HOKKAIDO

ELEVATIONS

☐	0 - 100 METERS.
⠿	100 - 1000 "
▨	1000 - 2000 "
■	OVER 2000 "

SCALE

0   50   200 KM.

P9-CBJ-102

Japan: A Physical, Cultural, and Regional Geography

Photograph on title page by Natori, Black Star

JAPAN

A PHYSICAL, CULTURAL
& REGIONAL GEOGRAPHY

BY GLENN THOMAS TREWARTHA

PROFESSOR OF GEOGRAPHY IN THE UNIVERSITY OF WISCONSIN

THE UNIVERSITY OF WISCONSIN PRESS

DRAWN

17552

Copyright 1945 by

THE UNIVERSITY OF WISCONSIN

All rights reserved. No part of this book may be reproduced in any form without the written permission of the publisher. Permission is hereby granted to reviewers to quote brief passages in a review to be printed in a magazine or newspaper.

FIRST PRINTING JANUARY 1945
SECOND PRINTING JUNE 1945
THIRD PRINTING NOVEMBER 1945
FOURTH PRINTING JULY 1947

PRINTED IN THE UNITED STATES OF AMERICA

GF 666
.T68

Introduction

Nations, like individuals, do not exist in isolation. They operate in an environment, as a plant is in the air and the soil. Japan is a single unit, and a very small one at that, of the immense Monsoon Realm of eastern and southeastern Asia, one of the most distinctive and most important of the earth's large geographic subdivisions. It is in the geographical, political, social, and economic climate of this Oriental realm that Japan has developed, and by which she has been greatly influenced.

The Monsoon Realm occupies the hilly borderlands of eastern and southeastern Asia from Manchuria and maritime Siberia on the north to India on the south and west. Between these pole areas lie Japan, Korea, China, French Indo-China, Thailand, Burma, Malaya, and the large island groups of the Philippines and the East Indies.

On its inner borders the Monsoon Realm is terminated by the great mountain masses and lofty plateaus which form the highland core of the continent. The 5,000-foot contour has been suggested as the region's approximate boundary on the land side. Essentially it is a hilly land in which slopes predominate and low level land is at a minimum. With one important exception, the Manchurian Plain, its lowlands are all plains of river deposition. They are, therefore, alluvial floodplains and deltas whose surfaces are essentially flat and hence easy to irrigate.

Partially offsetting the handicap of rough terrain is the fact that southeastern Asia is a humid land with relatively abundant rainfall, which greatly enhances its capacity for production. The seasonal winds, known as monsoons, which are most perfectly developed in eastern and southern Asia, are one of the important unifying bonds of the realm. In summer these monsoon winds blow from over warm tropical and subtropical seas into the heated continent, bringing with them an abundance of moisture which falls as rain. In winter, on the other hand, cold, dry winds of land origin blow from the colder continent toward the warmer seas. Over most of southeastern Asia these winter monsoons yield little rain. The result is a region with a marked seasonal rhythm in precipitation, a land of winter drought and summer rains. In general the monsoon rains penetrate the continent for several hundred up to a thousand miles. Beyond that are the dry lands of inner Asia, the land of the pastoral nomads. The 20-inch rainfall line may also be taken as a fairly satisfactory boundary of the landward limits of the Monsoon Realm.

v

Because it is a humid land most of southeastern Asia was originally covered with forests or with forests mingled with grass. Here is still another feature, therefore, that sets the monsoonal margins of the continent apart from the dry interior where sparse grasses and shrubs prevailed. Because of the relatively abundant precipitation and high temperatures characteristic of most of the realm the soluble mineral plant foods have been removed from the soil materials by solution, with the result that the residual soils are of low fertility. Organic as well as inorganic materials are deficient, for the forest cover does not yield abundant humus as grass does. Only in the subhumid North, Manchuria for example, where grasses were important in the plant cover, or where basic lavas prevail, are the residual soils of high quality. Elsewhere the uplands and slopes are thinly mantled with ruddy soils of low fertility. To a large extent, however, it is the fresh, unleached, fertile alluvial soils of the deltas and floodplains that are intensively used in the Monsoon Realm; the poor ruddy residual soils are avoided so far as possible. Unfortunately, these fertile lowland soils occupy only a limited portion of the realm's total area.

Asia's monsoon lands are not large producers of economic minerals. In part this reflects the stage of economic development in the Far East, a region in which factory industry is only meagerly and very spottily developed. In part, however, it reflects actual deficiencies or limited distribution of the basic minerals. The one really large reserve of good coal is in China, in the Loess Highlands inland from the North China Plain. This is one of the world's great coal deposits of high quality. Modest, but still significant, deposits are located in southern Manchuria, Japan, several parts of China, northern Indo-China, and northeastern India. The only first-class iron ore deposit is in northeastern India, about 150 miles west of Calcutta. There are other less important deposits in Malaya, Manchuria, and the Philippines. The Far East is deficient in petroleum, the only significant producing area being in the Netherlands Indies and in Burma. Malaya and the lands surrounding it are the world's most important sources of tin; India is one of the world's largest producers of manganese, and the China-Malayan area of tungsten. India also ranks high as a producer of mica; Ceylon of graphite; the Philippines of chromite; China of antimony. The Netherlands Indies and Malaya are important sources of bauxite. It is clear that while Monsoon Asia has some important mineral deposits, they are unfortunately widely scattered and not under the control of a single political unit, which might integrate their use. It is dubious whether the mineral reserves of the region are of such quality, magnitude, and geographic distribution as to make them capable of supporting an industrial development comparable to those in the lands on either side of the Atlantic Basin.

Culturally the Monsoon Realm is one of the world's most distinctive large geographic subdivisions. It is one of the two Old World centers of ancient civilization and culture diffusion. And although the civilizations of China and India did not develop as early as those of Egypt and Mesopotamia in the Mediterranean and Near East area, they have persisted down to the present time, whereas the earlier ones died centuries ago. Chinese civilization has flourished through nearly forty centuries, so that by contrast Japan's development seems recent.

Close to a billion people are crowded on the lands of southeastern Asia. Thus on about seven or eight per cent of the earth's land area are concentrated nearly half of the human race. Among the various measures of the importance of a region is the number of human beings making it their home. However small the per capita wealth, however meager the output of goods, the count of men alone is enough to establish the importance of the Monsoon Realm. The concentration of so large a part of the earth's population in eastern and southeastern Asia makes it the most densely inhabited large area on the earth, its density of about 200 persons per square mile being considerably greater than even that of industrial Europe. Moreover, this figure gives no proper concept of real population density, since the people are highly concentrated on the fertile plains of new alluvium; the hilly lands of steep slopes and poor soils are much more empty of inhabitants. The result is a very patchy, fragmented pattern of population distribution with densities of 500–1000 and even more per square mile on the lowlands. The Far East, like ancient Egypt and Babylon, is a river-valley civilization.

Not only is the population already dense but the high birth rates seem to portend an increased density in the future. To be sure, death rates are likewise high, but the annual increment of growth is still large. In China alone it may amount to 5 million or more a year. One hesitates to even imagine what effects on population increases and densities might result from improved health through better living conditions and more widespread sanitation, or from increased income associated with industrialization. Opportunities for large-scale emigration are not great, for most of the good land within the Monsoon Realm is already settled. Only in northern Manchuria, in the southeastern peninsula of Further India (French Indo-China, Thailand, Burma, Malaya), and in the East Indies, except Java, are there lower-than-average densities of population and considerable unoccupied land fit for agriculture.

By far the largest number of these nearly a billion people in the Monsoon Realm are impoverished peasant farmers engaged in intensive subsistence agriculture. Their interest is primarily in the production of food crops for local consumption. Forests, except in Japan, are inefficiently utilized or conserved. There is almost no pasture land, so essential in the economies of many world regions. Animals exist not in herds but singly or in pairs, chiefly as work animals on the farms. Animal foods are mainly those from scavenger animals, such as swine and poultry, or from fish. Rice is the great food crop of the general monsoon region, and over 90 per cent of the world's production of rice comes from this part of Asia. It is chiefly in subhumid northern China and Manchuria that irrigated paddy lands are not important. In certain restricted areas of southeastern Asia the raising of special commercial crops or products by the natives, or on plantations supervised by Occidentals, has reached a high degree of development. Thus much of the larger part of the world's raw silk supply comes from Japan and China; its tea from India, Ceylon, Japan, the Netherlands Indies, and China; its rubber from Malaya and the Netherlands Indies; its jute from northeastern India; its Manila hemp from the Philippines; its cinchona from Java, and its coconuts from the coastal lands of tropical southeastern Asia in general. In addition, Manchuria is a large producer of soybeans; the Netherlands Indies of tobacco, sugar, coffee, spices, and kapok; India and China of cotton. In spite of the fact that it is the world's largest and most important region of subsistence farming, it is at the same time the world's most important region of commercial tropical plantation agriculture. European capital and supervision are joined with native labor in this profitable enterprise.

A corollary to the predominance of subsistence agriculture is the fact that the Monsoon Realm is relatively undeveloped in factory industry. The industrial revolution has scarcely touched the larger part of the area. Only in a few of the larger cities are great modern factories conspicuous. Most manufacturing is still in the workshop stage, and craft products are among the best known of the Oriental wares. What factory industries do exist are chiefly of the light variety, textiles predominating. The two principal centers of heavy industry outside Japan are in the vicinity of Mukden in Manchuria and of Jamshedpur in northeastern India.

Trade, like manufacturing, is meagerly developed, and communications are still crude and inefficient. The two primary functions of cities, therefore, exist only on a small scale, and for this reason great cities are relatively few. Those that do exist are chiefly port cities, such as Dairen, Shanghai, Tientsin, Hongkong, Singapore, Bombay, and Calcutta whose development during the modern period has been partly, if not largely, the result of foreign initiative.

It is also worth noting that the Monsoon Realm is the most important focus of profitable, exploited colonial empire anywhere on the earth. Here the European powers found natives who had been husbandmen for long centuries and thus were accustomed to tilling the soil. This was not true in much of tropical Africa and South America. And while China has not been a colony of any single power, it was nevertheless exploited by several and was not master of its own house. Like other colonial regions of exploitation, the ambition of the white masters was to obtain large profits; the welfare and development of the native populations was of secondary importance.

Within the Monsoon Realm Japan is the outstanding exception to the standard pattern of a simple agrarian economy. There she stands as the single strong and independent nation and far more Westernized and modernized than any of the other political units. In a realm that was for the most part subservient to, or at least developed by, Occidental nations, Japan looms up by contrast. Possessed of a modern industrial structure, of efficient communications, a large foreign and domestic trade, a modern financial system, a large merchant marine, and a powerful army and navy, Nippon was the one political unit in the Orient that commanded the attention and respect of the Great Powers. It was a unique position that Japan held, a position that gave her a unique opportunity to become the unselfish leader of the Oriental peoples. The treatment accorded the native peoples of Asia by the whites was not such as to endear the masters, so that if Japan had really meant what she said when she coined the phrase "The Greater Sphere of Co-prosperity in Eastern Asia," and if she had really had the interests of the other Asiatic countries at heart, along with her own, she might have elicited genuine cooperation from them in a non-violence program emphasizing "Asia for the Asiatics." The one strong Asiatic nation striving for the wellbeing of all the Orient might have become the channel through which the conditions of all were improved. In retrospect it looks as though Japan may have missed the opportunity of a nation's lifetime in not offering herself as the Moses of the peoples of Monsoon Asia. It seems likely that they could have been led.

      *   *   *   *   *

In 1932–33 when *A Reconnaissance Geography of Japan,* the ancestor of the present book, was being written, Nippon was scarcely launched upon those momentous developments of the thirties which eventually led to the present war in the Pacific. To be sure, portents of the army-instigated expansionist policy in Asia were already observable in the 1931 invasion of Manchuria, and subsequently in the flaunting of international censure by a haughty withdrawal from the League of Nations. But the revamping of the industrial and commercial structure of the country to fit the requirements of a nation bent upon conquest in eastern Asia had scarcely begun. That was a feature of the remaining years of the decade, following 1932. The earlier book described a Japan as of about 1930, before it had undergone those transformations required by an army-ridden country determined to solve its national problems through the use of force.

The present book treats the geography of Japan as of about 1940, or before the outbreak of the present war in the Pacific. A span of only ten years, therefore, separates the datum planes of the two volumes. But in that decade basic changes occurred in Nippon's national economies which made parts of the earlier book obsolete. The first concrete suggestion for a revision of *A Reconnaissance Geography of Japan* came from certain army and navy officials in Washington who believed that a modernized and expanded version of the earlier book would be useful in various phases of the war effort. The fact that government purchases of the old edition had exhausted the supply, compelling its reprinting in 1943, served to substantiate the opinion that a new geography of Japan would be serviceable.

In the preparation of the present book there has been some salvage from its predecessor. Some of the facts concerning Nippon's geography had changed little or not at all during the decade of the thirties. This was particularly true of its physical geography, though even in this field important new materials on such topics as the country's terrain, climate, soils, and mineral resources became available. In the field of Japan's cultural geography the decade brought not only fundamental changes, but a wealth of new materials. The dangers inherent in empire building required a Japan strong in those industries which directly or indirectly strengthen a nation's ability to wage war. An unprecedented expansion in heavy industries was required, and in the train of this conversion from consumer's to producer's goods, changes resulted not only in industry, but also in the other economies as they were geared to war. At the same time population revealed new trends and new regional concentrations. The result has been that while some use could be made of the materials in *A Reconnaissance Geography of Japan*, the present book has been so largely rewritten and expanded that only in restricted parts does it resemble the earlier edition. More than doubled in size and nearly tripled in number of illustrations it is more comprehensive than its predecessor.

The brief introduction is designed to give Japan its proper geographic setting within the larger Monsoon Realm of eastern and southeastern Asia. Parts I and II treat of Japan Proper in its entirety. In these sections those geographic characteristics belonging to the archipelago as a whole have been emphasized, while intra-regional contrasts have received little attention. Part I concentrates on the physical aspects of Japan's geography and analyzes such resource elements and features of natural equipment as terrain, climate, soils, native vegetation, and economic minerals. Here there was the dual aim of (1) supplying foundation material for an understanding of the subsequent treatment of the cultural geography, and of (2) providing the reader with a concrete picture of the physical face of Nippon. Part II does for the cultural elements of Japan's geography what Part I does for the physical. Population, settlements, agriculture, fishing, industry, and communications are the principal themes elaborated. Part III is concerned with the regional contrasts within Japan. To a notable extent its content is based upon personal observations made during two periods of field investigation in Nippon. This regional treatment, it is hoped, will not only be intrinsically valuable, but will provide a geographic framework for Japan into which past and future detailed studies of limited area will fit and have a place. Unless preceded by a study in gross morphology, such detailed studies are less useful than they should be because they are isolated fragments not clearly related to the larger whole of which they are a part. For a regional treatment of the reconnaissance type, such as Part III contains, Japan presents peculiar difficulties. The country is composed of numerous small, isolated units which almost defy generalized synthesis. This individualism of numerous small areal units, resulting from the complicated relief as well as from the country's long history and earlier feudal organization, is such a characteristic feature that a description employing broad strokes is less satisfactory than it would be in regions where the terrain and occupance patterns are coarser and less complicated. In Part III this had led to a brief analysis of many more individual areas than would ordinarily be the case in what purports to be a regional study of reconnaissance type.

It seems the part of wisdom to admit that the book has been written with several types of readers in mind. This diverse focus has resulted in the inclusion of a greater variety of materials at a number of professional levels than would ordinarily be the case where only one audience is considered. Since its predecessor was used in many government offices engaged in war work, and in a number of military training programs, and likewise because the present revision was first suggested by army and navy officials, the needs of the military and government personnel have been considered. At the present time, moreover, there is a larger lay public in the United States interested in Japan's geography than has ever existed before. It is hoped that some sections of the book will prove interesting and profitable to this group. The nearly three hundred illustrations were intended as an aid to the non-professional readers. And finally there has been kept in mind the needs of professional geographers, especially those engaged in instructing at the college and university level.

A distinctive feature of the book is the numerous illustrations in the form of maps, sketches, and photographs. Graphic representation of portions of the earth's surface is used in many fields of learning, but especially by the earth sciences. The map is an essential tool of the geographer by which he clarifies and vivifies word descriptions of areas. The photographs have been carefully selected more for their geographic than for their artistic qualities. This has resulted in the inclusion of some illustrations which, though they fall short of photographic excellence, portray with great honesty a desirable combination of geographic features.

The fact that specific acknowledgement of assistance and courtesies received are so few is only an indication that the sources are unusually numerous. In other words, the ratio of number of acknowledgements to assistance received is an inverse one. Courtesies or aid in the form of maps and photographs are specifically mentioned by credit lines at the point of use in the book. Many of the footnotes perform the same service, although numerous ones are included chiefly for the purpose of suggesting sources where a more complete treatment of the subject may be found. Grateful acknowledgement is made to Akira Watanabe and H. Sasaki, at the time geography instructors at the Tokyo Imperial University, for aid given in the field. The John Simon Guggenheim Memorial Foundation generously subsidized my first field research in the Far East, and again in 1943-44 provided funds which released me from university duties in order to carry out the preparation of this book. From the National Research Council and the University of Wisconsin Research Fund was received the financial aid that made the second trip to Japan possible. The University of Wisconsin again provided liberally in money and time for the writing and publication of the present book.

GLENN T. TREWARTHA

Madison, Wisconsin
January, 1945.

Contents

INTRODUCTION v

Part I. The Country as a Whole: Physical Equipment and Resources

CHAPTER I   EARTH MATERIALS AND SURFACE CONFIGURATION..   3

CHAPTER II   CLIMATE   32

CHAPTER III   NATURAL VEGETATION AND SOILS   62

CHAPTER IV   ECONOMIC MINERALS: RESOURCES AND PRODUCTION   81

Part II. The Country as a Whole: Cultural Features

CHAPTER V   POPULATION AND CULTURE 121

CHAPTER VI   SETTLEMENTS AND HOUSES 151

CHAPTER VII   AGRICULTURE AND FISHING 193

CHAPTER VIII   MANUFACTURING 258

CHAPTER IX   COMMUNICATIONS AND TRADE 305

Part III. The Regional Subdivisions of Japan

CHAPTER X   HOKKAIDO 341

CHAPTER XI   THE OU OR TOHOKU DISTRICT OF NORTHERN HONSHU 395

CHAPTER XII   CENTRAL AND SOUTHWESTERN JAPAN 430

CHAPTER XIII   TOKAI: THE PACIFIC SIDE OF CHUBU 467

CHAPTER XIV   THE INNER ZONE OF SOUTHWEST JAPAN, PART 1 ... 512

CHAPTER XV   THE INNER ZONE OF SOUTHWEST JAPAN, PART 2 ... 538

CHAPTER XVI   THE INNER ZONE OF SOUTHWEST JAPAN, PART 3 ... 563

CHAPTER XVII   THE PACIFIC FOLDED MOUNTAINS OR THE OUTER
                      ZONE OF SOUTHWEST JAPAN 585

Japanese Weights and Measures

LENGTH

JAPANESE		METRIC		AMERICAN AND ENGLISH
1 ri	equals	3.92727 kilometers	equals	2.44030 miles

AREA

1 tan	equals	9.91735 ares	equals	0.24506 acres
1 cho	equals	99.17355 ares	equals	2.45064 acres
1 square ri	equals	15.42347 sq. kilometers	equals	5.95505 sq. miles

WEIGHT

1 momme	equals	3.75000 grams	equals	0.13228 ounces (avoir.)
1 kin	equals	0.60000 kilograms	equals	1.32277 pounds
1 kwan (kan)	equals	3.75000 kilograms	equals	8.26733 pounds

CAPACITY

1 koku	equals	1.80391 hectoliters	equals	4.96005 Imperial bushels 5.11902 American bushels 47.95389 American gallons
1 koku (timber)			equals	about 10 cubic feet
1 koku (fish)	is about	40 kwan in weight		

MONEY

1 yen (100 sen)				
at par			equals	0.49846 American dollars
in 1940			equalled	0.2344 American dollars

Pronunciation of Japanese Names

Unlike the English language, the Japanese has little or no accent upon individual syllables except where certain vowels are prolonged, such as the *o* in *Osaka*, which is held about twice as long as the long *o* in English.

Vowels are pronounced nearly the same as the vowels of the musical scale: *a* as in *fa*, *e* as in *re*, *i* as in *mi*, *o* as in *do*; *u* has the sound of *oo* in *boot*. In the diphthongs *ei* and *ai* both vowels are pronounced, but so rapidly as to give the impression of a single sound.

Consonants have much the same sound as in English. Double consonants are both pronounced. The letter *g* is always hard. The letters *l* and *v* are lacking. In such names as *Tokyo*, *Kyoto*, and *Kyushu* the *y* is pronounced as a consonant, so that *kyo* or *kyu* is rendered as one syllable. Thus *Kyushu* is pronounced *Kyoo-shoo*.

PART ONE

The Country as a Whole: Physical Equipment and Resources

CHAPTER I

Earth Materials and Surface Configuration

NATURE did not cut the resource pattern of Japan on a scale befitting a great power. Small in area, rugged of surface, and sparingly supplied with most of the economic minerals, Japan in her climb to a position of world eminence has been beset with many handicaps growing out of this poverty of resources. That these handicaps did not prevent her from becoming a world power merely illustrates how fallacious is the doctrine of environmental determinism as it applies to nations. On the other hand, to belittle the effects of Japan's natural endowments upon the nation's economies and culture is as mistaken as to overemphasize and oversimplify their influence. Certainly military power, and in a measure economic greatness as well, have been achieved in resource-poor Japan only by sacrificing the well-being of her citizenry, for the country's physical endowments have scarcely permitted an abundance of both butter and guns.

The early chapters of this book present a picture of the land of Japan in its original and man-modified natural aspects. This is physical geography. Such an inventory of the natural endowments and resources provides a background against which to view and understand the development of a nation, for surface, climate, forests, soil, minerals, etc., are the tools with which a people fashions its civilization. These elements are more than merely a set of natural features combining to form the varied and attractive physical face of Nippon. Along with other factors, they have influenced the structure of anthropo-Japan. "The civilization of a race is simply the sum-total of its achievement in adjusting itself to its environment" (Hu Shih).

* * * * *

Off the Pacific coast of Asia and forming its outer ramparts is a festoon of mountainous volcanic islands arranged in the form of three great bows or arcs, all convex toward the ocean. The main and central of these mountain arcs is Japan Proper, consisting of four principal islands, Hokkaido, Honshu, Shikoku, Kyushu, and hundreds of smaller

3

ones, the archipelago having a total area of nearly 150,000 square miles, or approximately that of California. The main islands are separated from one another by narrow straits of relative local subsidence.

At its northern or Hokkaido end the main Japan Arc is intersected by the Kurile Arc; at its southern or Kyushu extremity it fuses with the Ryukyu Bow. The Kurile and Ryukyu arcs are themselves represented by large numbers of small volcanic islands. The areas of arc intersection are marked by massive irregular bunches of highland with associated clusters of volcanoes.

EARTH MATERIALS

A layman examining a colored geological map of Japan is likely to be struck by the complicated and seemingly patternless arrangement of the great number of small color splotches on it. But when he learns that the colors represent different types of surficial rock differing in age, structure, and resistance, he recognizes that the Japanese islands are a minutely subdivided mosaic of various kinds of surface rocks and earth materials, reflecting a very long and complicated geological history. What at first appears to him as a meaningless patchwork of colors without pattern is not actually the case, for to the trained eye there is an understandable arrangement of the colors on the geologic map and of the rock strata they represent, even though the patterns are complicated and the individual geologic units of small size (Fig. 1). The linear character of the islands and the approximate parallelism of the Pacific and the Japan Sea coasts suggests a medial backbone of resistant rock, but this is not the prevailing structure. It is outside the scope of this book to trace the geological evolution of the Japanese islands. But since the character and structure of the rock of a region find expression in such areally important features as landforms, drainage patterns, soils, and minerals, a description of the kinds and distributions of earth materials is geographically significant and has a place here.

Table 2 shows the distribution of the principal large classes of surface rock and earth materials in Japan, together with the percentage of the country's total area that each occupies (Fig. 1). The old Archean rocks. mostly gneisses and crystalline schists, are least abundant, occupying only about 4 per cent of the Japanese islands. They occur chiefly in the Abukuma Hill Land, a spindle-shaped highland just north of the Tokyo Plain, and in Kii Peninsula and Shikoku in southwestern Japan. Granites, characteristic of 12 per cent of the area, are more abundant and are widely dispersed throughout all the islands, being especially prominent in central

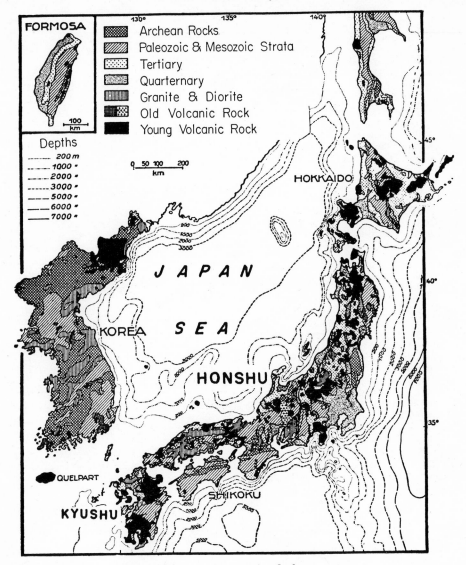

FIG. 1. After K. Haushofer.

and southwestern Honshu, and in northern Kyushu. Older sedimentary rocks (Paleozoic and Mesozoic), typically folded and faulted, occupy 21 per cent of the country and form some of its most rugged terrain. They are particularly conspicuous in central Hokkaido, central Honshu, and in the southern portions of Kii Peninsula, Shikoku, and Kyushu. Most extensive of all are the volcanic rocks, both old and young (26 per cent) which are present throughout the entire extent of Japan. Especially wide-

TABLE 1.—AREA OF JAPAN PROPER AND ITS EMPIRE

Subdivision	Square Miles	
Japan Proper (including outlying islands)	147,492	
Hokkaido		34,276
Honshu		88,622
Shikoku		7,228
Kyushu		16,246
Ryukyu		921
Taiwan (Formosa)	13,884	
Karafuto (Sakhalin)	13,934	
Chosen (Korea)	85,239	
Total	260,783*	
Kwantung Leased Territory	1,336	
Pacific Mandated Islands	829	

Source: *Far East Year Book*, 1941, p. 15.　*Includes other small islands.

TABLE 2.—PREVALENCE OF CERTAIN GEOLOGICAL FORMATIONS IN JAPAN

Geological Formations	Percentage of Country's Total Area	Geological Formations	Percentage of Country's Total Area
Granite rocks	12	Tertiary rocks	20
Archean rocks	4	Diluvium	6
Paleozoic rocks	14	Alluvium	12
Mesozoic rocks	7	Volcanic rocks	26

Source: Japanese Geological Laboratory Office as quoted by Shiroshi Nasu in *Aspects of Japanese Agriculture* (New York, 1941), 28.

TABLE 3.—RELATIONSHIP BETWEEN GEOLOGICAL FORMATIONS, SLOPE OF LAND, AND EXTENT OF CULTIVATION

Geological Formation	Percentage of Total Area of Formation Having Slope of 15° or Less	Percentage of Total Area of Formation under Cultivation	Cultivated Area in Cho per Square Ri*
Granitic rocks	16	10.1	157
Volcanic rocks	25	7.9	122
Archean rocks	15	8.8	137
Paleozoic rocks	15	7.9	122
Mesozoic rocks	21	6.1	94
Tertiary rocks	46	10.7	167
Diluvium	91	23.8	370
Alluvium	96	43.9	683

Source: Japanese Geological Laboratory Office as quoted by Shiroshi Nasu in *Aspects of Japanese Agriculture*, 28.
* 1 cho=2.45 acres; 1 square ri=5.955 square miles.

spread are the young volcanic materials in a variety of forms—ash-and-lava cones, lava plateaus, and ash plateaus. Thus these five types of rock (Archean, granite, Paleozoic, Mesozoic, volcanic), most of them very resistant to erosion, constitute 63 per cent of the country's area. They form its high and rugged mountain and hill land, a minimum amount of which is land level enough for agricultural use.

Of the younger and less resistant earth materials only the Tertiary strata (sandstone, shale, conglomerate, tuff) can be regarded as consolidated sedimentary rock. This formation is most common at rather low elevations, and because it is weak and poorly consolidated it characteristically forms low, thoroughly dissected hill country with moderate slopes and a considerable valley-floor area. Also of geographic significance is the fact that the Tertiary rocks are the source of much of Japan's coal and oil. Unconsolidated deposits, both older alluvium (diluvium) and new alluvium, forming the genuine lowlands of Japan, comprise only 18 per cent of the country's area, but it is this small area on which is concentrated a great part of the human life, agriculture, and industry of Nippon. Much of the old alluvium exists in the form of benches or terraces, which rise somewhat above the fans, floodplains, and deltas of new alluvium.

Table 3 shows how striking is the relationship between rock types, slope of land, and the percentage of area cultivated. Clearly it is the younger and less resistant rocks that have the gentler slope and hence the largest proportion of land under cultivation. Over 90 per cent of both the alluvium and diluvium is characterized by slopes of 15° or less. In view of the fact that so large a proportion of both the alluvium and diluvium has a slope of 15° or less, it may seem surprising that they should differ so much with respect to proportion of land under cultivation. The explanation lies partly in the greater surface unevenness of diluvial areas even where slopes do not exceed 15°, but still more, probably, in differences in soil fertility and ease of irrigation. Next to the alluvium and diluvium in prevalence of moderate slopes come the Tertiary rock areas, about 46 per cent of whose total area has slopes not exceeding 15°. Thus they are intermediate in character between the older rocks with their prevailingly steep slopes and the much more recent alluvium and diluvium, where steep slopes are at a minimum. With respect to percentage of land under cultivation, however, the Tertiary rock areas more nearly resemble the older rocks and are distinctly below the alluvium and diluvium. This no doubt reflects the difficulties of tilling slopes of even somewhat less than 15° inclination, such as are common in Tertiary areas, more especially in a country where inundated rice is the favored crop.

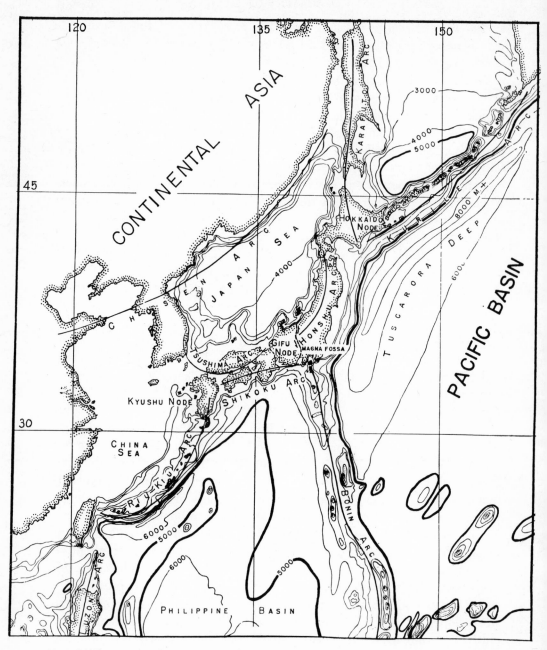

Fig. 2. The arcs and nodes in the Japanese Archipelagoes. Note the difference in depth of the Japan Sea and the China Sea. Depths are in meters. Map by Bailey Willis.

8

ORIGIN AND PHYSICAL FRAMEWORK

According to Japanese legend a number of gods were born in the "Plain of High Heaven," whose lives were very uneventful until the advent of Izanagi and Izanami, who eventually became man and wife and gave birth to many offspring. Among his numerous heroic gestures Izanagi on one occasion thrust his heavenly jeweled spear into the deep, and as he withdrew it the shower of drops that fell from the spear were transformed into the dragon-shaped island group of Japan. Actually the origin of the archipelago was not much less dramatic. Only instead of showering down from above, the islands were thrust upward from mighty ocean deeps, for they are the rugged crests of submarine mountains. Some geologists regard Japan's mountainous islands as essentially Alpine in type; others contend that they represent summits of one of the outermost series of tilted blocks forming the Pacific margins of the Asiatic land mass, from which they are separated by subsidence areas occupied by the intervening seas. Willis[1] believes the islands to be submarine ridges which over a period of sixty million years have risen through the floor of the Pacific Ocean. The great variety of igneous rocks comprising the archipelago suggests that multiple centers and multiple periods of volcanic activity were involved in the long period of mountain building.

Only a few score miles off the eastern side of Japan is one of the greatest series of submarine trenches known to exist in any ocean basin, with depths below sea level of 20,000 to 30,000 feet (Fig. 2). Not far to the southeast of the mouth of Tokyo Bay a depth of 10,550 meters (34,600 feet) has been recorded. Thus on the east the Japanese islands rise sharply from an ocean bottom five to six miles below sea level to heights of more than two miles above. In other words, the difference in elevation between the greatest depths of the Japan Submarine Trench and the high mountain peaks of Japan must be at least seven or eight miles.

This immense range of elevation within lateral distances of a few score miles inevitably develops enormous strains and stresses, with the result that this becomes a weak and unstable portion of the earth's crust in which readjustments of the rock masses are constantly occurring. Like the rest of the unstable circum-Pacific region, the Japanese islands are an area of numerous volcanoes and frequent earthquakes. There are well over five hundred volcanoes within Japan (including the Kurile and Ryukyu Islands to north and south), and there are historic records for eruptions

[1] Bailey Willis, "Why the Japanese Islands?" in the *Scientific Monthly*, 51:99–111 (August, 1940).

of exactly sixty.[2] Japan has on the average about fifteen hundred earthquakes annually, or approximately four shocks a day. In the Tokyo area there is a sensible shock on the average of once every three days. Since 1596 there have been twenty-one major earthquakes, each of which has cost the lives of more than a thousand persons.[3]

The seas to the west of the Japan Arc are not nearly so deep, yet the Japan Sea has a depth of more than 10,000 feet, indicating that it is a genuine ocean basin, not merely a submerged portion of the Asiatic continental platform. The China Sea, on the other hand, which in most places is no more than 125–150 feet deep, is only an inundated portion of the continent itself.[4] But between this shallow basin and the northwest side of Kyushu is a submarine trough having a maximum depth of nearly 9,000 feet. The considerable ocean depths on the continental side of Japan as well as the mighty deeps to the east support the hypothesis that the islands are the crests of heroic mountains rising through the ocean floor.

The arc form of mountain ranges, which is characteristic of many other parts of the globe, is particularly conspicuous in the island groups and associated submarine ridges of the western Pacific. The meeting of two arcs is usually marked by a massive irregular bunch or knot of mountainous terrain, which may be termed a node. In Japan the following arcs and nodes may be distinguished[5]:

The Hokkaido Node, where the Karafuto and Kurile arcs join, and in turn connect with the Honshu Arc (Fig. 2).

The Honshu Arc, extending from the Hokkaido Node to the Gifu Node, the central and broadest part of the main island.

The Gifu Node at the junction of three arcs: the Honshu on the north, the Tsushima and Shikoku arcs forming southwestern Japan, and the Bonin Arc entering as a submarine ridge from the southeast.

The Tsushima and Shikoku arcs, convex in opposite directions.

The Kyushu Node, at the junctions of the Tsushima and Shikoku arcs with the Ryukyu Arc.

The Ryukyu Arc, extending to Formosa.

The Four Zones

Along the whole length of Japan Proper from Hokkaido to Kyushu two zones of contrasting geological and morphological structure lie parallel to each other. The one on the Pacific side is known as the Outer Zone and

[2] Akira Watanabe, "On the Distribution of Volcanoes in Japan," in *Papers of the Michigan Academy of Sciences, Arts, and Letters*, 14 (1930):433–436.

[3] *Japan Year Book*, 1938–39, p. 30.

[4] Willis, *op. cit.*, 104.   [5] Willis, *op. cit.*, 102–103.

that on the Asiatic side as the Inner Zone (Fig. 3). Fault scarps and tectonic depressions mark the contact between the two, except in the great Gifu Node of central Honshu, where the arrangement of the principal features is confused and complex. In the Outer Zone the geological formations tend to have a more regular arrangement than in the Inner Zone, where the structure is more complex, the rock strata less regular in arrangement, and eruptive rock abundant.

The Honshu Arc may be still further subdivided into dissimilar northern and southern halves by a great depressed zone, the Fossa Magna of Naumann, which traverses the mid-part of the main island from the Pacific Ocean to the Sea of Japan. It appears as though the mountain arc had been bent backward along this fracture and the resulting rift subsequently filled, in part at least, by younger strata and great volcanic piles. A series of local structural basins occupy positions at the bases of the fault-scarps. Along this depressed zone runs the Fuji Volcanic Chain, whose magnificent cones, among them Fujiyama, stand as boundary posts between the two morphologically unlike districts of northern and southern Japan.

On the basis of geologic and morphologic contrasts, therefore, Japan may be subdivided into four zones: North Inner, North Outer, South Inner, and South Outer (Fig. 3). The arrangement may be likened to a bent capital *H* convex to the east, the crossbar of which is the Gifu Node separating the unlike northern and southern halves of Japan, and the two longer parallel bars are the Inner and Outer zones.

The Outer Zone of southwest Japan, designated the Pacific Folded Mountains, is separated from the Inner Zone by a line of great dislocation, with which are associated several graben valleys and a conspicuous fault-scarp extending from central Honshu through Kii Peninsula and northern Shikoku to western Kyushu. These mountains are characterized by well developed longitudinal dislocation lines. They are for the most part high and rugged and contain few sizeable plains. The predominant rocks are crystalline schists and older sedimentaries greatly folded and contorted. Granites and younger volcanics are rare. The mineral wealth is in the form of precious and semi-precious ores, chiefly copper, gold, and silver. In central Honshu this Outer Zone is represented by the high Akaishi Mountains (Akaishi Sphenoid), which terminate on the east in a bold fault-scarp overlooking the Fossa Magna. Declining gradually in elevation, the Pacific Folded Mountains continue westward in the southern parts of Kii Peninsula, Shikoku, and Kyushu; local subsidence in the vicinity of Kii Channel and Bungo Strait divides them into separate mountain masses. In southern Kyushu the Outer Zone is intersected by the Ryukyu Arc; this results in a southern appendage of volcanic materials consisting of an ash plateau, volcanic cones, and lava flows.

In contrast to the Outer Zone, the Inner Zone of southwest Japan is a series of dissected block plateaus. Slope prevails throughout, and some parts are genuinely mountainous, though more of the area is rugged hill country. Granite is abundant, hence rounded forms and slopes covered with a whitish crust of weathered rock are more prevalent here than in any other subdivision of Japan. The geological structure and physiographic history of the area are extremely complex. Ancient sedimentary rocks, pierced by granitic intrusives, have been peneplaned and cut by a complicated system of faults, some of the resulting blocks suffering upheaval, others depression. Throughout most of the area fault-block structures with associated tectonic valleys and basins are common. Volcanic activity is widespread. Elevations are highest in central Honshu, where the Hida Range (Japanese Alps), some of whose peaks exceed 3,000 meters, terminates abruptly at the tremendous fault-scarp overlooking the Fossa Magna. Farther west in Chugoku Peninsula, northern Shikoku, and northern Kyushu, elevations are lower, relief less, and the landscape hilly rather than mountainous. The Inland Sea, enclosed by Chugoku, Shikoku, and Kyushu, and its channel outlets to the open ocean occupy depressed zones. The western end of the Inland Sea subsidence area has been filled with volcanic material forming the ash and lava plateaus of North Kyushu.

The northern half of Japan, the area north of the Fossa Magna, is composed of three parallel chains of north-south mountains or hills separated from one another by structural depressions. This distinctive linear and parallel arrangement of ranges and basins is lost toward the south, where they all coalesce to form the Gifu Node of central Honshu.

The Outer Zone (east) of North Japan is separated from the Inner Zone by a line of structural depressions extending southward from the Ishikari-Yufutsu Lowland in Hokkaido, through the Mabechi, Kitakami, and Abukuma valleys, to the bay-head plain of Kwanto. In some places this series of depressions has fault-scarp margins, in others flexure-scarps. Gneisses, crystalline schists, older sedimentaries, and notable amounts of intrusives are characteristic. It is composed of five separate segments of highland: the Kwanto and Ashio blocks, forming the western margins of the Kwanto Plain and not conspicuously separated from the Inner Zone; the two spindle-shaped highlands of Abukuma and Kitakami farther north in Honshu; and the Hidaka Mountains of central Hokkaido. In general they all have the appearance of uplifted, tilted, and dissected peneplains developed upon complicated structures. In the central and eastern part of Hokkaido, where the Outer Zone is intersected by the Kurile Arc, great volcanic piles are a prominent feature.

The Inner Zone (west) of North Japan comprises two parallel ranges of hills and mountains, separated by a series of detritus-floored fault basins. The mountains are elongated domes with flexure-scarps along their margins. The central range, which is the backbone and watershed of northern Japan, is composed chiefly of recent sedimentary strata overlying a core of gneiss and granite. It is capped with volcanic cones which have greatly altered the original features of the mountain. The range extends continuously through northern Honshu and forms the northernmost knob of Mutsu Peninsula (Honshu) and the eastern volcanic portions of peninsular Hokkaido. The western range is geologically similar to the central one but varies more in altitude. Several streams draining the western basins cross it in antecedent valleys, their deltas forming various-sized plains along the Sea of Japan, some of them in cauldron-shaped depressions partially occupied by volcanoes.[6]

CHARACTERISTICS OF THE TERRAIN

Complexity and fineness of pattern are characteristic not only of the lithic features of Nippon but also of its terrain. Broad generalization is therefore difficult. Even within small areas the earth materials, their structures, and the resulting landforms are often of the greatest diversity. The lofty folded ranges that form the axis of the archipelago have been altered by block movements, hence faulted and folded forms are much intermingled. Remnants of flattish erosion surfaces at relatively high altitudes are widespread throughout the mountain country, contrasting curiously with the steep slopes and great relief. Repeated volcanic eruptions and intrusions, extensive and widespread, have added further to the complexity of the terrain. Moreover, these tectonic forces are still active, as is manifest in the recurring showers of volcanic ash, outpourings of lava, earthquakes, and changing strand lines. Short, vigorous, steep-gradient streams, acting upon these complex structures and materials have sculptured a land surface whose lineaments are varied and intricate.

[6] A more complete analysis of the individual physical subdivisions of Japan is presented in Part III of this book. See also Naomasa Yamasaki, "Geographical Sketch of Japan," in *Scientific Japan, Past and Present* (Kyoto, Japan, 1926), 1–32; and Robert B. Hall and Akira Watanabe, "Landforms of Japan," in *Papers of the Michigan Academy of Science, Arts, and Letters*, 18 (1932):157–207.

Hill and Mountain Lands

A core of moderately rugged hill land and mountain containing a number of debris-choked depressions, with small discontinuous fragments of river- and wave-deposited plains fringing the sea margins of the mountain land—such is the gross geomorphic pattern of Japan (Fig. 4). Along great stretches of the coast, plains are absent and the hill lands reach down to tidewater. Seventy-five per cent of the country is rugged hill and mountain land whose average slopes exceed 15° and are hence unfit for normal cultivation. Although nearly 65 per cent of the land with a gradient of 15° or less is tilled, the total area under cultivation amounts to less than 16 per cent of the country's total area.[7] The highest elevations

TABLE 4.—AREAS WITH SLOPE OF LESS THAN 15°
(in thousands of cho*)

Region	Area with Gradient below 15°		Percentage of Total Area
Honshu †		5602	24.1
Tohoku	1421		20.8
Hokuroku	631		25.1
Kwanto	1509		30.1
Tokai	794		24.6
Kinki	515		24.7
Sanin	252		18.1
Sanyo	478		22.2
Shikoku		439	23.2
Kyushu		1102	26.0
Hokkaido		2158	26.6
Total		9303	24.8

Source: Nasu, *Aspects of Japanese Agriculture*, 29.
* 1 cho = 2.45 acres.   † See Fig. 88 for locations of Honshu subdivisions.

and the most mountainous terrain of Japan is to be found in the Gifu Node of central Honshu, where a dozen or more peaks rise to about 10,000 feet. These highlands are known as the Japanese Alps. In this area is Mt. Fuji, Japan's highest peak, which attains an altitude of 12,461 feet. Just to the south of the Gifu Node, along the line of the Biwa Depression, is the most complete break in the Honshu highland barrier separating the Pacific and Japan Sea coasts. Except for relatively low ridges at the northern and southern ends of Lake Biwa there is here a water-level route across the narrow highlands from Wakasa Bay on the northwest to the eastern end of the Inland Sea, where are located the great industrial cities of Osaka, Kobe, and Kyoto (see front end papers).

[7] Shiroshi Nasu, *Aspects of Japanese Agriculture* (New York, 1941), 29.

In humid forest climates, especially where temperatures are subtropical, one expects to find rounded landforms mantled with a deep layer of weathered rock material. Throughout the rugged interior of Japan, however, it is not this type of terrain but sharp angular forms that prevail; concave slopes with narrow knife-edge ridge tops are characteristic (Fig. 5). This inconsistency is probably the result of the recent and rapid uplift of many of Japan's mountain areas and the associated vigorous downcutting and removal by streams.[8] The mantle of weathered rock material is consequently thin, with the result that the rugged outlines of the terrain have been little softened. Youthful and imposing fault- and flexure-scarps are conspicuous features, and commonly serve as the boundary zones between geomorphic subdivisions. It may also be that the frequent landslides caused by earthquake tremors have appreciably sharpened the contours of the landforms. The field geographer is much impressed by the evidence of recent slides in Japan: the numerous ruddy scars on the mountain flanks where the mantle of vegetation and a mass of regolith have recently been removed, exposing the raw bedrock beneath. Contrasting strangely with these features in some places, even in areas of steep slopes and sharp divides, there are still preserved fairly extensive upland erosion surfaces. This, too, is evidence of relatively recent uplift. Especially where granite is the predominant rock type, rounded cupola features, covered with a thin mantle of weathered rock materials, are common (Fig. 6). Southwesternmost Honshu (Chugoku), north of the Inland Sea, is representative of this latter type of terrain.

VOLCANIC CONES

Another element giving variety and contrast to the terrain are the scores of volcanic cones, with their associated lava and ash plateaus, in various stages of activity as well as dissection. These cones provide some of the highest elevations of the archipelago. The symmetrical concave slopes of the young cones, and the radial patterns of drainage lines and divides, make these highland areas easy to distinguish both in the field and on the topographic maps. Although they occur throughout the entire length of Japan, volcanoes are distributed according to a pattern, being numerous in some areas and almost lacking in others. Highest concentrations are at the intersections of the several arcs. The specific regions of concentration are as follows[9]:

[8] Francis Ruellan, "La Viguer de l'erosion normale au Japon," in the *Proceedings of the Third Pan-Pacific-Science Congress,* Tokyo, 1926, 2:1860–1862.
[9] Akira Watanabe, "On the Distribution of Volcanoes in Japan," *op. cit.,* 433–436.

1. Eastern Hokkaido and the Kurile (Chishima) Islands. Thirteen active volcanoes are located within this area of concentration.

2. Western Hokkaido and the central and western parts of North Honshu. Here there is a distinctly linear arrangement of the cones, beginning in the tail-like peninsular appendage of western Hokkaido and extending southward along the central range of northern Honshu. The volcanoes exist in the form of small compact agglomerations more or less equally spaced. Recent volcanic features are lacking on the Pacific side of North Honshu, although there are several splendid cones along the Japan Sea margins. Eighteen active volcanoes are present in this region.

3. Central Honshu and the islands of the Bonin Arc to the southeast. Here the volcanoes are arranged in a northwest-southeast line along the great depressed zone known as the Fossa Magna. Fujisan, one of the earth's most perfectly symmetrical ash cones, is located within this zone of concentration. For fifteen of the volcanoes there are records of eruptions during historic times, three in Honshu and twelve in the islands of the Bonin Arc.

In southwestern Honshu and Shikoku there are no volcanoes except in the Inner Zone or Tsushima Arc. None is active.

4. Kyushu and the islands of the Ryukyu Arc southward to Formosa. Fourteen volcanoes are classed as active. These too are arranged in a series of compact groups.

Tertiary Areas.—As has been said, the Tertiary rock areas, which are widely distributed throughout Japan, also have a distinctive terrain. Being weak and often poorly consolidated strata, they tend to form a low and thoroughly dissected hill country of moderate relief and slopes, and their drainage basins have a considerable valley-floor area.

Mountain Streams.—The mountain streams are short, swift, and shallow, and hence usually unnavigable; their drainage basins are small and their valleys narrow, with restricted floodplains. The headwaters and usually the greater part of the drainage basins of all Japanese rivers lie in the highlands. This fact, together with the abundant precipitation, results in swift rivers capable of vigorous erosion and in a close network of drainage channels over the country. Because of Japan's small size none of its rivers is long or has an extensive drainage basin. Of the twenty-four principal rivers listed in the *Japan-Manchukuo Year Book* for 1940, eight are less than 100 miles in length, fourteen are between 100 and 200 miles long, and only two are over 200 miles. These two rivers are the Ishikari in Hokkaido (227 miles) and the Shinano in central Honshu (229 miles), having drainage basins of only 5,401 and 4,734 square miles respectively.

FIG. 5. Sharp, angular terrain features are characteristic of a great deal of Japan's highlands.

FIG. 6. A region of granite rock where rounded features are more characteristic. The mantle of regolith is not thick. The forest cover is thin. A scene in the Kinki region.

FIG. 7. A mountain stream at the point where it debouches onto the plain. The bundles which have been rafted down-stream contain charcoal.

Of necessity the volume of such a stream is small. The restricted areas and steep slopes of their drainage basins cause the rivers to respond quickly to local rains and hence to vary greatly in regimen; they often flood seriously after heavy rains. Of small use for transport, except for rafting logs (Fig. 7), the mountain streams are important chiefly as sources of hydroelectric power and of irrigation water for the rice fields on the plains. In many sections the narrow floors of the river valleys are the principal sites of mountain agriculture. River terraces in multiple steps are striking features of the mountain valleys.

Lowlands

Nippon lacks extensive lowlands, and the diminutive ones that lie within her borders are almost exclusively surfaces of deposition. There are no extensive structural plains underlain by relatively horizontal strata as in central and eastern North America and in northern and western Europe. Hardrock areas in Japan are practically coextensive with hill and mountain land, almost the only exceptions being the fragments of wave-planed terrace along the coast. The typical plain of Japan is a small isolated patch of river- and wave-worked sediments developed in a coastal indentation or in a mountain basin. Even the largest of these, the Kwanto or Tokyo Plain in east-central Honshu, has an area of only about 13,000 square kilometers or 5,000 square miles. Being predominantly peripheral, most of the plains have frontage upon saltwater (Fig. 8). Seldom are they continuous along the coast for any considerable distance because of the frequent interruptions by spurs and larger masses of hardrock hill land that extend down to the sea (Fig. 9). The main railway line between Tokyo and Shimonoseki at the western extremity of Honshu, which roughly parallels the coast, goes in and out of smoky tunnels with a frequency that almost spoils one's enjoyment of the journey, so often are attractive views of plains and sea blacked out.

Origin.—Most of the Japanese plains are the result of river deposition. They are here designated as delta-fans. This is not to suggest that portions of the lowlands were not at one time below sea level, and their sediments reworked by waves and currents. Technically speaking, therefore, those portions of the plains which were submarine in origin are coastal plains, but in general no distinction will be made here between subaerial and submarine origin. The fact that almost every Japanese plain is associated with a river, and that most rivers have plains at their sea ends, clearly indicates the riverine origin of most of the sediments comprising the Japanese lowlands. Many plains in Nippon also contain considerable additions of volcanic ash.

As the swift, turbulent mountain streams of Japan debouch from their mountain valleys onto the plains, rapidly losing gradient, they deposit their loads of coarse sand, gravel, and boulders near the base of the mountain in the form of alluvial cones and fans. Most Japanese delta-fans steepen very perceptibly as the mountain hinterland is approached and the materials comprising the deposits become coarser. Nevertheless, because of the small size of most Japanese plains, the mountain-fed rivers in time of flood are able to carry clear to the sea much coarser materials than one ordinarily finds in deltas.

Seaward Margins.—The outer margins of the delta-fans are usually

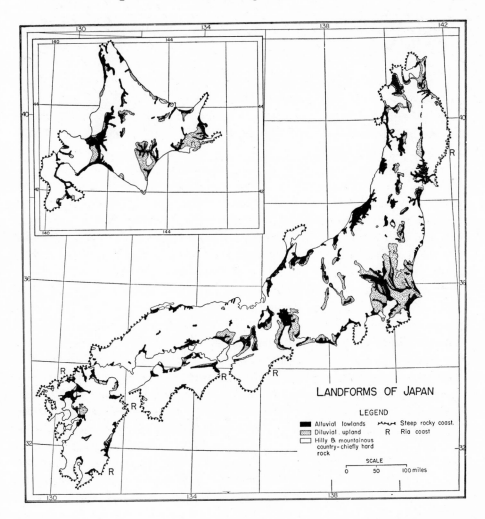

LANDFORMS OF JAPAN

LEGEND

■ Alluvial lowlands   〰〰 Steep rocky coast.
▨ Diluvial upland   R Ria coast
☐ Hilly & mountainous
  country—chiefly hard
  rock

SCALE

0   50   100 miles

Fig. 8

Fig. 9. The inner portion of a small coastal alluvial plain wedged in between spurs of highland. A portion of the Abe delta-fan in Shizuoka Prefecture.

flanked by beach ridges and dunes, the width and height of which depend on the strength of the winds and waves along any particular section of coast and the type of recent vertical movements of the strand line (Fig. 15). Where a low coast faces the open sea, dunes and beach ridges are usually conspicuous features, but along coasts fronting on the quiet waters of deep bays, and especially the Inland Sea, they may be very inconspicuous or lacking altogether. It is along the stormy Japan Sea coast that dunes and multiple beach ridges are best developed. On the Niigata Plain, for example, the parallel beach ridges and dunes, separated by narrow, partially filled lagoons, attain a width of several miles. The parallelism of the littoral terrain features is conspicuous. Not infrequently

Fig. 10. Looking seaward, crest of a beach ridge planted in conifers. Vegetables and orchards inland from conifers.

the coastal dunes and beach ridges so obstruct the natural seaward movement of drainage waters that poorly drained land, or even lake and swamp, develop back of them (Fig. 209 on page 449 and Fig. 217 on page 457). Rivers are noticeably deflected from a direct

20

seaward course and often are forced to flow parallel with the coast for some distance before they succeed in breaking through the dune and beach-ridge barriers to the sea. Many of the ridges have been planted with pine forests to prevent the sand from being blown inland over the fertile rice land, and to serve as wind breaks (Fig. 10). These elevated features, composed of coarse sand, are obviously unsuited to paddy rice,

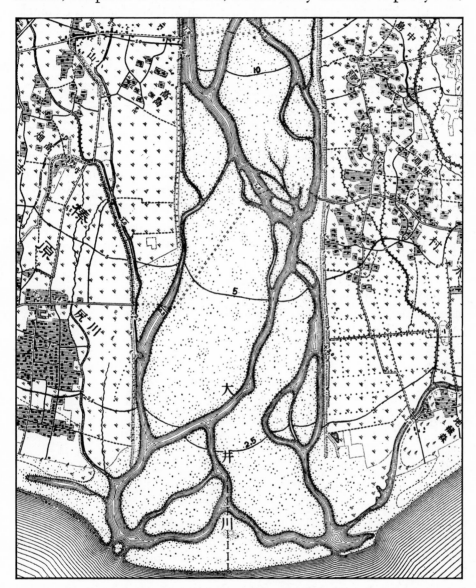

FIG. 11. Oi River in Shizuoka Prefecture. Note braided channel and the seaward bending of the contours. From Japanese army topographic sheet, scale 1: 25,000.

and hence their fields of orchards, vegetables, cereals, and other unirrigated crops are another feature that distinguishes them from the plain proper to the rear, where paddy rice is usually the chief crop.

Rivers on the plains are shallow and braided. They flow in broad gravel-choked beds, the several channels, except in flood periods, occupying only a small part of the total width of the bed (Fig. 11). Characteristically, the rivers are *on* the plains rather than *in* them, for their channels and levees are the most elevated portions of the plains; that is, the land slopes downward away from the rivers (Fig. 12). When bicycling in con-

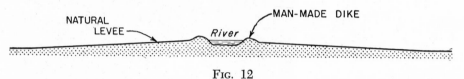

FIG. 12

nection with my field work in Japan, I could usually tell when I was approaching a river because the pedaling became harder by reason of the upgrade. After crossing the bridge over the stream, it was possible to coast or pedal leisurely for a short distance. In a number of places in Japan the streams are so much higher than the adjacent country that roads and even railroads pass under their channels in tunnels instead of surmounting them (Fig. 13). On the topographic maps contours usually bend downstream in the vicinity of river channels, indicating that they are above the general country level (Fig. 11). Natural and man-made levees and dikes, often more than a single series of the artificial variety, hold the lowland stream within its raised channel (Fig. 14). Such elevated streams are both asset and liability—an asset in that a simple gravity system ordinarily serves to distribute their waters for irrigation purposes over the rice fields on the plain; a liability in that they often break their levees in time of flood and do an inordinate amount of damage.

Diluvial Terraces.—The inner margins of the delta-plains frequently terminate abruptly, with no marked increase in slope, at the bases of the encircling hardrock foothills. At the points where rivers debouch upon a plain the transition is made less abrupt by the presence of steeply inclined, coarse-textured alluvial fans or cones, which in certain areas are continuous enough to form piedmont belts. It is very common also for the descent from interior mountain to new alluvial plain to be broken by one or more intermediate steps in the form of sand and gravel terraces (Fig. 15). These terraces are of unconsolidated materials deposited by rivers and probably reworked by waves and currents. They are alluvium in part at least, but it is alluvium whose fertility has been sapped by long-continued leaching without being replenished by additions of new sediment. This older alluvium, as it is commonly called in this country, the Japanese geologists and geographers call *diluvium*. Most of the diluvial terraces are the result of uplift associated with mountain building, which has raised to their present positions coastal plains and delta-fans that were once near sea level. With the uplift the streams were rejuvenated and a portion of the elevated alluvium was cut away and carried

FIG. 13. Tokaido Railroad carried by tunnels under an elevated stream channel in Biwa Basin.

seaward to form the newer alluvial plains. The presence of diluvial terraces in almost all parts of the country from Hokkaido to Kyushu has led one group of geomorphologists to conclude that rather general and contemporaneous uplift of the Japanese island group has taken place. In some places there are multiple terraces, indicating several periods of

FIG. 14. Elevated and diked stream. A road follows the crest of one levee. A village has also sought out the elevated dry site. Bamboo groves protect against washing.

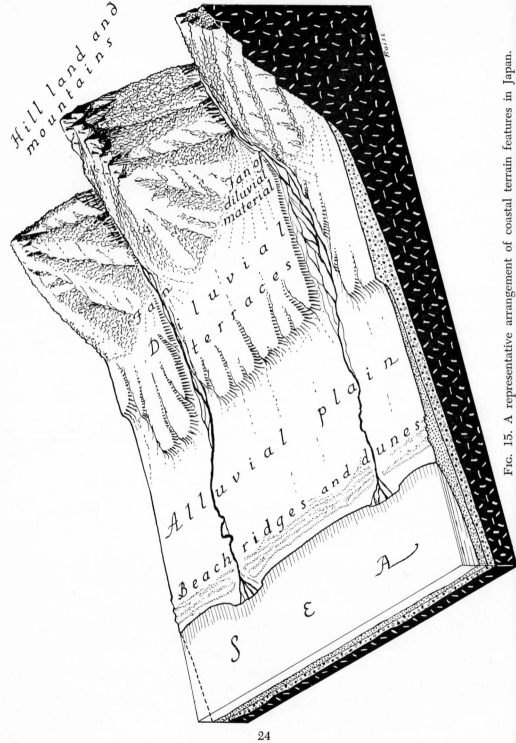

Hill land and mountains

Fan of diluvial material

Diluvial terraces

Fan

Alluvial plain

Beach ridges and dunes

SEA

Raisz

Fig. 15. A representative arrangement of coastal terrain features in Japan.

24

relatively rapid uplift. In certain coastal areas there are conspicuous terraces of considerable extent which are chiefly the result of wave planation. These benches are composed largely of hardrock with only a veneer of gravel and sand covering the erosion surface (Fig. 16). The Kushiro and Nemuro plains of southeastern Hokkaido are of this origin.

The usual form of the diluvial terrace in Japan is that of a low, flat-crested upland rising in fairly abrupt slopes above the adjacent surfaces of new alluvium (Fig. 17). They vary markedly in elevation; some are so low as to be almost indistinguishable from the new alluvium, whereas others rise by precipitous slopes to a height of several hundred feet. Vertical downcutting by streams is rapid in these elevated unconsolidated sediments, creating a terrain of shallow, canyon-like valleys with flat to gently sloping interfluves. This latter feature is a remnant of an earlier depositional (or erosional) surface; its preservation indicates how short a time, geologically speaking, has elapsed since the uplift. Within a relatively brief time, measured geologically, these diluvial crests are bound to disappear. As it is, the relatively even skylines of the diluvial uplands are one of the distinctive characteristics of their profiles as seen from a distance, distinguishing them from hardrock hills.

Less common are certain diluvial terraces, ordinarily older and higher, that have been so intricately carved by streams that level upland surfaces are infrequent and the re-

Fig. 16. Multiple marine abrasion terraces along a portion of Japan's coast. From a Japanese source, author unknown.

gion has been reduced to a bad-land condition in which slopes predominate, thus much resembling the Tertiary rock areas. The Tama terraces of the Kwanto or Tokyo Plain are of this type, as are certain others in the southern part of the Lake Biwa Basin north of Kyoto, and along the margins of the Osaka and Nagoya plains.

Throughout Japan the diluvial terraces are much less intensively utilized than are the lower plains of new alluvium. Rice is not a common crop on the diluvial uplands, unirrigated crops being more characteristic—wheat, barley, vegetables, mulberry, tea, and orchard fruits. Large areas are in planted forest and parts would be classed as virtual wasteland (Fig. 17 at the left). This less intensive use of the diluvial terraces is partly a reflection of the difficulty of raising irrigation water from the deeply incised valleys to the upland levels. And to the Japanese any land that cannot be inundated and therefore planted to paddy rice is, *ipso facto*, inferior land. In any case, much diluvial terrace land is composed of such coarse materials that water would not remain long on its surface (Fig. 18). Moreover, much of it has

FIG. 17. Diluvial terrace. *Above,* the flattish crest of a terrace. Note the deeply incised valley with steep margins. *Below,* a level terrace surface with a cover of wild grasses and shrubs. Such areas, designated *gen-ya,* are used to some extent for grazing and as sources of firewood.

become infertile. Leached of the soluble minerals and shy of humus, the diluvium is low in plant foods and inferior in structure. The addition of acidic volcanic ash in some parts of Japan has done little to improve the condition of the soil. Where the veneer of ash is not present the soil may be quite sandy or even gravelly.

The Larger Plains.—Among Japan's largest and most important plains are the three on the Pacific side of southwestern Honshu, each at the head of a large and deep indentation formed by subsidence: (1) the Kwanto Plain (13,000 sq. km.) at the head of Tokyo Bay, containing the two great urban centers of Tokyo and Yokohama and boasting a total population of over 15 million; (2) the Nobi Plain (1,800 sq. km.) at the head of Ise Bay, with the great industrial city of Nagoya and a total population of over 5 million; and (3) the Kinai or Settsu Plain (1,250 sq. km.) at the head of Osaka Bay, on which are located the three great cities of Kyoto, Osaka, and Kobe, and which is coextensive with a population cluster of over 9 million people. A similar fourth bay, Suruga, between Tokyo and Ise

Fig. 18. Materials composing a diluvial terrace. Beneath the top humus layer is a porous mass of sand, gravel, stones, and even sizeable boulders.

bays, has no comparable bay-head plain with a large cluster of population, for the head of Suruga Bay marks the southern end of the Fossa Magna, from which rises the immense volcanic cone of Fujisan and its satellite Ashitaka. On the three plains named are located all six of Japan's great cities of nearly a million or more population, her three chief foreign trade ports, and three of her four great nodes of industrial development. Other large and important plains in Japan are the Ishikari (2,100 sq. km.) in southwestern Hokkaido; the Echigo (1,800 sq. km.) in western North Honshu, where the city of Niigata is situated; the Sendai (1,500 sq. km.) in eastern North Honshu, which supports the city of Sendai; and the

Tsukushi (1,200 sq. km.) in northwestern Kyushu, of which Kurume is the metropolis.

Interior Lowlands.—Although the greater number of Japanese plains, including the most important ones, front upon the sea, a considerable number of isolated basins, a few fairly large but most of them small, are located in the mountainous interior. These are striking in the small amount of genuinely level land characteristic of their alluvial and diluvial deposits. From the enclosing hill and mountain ramparts numerous torrential streams debouch into the basins, building a series of converging and coalescing alluvial cones and fans (Fig. 199 on page 438). The resulting terrain is one of smooth, moderately inclined slopes with a very conspicuous cone pattern. Coarse materials predominate. Characteristically these interior basins are arranged in lines or rows, following important zones of crustal fracture and subsidence. Illustrating this linear arrangement are (1) the series of north-south basins in central Hokkaido; (2) the two parallel north-south rows of basins on either side of the central range in northern Honshu; (3) the northwest-southeast chain of basins across central Honshu, coinciding with the Fossa Magna; and (4) the series of northeast-southwest basins corresponding with the great medial dislocation line in Kii Peninsula and northern Shikoku.

The Coastline[10]

Few regions of the earth have so great a variety of interesting coastal features as does Japan. Nippon Proper has a remarkably long coastline, approximately 17,000 miles, or one linear mile of coast for each 8.5 square miles of area.[11] The influence of this unusually long line of contact with the sea is increased by the fact that most of the lowlands, the only areas capable of large-scale production and consequently the areas of large population, have sea frontage. To an unusual degree, therefore, the people of Japan have a maritime outlook.

Coastal features of first magnitude in Nippon are due principally to faulting and warping; broad regional contrasts represent differences in fault patterns and in the crustal movements that have occurred along the fault lines. Thus the coastline of the Japan Sea littoral is relatively smooth because it roughly parallels a fault system. Only occasionally, as at Wakasa Bay, does a fault system which has developed at an angle to the coast produce major irregularities. Along the east coast of North Honshu

[10] For a fairly comprehensive treatment of this topic, in both its general and its regional aspects, see Ludwig Mecking, *Japans Häfen* (Hamburg, 1931), 180–207.
[11] The ratio is about 1:13 for Great Britain.

the fault system cuts the north-south highlands at an oblique angle, resulting in an echelon type of development with some stretches of the coast paralleling the fault lines and others trending at an angle with them. The Pacific side of southwestern Japan is indented by a series of channels and bays of fault origin oriented in a general north-south direction and consequently cutting across the trend of the coast. The result is a number of major irregularities. And finally the Inland Sea and midwestern Kyushu owe their coastal complexity and irregularity to subsidence along a mosaic of fault lines crossing each other at several angles.

In general the minor features of any portion of Japan's coast are the result of two elements: (1) the relative resistance of the rock and (2) the nature of the crustal movements. Irregular and deeply indented coasts are most commonly developed in resistant rocks, whereas the hinterlands of smooth coasts are usually composed of weak rocks.[12] Geologists believe that during the earliest alluvial period there was a general subsidence of the Japanese islands which created a coastline much more irregular than the present one.[13] Wave action has since eroded the promontories and filled in the bays, thus gradually smoothing the coastline. In general two types of coastline are recognized. One, usually the smoother, has raised beaches and terraces, and the incised rivers give evidence of emergence. In the other type, which is more irregular, submergence is indicated.

The shoreline of Japan facing Asia is much less diversified than that along the Pacific, the ratio of their lengths being about 1:3.7. The most marked irregularity in the prevailingly regular coastline along the Japan Sea is the much-indented and island-studded coast of western Kyushu, where a mature land surface cut by a complicated system of faults has suffered subsidence.[14] It is on this much indented coastal area that the well protected deepwater port of Nagasaki is located. Northeast from Kyushu are the lesser irregularities of the Shinji Horst region in northern Chugoku, where the old city of Matsue is located; the deeply indented ria coast of the Wakasa Bay region, in what is the most constricted part of Honshu; and Noto and Oga peninsulas farther north. The coasts of the plains along the Japan Sea side are often bordered by dunes and

[12] Y. Otuka, "The Japanese Coastline" (in Japanese with English summary), in the *Geographical Review of Japan* (*Chirigaku Hyron*), 9 (1933):818–843.

[13] Dr. Jörn Leo, "Küstengestaltung Japans nach neuesten Forschungen," in *Petermanns Mitteilungen*, 80 (1934):260.

[14] Shinji Yamane, "Physiographic Changes in the Northwestern Coast of Kyushu in the Quarternary Period," in the *Proceedings of the Fifth Pacific Science Congress*, Toronto, 1933, 2:1599–1603.

belts of beach ridges, enclosing lagoons on their land sides. Relatively smooth and abrupt coasts are characteristic of the Pacific side of Japan north of the latitude of Tokyo, the single important exception being the irregular ria coast of the southern part of the Kitakami hill land in northern Honshu. Pacific southwestern Japan has many more large irregularities. The four great bays between Tokyo and Osaka have already been described and their importance suggested. Farther to the southwest is the island-studded Inland Sea with its ragged coastal margins, and the ria coasts of Kyushu, Shikoku, and Kii Peninsula bordering Bungo and Kii channels leading to that sea. The coastal outlines of the Pacific Folded Mountains, or the Outer Zone of southwest Japan, in southern Kii Peninsula, southern Shikoku, and southern Kyushu, are more regular, although minor irregularities are numerous.

Unfortunately Japan's best natural harbors are situated in regions that in other respects are unsuited to the development of important ports. In general the hinterlands of the deeply indented coasts where good harbors are plentiful are regions of rugged terrain which are relatively unproductive and are unconnected by easy natural routes with productive regions to the rear. Conversely, the productive plains regions are ordinarily paralleled by shallow silted waters, have smooth shorelines, and on their sea sides are bordered by belts of dunes and beach ridges or by abrupt terrace fronts. Often the local port of a small plain is located not on the sea margin of the plain itself but at some coastal point farther distant, where spurs of the hardrock hills, descending to tidewater, create a better harbor. Where rivers enter the sea at the heads of large indentations, such as Tokyo, Ise, and Osaka bays, forming relatively extensive bay-head plains, so much sediment is deposited that artificially dredged channels are necessary to permit ships of any size to reach the river entrance. Moreover, the rivers are so small and shallow that seagoing vessels are unable to enter the plains. There are no deep and extensive estuaries, such as Delaware or Chesapeake Bay, which would permit the development of great ports scores of miles inland.

SELECTED REFERENCES

CUSHING, SUMNER. "Coastal Plains and Block Mountains in Japan." *Annals of the Association of American Geographers*, 3 (1913):43–61.

HALL, ROBERT B., and AKIRA WATANABE. "Landforms of Japan." *Papers of the Michigan Academy of Science, Arts, and Letters*, 18 (1932):157–207.

ROSINSKI, HERBERT. "Das Japanische Kaiser-reich." *Handbuch der geographischen Wissenschaft*, 7:435–557. Pottsdam, 1937.

RUELLAN, FRANCIS. "Le relief et la structure du Japon du sudouest." *Annals de Géographie,* 41 (1932):141–166.

———. *Le Kwansi: étude geomorphologique d'une region japonaise.* Arrault et cie, Tours, 1940.

SION, JULES. "Asie des Moussons, Part I: Chine-Japon." *Géographie Universelle,* 9:189–198. Paris, 1928.

TSUJIMURA, T. *The Regional Physiography of Japan* (in Japanese). Tokyo, 1929.

———. "Summary of the Physiographic Division of Japan." *Proceedings of the Fifth Pacific Science Congress,* Toronto, 1933, 2:1619–1628.

WATANABE, AKIRA. "On the Distribution of Volcanoes in Japan." *Papers of the Michigan Academy of Science, Arts, and Letters,* 14:433–436. Ann Arbor, 1930.

WILLIS, BAILEY. "Why the Japanese Islands?" *Scientific Monthly,* 51:99–111 (August, 1940).

YABE, H. "Problems Concerning the Geotectonics of the Japanese Islands." *Science Reports of the Tohoku Imperial University, Sendai,* Second Series, 4:75–104. 1917.

YAMASAKI, NAOMASA. "Geographical Sketch of Japan." *Scientific Japan, Past and Present,* 1–32. Kyoto, 1926.

CHAPTER II

Climate

THE CLIMATES of Japan are a mixture of continental and marine elements, the former predominating. This is what one would expect to find in a mountainous island group stretched out in subtropical and middle latitudes along the eastern or leeward side of the earth's greatest land mass. In some respects the climates of the islands are very similar to those of the North American Atlantic seaboard between Maine and southern Georgia.

Some Important Controls of Climate in Japan

Extending from about 31° to 45° N., Japan has a range of latitude which in itself tends to produce marked climatic contrasts between the northern and southern parts. Latitudinal differences in winter temperatures and in length of frost-free season are striking, being equivalent to those between the spring-wheat area in South Dakota and the sugar-cane region of Louisiana in the United States. Fortunately a large part of Japan lies in subtropical latitudes, where the climatic energy is abundant and the climatic potentialities for plant growth high. Intricacy of surface configuration and differences in altitude of 10,000 feet and more are other factors that make for marked local differences in climate.

MONSOONS AND ASSOCIATED AIR MASSES

Probably the greatest of all the controls operating to produce the climates of Japan are the monsoonal air masses that so dominate the weather conditions throughout southeastern Asia. In winter the cold Asiatic continent develops an immense thermal anticyclone whose center is in the Lake Baikal area of Siberia. From this region great surges of dry, cold, polar-continental air stream centrifugally oceanward. This is the northwest winter monsoon of China and Japan (Fig. 19a). In summer, on the other hand, when the continent is warm, a thermally induced low-pressure center-of-action replaces the winter anticyclone over Asia. The pressure gradient is consequently the reverse of that which prevails in

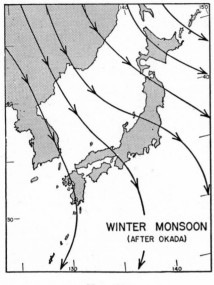

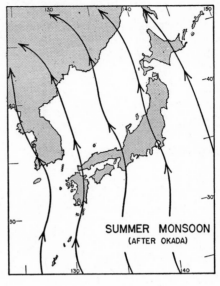

FIG. 19a   FIG. 19b

winter, and moist tropical and subtropical maritime air masses (mT) originating over the warmer parts of the Pacific Ocean converge upon eastern Asia. This is the weaker and more intermittent southeast summer monsoon (Fig. 19b). Throughout the winter months, therefore, winds in Japan are prevailingly from the northwest, having originated over the cold land mass of eastern Siberia; in summer they are from the southeast, having originated over tropical seas. As shown by the wind roses (Fig. 20) the winter and the summer monsoon and the air masses of which they are composed are not continuous air streams, for there are frequent interruptions in the seaward flow of polar-continental air in winter and the landward flow of tropical-maritime air in summer. That is to say, in all seasons winds do blow from the several points of the compass. But the fact that they are predominantly from cold Siberia and Manchuria in winter and from a subtropical ocean in summer results in colder winters and hotter, more humid summers, than are normal for Japan's latitude.

As Table 5 shows, the winter monsoon is stronger than that of summer. The maximum difference between January and July wind velocities is greatest at Akita, which receives the full force of the winter winds from the Asiatic continent. At Osaka on the Pacific side the difference in strength between the summer and winter winds is less marked.

According to Arakawa the four air masses which influence Japan's weather most are:

TABLE 5.—AVERAGE VELOCITY OF WIND AT SELECTED STATIONS
(meters per second)

Station	Jan.	Feb.	Mar.	Apr.	May	June	July	Aug.	Sept.	Oct.	Nov.	Dec.	Yr.
Osaka (Inland Sea)	3.2	3.2	3.1	2.0	2.8	2.7	2.8	2.8	2.7	2.5	2.7	3.3	2.9
Akita (Japan Sea)	5.9	5.5	5.4	4.5	4.0	3.3	2.8	2.7	2.8	3.3	4.6	5.9	4.2
Nemuro (western Hok-kaido)	5.4	4.8	4.9	5.1	5.1	4.3	3.9	3.8	4.2	5.1	5.6	5.7	4.8

Source: Okada, *The Climate of Japan*, 280.

TABLE 6.—AIR MASSES IN THE VICINITY OF JAPAN

General Latitude	Nature	Local Source Region	Name of Air Mass	Season of Prevalence	Bergeron Classification
Polar	Continental	Siberia	Siberian Continental	Mainly in winter; also spring and fall.	cPK (Japan Sea side of Japan) cPW (Pacific side of Japan)
	Maritime	Okhotsk Sea and region of Kuriles	Okhostk Maritime	Mainly in *Bai-u* season in late spring and early summer; often in spring and fall.	mPK
Tropical	Maritime	Subtropical seas south of Honshu	Ogasawara	Mainly summer; also in spring and fall.	mTW
	Continental	Yangtze region and South China	Yangtze	Most often in spring and fall.	Varies with route taken.
Equatorial	Maritime	Equatorial Pacific north of equator	Trade wind	No particular season.	mE
	Maritime	Equatorial Pacific south of equator	Southwest Monsoon	Typhoon season of late summer and fall.	

Source: H. Arakawa, "Air Masses of Japan," *Journal of the Meteorological Society of Japan*, 13 (1935): 391.

1. Polar continental (cP). Source region Siberia and Manchuria.

2. Polar maritime (mP). Source region the Okhotsk Sea and the higher latitudes of the north Pacific.

3. Tropical maritime (mT). Source region the subtropical latitudes of the north Pacific.

4. Tropical continental (cT). Source region the subtropical latitudes of China.[1]

Polar Continental or Siberian Air.—At its source in eastern Siberia winter cP air is cold, dry, and stable. Usually there is a strong temperature inversion in the lower layers. As it moves southeast over the rough lands of eastern Siberia and Manchuria, turbulence tends to destroy the inversion and to increase the temperature of the surface layers. After the cP air leaves the continent and moves over the Sea of Japan the lower layers of the continental air mass are distinctly warmed and humidified, and by the time it reaches Japan it is a modified type of cP air (nPc), one that is conditionally and convectively unstable. Its trajectory over the Japan Sea has not been long enough, however, to transform it into genuine maritime air. It is still raw and cold, but its lower layers have acquired considerable moisture. As this unstable, modified-continental air mass is thrust upward by the highlands of western Japan, it produces a heavy winter precipitation, much of it in the form of snow. Dark, gloomy winter weather with a heavy cloud cover is characteristic of the Japan Sea side of Nippon. After crossing the highlands the polar air descends on the lee side as a drier and warmer air mass, and the weather associated with it is likely to be relatively fair. It moves southeastward in successive gushes, each new invasion extending somewhat farther toward the equator. As it advances with decreasing velocity toward the lower latitudes it warms markedly at the surface, and ultimately its temperature becomes enough higher than that of the fresher cP air advancing from the north to produce extensive fronts between the two polar air masses, resulting in cyclone development with associated cloud

---

[1] The discussion of Japanese air masses is based chiefly on the following: H. Arakawa, "The Air Masses of Japan" (in Japanese with English abstract), in the *Journal of the Meteorological Society of Japan,* 13:385–402 (September, 1935); 14:328–338 (July, 1936); 15:185–189 (May, 1937); H. Arakawa, "Die Luftmassen in den japanischen Gebieten," *Meteorologische Zeitschrift,* 54:169–174 (May, 1937); H. Futi, S. Tazima, and N. Murase, "On the Structure of an Extratropical Cyclone" (in Japanese with English abstract), *Journal of the Meteorological Society of Japan,* 17:450–453 (November, 1939); K. Takahashi, "On the Transformation of the Cold Dry Air-Mass by Traveling over Warm Sea" (in Japanese with English abstract), *ibid.,* 18:77–80 (March, 1940); T. Yamanaka and C. Ikeda, "On the Three Principal Air Masses in Japan" (in Japanese with English abstract), *ibid.,* 17:450–453 (September, 1939).

TABLE 7.—SIBERIAN AIR MASSES (cP) AT PEKING, CHINA

Elevation in Meters	FALL			WINTER			SPRING		
	Temp. F°	Specific Humidity g/kg.	Relative Humidity %	Temp. F°	Specific Humidity g/kg.	Relative Humidity %	Temp. F°	Specific Humidity g/kg.	Relative Humidity %
70.5	54.5	3.7	38	24.1	0.8	28	60.8	3.0	25
500	46.2	3.0	41	16.7	0.7	29	54.0	2.5	26
1000	38.1	2.6	45	9.0	0.6	30	45.5	2.1	28
1500	29.7	2.3	49	1.9	0.5	31	36.5	1.8	30
2000	23.5	1.9	52	−4.7	0.4	32	27.3	1.4	33
2500	—	—	—	—	—	—	19.9	1.2	35

Source: H. Arakawa, "Air Masses of Japan," in the *Journal of the Meteorological Society of Japan*, 13 (1935): 395.

TABLE 8.—SIBERIAN AIR MASSES (cP) AT TATENO, JAPAN
(36°3′N., 140°8′E.; northeast of Tokyo on Kwanto Plain)

Elevation in Meters	FALL			WINTER			SPRING		
	Temp. F°	Specific Humidity g/kg.	Relative Humidity %	Temp. F°	Specific Humidity g/kg.	Relative Humidity %	Temp. F°	Specific Humidity g/kg.	Relative Humidity %
26	61.5	7.3	63	40.6	3.1		55.6	5.7	60
200	55.9	6.0	62	37.6	2.8		49.6	4.7	60
500	50.2	5.3	66	34.3	2.8		43.9	4.1	63
800	45.3	4.8	69	31.5	2.8		38.7	3.8	67
1000	43.2	4.3	66	29.1	2.6		35.2	3.2	71
1200	42.3	3.8	59	27.1	2.3		33.3	3.0	64
1500	39.6	3.2	53	25.7	1.9		31.8	2.6	55
2000	36.1	2.5	45	22.6	1.7		27.9	2.0	54

Source: H. Arakawa, "Air Masses of Japan," in the *Journal of the Meteorological Society of Japan*, 13 (1935): 396.

TABLE 9.—SUMMER OKHOTSK AIR MASS (mP) AT TATENO, JAPAN

Elevation in Meters	Temperature F°	Specific Humidity g/kg.	Relative Humidity %
26	71.4	12.6	77
200	68.0	12.3	82
500	64.0	11.4	84
800	61.2	11.0	87
1000	59.4	10.7	89
1200	58.1	9.9	83
1500	58.1	9.3	76
2000	54.9	8.4	73

Source: H. Arakawa, "Air Masses of Japan," in the *Journal of the Meteorological Society of Japan*, 13 (1935): 397.

and precipitation. Japan experiences cP air chiefly in winter, less frequently in spring and fall, rarely in summer.

Polar Maritime or Okhotsk Air.—As it leaves its source region over the
Okhotsk Sea and the Kurile region polar maritime air is cool and moderately moist. Because of the general west-to-east direction of atmospheric
circulation in these latitudes mP air is not common in Japan. In late
spring and early summer, however, when west-to-east circulation weak-
ens and an abundance of cold
water is brought south into the
vicinity of the Kuriles, high-pres-
sure centers develop. Air from
these centers moves southward,
becoming warmed and absorbing
moisture en route. This mP air
may reach central and southern
Japan, bringing with it the overcast, sultry, and drizzly weather
which is known as the *bai-u* or
plum season. Occasionally, when
the lower strata of the mP air are
rapidly warmed, the rain is of
convectional origin but more frequently it is of frontal origin, for
the upper surface of the mP air
mass is a sloping discontinuity
surface over which the mT air is
forced to rise. The comparatively
stagnant nature of these fronts
may cause the unpleasant drip-
ping weather to continue for days
on end.

*Tropical Maritime or Ogasa-
wara Air* originates in the warm
subsiding air masses of the subtropical anticyclone over the
western Pacific southeast of Japan. At its source, therefore, it is
warm, dry, and stable. Moving
north as the summer monsoon, its
lower layers are cooled somewhat,

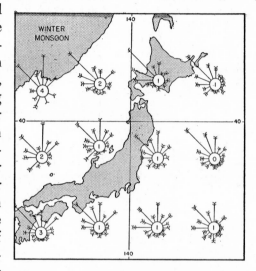

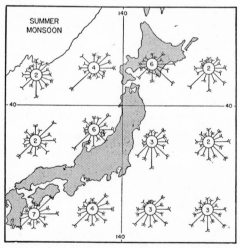

Fig. 20. Length of arrow indicates prevalence of wind from that direction; figures
in circles, percentage of calms; number of
feathers on arrows, relative strength of winds.

TABLE 10.—SUMMER OGASAWARA (mT) AIR AT TATENO, JAPAN

Elevation in Meters	Temperature F°	Specific Humidity g/kg.	Relative Humidity %
26	82.6	19.5	81
200	79.2	17.9	81
500	74.7	15.9	81
800	71.6	14.2	77
1000	70.0	12.9	73
1200	68.5	11.8	68
1500	67.1	10.4	62
2000	62.4	9.0	60

Source: H. Arakawa, "Air Masses of Japan," in the *Journal of the Meteorological Society of Japan*, 13 (1935): 398.

TABLE 11.—YANGTZE AIR MASSES (cT) AT NANKING, CHINA

Elevation in Meters	FALL			WINTER			SPRING		
	Temp. F°	Specific Humidity g/kg.	Relative Humidity %	Temp. F°	Specific Humidity g/kg.	Relative Humidity %	Temp. F°	Specific Humidity g/kg.	Relative Humidity %
10	87.6	15.0	54	61.7	6.2	52	49.1	4.8	65
500	87.4	14.6	49	53.2	5.3	56	42.3	4.0	66
1000	86.0	15.1	49	45.3	4.9	59	36.3	3.3	64
1500	81.3	12.7	45	42.4	3.5	51	30.2	2.7	63
2000	76.3	11.5	45	43.2	2.1	33	27.5	2.3	56
2500	67.3	9.0	47	41.0	1.9	34	23.6	2.0	52
3000	59.4	7.4	50	36.3	1.3	27	20.3	1.5	45

Source: H. Arakawa, "Air Masses of Japan," in the *Journal of the Meteorological Society of Japan*, 13 (1935): 399.

TABLE 12.—YANGTZE AIR MASSES (cT) AT TATENO, JAPAN

Elevation in Meters	SPRING			AUTUMN		
	Temperature F°	Specific Humidity g/kg.	Relative Humidity %	Temperature F°	Specific Humidity g/kg.	Relative Humidity %
26	67.8	9.0	62	64.6	7.9	64
200	64.6	7.9	60	61.5	7.6	62
500	59.0	6.8	61	55.9	6.7	65
800	53.4	6.2	66	50.7	6.0	68
1000	50.0	5.7	65	47.8	5.5	69
1200	46.9	5.3	69	45.5	5.0	67
1500	41.9	4.6	68	42.3	4.4	64
2000	37.6	3.8	64	36.3	3.6	60

Source: H. Arakawa, "Air Masses of Japan," in the *Journal of the Meteorological Society of Japan* 13 (1935): 399.

and it becomes thermally more stable, but at the same time large additions of moisture cause it to become convectively and conditionally unstable. The air movement is chiefly laminar rather than vertical. Clear, calm summer days with sultry heat and a moisture haze are the typical manifestation of Ogasawara air over Japan. Since much surface heating is required to produce thermal convection, local thunderstorms are less frequent than one might expect. On the other hand, because of the large moisture content of the convectively unstable mT air, upward propulsion by highlands or along a front results in abundant rain. Most of Japan's precipitation is from Ogasawara air. This air mass is dominant in Japan in summer, the time of the summer monsoon, and is frequent also in spring and fall. In winter it is infrequent at ground level because polar air masses are dominant during that season, although it may be the precipitating air mass in a cyclone above the front.

Tropical Continental or Yangtze Air Masses originate over subtropical China. According to Arakawa, they affect Japan's weather chiefly during the transition seasons, spring and fall. At their source they have relatively high temperatures and a comparatively low moisture content. Although they are somewhat unstable, the dearth of moisture results in few clouds, and associated weather conditions tend to be good. With their passage over the East China Sea and the waters adjoining Japan the Yangtze air masses are considerably modified; by the time they arrive in Japan they have acquired many of the characteristics of maritime air and are potential rain-bringers. What kind of weather they produce in Japan depends upon the trajectory of the air mass after it leaves China, and the length of time it remains over the sea.

Equatorial Air Masses and their influence upon Japanese weather receive slight attention from Arakawa. It appears that they affect Japan only occasionally and then indirectly as a factor in the development of typhoons.

Influences of Surrounding Seas and Ocean Currents.—Other controls of Japan's climate are her insularity and the nature of the ocean waters surrounding her. The fact that cP air masses from Siberia must cross from two to six hundred miles of moderately warm ocean surface before reaching Japan Proper has a pronounced effect on the country's winter weather conditions. For although the trajectory of this air mass is not long enough to transform the cP air into one with genuine maritime characteristics, its temperature and humidity are so increased by the Japan Sea as to produce less severe winter temperatures and much heavier winter precipitation in Japan than in Manchuria and Siberia.

Two ocean currents, a cold one from the north, the *Oyashio* or Okhotsk Current, and a warm one from the south, the *Kuroshio* or Japan Current, have some influence upon Japan's climate (Fig. 21). The Japan Current bifurcates at the southern extremity of Japan Proper, the main stream flowing northward along the Pacific coast of Honshu to nearly the latitude of Tokyo (35°) before it turns northeastward into the Pacific. The surface temperatures of this warm current range from about 82° in late summer to 68° in late winter. Because it is on the lee side of Japan during the winter monsoon, its direct effects on the temperatures of Nippon are minimized. The western branch of the *Kuroshio*, the *Tsushima* Current, containing a much smaller amount of warm water, enters the Japan Sea through the *Tsushima* (Korea) Strait and flows northward in the eastern part of that sea as far as northern Hokkaido.

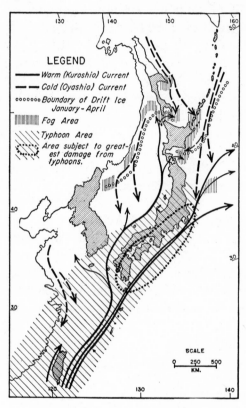

The cold *Oyashio* Current, flowing southward from the Okhotsk Sea, hugs the Pacific side of Japan down to about latitude 36°, where it sinks below the waters of the *Kuroshio*. In the western part of the Japan Sea cold water is likewise present, but this can scarcely be regarded as a western branch of the Okhotsk Current, inasmuch as the strait between Sakhalin Island and the Asiatic mainland is only about 7 kilometers wide and 12 meters deep at its narrowest part. It is probably the result of excessive cooling in winter, when seaward moving cP air masses are prevalent. In the western part of the Japan Sea the sea surface temperature in summer is only about 67°, whereas in the eastern part it is approximately 81°, a difference of nearly 14°.[2] Since the cold *Oyashio* is on the windward side during the summer

Fig. 21. After Haushofer.

---

[2] H. U. Sverdrup, Martin W. Johnson, and Richard H. Fleming, *The Oceans: Their Physics, Chemistry, and General Biology* (Prentice-Hall, Inc., New York, 1942), 734.

monsoon, it produces distinctly lowered summer temperatures and much fog on the Pacific side of North Honshu and Hokkaido.

Storm Control.—Japan is a region of numerous fronts with associated cyclonic storms. In fact, the winter temperature gradients along the Pacific margins of Asia are some of the steepest on earth. Such regions, where air masses of different temperatures are in close juxtaposition, are ideal for the development of fronts and their cyclonic storms, with which are associated conditions of cloud and precipitation. The frequent nonperiodic weather changes during the winter and the summer monsoon, giving Japanese weather its variety and changeability, especially in the winter, result from the passage of cyclones with their associated air masses and fronts. These storms are most frequent in winter and spring, least frequent in late summer. Figs. 22 and 23 show the characteristic tracks of cyclones in the Far East during February and August, when cyclones reach their maximum and minimum frequency in the Japan area. In winter the storms appear to come both from the Yangtze region of central China and from southern Siberia and Manchuria.[3] Both from the southwest and the northwest the tracks converge upon Japan. In summer most storms come from northerly latitudes and appear to travel more northerly routes; hence at this season southern Japan is less affected by well developed surface fronts. The summer map (Fig. 23) shows the ty-

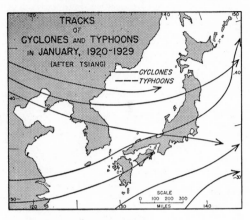

Fig. 22

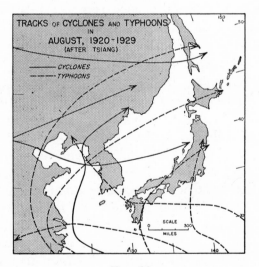

Fig. 23

[3] P. J. Tsiang, "On the Distribution of Typhoons and Depressions in the Far East," in the *Proceedings of the Fifth Pacific Science Congress,* Toronto, 1933, 3:1119–1936.

phoon tracks passing over southern Japan. From mid-June to about mid-July there is a high frequency of relatively weak, slow-moving cyclones and fronts which travel slowly northeastward, or even stagnate over subtropical Japan. Some of these storms appear to originate in the Yangtze lowlands of China, others in the immediate vicinity of Japan. They appear to be associated with a southward movement of Okhotsk air masses in late spring and early summer. Much cloudiness, abundant rain, high humidity, and high sensible temperatures make the so-called *bai-u* or plum rains a very uncomfortable and gloomy season.[4] The early-summer rainfall maximum of subtropical Japan appears to be associated with this seasonal concentration of *bai-u* storms.

TABLE 13.—MEAN NUMBER OF DAYS WITH THUNDERSTORMS AT SELECTED JAPANESE STATIONS

Station	Jan.	Feb.	Mar.	Apr.	May	June	July	Aug.	Sept.	Oct.	Nov.	Dec.	Yr
Kagoshima	0.4	—	0.8	0.8	0.6	0.4	3.2	2.8	3.0	0.6	0.8	1.2	14.6
Fukuoka	0.2	—	0.8	0.6	—	0.6	4.0	4.0	4.0	0.2	0.2	0.6	15.2
Osaka	—	0.2	0.2	0.6	0.6	0.6	1.6	2.2	2.6	0.4	0.2	0.4	9.6
Tokyo	—	—	0.4	0.4	1.2	0.6	2.0	3.0	1.2	0.2	0.2	0.2	9.4
Kofu	0.2	—	0.2	0.8	1.8	2.8	7.8	4.8	1.4	0.4	0.2	0.2	20.8
Niigata	0.6	—	0.6	0.4	1.0	1.4	1.2	2.4	2.4	2.4	1.2	1.4	15.6
Sapporo	—	—	—	—	0.4	0.6	0.8	1.6	1.6	1.2	0.6	—	6.0

Source: T. Okada, *The Climate of Japan*, 349.

Typhoons, those intense cyclones of tropical origin, comparable to our North American West Indian hurricanes, are an important element in the weather of southern Japan. These violent storms, which occur oftenest in late summer and early fall, originate in the Pacific Ocean near the Carolines, Marshall, or Mariana Islands and thence progress toward the northwest. About half of them enter South China or cross the Philippines, and the rest curve to the northeast and pass over southwestern Japan or the adjacent seas. Fortunately these severe storms are not very frequent, averaging only one to two a month from July to October inclusive over the entire typhoon area of eastern Asia. Far fewer than that affect Japan, not more than two a year on the average. The violent wind and rain accompanying typhoons often do great damage, beating down the ripening rice and flooding the rice fields, causing the short, steep-gradient rivers to overflow their banks, and visiting death and destruction upon the villages.

Considering how prevalent are the tropical maritime air masses in

[4] T. Okada, *On the Bai-u or Rainy Season in Japan* (Bulletin of Central Meteorological Observatory of Japan, No. 5, Tokyo, 1910).

summer, and how rugged is the terrain, it is noteworthy that Japan has far fewer thunderstorms than similar subtropical latitudes in the United States. Only 3 to 5 per cent of the days are marked by thunderstorms compared with 20 per cent in the Gulf States of the United States, and between 10 and 20 per cent in most of the Mississippi Valley south of Wisconsin. Even where most frequent, they occur on only about 20 days of the year on the average, and in Hokkaido the number is usually less than 10.[5] By contrast, the eastern American Gulf States have an average of 60 to 80 thunderstorms a year. The reason for this difference is none too clear, for the summer Ogasawara air mass at Tateno, Japan, is warmer and has a higher surface specific humidity than does tropical-gulf air at Miami, Florida.

The Important Climatic Elements

TEMPERATURE

More continental than marine in temperature because of its east-coast location in a region of well developed monsoons, Japan has a distinctly colder winter climate than is normal for its latitude. Actually the Japanese area has a negative January temperature anomaly amounting to about 15 degrees. Summers in Japan, although more normal for the latitude, are for the most part hot and sultry. The statement made in a recent, fairly authoritative publication that the climate of northern Japan is like that of our American Pacific Northwest is decidedly erroneous. The latter is a marine climate whose temperatures are dominated by maritime air masses. Like western Europe, it occupies a windward position on the continent. Japan, on the other hand, is under the influence of air masses from Asia, for a part of the year, with the result that its climate is more severe. It is much more like the climate of our Atlantic seaboard or Mississippi Valley states in similar latitudes, areas which, like Japan, are on the lee side of a great land mass. To be sure, Japan's insularity moderates her winter temperatures somewhat, but Siberian air is so intensely cold at its source that, despite the warming influence of intervening seas, it is still cold continental air when it arrives in Nippon. Thus Asahigawa in Hokkaido at 44° N. has winter and summer temperatures that closely approximate those of St. Johnsbury, Vermont; Tokyo in mid-Japan, at about 36° N., is comparable to Winston-Salem, North Carolina, and Kagoshima in the extreme south at about 31° or 32° N. to Birmingham, Alabama. (For data on Japan's temperatures see Table 14.)

[5] Noto, Hisashi, "Statistical Investigations of Thunderstorms in Japan," in the *Japanese Journal of Astronomy and Geophysics*, 9 (1932):207–243; 10 (1932):51–79.

TABLE 14.—CLIMATIC DATA FOR VARIOUS STATIONS

Station	TEMPERATURE F.				GROWING SEASON IN DAYS	PRECIPITATION												
	Mean of Warmest Month	Mean of Coldest Month	Mean Maximum	Mean Minimum		Jan.	Feb.	Mar.	April	May	June	July	Aug.	Sept.	Oct.	Nov.	Dec.	Year
Kagoshima	A 79.9	J 45.0	A 87.3	J 37.4	253	3.4	4.0	6.4	8.7	8.2	17.0	12.2	7.3	8.7	5.2	3.7	3.4	88.4
Kumamoto	A 80.4	J 40.6	A 90.5	J 31.1	211	2.6	2.8	5.2	6.3	6.5	14.5	12.3	6.4	6.8	4.4	2.8	2.3	72.9
Fukuoka	A 79.5	J&F 41.1	A 88.2	F 33.6	203	2.8	3.3	4.4	5.2	5.1	10.2	9.7	5.2	8.1	4.2	2.9	3.0	64.0
Hiroshima	A 80.2	J 39.5	A 89.1	J 30.0	221	2.2	2.5	4.3	6.3	6.1	10.1	8.9	4.3	8.3	4.1	2.4	2.0	61.3
Tadotsu	A 80.8	F 41.3	A 88.9	J 34.7	235	1.7	1.9	3.3	3.6	4.3	6.5	5.3	3.9	7.9	4.1	2.3	1.9	46.6
Osaka	A 81.1	J 39.9	A 89.8	J 33.1	219	2.0	2.3	4.0	5.2	5.2	8.2	6.4	4.2	7.5	5.0	2.7	1.9	54.6
Kochi	A 79.0	J 41.9	A 87.8	J 33.6	241	2.8	3.9	7.4	10.6	10.9	14.0	12.9	13.0	15.9	8.0	4.2	3.0	106.5
Nagoya	A 79.9	J 37.9	A 88.0	J 30.4	207	2.4	2.8	4.8	6.4	6.5	9.0	7.0	6.9	9.6	6.1	3.2	2.4	67.1
Hamamatsu	A 78.4	J 41.2	A 86.0	J 34.3	281	2.7	2.8	5.7	7.2	8.1	10.0	8.5	8.9	11.8	7.1	4.1	2.8	79.5
Tokyo	A 77.7	J 37.4	A 85.5	J 29.7	215	2.3	3.0	4.3	5.3	5.9	6.8	5.6	7.1	10.1	7.9	3.5	2.2	64.0
Onahama	A 74.5	J 36.3	A 81.1	J 27.3	206	1.7	3.3	4.2	5.2	6.5	6.2	4.8	5.5	8.9	8.7	3.8	2.3	61.0
Sendai	A 74.8	F 30.7	A 82.9	F 23.7	181	1.3	1.3	2.3	6.0	5.3	3.9	3.6	4.4	6.0	5.7	2.7	2.0	44.5
Miyako	J 71.6	J 31.1	A 80.2	J 22.6	171	2.9	3.0	3.2	3.5	4.5	5.0	5.0	7.2	9.5	6.8	3.0	2.6	56.2
Kofu	A 77.7	J 34.1	A 88.7	J 23.7	191	1.8	2.1	3.0	3.5	4.0	5.1	5.2	7.0	8.2	5.2	2.5	1.8	49.6
Nagano	A 75.4	J 29.1	A 86.9	J 21.6	166	2.3	2.0	2.3	2.7	3.1	4.4	5.7	3.8	5.8	3.4	2.1	2.3	39.7
Morioka	A 73.4	J 25.5	A 82.9	J 17.8	148	2.1	1.7	2.8	2.2	2.8	2.8	4.4	6.3	5.0	3.7	3.3	3.1	40.2
Sakai	A 78.6	J&F 39.4	A 86.0	F 33.1	200	8.0	6.2	5.7	4.7	4.5	6.6	6.3	4.8	9.7	6.4	6.1	8.2	77.2
Fukui	A 78.6	J 36.3	A 88.9	F 30.4	205	11.1	7.9	6.3	5.7	5.6	7.1	7.7	5.7	9.1	6.9	8.7	13.5	95.4
Takada	A 79.1	J 33.3	A 88.0	J 27.3	191	17.5	14.9	8.8	4.3	3.9	3.5	5.0	4.5	8.4	8.5	9.3	20.0	112.6
Akita	A 74.7	J 29.5	A 83.3	F 22.6	175	5.6	4.1	4.1	4.3	4.0	5.0	7.8	7.4	8.3	7.4	7.5	7.0	72.8
Sapporo	A 69.4	J 21.0	A 78.8	J 11.5	129	3.5	2.6	2.4	2.2	2.7	2.8	3.3	3.7	5.0	4.6	4.4	3.9	41.0
Haboro	A 69.3	J 21.0	A 76.1	J&F 14.2	165	3.8	2.4	2.0	2.1	3.2	2.2	4.6	4.6	6.1	6.7	6.3	5.0	49.0
Asahigawa	A 68.5	J 14.1	A 80.1	J 3.0	127	2.8	2.0	2.1	2.0	2.6	3.1	4.5	5.1	5.8	4.2	4.2	4.0	42.4
Kushiro	A 64.0	J 19.8	A 70.5	J 8.4	141	2.0	1.4	2.6	3.7	3.7	4.4	4.5	5.6	5.6	4.6	2.9	2.0	43.3
Nemuro	A 62.4	F 21.7	A 69.1	F 14.2	185	1.6	1.2	2.2	3.0	3.6	3.5	3.7	4.0	5.9	4.1	3.1	2.1	37.9

Source: T. Okada, *The Climate of Japan.*

44

Winter Temperatures.—January temperatures range from about 10° or 15° in northern and central Hokkaido to 35° or 40° on the lowlands of central Japan, and 45° in the extreme south of Kyushu (Fig. 24). Thus the latitudinal temperature gradient, or rate of change of temperature, is very steep in Japan—approximately 2.6° for each degree of latitude, which is almost the same as on the American Atlantic seaboard. The freezing isotherm for January is at about latitude 38°, in the general vicinity of Sendai. The January isotherms tend to loop far southward over the islands, roughly parallel to the coasts, showing the effects both of altitude and of the colder land. Thus the January isotherm of 38°, which skirts the southern part of the Tokyo Plain, follows the coastal lowlands southwestward to about the mid-Inland Sea region.

Despite the fact that the west coast faces the cold Asiatic continent, from which the polar air masses arrive in winter, there is little difference between the winter air temperatures of the Japan Sea side and those of the Pacific coast at a given latitude. Actually the Japan Sea side north of 36° (northern Honshu and Hokkaido) is slightly warmer than the Pacific side. This is due to the rather constant cloudiness and heavy precipitation along the Japan Sea coast in winter, which tends to mitigate the cold. The clearer skies of the Pacific side, which accelerate earth radiation, are inclined to produce colder nights but warmer, sunnier days. But thermometer recordings notwithstanding, there is no doubt that the windy, cloudy, and more humid west side *feels* colder in winter than

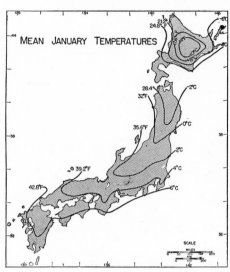

FIG. 24. After Okada.

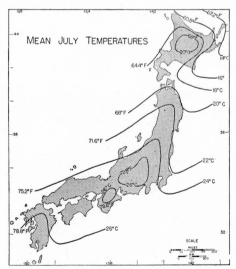

FIG. 25. After Okada.

the quieter, brighter and drier east side, where the winds are both descending and offshore.

   Summer Temperatures.—High temperatures combined with high humidity make the summer weather of much of Japan extremely sultry
and oppressive (Fig. 25). Most foreign residents and many Japanese as
well trek to high altitudes or to seacoast resorts in summer just as whites
do in tropical locations. July temperatures in central and southern Japan
range from 77° to 80°, and August is slightly warmer than July at most
Japanese stations. The rate of change in temperature from north to south

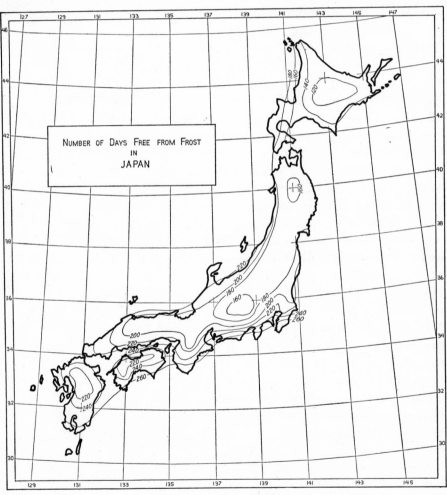

NUMBER OF DAYS FREE FROM FROST
IN
JAPAN

FIG. 26. After Okada.

is much less in summer than in winter, the latitudinal temperature gradient being only 1.3° for each degree of latitude, or approximately half that of January. Northern Japan largely escapes the uncomfortable heat. The July isotherm of 61° skirts the eastern and southeastern lowlands of Hokkaido, which are paralleled by a cool current; most of central and western Hokkaido has July temperatures of about 65° to 68°. These are much the same as the midsummer temperatures of northern New England. The cool *Oyashio* Current paralleling the east coast of Honshu down to about latitude 35° or 36° makes the Pacific coast of northern Japan definitely cooler and also somewhat foggier in summer than the Japan Sea lowlands in similar latitudes. Interior basins at considerable elevation are also somewhat cooler.

Growing Season.—The length of the frost-free, or growing, period ranges from about 120 or 130 days in central and eastern Hokkaido to 250 days or more along the extreme southern and eastern littoral (Fig. 26). To be sure, these data apply to the period between the first and last hoarfrosts, but in humid Japan any temperature drop below 32° is almost invariably accompanied by a white deposit of frost. A deposit of hoarfrost is usually associated with temperatures destructive to vegetation. In the United States northern New England and North Dakota are comparable to Hokkaido in length of frost-free season. Thus St. Johnsbury, Vermont, has a frost-free period of 127 days, which is identical with that of Asahigawa in central Hokkaido; Grand Forks, North Dakota, is without frost for 132 days. The 250-day frost-free season in the extreme south of Japan is duplicated in southern Georgia, Alabama, and Mississippi. Tokyo in the middle latitudes of Nippon has a growing season of about 215 days and Nagoya 207, which is comparable to the northern part of the American Cotton Belt. The fact that the isorithms connecting places with the same number of frost-free days tend to parallel the coasts shows that land-and-water and altitude controls operate quite as much as latitude in frost distribution. In northern Japan, especially in Hokkaido, early autumn frosts often do serious damage to rice fields, and in the northern part of subtropical Japan late spring frosts not infrequently damage vegetables, mulberry, and tea.

PRECIPITATION

Unlike subhumid North China and Manchuria in about the same latitude, Japan is a humid land no section of which suffers from a yearly or seasonal deficiency of rainfall. There are no winter-dry climates as in

North China and Manchuria. Although the country is strongly affected by the winter monsoon, these prevailingly dry winter air masses have been sufficiently humidified over the Japan Sea to furnish an abundance of cool-season precipitation.

It is hard to generalize about areal distribution of·precipitation. The variable relief results in an exceedingly confused and patchy rainfall map, the larger patterns being obscured by the numerous closed isohyets and

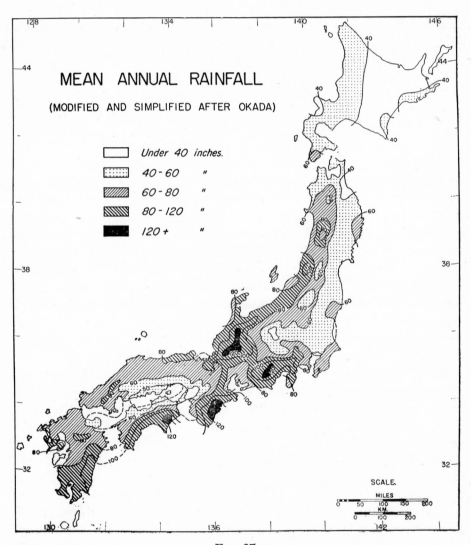

FIG. 27

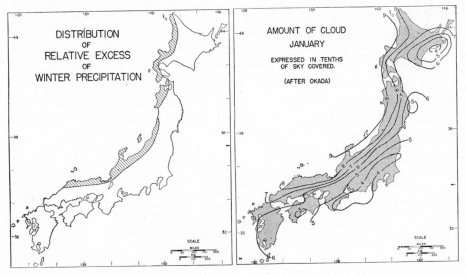

FIG. 28. After Okada.   FIG. 29

the very circuitous courses of others (Fig. 27). In general there are
three areas of heavier than normal precipitation (80 to 120 inches):
(1) the Pacific side of Japan Proper from Kyushu to Izu Peninsula
south of Fuji (35° N.); (2) the Japan Sea coast north of latitude 35° or 36°
to about Akita (40° N.); and (3) the Hida Highlands of central Honshu
west to the Fossa Magna. In many localities in these areas the precipitation
exceeds 120 inches, and here and there it approaches 160 inches. There
are at least four areas of less than normal rainfall, where the annual
totals are in the neighborhood of 40 inches: (1) a large part of Hokkaido,
especially its eastern portions; (2) the basins of the Fossa Magna in central
Honshu; (3) the Inland Sea borderlands; and (4) the eastern and northeastern sections of North Honshu.

Over much of the country precipitation is heaviest in the warm months
of the year, and lightest in the winter. This is what one would expect in a
region where monsoon wind systems are highly developed. The surprising
thing is that the difference between winter and summer precipitation
is not greater. Even in the driest cool-season months there is normally
from two to three inches of precipitation, and several times this amount
in the warm months. Often there are two secondary maxima in the precipitation curves of stations in eastern subtropical Japan, the first in early
summer, associated with the *bai-u* rains, and the second in late summer
and early fall, at the time of the typhoons. The secondary minimum in

midsummer is perhaps associated with a westward extension of the Pacific subtropical high, for the same phenomenon is observable in the precipitation curves of many West Indies stations.

The most marked exception to a warm-season maximum of precipitation in Nippon is an area on the Japan Sea side of the islands, from Hokkaido nearly to the southwestern tip of Honshu (Fig. 28). There the cP air masses, warmed and humidified in their lower strata, come onshore in winter as conditionally and convectively unstable air masses. As they are forced to ascend the orographic barriers, or perhaps surmount local masses

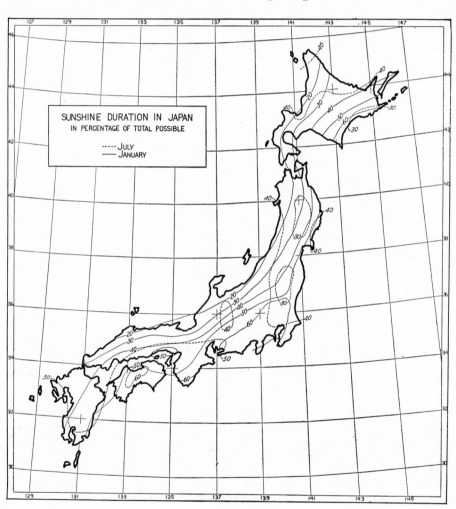

FIG. 30. After Okada.

of colder air lying over the western plains and mountains, they yield heavy precipitation, much of it in the form of snow. Farther to the east, where these same air masses are descending, the winter weather is clearer and precipitation lighter (Figs. 29, 30). Summers, too, are wet along the Japan Sea side, there being no marked difference in warm-season precipitation between the northwestern and southeastern coasts. The weaker summer monsoon produces less distinct windward and leeward coasts than does the stronger winter monsoon.

Snow falls over the whole of Japan Proper and remains on the ground all winter in Hokkaido, on the Pacific side of Honshu down to about latitude 37° or 38°, and on the Japan Sea side almost down to Kyushu. In many places in the mountainous western parts of northern Japan the snow reaches a depth of six or seven feet in January, and at a number of stations snow lies on the ground for more than 100 days in the year, and there may be as many as 25 days with snowfall in the midwinter months.

TABLE 15.—MEAN MAXIMUM DEPTH OF SNOW COVER AT SELECTED STATIONS
(in cm.; five-year average)

Station	Nov.	Dec.	Jan.	Feb.	Mar.	Apr.
Sapporo	13	59	98	110	100	27
Kushiro	3	23	29	32	22	5
Obihiro	6	40	42	50	54	11
Takada	0	66	136	177	134	37
Morioka	6	23	27	25	16	—
Nagaoka	0	56	109	129	83	6
Kamaishi	0	6	7	13	6	4

Source: T. Okada, *The Climate of Japan*, 264–269.

TABLE 16.—AVERAGE NUMBER OF DAYS WITH SNOWFALL AT SELECTED STATIONS

Station	Jan.	Feb.	Mar.	Apr.	May	Oct.	Nov.	Dec.	Yr.
1897–1926									
Kagoshima	2.4	2.9	0.9	—	—	—	—	0.9	7.1
Kumamoto	3.9	4.1	1.2	—	—	—	—	2.1	11.4
Hiroshima	8.0	7.6	3.4	0.2	—	—	0.3	4.3	23.7
Kobe	7.0	7.6	3.8	0.1	—	—	0.1	2.6	21.1
Tokyo	4.1	4.7	3.4	0.4	—	—	0.1	1.6	14.3
Takada	24.4	19.6	16.1	2.0	0.1	—	1.0	15.9	79.1
1922–1929									
Morioka	26.7	23.8	21.8	3.8	0.2	0.3	5.0	19.5	101.1
Aomori	26.5	23.8	20.4	3.7	—	0.5	9.9	24.1	108.8
Sapporo	26.6	23.4	22.6	6.6	0.2	1.5	14.7	25.2	120.6

Source: T. Okada, *The Climate of Japan*, 269–271.

Climatic Types and Regions

Two of the most detailed schemes of climatic subdivision that have been devised for Japan unfortunately do not fit into any recognized world scheme of climatic classification. Okada's[6] and Fukui's[7] maps, therefore, show only regional subdivisions, and no relationship to world patterns of climate are suggested. Actually Okada calls his map one of geographical, not climatic, subdivisions, although his discussion of regional climates follows the subdivisions shown on the map. Fukui's map, which is more detailed, is designated a map of "climatic divisions." It bears some resemblance to the Thornthwaite map of climatic subdivisions of Japan.[8]

In the modified Köppen system[9] of climates here employed, the 32° cold-month isotherm is adopted as the boundary between the relatively mild, or mesothermal, and the more severe, or microthermal, groups of climate—called, respectively, the C and D groups. Northern Honshu and Hokkaido are shown in the D group, the rest of Japan in the C group. All the C climates are of the Caf variety, which may be described as humid subtropical. North of about latitude 38° Honshu has a Da or humid continental–warm summer climate, as does also the elevated interior farther south (Fig. 32). Hokkaido with its cooler and shorter summers has the Dbf or humid continental–cool summer climate. On the map of climatic subdivisions, Fig. 32, page 56, some subdivisions of the principal Köppen types have been added.

The Dbf Climates of Hokkaido.[10]—Hokkaido, in the general latitude of the northern tier of American states, resembles climatically the northeastern part of New England and the Maritime Provinces of Canada. Summers tend to be short and also cool, the average for the warmest month usually being below 70° (Asahigawa, 68.5°; Sapporo, 69.4°;

[6] T. Okada, *The Climate of Japan* (*Bulletin of the Central Meteorological Observatory of Japan*, vol. 4, no. 2, Tokyo, 1931), 1–416; map on p. 90. This source has been drawn upon freely in the discussion of regional climates.

[7] Eiichiro Fukui, "The Climatic Provinces of Japan" (in Japanese with English summary), in the *Geographical Review of Japan*, 9 (1933):1–17, 109–127, 195–219, 271–400. See also Fukui, "Climatic Divisions of Japan," in *Comptes Rendus du Congrès International de Géographie*, Amsterdam, vol. 2 (1938), sec. C, pp. 300–304.

[8] C. W. Thornthwaite, "The Climates of Japan," in the *Geographical Review*, 24: 494–496 (July, 1934).

[9] See Glenn T. Trewartha, *An Introduction to Weather and Climate*, 2d ed. (McGraw-Hill Book Co., 1943), 309–314.

[10] The definition of the climatic symbols is as follows: D = temperature of coldest month under 32°F. (0°C.), warmest month over 50°F. (10°C.); b = warmest month below 71.6°F. (22°C.); f = no distinctly dry season; driest month of summer receives more than 1.2 inches of precipitation.

Nemuro, 62.4°; Obihiro, 67.1°). These are delightful temperatures for human comfort but less desirable for the growing of crops. The eastern and southeastern littorals, washed by the cool Okhotsk Current, are particularly cool in summer, warm-month averages being below 65°. Summer fog is prevalent along these cool-water coasts. At Sapporo the mean maximum temperature of the air in August is only 80°, hence summer days are not oppressive and sultry as they are farther south. The normal frost-free season is between four and five months. Winters, on the other hand, are long, cold, and snowy. Except in the southwestern peninsula of Hokkaido average temperatures in the four winter months are below freezing. Average January temperatures in most of Hokkaido range between 14° and 23°; mean January minimum temperatures at interior stations range from 3° to 12°; at Asahigawa 42° below zero has been recorded.

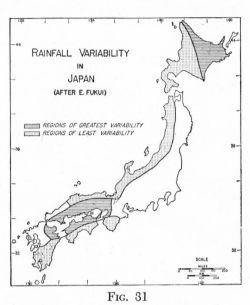

FIG. 31

Winter weather is likely to be changeable, but numerous overcast days with snow and boisterous winds are characteristic. The first snowfall usually occurs in late October or early November and the last snow of the year in late April or early May. Snow lies on the ground ten to twenty inches deep for several months, being much deeper on the windward west side than to the east of the central mountain chain. On the Ishikari Plain in western Hokkaido the snow in midwinter is two to three feet deep on the level; at Kutchan it may reach a depth of six to seven feet. The transition seasons of spring and fall are short. Hokkaido is one of the driest parts of Japan; at most of its stations precipitation totals only about 40 inches. There is no distinctly dry season in Hokkaido, although there are seasonal differences in precipitation. Stations close to the west coast have more in the winter half year than in the summer half year, whereas the converse is true of stations on the eastern side. September is likely to be the wettest month. One of the principal defects of Hokkaido's climate is the deficiency of bright sunshine (Fig. 30). In western Hokkaido this deficiency is most marked in winter when the strong winter monsoon winds blow from off the Sea of Japan. Eastern Hokkaido has the least sunshine in summer, when dense fogs prevail along the coasts washed by the cool Okhotsk Current.[11]

Subprovinces 1 and 2 in Hokkaido are separated by a boundary line coinciding with the average temperature of 65° for the warmest month. In western subprovince 1 August temperatures are higher, and in the eastern subdivision lower, than 65°. The summer climate of eastern Hokkaido, cool and foggy, is a distinct handicap to cereal agriculture. Winters are somewhat less cloudy and snowy than in subprovince 1.

The Daf[12] Climates of Northern Honshu (Tohoku District).—The chief distinction between Daf and Dbf climates is the difference in summer temperatures. It is therefore the warmer summers of northern Honshu that set it apart climatically from Hokkaido, although there are other differences too. Throughout all the Daf region the average temperature of August, the warmest summer month, is above 71.6°F. (22°C.) and at most stations it is between 73° and 76°. These approximate the summer-month temperatures in the American Corn Belt. As a rule the temperatures at stations along the Pacific coast, which is paralleled by the cool Okhotsk Current, are a few degrees lower than at interior and west-coast stations. Thus Miyako on the Pacific coast in eastern Iwate Prefecture at about 39°40′ N. has a mean August temperature of only 71.8°, whereas Morioka, an interior station, and Akita on the west coast, in about the same latitude, have August means of 73.4° and 74.7°. In fact, this whole eastern littoral of northern Honshu comes close to having a Dbf climate. It is partly because of these lower summer temperatures that the Pacific side of northern Honshu is less a rice-growing region than is the Japan Sea littoral. The period between killing frosts ranges from 160 to 180 days.

Winters in Tokoku are considerably milder than in Hokkaido, average January temperatures being only a few degrees below freezing (January at Akita, 29.5°; Miyako, 31°; Morioka, 25.5°; Fukushima, 29.3°). At most stations in this climatic subdivision average temperatures fall below 32° in only one or two months. Such winter temperatures are comparable to those of southern New England, New Jersey, Pennsylvania, and the warmer portions of the American Corn Belt.

Precipitation is heavier than in Hokkaido, virtually all the Daf region

[11] For a more detailed description of Hokkaido's regional climates, see Part III below, which deals with the regional geography of Japan

[12] The definition of the climatic symbol is as follows: D = temperature of coldest month under 32°F. (0°C.), warmest month over 50°F. (10°C.); a = warmest month above 71.6°F. (22°C); f = no distinctly dry season; driest month of summer receives more than 1.2 inches of precipitation.

having over 50 inches and much of the western part over 60. Rainfall is least abundant on the eastern side and in the interior basins. Western Tokoku is one of the wetter sections of Japan, some stations recording 80 to 100 inches. For the Pacific side the rainfall curve is typically monsoonal in seasonal distribution, precipitation being three to four times as heavy in the midsummer as in the midwinter months. The reverse is true of the Japan Sea side, in most parts of which the winter precipitation equals or even exceeds that of summer. The region north of Koriyama is usually mantled with snow for several months in the winter, the depth being much greater on the western than on the Pacific side. Snow begins to lie on the ground early in November, and usually remains until April. East of the Central Range its mean maximum depth in the three midwinter months is only six to eight inches, but on the Japan Sea side it is commonly several feet deep, often suspending railway traffic temporarily.

Subprovinces of Daf.—Three subdivisions of the Daf climate are shown in Fig. 32. The boundary between 1 and 2, which purports to be approximately the line of 30 inches winter precipitation (six months), is somewhat conjectural, since the region has few weather stations. On Fig. 32 it is made to coincide roughly with the central meridional mountain range. West of

TABLE 17.—MEAN MAXIMUM DEPTH OF SNOW COVER AT SELECTED STATIONS
(in cm.)

Station	Nov.	Dec.	Jan.	Feb.	Mar.	Apr.	May
Aomori	17	46	92	107	89	12	—
Akita	2	30	64	68	41	—	—
Towada.	4	107	170	214	264	170	6
Morioka	6	23	27	25	16	—	—
Miyako.	0	23	15	20	12	2	—
Fukushima . . .	—	16	16	18	10	8	1

Source: T. Okada, *Climate of Japan*, p. 107.

TABLE 18.—AVERAGE NUMBER OF CLEAR AND CLOUDY DAYS PER MONTH AT SEVERAL STATIONS ON THE EASTERN AND WESTERN SIDES OF NORTHERN HONSHU, 1897–1926

Month	WEST				EAST			
	Aomori		Akita		Miyako		Fukushima	
	Clear	Cloudy	Clear	Cloudy	Clear	Cloudy	Clear	Cloudy
December	0.5	21.5	0.4	26.2	6.9	4.7	1.8	8.9
January	0.2	21.0	0.2	26.6	6.2	5.3	1.7	8.2
February	1.0	16.7	0.4	22.4	3.5	6.2	1.5	8.9

Source: T. Okada, *Climate of Japan*, 109.

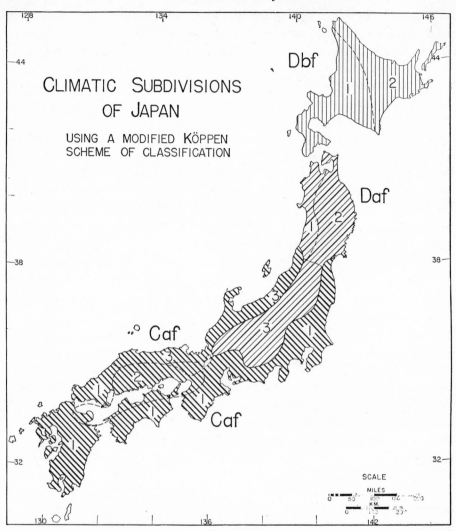

CLIMATIC SUBDIVISIONS
OF JAPAN

USING A MODIFIED KÖPPEN
SCHEME OF CLASSIFICATION

Dbf

Daf

Caf

Caf

SCALE

MILES

K.M.

Fig. 32

this line, in subprovince 1, the precipitation of the winter half year exceeds 30 inches, and in many parts exceeds that of the summer half year. Further evidence for the location of the boundary was obtained from the detailed seasonal rainfall maps published by the Central Meteorological Observatory in Tokyo.

In *subprovince 1* winters are dark and gloomy, and bright sunshine is infrequent (Figs. 29, 30). Winds are strong and boisterous. Annual precipitation is relatively heavy, and since half or more of the total falls in winter, the snow cover is very deep. Sensible temperatures are low and the air is raw and penetrating, although the actual temperature is no lower than in the eastern subprovince, if quite as low. Relatively high summer temperatures and high humidity make for sultry heat. *Subprovince 2* has sunnier winter weather, cloudy days being only a third or a fourth as numerous as in subprovince 1, and clear days 10 to 30 times as numerous. Snow falls on a majority of the winter days, but the total fall is much less and the snow cover much shallower than on the Japan Sea side. Winter temperatures are about the same as to the west, but the cold is less penetrating. Summers are cooler than in subprovince 1. Rainfall is between 40 and 60 inches, and there is a definite summer maximum, although winters are by no means dry.

Subprovince 3 is the southward extension of the relatively severe D climates following the central highlands. Marked altitudinal differences result in a variety of climates. Elevated interior basins, such as the Nagano, Matsumoto, and Suwa basins, have local continental climates. Winters are relatively severe, the January average temperature at Matsumoto being 28.2° and at Nagano 29.1°, about the same as in northern Honshu. In these mountain-enclosed interior basins, August temperatures are relatively high, usually between 73° and 75°. Outside the basins, however, altitude makes for cool summers. There are great local variations in amount of precipitation. During the winter the mountains are covered by a deep snow mantle. Cool summers and snowy winters, plus the attractive mountain scenery, have made famous a number of summer resorts and skiing centers. In contrast to the mountains, the enclosed basins have considerably less precipitation. As the air descends into these depressions after crossing the surrounding highlands, at the time of either the winter or the summer monsoon, it is warmed and made relatively drier, and thereby rendered less capable of producing precipitation. In some basins the rainfall is less than 40 inches, but in more of them it is between 40 and 50 inches (Ueda, 37.9; Nagano, 40.1; Matsumoto, 44.3; Kamisuwa, 52.6). With eastern Hokkaido and the Inland Sea district, these mountain basins of central Honshu are the driest parts of Japan. In all of them summer is the period of maximum precipitation, for the summer monsoon is the dominant control. Normally the wettest summer month has three to five times as much precipitation as the driest winter month.

The Caf[13] Climates of Subtropical Japan.—This is the part of Japan

---

[13] The definition of the climatic symbol is as follows: C = temperature of coldest month above 32°F. (0°C.) but under 64.4°F. (18°C.); a = warmest month above 71.6°F. (22°C.); f = no distinctly dry season; driest month of summer receives more than 1.2 inches of precipitation.

best known to Occidentals, who are likely to assume that it is typical of the entire country. Summer temperatures are high, the average for the warmest month being between 75° and 81°. At a majority of weather stations midsummer temperatures approximate those of the wet tropics. And since rainfall is abundant and humidity high, sensible temperatures as well as air temperatures are veritably Amazonian. This sultry, humid heat, virtually unrelieved by air movements, makes the summer season very uncomfortable and enervating, much like that of the American Atlantic seaboard from about Washington, D.C. to southern Georgia. The growing season is long, from 180 days in the northern part to 260 days along coastal locations on the Pacific side.

Winters are relatively mild, the coldest winter months having a mean temperature above freezing. During January Tokyo has an average temperature of 37.4°, Osaka 40°, Kagoshima 45°. On sunny winter days midday temperatures are very pleasant, but when it is overcast and a strong wind is blowing, the humid cold is raw and penetrating. Japanese homes are so ineffectively heated that indoor winter temperatures are distinctly uncomfortable; indeed, the foreigner in Japan is likely to have as unpleasant recollections of the winter cold as of the summer heat. Because the winter chilliness is much less prolonged than the summer heat, Japanese houses, clothes, and ways of living are much better adjusted to heat than to cold. The number of days with a mean temperature below freezing is small—only 3.2 a year at Tokyo; 0.7 at Osaka; 2.7 at Hiroshima; and 19.2 at Niigata. Frosts are widespread throughout subtropical Japan in midwinter. Thus at Kumamoto, far to the south in central-western Kyushu, night temperatures drop below freezing on an average of 64 days a year, of which 15 occur in December, 20 in January, and 17 in February. Thus it is obvious that despite its insular location, subtropical Japan has relatively severe winter weather for its latitude.

Precipitation varies in amount. Heavy average annual rainfalls of over 100 inches are recorded at stations along the mountainous Pacific coast, facing the inflowing summer monsoon, and also along the Japan Sea coast, which is windward during the winter monsoon. By contrast many sections of the borderlands of the Inland Sea depression have only 40 to 50 inches of rainfall. Seasonal distribution of precipitation is no more uniform than the amounts. Over the larger part of the Caf region summer rainfall greatly predominates, but the Japan Sea side of Honshu receives an excess of winter precipitation (Fig. 28). Snow falls on occasion over the whole of subtropical Japan; even Kagoshima in the extreme south of Kyushu records an annual average of 6 to 7 days with snowfall, Tokyo 13, and Osaka 14 to 15. Over much of the larger part of this region snow remains on the ground for only a few hours or days at the most, and there is no lasting snow cover. Only on the northwestern side, facing the Sea of Japan, does snow lie deep on the ground throughout the winter, in some mountain localities to maximum depths of six to ten feet.

Subprovinces of Caf.—Subprovince 1, occupying the Pacific side of Japan, is so typical of the Caf region that it requires no further description. *Subprovince 2* is comprised chiefly of the borderlands of the Inland Sea. The boundary as drawn follows closely the 60-inch isohyet. The central portion of this subprovince, having an average annual rainfall of less than 45 inches, is one of the driest regions in Japan. The Inland Sea district, on the other hand, is famous for its prevailingly sunny weather, moderate cloudiness, and the lowest relative humidity anywhere

TABLE 19.—MEAN PERCENTAGE OF BRIGHT SUNSHINE AT SELECTED STATIONS

Station	Jan.	Feb.	Mar.	Apr.	May	June	July	Aug.	Sept.	Oct.	Nov.	Dec.	Yr.
Okayama (Inland Sea)	53	51	55	56	56	45	58	65	50	57	59	55	55
Niigata (Japan Sea)	18	26	35	46	46	45	44	55	38	39	30	18	37
Hamamatsu (Pacific Coast)	62	57	54	49	46	37	46	55	42	43	36	60	51

Source: T. Okada, *The Climate of Japan*, 118, 125, 132.

in the country. The high evaporation rate has led to the establishment here of numerous plants for the extraction of salt from seawater. In this subdivision there are fewer rainy days than anywhere else in Japan—139 at Hiroshima and 129 at Okayama, as compared with 166 at Nagasaki, 197 at Sapporo, and 227 at Niigata.

Subprovince 3, comprising the Sanin and southern Hokuroku districts of Japan, is the subtropical southward extension of the Japan Sea climates of northern Honshu (subprovince 1 of Daf). This region is unquestionably unique among the subtropical climates of the earth, for although it has the normal hot and rainy summers with an average August temperature of 77°–79°, it has also excessively heavy snow in winter. No other region of the earth has such a combination of tropical heat and humidity in summer and a great depth of snow in winter. The explanation is to be found in the location of these subtropical mountainous islands, which lie almost at right angles to the trajectories of air masses associated with the earth's best developed winter monsoons. January temperatures in the subprovince are moderate, ranging from about 34.5° at Niigata near the northern limit to 41.7° at Hamada. These resemble midwinter temperatures along the American Atlantic seaboard from Maryland to North Carolina. Strong winds, often of gale strength, accompanied by driving snow, and a heavy cloud cover make the winter raw and penetrating even though the air temperatures are not low. There is less winter sunshine than in any other part of Japan; Niigata has only 18 per cent of the amount possible in December and January. Snow falls on one- to two-thirds of the days in midwinter, the total for the year ranging from 70 at Niigata, the station farthest north, to 30 at Hamada at the extreme southwest. Total precipitation is heavy; almost the whole area has over 80 inches, and in some highland areas it exceeds 120 inches. Throughout the subprovince pre-

TABLE 20.—MAXIMUM DEPTH OF SNOW COVER IN CM. AT SELECTED STATIONS IN
SUBPROVINCE 3 OF THE Caf CLIMATE

Station	Nov.	Dec.	Jan.	Feb.	Mar.	April	May
Takada	0	66	136	177	134	37	—
Tsuruga	—	24	59	62	21	—	—
Siramine	7	110	199	233	193	91	—
Fukui	—	37	74	84	38	—	—

Source: T. Okada, *Climate of Japan*, 124–125.

cipitation is greater in winter than in summer, although warm-season rainfall is also heavy and there is a secondary maximum in late summer. So heavy is the winter snowfall that special forms of house construction are required and farmers often leave their snowbound villages for several months to find employment elsewhere. It is not unusual for rail traffic to be suspended for days because of snow blockades, and frame snowsheds protect the rail lines for long distances. West of Wakasa Bay the snow cover is much less deep than to the north and east.

SELECTED REFERENCES

ARAKAWA, H. "The Air Masses of Japan" (in Japanese with English summary). *Journal of the Meteorological Society of Japan*, 13:385–402 (September, 1935); 14:328–338 (July, 1936); 15:185–189 (May, 1937).
———. "Die Luftmassen in den japanischen Gebieten." *Meteorologische Zeitschrift*, 54:169–174 (May, 1937).
The Climatic Atlas of Japan and Her Neighboring Countries. Central Meteorological Observatory, Tokyo, 1929.
FUJIWHARA, SAKUHEI. "The Present Status of Investigations of Typhoons and Depressions in Japan." *Proceedings of the Sixth Pacific Science Congress*, Berkeley, 1940, 3:675–689.
FUKUI, EIICHIRO. "Climatic Divisions of Japan." *Comptes Rendus du Congrès International de Géographie*, Amsterdam, 1938. vol. 2, sec. C, pp. 300–304.

———. "The Climatic Provinces of Japan" (in Japanese with English summary). *Geographical Review of Japan*, 9 (1933):1–17, 109–127, 195–219, 271–400.

HUKUI, EITIRO. "Distribution of Air Temperature on the Pacific Side and on the Japan Sea Side of Japan" (in Japanese with English summary). *Geographical Review of Japan*, 6 (1930):266–276.

LANDSBERG, H. *A Climatic Study of Cloudiness over Japan.* Institute of Meteorology, *Miscellaneous Reports*, No. 15. University of Chicago Press, Chicago, Illinois, 1944.

LOSCH, WOLFGANG. "Das Klima von Japan." *Geographische Zeitschrift*, 38 (1932): 82–95.

OKADA, T. *The Climate of Japan (Bulletin of the Central Meteorological Observatory of Japan*, vol. 4, no. 2). Toyko, 1931. 416 pages. The most complete compilation of weather data and the most complete text on the climates of Japan. Fifty-five plates, most of them in color.

———. "The Climate of Japan, with a Note on the Meteorological Service of Japan." *Scientific Japan, Past and Present*, 34–53. Tokyo, 1926.

TAKAHASHI, K. "On the Transformation of the Cold Dry Air Mass by Traveling over Warm Sea" (in Japanese with English summary). *Journal of the Meteorological Society of Japan*, 18:77–80 (March, 1940).

THORNTHWAITE, C. W. "The Climates of Japan." *The Geographical Review*, 24: 494–496 (July, 1934).

TSIANG, P. T. "On the Distribution of Typhoons and Depressions in the Far East." *Proceedings of the Fifth Pacific Science Congress*, Toronto, 1933, 3:1919–1936.

YAMANAKA, T., and C. IKEDA. "On the Three Principal Air Masses in Japan." *Journal of the Meteorological Society of Japan*, 17 (1939):450–453.

CHAPTER III

Natural Vegetation and Soils

FORESTS

JAPAN is one of the most completely forested of the civilized nations, rivaling even Finland and Sweden. The luxuriant mantle of trees that covers the slopes throughout the mountain regions is among the foreign traveler's most vivid and lasting impressions of Nippon's landscape. The Japanese love of trees is demonstrated by the stately cryptomeria which surround the nation's temples and shrines. Leading to the celebrated Nikko Shrine is an avenue of great cryptomerias over thirty miles long—one of the tree wonders of the world.

The Japanese Ministry of Agriculture and Forestry classifies 54.5 per cent of Japan Proper as forest land. Another 8 or 9 per cent, designated *gen-ya*, or wild land, may be regarded as potential forest land.[1] The term *gen-ya* is translated in various ways—wild land, wasteland, prairie, meadow, pasture—but essentially it is treeless land most of which will one day doubtless be devoted to planted forests. At present it is covered with weedy plants, grasses, and shrubs, some elements of which are being used for grazing or forage, some for fuel or fertilizer material. No accurate survey of actual forest and *gen-ya* lands has ever been made, but their extent has probably been underestimated; it is not unlikely that a considerable part of the 19 or 20 per cent of the country's area classified as "miscellaneous" should be added to the forest land.[2]

The fact that more than half the country, though occupied for millenniums, is still in forest is explained by the preponderance of hill land and mountains unsuited to widespread agricultural utilization. But while a greater area of fertile arable plains would undoubtedly make for greater prosperity, it must not be assumed that because this rugged land cannot be cropped it is largely without economic value. It is not only a source of timber, but of charcoal, wood fuel, wood pulp, and various foods, such as nuts, fruit, and bamboo shoots. It is in these forested mountain lands,

[1] *Far East Year Book,* 1941, p. 285.
[2] Shiroshi Nasu, *Aspects of Japanese Agriculture* (Institute of Pacific Relations, New York, 1941), 37.

too, that most of the country's waterpower is generated. About three-fourths of the Japanese forest land is still in its natural state; nearly half of this has a cover of dwarf species and shrub, which is suitable chiefly for fuel. Broadleaf forests greatly predominate, occupying 44 per cent of the total forest area. Coniferous and mixed forests are about equally divided—occupying 26 and 27 per cent respectively. Much of the broadleaf forest area, however, consists of young trees unfit for timber; the area of large broadleaf trees is unfortunately small. Hence it is the coniferous forests that supply a large proportion, approximately 85 per cent, of domestic lumber production. The total area in forests has not only been maintained but actually expanded, the increase between 1915 and 1936 having been 13 per cent. Of the three classes of forests only the mixed type declined (22 per cent); the area of coniferous forest increased 36 per cent and that in broadleaf trees 30 per cent.

A distinctive and remarkable feature of the Japanese flora is the great variety of its forms, which include, at various latitudes, many elements belonging to much warmer regions. To most botanists this indicates recent climatic oscillations. Japanese forests have a dense undergrowth, reflecting heavy rainfall and high temperatures during the vegetative period.

Long occupance of the country by a civilized people has added to the confusion in the vegetation cover, which contains many recent, relict, and cultivated forms in addition to the original forms. The confusion prevailing in the forest cover makes it difficult to define simple vegetative zones, and many botanists prefer different groupings and combinations.[3]

Forest Zones[4]

In a region having so wide a range of latitude and altitude as Japan, and hence of temperature, there are bound to be different forest types in contrasting latitudinal and altitudinal zones. Each zone is bounded by approximate temperature limits. The boundary planes of each altitudinal forest zone in Japan slope downward toward the north, intersecting Japan's sea level surface at various latitudes and forming the latitudinal belts (Fig. 33). Three general latitudinal forest zones, the subtropical, the temperate, and the boreal, are usually recognized (Fig. 34).

The *Subtropical Forest Zone* descends to sea level at about the latitude of the Tokyo Plain (37° or 38°) and occupies the lowlands and lower slopes of southwestern Japan, where the mean annual temperatures

[3] Mrs. O. N. Mikhailovskaia, "On the Soils of Japan: Contributions to the Knowledge of the Soils of Asia," in *Academy of Sciences of the U.S.S.R.,* 1 (1930):9–30.

[4] Mitsunaga Fujioka, "Forest Resources of Japan," in the *Proceedings of the Fifth Pacific Science Congress,* Toronto, 1933, 2:961–971.

are between about 55° and 70° F. At increasingly higher altitudes to the south, above the isothermal surface of about 55°, are deciduous and mixed forests, which are characteristic of the lowlands in northern Japan. The original vegetation of this subtropical forest consisted of broadleaf evergreen trees (*Boxus sempervirens, Quercus ilex, Quercus silva, Quercus vibrayeana, Quercus abuta*), and remnants of these forests still survive in the isolated mountain districts of Kyushu and Shikoku (Fig. 35). With human occupancy, however, attended by careless cutting, fires, and partial reforestation, there has been an intrusion of deciduous broadleaf

TABLE 21.—FOREST AREA IN JAPAN PROPER CLASSIFIED BY KINDS OF TREES

Type of Forest	Area in Square Miles	Percentage of Total Area
Coniferous forest	20,925	26.4
Broadleaf forest.	35,073	44.1
Mixed forest	21,056	26.5
Bamboo forest	572	0.7
Miscellaneous.	1,798	2.3
Total forests	79,424	100.0

Source: Nasu, *Aspects of Japanese Agriculture*, 58.

species (*Quercus serrata, Quercus glandulifera*) and pines (*Pinus densiflora, Pinus tunbergii*). Oaks predominate and are the most widely used of the broadleaf trees. On the whole, however, this forest zone is not very rich in good timber trees. Several varieties of bamboo, which grow in small groves rather than in extensive contiguous areas, the Japanese tallow or wax tree (*Rhus succedanea*) and the camphor tree (*Cinnamomum camphora*) are common species which have special industrial uses. In the extreme southern part of Kyushu are found numerous tropical elements, both among the trees and among the plants which comprise the underwood. Here are to be seen such forms as palms and banana trees.

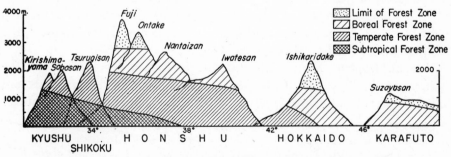

NORTH-SOUTH PROFILE OF FOREST ZONES (After A. Hofmann)

FIG. 33

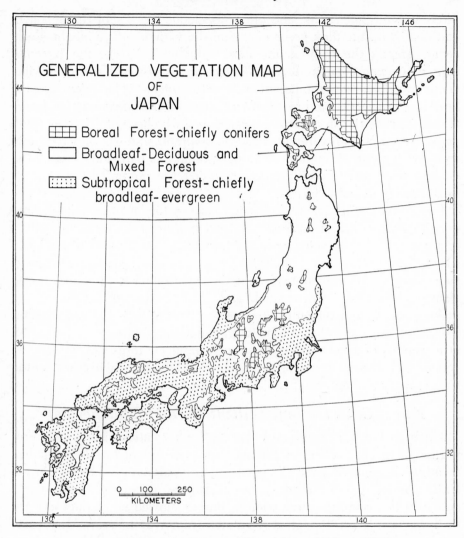

FIG. 34. From *The Newest Atlas of Japan* (Tokyo, 1929).

The *Temperate Mixed-Forest Zone* includes Honshu north of about latitude 37° or 38°, southwestern Hokkaido to about 43½°, and certain higher elevations south of latitude 37°—all regions where the mean annual temperatures are between 43° F. and 55° F. Here the original cover was comprised of broadleaf deciduous forests and stands of mixed hardwoods and conifers. Deciduous trees still predominate, although the conifers are commercially more important and in the planted woodlands greatly outnumber all others. Mixed forests are most common. In autumn these produce a riot of colors: the rich yellow, brown, and red of the maple, birch, beech, poplar, oak, and other deciduous trees, shot through here and there with the dark green of the needle varieties—fir, pine, hemlock, cedar. Among the conifers the most valuable trees are the Japanese cypress *(Chamaecyparis obtusa, Chamaecyparis pisifera),* the arbor vitae *(Thujopsis dolabrata),* the Japanese cedar *(Cryptomeria japonica),* and the fir *(Abies firma).* Of the broadleaf trees, Keyaki *(Zelkowa serrata),* beech *(Fagus sylvatica),* ash *(Fraxinus mandschurica),* chestnut *(Castenea vulgaris),* poplar *(Populus tremulus* and *balsamifera),* and oak *(Quercus dentata)* are of greatest commercial value. Within this temperate zone of deciduous and mixed woodland are included the larger part of Japan's economically valuable forests.

In northern and eastern Hokkaido, where the average annual temperatures are below 43° F., is the *Zone of Boreal Forests,* where conifers predominate, principally fir *(Abies veitchii, Abies sachaliensis)* and spruce *(Picea ajanensis)* (Fig. 36). A great variety of broadleaf deciduous trees, of little value for timber, are also present either in pure or in mixed stands. The undergrowth is thick, and dead timber clutters the forests, making penetration difficult. Many of the river valleys are wet, tundra-like areas. This boreal forest type is also found in a limited area of Honshu at elevations of 1800–2800 meters. Such highland forests are of limited commercial value because of their inaccessibility, but their effect on the water supply and on runoff is of great importance.

Forest Conservation, Utilization, and Management

Although Japan, as compared with most other nations, has a large proportion of its land in forests, the per capita acreage of forest land is less favorable—about 0.78 acre per person as compared with 3.8 acres in the United States and 5.5 acres in Soviet Russia. Between World War I and 1930 the domestic production of timber showed no distinct upward or downward trend, though it fluctuated from year to year. After 1930, however, the value and volume of timber output increased sharply. Normally imports of timber amount to about one-quarter of the total consumption. After 1937 both lumber and pulp imports declined markedly, at the same time that exports, chiefly to Yen-Bloc countries, increased. This is undoubtedly attributable to the necessity for loading incoming ships with more urgently needed war-time materials. It also suggests that in the emergency the home forests were being sacrificed at an accelerated rate. The sources of the imports have also shifted. Formerly more than 50 per cent of the timber imports came from the United States, another 15–20

FIG. 35. A portion of the forest of broadleaf evergreens in Kyushu.
United States Forest Service photograph.

FIG. 36. A virgin forest of conifers in the central part of Hokkaido.
United States Forest Service photograph.

per cent from Canada, and 20–30 per cent from tropical southeastern Asia. In recent years the Asiatic region has greatly improved its relative position. Whereas in 1929 it supplied only 4.8 per cent of Japan's imports of timber, in 1937 it supplied 33 per cent and in 1938 about 40 per cent. It seems fairly obvious that Japan can maintain its present per capita consumption of lumber only by increasing imports or by cutting socially and strategically located protection forests which can scarcely be sacrificed without unpleasant consequences. In recent years Old Japan south of Hokkaido has contributed from 50 to 65 per cent of the country's requirements of timber, and Hokkaido about 15 per cent. Approximately one-fifth of the standing timber is in Hokkaido, the remainder in Old Japan.

TABLE 22.—IMPORTS OF TIMBER BY COUNTRIES OF ORIGIN
(in thousands of yen)

Year	United States	Canada	Dutch East Indies	British Borneo	Thailand	Philippines	Total, Including Others
1929	67,316	5,110	1,150	—	1,851	—	88,838
1937	30,077	11,517	2,477	3,198	3,102	11,260	64,817
1939	9,448	5,171	1,793	2,159	1,083	10,366	32,326

Source: *Far East Year Book*, 1941, p. 310.

TABLE 23.—DISTRIBUTION OF TIMBER STANDS
(in millions of cubic feet)

Region	Conifers	Broadleaf	Total
Old Japan	42,074	45,774	87,848
Hokkaido	7,816	12,962	20,778

Source: Ivan Elchibegoff, "Japanese Forest Resources and Requirements of Timber," in the *Paper Trade Journal*, 106: 23 (June 2, 1938).

Forest Ownership and Management.—For some decades the Japanese government has realized that only by the most exemplary system of forest management and control can any considerable part of the country's timber needs continue to be supplied from its own forests. The type of destructive exploitation of forests practised in the United States has been checked in Japan, and until 1937 at least they have been utilized as a replaceable natural resource should be. About half the forest area in Old Japan is owned by the government or by other public bodies and is managed under an efficient administrative system. In Hokkaido, which was settled relatively recently, forests have never been considered merely as exploitable materials, but as renewable resources to be perpetuated and

improved. Destruction by fire and ruthless cutting has been much reduced, and the actual cutting of timber is restricted to an amount not
greater than the annual growth. Careful forest management is becoming
more widespread everywhere in Japan, not only in the state and publicly
owned forests but also in the private forests. The latter are divided among
a relatively large number of owners on much the same basis as ownership of arable land. This fact, together with the Japanese concept of
the forest as a crop, helps to explain the unusual mosaic of large and
small plots of trees of different species and ages which characterizes large
areas of Japan's forested mountain slopes (Fig. 5).

TABLE 24.—OWNERSHIP OF FOREST LAND
IN OLD JAPAN

State	Public	Private
28.9	21.9	49.2

Source: Nasu, *Aspects of Japanese Agriculture*
(Institute of Pacific Relations, New York,
1941), 60.

TABLE 25.—OWNERSHIP OF STANDING
TIMBER IN HOKKAIDO

Crown	State	Commercial	Private
16.2	68.0	12.2	3.6

Source: Mitsunaga Fujioka, "Forest Resources
of Japan," in the *Proceedings of the Fifth Pacific
Science Congress*, Toronto, 1933, 2: 966.

In 1937 Japan had over 5.2 million acres in "protection" forests, whose
value is social as well as economic and whose maintenance is required
for protection against soil denudation, floods, winds, and tides, for the
protection of headwaters, and the preservation of scenic beauties. Most
important of these is the protection of headwaters and the prevention of
soil denudation. Some stands of over-mature timber, even in the protection forest, are being cut to save them from decay and economic waste.

TABLE 26.—PROTECTION FORESTS, 1938, CLASSIFIED ACCORDING TO PURPOSE SERVED
(in millions of cho; 1 cho = 2.45 acres)

Against Soil Denudation	Protection of Headwaters	Against Floods	Against Winds	Against Tides	For Fish	For Scenery	Total includ-ing Others
948	999	6.6	76.3	9.2	51.9	38.6	2,144

Source: *Far East Year Book*, 1941, p. 306.

At least until the middle of the last decade the area of forests cut each
year was greater than the total area naturally afforested and artificially
planted. But since relatively less timber is produced from the natural
forests than from the planted forests, the increasing proportion of the
latter will tend to increase the per acre yield of timber. The striking
decline in imports since 1937, however, seems to portend a great increase

in the felling of domestic forests. In Old Japan the area of artificially planted forests represents about 19 per cent of the total forest-land area,[5] in Hokkaido only 1.6 per cent. The principle species artificially planted are Japanese cypress, Japanese cedar, and various kinds of pines, the area planted in conifers being roughly ten times that in broadleaf trees (Fig. 37). Two of the largest areas of planted forests are the basin of the Yoshino River in eastern Shikoku, where there are more than 200,000 acres of cryptomeria and Japanese cypress, and the basin of the Tenryu in

TABLE 27.—AREA OF FORESTS FELLED AND PLANTED, 1934
(in thousands of cho; 1 cho = 2.45 acres)

Year	Forests Felled	Newly Planted Area	Naturally Afforested	Number of Trees Supplementally Planted (in thousands)
1930	358,965	102,052	226,392	61,382
1934	444,430	112,627	273,827	64,756

Source: Nasu, *Aspects of Japanese Agriculture*, 63.

central Honshu, similarly planted.[6] The production of timber must always be subordinate to the more urgent need of soil conservation, both on the plains and on the slopes. Much forest not classed as "protective" is very essential to this conservation program, and cutting must be carefully regulated. Considerable portions of Japan's forests are in such inaccessible mountain areas that cutting is unprofitable.

Forest Utilization.—The principal products obtained from Japanese forests are timber, wood for charcoal, and firewood. In area of forest felled and volume of wood produced, the timber cut for fuel and charcoal exceeds that cut for lumber. In the cities coal is being used increasingly as a household fuel, but the rural areas still rely chiefly on wood and charcoal. In 1937 the volume of wood used for fuel and charcoal was more than twice that used for lumber, and its value was considerably greater. Under the head of "miscellaneous" in Table 28 are included such items as seeds for afforestation, bark, fruit, bamboo sheaths, grass, mushrooms, and others.

The cutting of timber and the production of firewood and charcoal are widely distributed throughout the country. Forestry is decidedly an industry of the hill and mountain lands, hence logging and transportation offer difficulties, many rivers being unsuited to rafting. In these highland

[5] Fujioka, *op. cit.*, 969.
[6] *Japan-Manchukuo Year Book,* 1940, p. 307.

districts forest products constitute the principal source of income for many settlers, who till the soil in summer and cut wood and burn charcoal in winter (Fig. 38). Bundles of firewood and charcoal piled around their residences, awaiting transportation to the markets on the lowlands, are a common sight (Fig. 39). Partly because of its greater size, Hokkaido leads all other prefectures in lumber production, accounting for nearly

TABLE 28.—OUTPUT OF FOREST PRODUCTS IN JAPAN

Kind of Product	Area Felled (thousands of cho)	Production (thousands of koku)	Value (thousands of yen)	Percentage of Total
Timber				
Coniferous				
1934	58	53,566	96,694	46
1937		67,069	———	
Broadleaf				
1934	27	10,806	16,056	8
1937		12,358	———	
Total timber				
1934	85	64,372	112,750	54
1937		79,427	189,089	
Wood for charcoal				
and fuel				
1934	198	139,503	59,789	28
1937		218,940	63,219	
Bamboo				
1934	10	5,419 (1,000	2,581	1
1937		bundles)	2,684	
Miscellaneous				
1934			35,269	17

Source: 1934 figures from Nasu, *Aspects of Japanese Agriculture,* 61; 1937 figures from *Japan-Man-chukuo Year Book,* 1940, p. 309. 1 cho = 2.45 acres; 1 koku = about 10 cubic feet of wood.

TABLE 29.—LUMBER PRODUCTION BY PRINCIPAL REGIONS, 1934
(in thousands of koku; 1 koku = 10 cubic feet)

Prefecture	Region	Quantity
Wakayama and Miye	Catchment of Kumano River	1,543
Akita	Catchment of Yoneshiro River	1,397
Shizuoka	Catchment of Tenryu River	772
Nara	Catchment of Yoshiro River	706
Nagano	Kiso district	704
Aomori	Higashi-Tsugaru	676
Oita	Hida district	610
Aichi	Catchment of Toyo River	548
Kochi	Nahara district	547
Aomori	Shomokita district	542
Miyazaki	Kobayaski district	508

Source: Nasu, *Aspects of Japanese Agriculture,* 62.

a quarter of the total. In Old Japan the northernmost prefectures of Honshu, including Aomori, Iwate, and Akita prefectures, constitute an important region of timber production. South of this region the areas of greatest timber cutting coincide in general with the remote mountainous districts. Table 29 shows the principal districts of lumber production in Old Japan.

A great deal of Japan's broadleaf forest is unfit for the production of lumber and is therefore more important as a source of fuel and charcoal. Since coniferous trees contribute most of Japan's lumber—80–85 per cent—they greatly predominate in the planted forests. The four species most important commercially are *sugi* or cedar *(Cryptomeria japonica); matsu* or pine *(Pinus densiflora, Pinus thunbergii); ezomatzu* or spruce and *todomatsu* or fir *(Picea jezoensis, Abies sachaliensis);* and *hinoki* or cypress *(Chamaecyparts obtusa).* The average unit-area timber production of Japanese forests is only about half that of German forests, for the reason that the natural forests comprise about three-fourths of the forest area. Of this nearly one-half is dwarf woods fit for

Fig. 37. A planted cryptomeria forest in the southern part of Hokkaido. United States Forest Service photograph.

little except fuel. The other half is composed of timber trees, but the yield is small as compared with that of planted forests. As the area of planted forests is expanded, domestic timber production will undoubtedly increase greatly.

FIG. 38. A charcoal pit in the mountains. It is by such crude methods as this that a large part of Japan's charcoal is manufactured.

In normal times general building and construction has been much the largest consumer of timber, taking more than 50 per cent of the total production. Most of this is used for the construction of dwellings. It is estimated that from 450,000 to 750,000 new homes are built in Japan each year, for which wood is used almost exclusively, although brick, concrete, and other materials are readily available and are being used increasingly for public, business, and factory buildings. The next largest user of timber is the pulpwood industry, which provides raw material for rayon, staple fiber, and paper manufacture; the amount so used increased rapidly in the decade of the thirties.

FIG. 39. The residence of a farmer-forester in the mountains. The roof is of bark. The straw-covered bundles contain charcoal.

The *gen-ya* and forest land is also used to some extent for grazing, though the natural herbage is of very inferior quality for this purpose. In 1933 some 479,088 cho of forest land and 366,922 cho of *gen-ya* were grazed over by 196,343 cattle and 241,468 horses;[7] this does not represent a very important form of utilization, and there is no indication that it is increasing.

SOILS

Until recently Japanese scientists have tended to ignore the influences of climate and vegetation on the composition of their soils, and have regarded them simply as geologic or petrographic features. This emphasis on bedrock as a soil determinant is understandable when one considers the history of soil science in Japan and the rugged terrain and steep slopes that prevail over most of the area, conditions making for immaturity in soils.

Development of Soil Science and Soil Maps.[8]—Soil study and research was begun in 1882 when an Agronomic Division was established within the Imperial Geological Survey. Thus soil science in Japan was founded on an agronomic-geologic basis, and the soil research program was developed by a government bureau whose primary interest was geology. Between 1886 and 1935 agronomic maps (scale 1:100,000) based upon geological surveys were published for most of Japan Proper; only Hokkaido and Aomori prefectures in northern Honshu have not been completed. On these maps geological formations are shown in solid colors, contours by brown lines, and soil types by an overprint of dots and lines. The emphasis is upon the surficial geological formation with which a given soil type is associated; indeed, for much of the mountainous area the maps are purely geological, omitting soil symbols altogether. The classification of soils is based on the mechanical analysis and size of soil particles.

In 1924 appeared the first sheets of a new soils map entitled *The General Soil Map of Japan Proper*, scale 1:500,000, published by the Imperial Agricultural Experiment Station in Tokyo under the direction of Dr. Toyotaro Seki.[9] This map was to cover all of Old Japan in sixteen sheets. Within two years six of these were published, covering the greater part of northern and middle Honshu. Actually this was no more than a synthesis and generalization of the already published Agronomic

[7] Nasu, *op. cit.*, 66.

[8] Leopold G. Scheidl, "Der Boden Japans," in *Mitteilungen der Deutschen Gesellschaft für Natur- und Völkerkunde Ostasiens,* vol. 30, pt. A (Tokyo, 1937).

[9] *Ibid.*, 9–10.

Charts (1:200,000), although a number of improvements were made. Watercourses, railroads, roads, and political boundaries are in black. No contours are shown, but several spot elevations are given. The petrographic and stratigraphic formations, as the foundation for soil classes, are delineated by brown-line boundaries and red-letter symbols. For the regions of nearly level land, soil types are shown in color. One sees at a glance how little of Japan can be classed as plain, for most of the map is left white. Seven groups of soils, ranging from sand through loam to clay are classified on the basis of particle size. Soils that are stony and very rich in humus are indicated in red symbols. This is an improvement over the older maps, on which the soils were indicated only by an overprint. However, the effect of climate and vegetation as soil-forming agencies was still ignored. The legends and place names are given in Japanese only.

In 1930 appeared the *Outline Soil Map of Japan* (scale 1:5,000,000), also compiled by Dr. Seki.[10] On this latest map the three primary colors are used to differentiate sandy, loamy, and clayey soils. Other symbols distinguish alluvium, diluvium, recent volcanic detritus, *onji* soils or slightly lateritic ash-loams, peat soils, moor soils, and red lateritic soils. By means of heavy black boundary lines Japan Proper is divided into three great soil groups whose designations reflect a recognition of the role climate and native vegetation play in soil formation (Fig. 40). These subdivisions are (1) the red soil area of southern and southwestern Japan; (2) the brown soil area of eastern Honshu between latitudes 35° and 38°; and (3) the slightly podsolized and moor soils of western and northern Honshu and of Hokkaido. Thus Dr. Seki is the first Japanese author to recognize the role of climate and vegetation in soil development, although a Russian author had published in 1930 a soil (and vegetation) map of Japan whose subdivisions were based upon climatic processes of soil formation.[11]

Mature Soils Uncommon.—Not historical antecedents alone retarded recognition by Japanese soil scientists of the role of climate and vegetation in soil formation but also the physical nature of the Japanese islands. Even as late as 1926, Aso and Seki, in announcing plans for a new soil map of Japan, proposed a classification based upon texture of soil particles, parent rock, and relief, and using no terminology relating to climatic

[10] A colored edition of this map is to be found in Scheidl, "Der Boden Japans," *op. cit.* A black and white reproduction of the colored original appears in P. Krische, "Bodenkarte Gross-Japans," in *Die Ernahrung der Pflanze*, vol. 34, June, 1938.

[11] Mrs. O. N. Mikhailovskaia, "On the Soils of Japan," in *Contributions to the Knowledge of the Soils of Asia*, 1:9–30 (Academy of Sciences of the U.S.S.R., 1930).

processes of soil formation.[12] This is understandable when one reflects that the country is largely mountains and hills whose slopes are so steep that the weathered rock materials are removed by erosion before the climatic and vegetation environments have been able to affect the soil and give it the characteristics of maturity. In such locations the layer of weathered rock is very thin, and soil profiles do not develop to maturity; what soils exist are young and bear strong resemblance to the parent rock, which is frequently exposed at the surface. Not only in the hill lands, however, but also on the lowlands of Japan mature climatically produced soils are none too common. On the plains of new alluvium the materials are often of such recent origin that mature profiles have not had time to develop. The soils on the flattish crests of some of the diluvial terraces show greater evidences of maturity; yet even these have not undergone the full effect of climatic forces because of the recent, or even current, additions of volcanic ash. The great relief energy everywhere prevalent leads to a thorough mixing of earth materials and thus retards the development of climatically induced mature soil profiles. Nevertheless, since *tendencies* toward general climatic soil types do exist even in Japan, such a threefold classification of the country's soils as Seki and Mikhailovskaia suggest are of some value. It should be noted that the subdivisions of these two authors differ rather markedly.

Soil Regions.—Seki's red-soils region, which includes all of Kyushu, Shikoku, and the greater part of southwestern Honshu south of latitude 35° is not coextensive with any particular forest type, although it is entirely within the region of the subtropical broadleaf evergreen forest (Fig. 40). In general it is the warmest and one of the rainiest parts of Japan, and has a marked maximum of precipitation in the warm season. Low in mineral plant foods and in humus, these red soils are infertile, although they break up readily and are easy to work. Patches of brown soil, limited in area, are also found within this zone, and at elevations above 3,000 to 4,500 feet slightly podsolized soils are common.

The brown-soil area of east-central Honshu is another region that is not coextensive with a particular forest type (Fig. 40). In general it is intermediate between the broadleaf evergreen forest to the south and the broadleaf deciduous and mixed forest to the north. Here rainfall is somewhat less abundant and winters cooler. Leaching is not quite so rapid in this area, and consequently the soils are less impoverished in

[12] Keijiro Aso and Toyotaro Seki, "New Schemes of Soil Classification and Soil Surveying in Japan," in the *Proceedings of the Third Pan-Pacific Science Congress,* Tokyo, 1926, 2:1955–1959.
[12] *Ibid.*

inorganic and organic plant foods. Slightly podsolized soils are found above elevations of about 1,500 feet.

All of Hokkaido and almost all of the Japan Sea side of Honshu fall within the area of slightly podsolized and moor soils (Fig. 40). Such soils are normally developed in cool, moist climates, in the presence of raw humus. They are gray in color and very low in soluble minerals. On the whole they are to be classed among the poorer soils of the earth. The

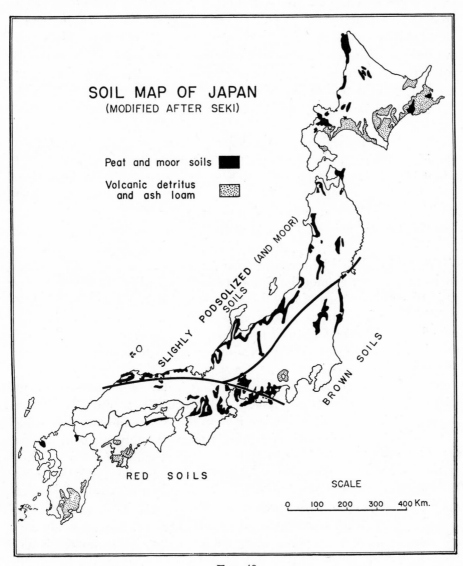

SOIL MAP OF JAPAN
(MODIFIED AFTER SEKI)

Peat and moor soils

Volcanic detritus
and ash loam

SLIGHLY PODSOLIZED (AND MOOR) SOILS

BROWN SOILS

RED SOILS

SCALE

0   100   200   300   400 Km.

Fig. 40

heavy precipitation of northwestern Honshu, especially in winter, and the poorly drained character of the delta-plains, lying as they do behind extensive belts of dunes and beach ridges, have resulted in the widespread development of acid moor soils in this region.

Soil Fertility.—Japanese soils in general are infertile. The abundant rainfall tends to remove the weathered rock from the slopes with great rapidity and to carry away in solution the soluble minerals needed by planted crops. They are particularly deficient in lime and nitrates. The prevalence of infertile acid soils explains in part why Japanese farmers must add enormous amounts of fertilizer to their croplands. Moreover, the soils are low in organic matter as well as mineral plant foods, for nowhere in Japan are there extensive natural grasslands whose rootmats would provide a rich supply of organic material. They are light in color, lacking the darker hues characteristic of fertile grassland soils.

Because of the very complicated lithic character of Japan, her predominantly young soils vary considerably. Even the small alluvial plains, nourished by rivers each of whose tributaries may be the source of a different kind of soil material, are likely to present complicated pattern of soil distribution varying greatly from one locality to another. Sandy soils are concentrated chiefly along the outer margins of alluvial plains where they front upon the sea. Because of their porous nature the sandy soils are unsuited to an amphibious crop like rice, which requires inundation of the fields. Their high porosity also makes for rapid loss of fertilizer. In large part these infertile, droughty soils are planted either in trees or in unirrigated crops of cereals and vegetables. Loam soils are characteristic of the largest part of the cultivated plains land and are the most prized soils of Japan. Clay soils in the rice fields are hard to work because they become waterlogged and because fertilizers decompose very slowly in them.

Alluvial and Diluvial Soils.—In Japan, as in the other monsoon countries of eastern and southern Asia, it is the young new alluvial soils that are most highly valued, and hence it is on the floodplains and deltas that human life is concentrated. Not only is the new alluvium more fertile, but it is associated with low and flattish surfaces which make inundation of the paddy fields easy. Even the diminutive alluvial plains, however, have diverse soils, varying from plain to plain according to the source of the sediments, and also from one part of a given plain to another. The beach ridges and the dunes along their coasts are porous and sandy, and adjacent to present and even relict stream channels the texture is also somewhat coarse. The upper part of a well developed fan is usually comprised of boulders and gravels. Because of the small size of Japanese plains, the rugged nature of their hinterlands, the vigorous character of the streams that feed them, and the prevalence of coarse-mineraled rocks such as granite, the alluvial soils of Japan are inclined to be loams rather than tight clays, a feature much valued in a region of heavy rainfall and prevalent rice culture.

The older alluvium (in Japan called diluvium) of the terraces is in general much less fertile than the new alluvium. Much of its surface material is coarse in texture, and porous sand and gravel subsoils are characteristic; hence it is unfit for rice fields, whose surfaces must be covered by water. Moreover, these older alluvial deposits have been subjected to the weathering effects of a humid forest climate much longer than has the new alluvium, whose fertility has more recently been renewed by additions of silt from floodwaters and from present-day irrigation waters. Volcanic ash, which mantles many of the terraces and also forms volcanic uplands of some extent, is on the whole infertile, being very deficient in basic minerals even though its physical properties are satisfactory.

Because the cultivated lands of Japan are so limited, comprising only 16 per cent of the total area, great care is taken to protect these precious soils of the plains from injury. Hillsides are kept well mantled with vegetation to prevent damaging floods and resulting deposits of coarse detritus on valuable farmland on the lowlands. Where hillsides are cultivated, the fields are usually terraced to check soil removal, and the upper slopes above the fields are left in trees and grass. Having learned by sad experience the costliness of denuded slopes, Japan is constantly waging a vigorous and scientific campaign against soil denudation. Check dams, artificial terraces, and restoration of the vegetation cover are the methods most commonly employed. In 1937 more than 2.25 million acres of forest were maintained primarily for the purpose of preventing soil denudation. On the plains the mountain-fed streams, which threaten to become raging torrents after any heavy rain, are flanked by high man-made multiple dikes to keep the flooding streams within their channels.

SELECTED REFERENCES

VEGETATION

ELCHIBEGOFF, IVAN. "Japanese Forest Resources and Requirements for Timber." *Paper Trade Journal,* vol. 106, no. 22 (June 2, 1938), 22 ff.

FUJIOKA, MITSUNAGA. "Forest Resources of Japan." *Proceedings of the Fifth Pacific Science Congress,* Toronto, 1933, 2:961–971.

LOWDERMILK, W. C. "Torrent and Erosion Control in Japan." *American Forests and Forest Life,* 35:474–479 (August, 1927).

NASU, SHIROSHI. *Aspects of Japanese Agriculture,* 58–67. Institute of Pacific Relations, New York, 1941.

SCHUMPETER, E. B., editor. *The Industrialization of Japan and Manchukuo, 1930–1940,* 188–204. The Macmillan Co., New York, 1940.

TURNER, E. PHILLIPS. "Japanese Forests and Forestry." *Empire Forestry Journal,* vol. 16 (1937).

SOILS

ASO, KEIJIRO and TOYOTARO SEKI. "New Schemes of Soil Classification and Soil Surveying in Japan." *Proceedings of the Third Pan-Pacific Science Congress,* Tokyo, 1926, 2:1955–1959.

CRAMER, P. J. S. "Notes on Agriculture in Japan Gathered during a Voyage in 1924." *Communications of the General Experiment Station for Agriculture,* Buitenzorg, Java, No. 22, pp. 6–15.

KRISCHE, P. "Bodenkarte Gross-Japans." *Die Ernahrung der Pflanze,* 34:198–200 (June, 1938). Contains a black and white reproduction of Seki's original map in color.

NASU, SHIROSHI. *Aspects of Japanese Agriculture,* 29–36. Institute of Pacific Relations, New York, 1941.

SCHEIDL, LEOPOLD. "Der Boden Japans." *Mitteilungen der Deutschen Gesellschaft für Natur- und Völkerkunde Ostasiens,* vol. 30, pt. A (Tokyo, 1937). Contains colored soils map of Japan by T. Seki, scale 1:5,000,000.

SEKI, TOYOTARO. "Distribution of Volcanic Ash Loams in Japan Proper and Their Characteristics and Agricultural Value." *Proceedings of the Third Pan-Pacific Science Congress,* Tokyo, 1926, 2: 1936–1941.

CHAPTER IV

Economic Minerals: Resources and Production

J APAN'S greatly accelerated industrial expansion during the decade of the thirties, especially in the chemical, metal, and machine industries, was paralleled by an extraordinary increase in domestic mineral production and consumption. Under the stimulus of wartime requirements the production of minerals had reached a peak in 1919, after which it had declined markedly. In the early years of the depression another marked decline occurred, low points being reached in 1931 and 1932. But from 1932 on, as the industrial and trade boom got under way, mineral production shot up so rapidly that in 1936, the last year for which official statistics are available, the value of domestic mineral production was 2.4 times as great as in 1931. This increase in value, to be sure, is partly attributable to price advances, but by no means entirely, as Table 31 shows.

But in spite of the stimulus of war preparations, domestic production could not keep pace with expanding industrial requirements. Even under normal conditions Japan is a large net importer of economic minerals; hence the prodigious increase in demand after 1932 could be met only by greatly increased imports. Importations of minerals rose from 220 million yen in 1931 to 660 million yen in 1936, a 300 per cent increase. Between 1931 and 1934 the ratio of domestic production to total mineral consumption fell from 60 to 51 per cent.

POWER MINERALS AND RESOURCES

The industrial expansion program undertaken by Japan during the decade of the thirties was contingent upon additional power resources. The output of coal and waterpower was greatly increased, but still remained insufficient, in the latter part of the decade, to permit attainment of many of the goals set by the government. Industrial power is supplied principally by coal, but hydroelectric power and petroleum are being used in increasingly greater proportions. Estimating four barrels of fuel oil as the equivalent of one metric ton of coal, and one installed horsepower

TABLE 30.—MINERAL PRODUCTION IN JAPAN PROPER

Year	Value in Millions of Yen	Percentage Rate of Change	Year	Value in Millions of Yen	Percentage Rate of Change
1929	384,558	−20	1934	432,308	+16.6
1930	307,673	−21.5	1935	504,419	+16.9
1931	241,836	+ 5.3	1936	589,400	+16.6
1932	254,782	+39.0	1937*	800,000	+36.0
1933	354,373	+21.9			

Source: *Oriental Economist*, 3(1936): 627–629; *Japan Year Book*, 1939–40.
* Estimated.

TABLE 31.—VOLUME INDEX OF MINERAL PRODUCTION IN JAPAN
(monthly average 1931–33 = 100)

1932	1933	1934	1935	1936	1937	1938	1939
96.3	106.8	115.4	123.8	137.8	150.0	159.5	164.5

Source: *Oriental Economist* as quoted by Kate L. Mitchell in *Japan's Industrial Strength*, 47.

TABLE 32.—SOURCES OF POWER IN JAPAN

Year	Coal Equivalent (in millions of metric tons)	Consumption Ratio of		
		Coal	Fuel Oil	Water Power
1913	19,113	94	—	6
1925	38,495	79	2	19
1929	46,548	76	2	22
1932	41,176	66	3	31
1936	67,500	68	10	22

Source: John R. Bradley and Donald W. Smith, *Fuel and Power in Japan* (U. S. Department of Commerce, *Trade Information Bulletin*, No. 821) p. ii. Data for 1936 computed.

TABLE 33.—JAPANESE COAL CONSUMPTION CLASSIFIED BY INDUSTRIES

Industry	Percentage of Total		Industry	Percentage of Total	
	1934	1937		1934	1937
Heavy industries . . .	15.6	19.5	Ceramic industry . . .	8.7	8.7
Chemical industry. . .	9.3	14.2	Electricity	6.8	8.0
Steamships	11.4	8.8	Gas and coke.	6.0	5.0
Railways.	10.0	9.6	Foodstuffs	5.6	4.9
Textiles and dyeing . .	9.6	8.9	Household, offices, etc..	17.0	11.9

Source: Schumpeter *et al.*, *The Industrialization of Japan and Manchukuo*, 425

in waterpower plants as equivalent to three tons of coal per annum, Table 32 shows the consumption of these three principal power sources in Japan over a quarter century. Although coal is still by far the most important source of power, its importance in relation to waterpower and fuel oil has declined. The striking shift in the relative importance of fuel oil and waterpower between 1932 and 1936 reflects the greatly increased imports of the former, a considerable proportion of which was stored in preparation for a possible national emergency. The waterpower capacity continued to increase, but less rapidly than fuel oil.

Coal

Although the production of coal in Japan Proper has declined in relation to that of other minerals, representing 63 per cent of the value of all minerals in 1931 and 52 per cent in 1936, its value still exceeds that of all other minerals combined. The principal demand for coal comes from the manufacturing industries, which consume from 50 to 60 per cent of the annual output. Only 12 per cent of the consumption is represented by household uses and the heating of office buildings, a much smaller proportion than in most Occidental countries. Though the demand for domestic briquettes has increased rapidly, charcoal consumption for household purposes still amounts to 2 million tons, or about 50 per cent of the quantity of coal used for this purpose.[1] Between 1934 and 1937 the most striking increase in coal consumption was in the heavy industries and the chemical industries, which accounted for 37.7 per cent of the coal used in 1937 as against 24.9 per cent in 1934. The greatest proportional decline during this period was in the use of coal for the heating of homes and office buildings.

Coal Resources.—Statistics on mineral reserves are often very confusing to the layman, for a number of seemingly dependable sources may present divergent figures. This does not necessarily mean that the sources are unreliable; it may simply mean that they have used different yardsticks. Some of them may include certain low-quality coals, others not. They may differ as to the thickness of seam that can be considered economically workable, the depth at which mining becomes uneconomical, and other points upon which even experts may disagree.

Japan is neither impoverished nor affluent as regards coal resources. In 1911 K. Inouye, director of the Imperial Geological Survey, estimated the reserves of coal in Japan Proper at 6.22 billion tons, of which less than

[1] *Transactions of the Third World Power Conference* (Washington, D.C., 1936), 3:681.

a billion tons represented "actual" reserves and the balance, 5.27 billion tons, "probable" reserves.[2] Inouye considered his estimate of actual reserves to be very conservative. Because of the very detailed character of his analysis and presentation the Inouye estimates, now more than thirty years old, are still highly regarded.

On the basis of a survey conducted by the Mining Bureau of the Japanese Department of Commerce and Industry in 1932, somewhat higher figures for coal reserves have been published. The survey report contains few details and fails to indicate whether or not the new estimates are based upon additional field work. Reasons for the departures from Inouye's estimates are not made clear. Actual or proved reserves of coal are placed at about 6 billion metric tons or more than six times the 1911 estimates,

TABLE 34.—COAL RESERVES OF JAPAN
(in thousands of metric tons)

Kind of Coal	Proved Deposits	Estimated Deposits	Potential Deposits	Total	Percentage of Total
Anthracite	454,745	131,944	132,093	718,782	4.3
Soft coal	5,439,905	3,780,975	6,278,211	15,499,091	93.0
Lignite	65,765	132,582	275,113	473,460	3.0
Total	5,960,415	4,045,501	6,685,417	16,691,333	100.0

Source: Mining Bureau, Department of Commerce and Industry, as quoted in Bradley and Smith, *Fuel and Power in Japan* (U. S. Department of Commerce, *Trade Information Bulletin*, No. 821), 2.

and the probable or estimated reserves at about 4 billion metric tons, a total of about 10 billion metric tons. If Inouye's 1911 figure of 6.22 billion tons is corrected for the amounts mined and consumed between 1911 and 1932 it will be reduced to about 5.7 billion tons. The Mining Bureau's 1932 figure exceeds this by about 80 per cent. In addition the Mining Bureau's estimate contains a third category, "potential reserves," amounting to about 6.7 billion tons, which is the most uncertain of all.

Whether one accepts Inouye's conservative figures or the Mining Bureau's more optimistic ones it is evident that Japan's coal reserves are far from bountiful. If they were being mined at the rate at which coal is produced in the United States, the "actual" reserve of Inouye would be consumed in about two years, and the actual and probable reserves combined in about fifteen years. Britain would consume this quantity of coal in twenty-five or thirty years. If the Mining Bureau's more liberal esti-

[2] Inouye, "The Coal Resources of Japan," in International Geological Congress, *The Coal Resources of the World* (Toronto, 1913), 1:291, 295.

mates are valid, these periods would be extended by 80 per cent. Perhaps these comparisons are better expressed by noting that Japan has a per capita reserve of only 80 (Inouye) to 140 (Mining Bureau) metric tons of coal as against 27,500 for the United States, about 4,000 for the United Kingdom, and 3,900 for Germany. If Japan were to continue mining coal at the rate she did in 1938 (44.6 million tons) her actual and probable reserves would last from 120 to 200 years, depending on which of the two estimates is valid. But projected plans for expansion of heavy industry, for coal liquefaction, and thermoelectric power development called for coal production at the rate of about 50–60 million tons a year in Japan Proper. Moreover, if Japan loses territory as a result of the present war she may be obliged in the post-war period to increase her manufacturing as a means of supporting her population. Obviously an accelerated rate of coal consumption would materially hasten exhaustion of her reserves. One to two hundred years is not long in the life of a nation, and years before there is a serious coal shortage the increased costs of mining thinner seams at greater depths will affect industry adversely. In summary, then, Japan is only moderately well supplied with coal, and though there is no danger that her reserves will be exhausted in the immediate future, neither is her supply bountiful or accessible enough to make careful conservation unnecessary.

Quality of Coal.—Because more than 90 per cent of the total coal mined is of mediocre quality—low bituminous or sub-bituminous—it is misleading to express value in terms of tonnage only. In this coal the volatile matter averages 30–45 per cent, the volume of carbon 35–55 per cent, and the calorific value 11,700–13,500 B.T.U.[3] In general, Japanese coal is not suitable for the production of high-quality metallurgical coke. Most of it is too porous and contains too much ash and volatile matter. A serious handicap to the iron and steel industry has been the high production cost of metallurgical coke. It has been common practice to mix Japanese coal with hard coking coal from Kaiping in North China, Penhsihu in Manchuria, and Hungchi in Indo-China in about the ratio 1:4. To some extent technological improvements in the dressing and treatment of local coal have meliorated this handicap. Another handicap to Japanese coal development is the fact that much of it exists in the form of thin seams which, being associated with complicated geological structures, are irregular in occurrence with frequent offsets. Moreover, the angles and positions of the coal strata make mining operations very difficult.

Anthracite comprises only a small part of the total coal reserve (0.4

[3] Bradley and Smith, *op. cit.,* 4.

per cent according to Inouye; the Mining Bureau gives 4 per cent). Most of the small amount of so-called anthracite is only semi-anthracite, and much of the mined product is virtually coaldust rather than lump coal. The semi-anthracite contains from 9 to 13 per cent of volatile matter and considerable ash; it has a short burning flame and a calorific value between 10,800 and 12,600 B.T.U. Japan's most important anthracite field is located at Omine in Yamaguchi Prefecture, in the extreme southwest of Honshu. Coal from this field contains little sulphur, and much of it is used for domestic purposes and for the manufacture of briquettes.[4] Lignite is un-important, amounting to only 3 per cent of the total coal reserve. The fields are widely scattered, and most of the production is for local domestic consumption.

Distribution of Coal Fields and of Coal Mining.—Although Japan is far from having the greatest reserves, she is the largest producer of coal in eastern Asia, and her output has increased rapidly in the last decade. Before World War I annual production was approximately 20 million metric tons; after the war, and until 1933, from 30 to 34 million metric tons. In 1932, a depression year, output dropped to 28 million tons, but by 1937, the last year for which reliable statistics are available, it exceeded 45 million tons.[5] The 1938 production of Japan Proper has been estimated at 44.6 million tons and that of the Empire at 70 million tons.[6] Despite the increases, however, coal production failed to keep pace with industrial demands. In 1938 and 1939 coal shortages impeded the government-stimulated program for wartime conversion and expansion of industry and was one reason for the industrial slump of 1940.

The two most extensive "actual" or "proved" coal deposits of Japan are located in Hokkaido and in Kyushu at the northern and southern ends of the country (Fig. 41). In 1932, according to the Mining Bureau's estimates (excluding the more dubious potential deposits), Kyushu contained 49 per cent of the country's coal and Hokkaido 39 per cent (Table 35).[7] The remaining 12 per cent is in small fields widely scattered throughout the main island of Honshu. There is virtually no coal in Shikoku. In 1936 about 70 per cent of the coal mined in Japan Proper came from the Kyushu fields, only 22 per cent from Hokkaido. This greater production in Kyushu is in part due to its closer proximity to the principal centers of population and industry and to the main shipping routes. It is sig-

[4] *Ibid.*   [5] *The Oriental Economist*, 7:215–217 (April, 1940).
[6] *The Mineral Industry during 1941*, edited by G. A. Roush (New York, 1942), 108–109.
[7] Inouye's estimates of 1912, adjusted for the amounts mined between 1913 and 1927, gave Hokkaido slightly larger reserves as of the latter date.

Table 35.—Coal Resources and Production in Japan Proper by Districts
(in thousands of metric tons)

District	Proved or Actual Deposits		Estimated or Probable Deposits		Possible or Potential Deposits	Production 1936
	Inouye (1900)	Mining Bureau (1932)	Inouye	Mining Bureau	Mining Bureau	
Hokkaido	336,000	2,032,825	2,339,000	1,766,699	4,219,558	9,300
Honshu	70,000		512,000			2,900
Northeast district		151,724		157,673	615,462	
Kwanto and middle district		56,876		131,228	103,252	
Kinki, Chugoku, and Shikoku		486,949		201,555	177,331	
Kyushu	542,000	3,166,276	2,374,000	1,655,764	1,304,701	29,600*
Total Japan Proper	948,000	5,894,650	5,225,000	3,912,919	6,410,304	41,800

Sources: Inouye, "Coal Resources of Japan," *op. cit.*, 289–295; Bradley and Smith, *Fuel and Power in Japan*, 2; Schumpeter *et al.*, *The Industrialization of Japan and Manchukuo, 1930–1940*, 265.
* Includes Yamaguchi Prefecture in Honshu.

Table 36.—Scale of Coal Mining Operations in 1935

Output of Mines (metric tons)	Number of Mines in Group	Output of Group (metric tons)	Average Output per Mine	Percentage of Total
Over 1,000,000	6	8,500,000	1,420,000	22.5
500,000 to 1,000,000	12	8,420,000	700,000	22.3
250,000 to 500,000	23	8,520,000	370,000	22.5
100,000 to 250,000	49	7,990,000	160,000	21.2
Under 100,000	360	4,330,000	12,000	11.5
Total	450	37,760,000		

Source: Schumpeter *et al.*, *The Industrialization of Japan and Manchukuo, 1930–1940*, 606.

Table 37.—Japan Proper: Production of Coal Mines in 1935

Number of Mines Producing over 250,000 Tons	Locality	Production in Metric Tons (mines over 10,000 T.)
0	Shirabeshi, (Hokkaido)	126,377
8	Ishikari (Hokkaido)	7,381,917
0	Tokachi (Hokkaido)	20,795
1	Kushiro (Hokkaido)	733,688
3	Fukushima (Joban)	2,218,170
0	Ibaraki (Joban)	345,344
2	Yamaguchi (Ube)	2,540,476
24	Fukuoka (northern Kyushu)	9,964,410
1	Saga (northwest Kyushu)	898,255
2	Nagasaki (northwest Kyushu)	3,048,580
41	Total	27,278,012
	Total all mines	37,800,000

Source: *Mining Industry of Japan, 1935* (Mining Bureau, Tokyo).

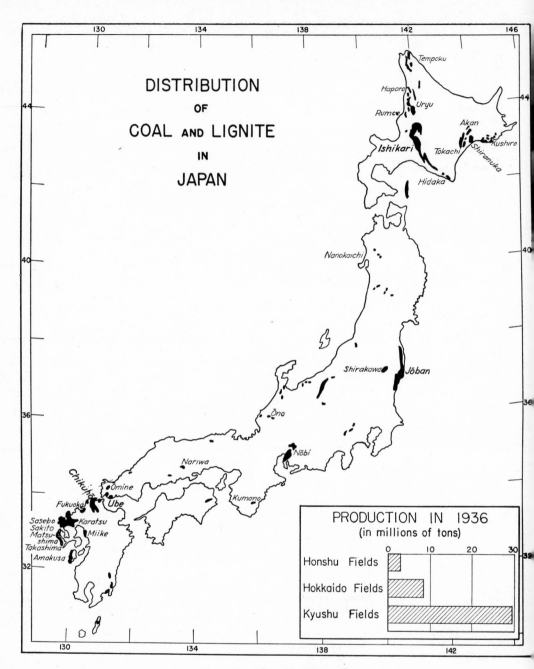

FIG. 41. After K. Watanabe.

88

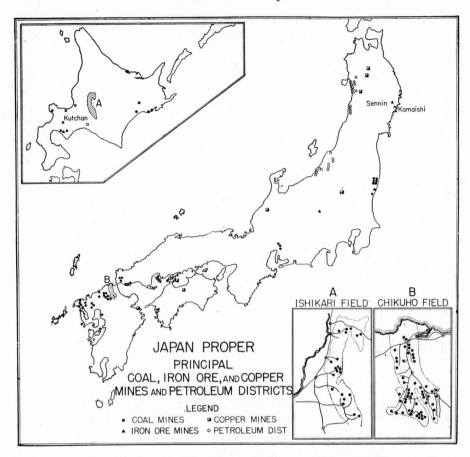

Fig. 42. Source: *The Mining Industry of Japan, 1935.*

nificant, however, that in recent years coal production has increased more rapidly in Hokkaido than in Kyushu, the respective ratios of increase in the decade 1925–36 being 64 and 29 per cent. Prospects for further rapid expansion are less favorable in Kyushu, where the mines have been worked for a longer period, than in the newer Hokkaido fields. The cost of production in Hokkaido is 5.60 yen per ton as against 6.50 yen in Kyushu.[8]

In 1935 about 450 coal mines were in operation in Japan Proper, but a large majority of these were very small producers. Only six mined over a million tons. Forty-one mines, each of which had an annual output of a quarter million tons or more, accounted for 67 per cent of the nation's

[8] Kaneo Nanyo, "Transportation and Distribution of Coal in Japan," in *Transactions of Sectional Meeting, World Power Conference*, Tokyo, 1929, 1:367.

total coal production. Their distribution is shown in Table 37 and Fig. 42. Nine were in Hokkaido, twenty-seven in Kyushu, and five in the Joban and Ube fields in Honshu. Judged by American standards coal-mining operations in Japan are not very modern. Virtually all the labor is manual, although there has been an increased installation of machinery in recent years. Most of the underground work is done with pick and shovel, and the product is carried in baskets to the mine entry by women and children.[9]

Kyushu Fields.—In northern and western Kyushu there are a number of separate coal fields. The most important of these, the Chikuho Field, occupies a hilly basin-like area of Tertiary rocks in the extreme north of the island, not far from the belt of heavy industry along the Straits of Shimonoseki (Fig. 41). Somewhat farther to the west and southwest are several less important fields: Fukuoka, Karatsu, Sasebo, Sakito, Matsushima, Takashima, Miike, and Amakusa.[10] Most of Kyushu fields lie close to the coast, and in a number of them submarine seams are being worked. Considerably less than half the Kyushu coal mined is consumed in the local industries of the island. The larger part goes by lighter, barge, sailer, and small steamer to districts south and west of the Tokyo region; and several million tons are consumed as bunker fuel. Much of it is shipped to industrial centers along the Inland Sea, especially the Osaka-Kobe-Kyoto center. About one-fourth to one-third as much as reaches this latter center finds its way northward as far as the Tokyo-Yokohama district.[11] The principal coal-shipping ports for the Kyushu coal are Wakamatsu, which handles nearly two-thirds of the total, Nagasaki, Miike, and Fukuoka. A portion of the Kyushu coal leaving the island requires no rail haul, since a number of the mines are on the immediate seacoast.

Hokkaido Fields.—Hokkaido, whose coal reserves approximate those of Kyushu, has one major field, the Ishikari, which is to Hokkaido what Chikuho is to Kyushu, and several minor ones (Fig. 41). According to Inouye, Ishikari has the largest reserves of coal of all the individual Japan fields, although it produces much less than Chikuho. The field lies in the Tertiary rock hill lands just east of the Ishikari plain in west-central Hokkaido. Being more remote from the country's principal industrial centers, it has not been tapped to the same extent as have the Kyushu fields. Most of its mines have been opened more recently, and hence equip-

---

[9] Nanyo, *op. cit.*, 367.

[10] Details concerning each of the coal fields are to be found in International Geological Congress, *The Coal Resources of the World*, 1:296–348. Further descriptions of individual fields are contained in Part III below.

[11] Nanyo, *op. cit.*, 386–387.

TABLE 38.—RESOURCES AND PRODUCTION OF COAL FIELDS OF KYUSHU

Coal Field	Thickness of Coal Seams	Actual Reserve, 1912 (estimated)		Probable Reserve, 1912 (estimated)		Aggregate Production, 1913–27
	meters	area sq. km.	thousands of metric tons	area sq. km.	thousands of metric tons	thousands of metric tons
Chikuko	1.4–11.1	71.2	405,500	229.3	1,255,000	213,246
Miike	3.0– 5.5	10.0	60,000	130.0	700,000	31,340
Karatsu	0.9– 4.2	8.0	17,000	53.0	112,000	28,163
Sasebo	0.5– 2.7	—	—	110.0	90,000 ⎫	
Sakito	4.5– 4.9	2.5	16,000	6.5	40,000 ⎬ 24,896	
Matsushima	3.6– 4.2	2.0	10,000	5.0	28,000	
Takashima	4.5–15.2	2.5	33,000	11.0	146,000 ⎭	
Amakusa	1.2– 1.8	1.4	3,500	8.0	15,000	749
Yaeyama	2.0– 4.0	—	—	3.5	3,000	627

Source: Inouye, in International Geological Congress, *Coal Resources of the World*, 1:289–295; and Kyukichi Watanabe, "Coal Resources of Japan," in *World Power Conference, Sectional Meeting*, Tokyo, 1929, Appendix II, pp. 315–317.

TABLE 39.—DISPOSITION OF COAL LEAVING KYUSHU
(no date given; probably about 1927)

Seaport	Tonnage Carried to Seaport	Tonnage Shipped from Seaport	Tonnage for Bunker Purposes
Wakamatsu	7,960,000	7,540,000	420,000
Moji	1,830,000	430,000	1,400,000
Fukuoka	790,000	730,000	60,000
Karatsu	730,000	470,000	260,000
Nagasaki	1,450,000	1,190,000	260,000
Miiki	1,650,000	890,000	760,000
Suminoye	270,000	260,000	10,000
Total	14,680,000	11,480,000	3,200,000

Source: Kaneo Nanyo, "Transportation and Distribution of Coal in Japan," in *World Power Conference, Sectional Meeting*, Tokyo, 1929, 1: 370.

TABLE 40.—DISPOSITION OF COAL LEAVING HOKKAIDO
(no date given; probably about 1927)

Seaport	Tonnage Carried to Seaport	Tonnage Shipped from Seaport	Tonnage for Bunker Purposes
Otaru	1,680,000	910,000	770,000
Muroran	2,300,000	1,960,000	340,000
Hakodate	120,000	60,000	60,000
Kushiro	420,000	36,000	60,000
Total	4,520,000	3,270,000	1,250,000

Source: Kaneo Nanyo, "Transportation and Distribution of Coal in Japan," in *World Power Conference, Sectional Meeting*, Tokyo, 1929, 1: 370.

TABLE 41.—RESOURCES AND PRODUCTION OF THE COAL FIELDS OF HOKKAIDO

Coal Field	Thickness of Coal Seams	Actual Reserves, 1912 (estimated)		Probable Reserves, 1912 (estimated)		Aggregate Production, 1913–27
	meters	area sq. km.	thousands of metric tons	area sq. km.	thousands of metric tons	thousands of metric tons
Ishikari	1.8–51.5	25.3	307,600	271.5	1,791,500	59,109
Tempoku	2.0–11.0	—	17,670	—	270,690	1
Haporo	3.0	—	8,220	—	29,980	—
Opiraushpetsu	1.0–10.0	—	20,082	—	76,982	--
Rumoi	1.5– 3.0	—	11,934	—	27,713	326
Uryu	—	—	38,707	—	151,000	—
Kushiro	0.5– 3.0	19.5	32,380	15.5	105,210 ⎫	
Akan	0.6– 4.3	—	57,270	—	84,630 ⎬	3,544
Shiranuka	—	—	9,720	—	12,120 ⎭	
Oraporo	1.0– 5.0	—	19,368	—	43,122	8
Kayanuma	1.8– 7.0	—	7,260	—	41,600	286

Source: Kyukichi Watanabe, "Coal Resources of Japan," in *World Power Conference, Sectional Meeting*, Tokyo, 1929, Appendix II, pp. 315–317.

TABLE 42.—RESOURCES AND PRODUCTION OF COAL FIELDS OF HONSHU

Coal Field	Thickness of Coal Seam	Actual Reserve, 1912 (estimated)		Probable Reserve, 1912 (estimated)		Aggregate Production, 1913–27
	meters	area sq. km.	thousands of metric tons	area sq. km.	thousands of metric tons	thousands of metric tons
Nanokaichi	1.8–2.7	—	1,000	—	19,500	372
Aburato	0.6–1.8	—	1,000	—	14,000	306
Joban	0.6–4.2	14.0	43,500	122.0	306,000	44,886
Ube	0.9–3.6	4.4	10,000	37.5	85,500	19,000
Mogami	0.8–0.9	—	—	17.0	20,000	204
Nobi	0.8–1.2	11.0	13,000	26.0	30,000	1,643
Sendai, Suzuka, etc.	0.5–1.2	0.6	1,000	37.4	37,000	507

Source: Kyukichi Watanabe, "Coal Resources of Japan," cited above.

TABLE 43.—COAL PRODUCTION, IMPORTS, AND EXPORTS
(in thousands of metric tons)

	1936	1937	1938	1939
Production, Japan Proper	41,803			
Imports				
From colonies				
Korea	638			
Formosa	114	271		
From foreign countries				
Manchukuo	2,273	2,277	1,463	764
China	1,034	1,308	1,647	2,474
French Indo-China	883	832	618	614
Others	11	9	14	5
Total	4,200	4,426	3,742	3,857
Exports to foreign countries	1,113	1,027	758	680

Source: Schumpeter *et al.*, *The Industrialization of Japan and Manchukuo, 1930–1940*, 265–266.

ment and mining methods are more up-to-date. Since the field is thirty to forty miles inland, the coal must be hauled to tidewater by rail. Most of it leaves from the ports of Muroran and Otaru; a considerable part goes to the Tokyo-Yokohama industrial region, and about a sixth as much to the Osaka-Kobe region.[12] The other Hokkaido fields are worked on a smaller scale. Among these are the Kushiro, Akan, and Shiranuka fields in the east, back of the port of Kushiro. Their coals exist in thin seams and are of inferior quality.

Honshu Fields.—Chief among the minor Honshu coal fields is Joban, located close to the seacoast of Fukushima Prefecture about 120 miles north and slightly east of Tokyo (Figs. 41, 42). Though its coal is of inferior quality, being rich in ash and sulphur, it has the advantage of proximity to the great Kwanto industrial node just to the south, with which it has excellent rail connections. In normal years Joban is the most important single source of supply for the Kwanto center, which is the destination of most of its coal. It also supplies northern Honshu in general. Since there is no nearby port, all coal movement is by rail.

Next to Joban in both reserves and normal production is the Ube (Onada) Field on the shores of the Inland Sea in the extreme southwestern part of Honshu (Yamaguchi Prefecture) (Figs. 41, 42). Most of the mines are small, and the reserves are limited. The coal is of inferior quality, but location on tidewater permits cheap transportation by small boat to the industrial centers—especially Osaka and Kobe—on the shores of the Inland Sea. Lignite is mined in the Nobi Bay region to the east of Nagoya and is used in the porcelain industry of that area. Lignite is also mined on a small scale for limited consumption at Takasaki, in the Kwanto district, and at Mogami and Sendai in northern Honshu.

IMPORTS AND EXPORTS OF COAL

Japan Proper is largely self-sufficient with respect to coal and could be entirely so except for certain coals, such as anthracite and coking coal, required by particular industries. Of the total coal consumed in 1936, domestic production supplied over 90 per cent; slightly less than 5 million metric tons was imported, of which 638,000 metric tons, chiefly anthracite, came from Korea, and 114,000 tons from Formosa. Thus 15 per cent of the imports into Japan Proper came from the colonies. About 2.3 million metric tons, or 46 per cent of total imports, came from the Japanese-controlled state of Manchukuo, chiefly from the Fushun colliery near Mukden. From China came 1.03 million metric tons or 21 per cent, much of this being coking coal from the Kaiping collieries. French Indo-China sent 883,000 metric tons, or 15 per cent of the imports, nearly all of which was anthracite.[13] Exports to foreign countries amounted to only 1.2 million metric tons.

Petroleum

Of the fuel and power resources of Japan, petroleum is the weakest unit, annual production being normally less than daily production in the United States. What is still more serious, the reserves too are small. No recent estimates of oil reserves have been published, but a description of the situation in the early thirties is available. Mr. W. B. Heroy, of the staff of the Sinclair Consolidated Oil Corporation, writes as follows: "Reserves of petroleum in unexhausted horizons of present producing fields were estimated by Redfield to be about 56,000,000 barrels at the end of 1924. Deeper horizons may be expected to be found in present producing fields and it is probable that further prospecting will lead to the discovery of other producing areas. However, the extensive exploration work in wildcat drilling which has been done in recent years without important new discoveries suggests that in this respect less may be expected in the future than in the past. . . . While estimates of future recovery have little or no quantitative value, it would be surprising if the ultimate production of petroleum from all sources were to exceed 500,000,000 barrels."[14] Bradley and Smith summarize the matter of reserves with the statement that "previous surveys indicated that the output of the wells developed prior to 1931 would be exhausted in less than thirty years and that the total reserves of the wells in operation were less than 75,000,000 barrels."[15]

On the basis of Heroy's estimate of ultimate reserves, Japan's per capita oil reserve would have been approximately seven barrels per capita in the early thirties; on the basis of Bradley and Smith's estimate, only about one barrel. For a country with so large and rapidly increasing a population, and one whose industrial expansion has been so rapid, the petroleum resources are extremely meager. On purely economic grounds the situation was not necessarily alarming. On strategic grounds, however, it was a matter of grave concern. Bent upon territorial expansion as she obviously was during the thirties, Japan regarded the matter of oil supply as so crucial that in 1934 the petroleum industry was placed under State control.

[13] E. B. Schumpeter, ed., *et al.*, *The Industrialization of Japan and Manchukuo, 1930–1940* (New York, 1940), 265–266.

[14] W. B. Heroy in J. Foster Bain, *Ores and Industry in the Far East*, revised edition (New York, 1933), 120–121.

[15] John R. Bradley and Donald W. Smith, *Fuel and Power in Japan* (U. S. Department of Commerce, *Trade Information Bulletin*, No. 821, Washington, D.C., 1935), 10.

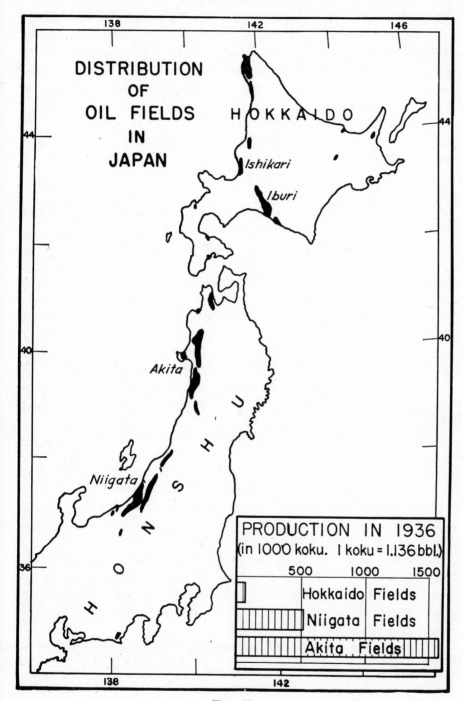

FIG. 43

95

Oil Production in Japan.—Domestic crude oil production reached an all-time high during the period of World War I. Thereafter, during the twenties, it declined, and the annual average for the years 1928–31 was only two-thirds that of 1916. Beginning about 1932, when Japan entered upon a period of territorial expansion, with the consequent danger of war that such a venture involved, domestic oil production again rose rapidly, until by 1936 it was 75 per cent greater than in 1933. If estimates are correct, the increase after 1936 was slight, indicating that even under wartime pressure further expansion was impossible. In 1936 domestic production provided only 9 per cent of the non-government requirements; the remaining 91 per cent had to be imported.

Japan's petroleum belt lies along the Japan Sea coast from Hokkaido on the north, through northern Honshu, to about parallel 37° on the south (Figs. 42, 43). The fields are associated with anticlinal folds in Tertiary rocks. The western part of North Honshu includes the country's two principal oil fields, the Akita and the Niigata, each of which contains a number of producing districts. From these two fields 95 per cent of Japan's domestic oil supply is derived. The Akita Field has been rapidly increasing in importance since 1933, its output climbing from 40 to 73 per cent in the period 1932–36.[16] The Niigata Field, on the other hand, which reached its peak production of about 2 million barrels in 1914, has been declining both absolutely and relatively in recent years; in 1932 its output was 54 per cent of the nation's total, but by 1936 it was only 24 per cent, or 600,000 barrels.

The Akita Field, located in the prefecture of the same name, is included in a north-south coastal belt about 170 kilometers long and thirty to fifty kilometers wide.[17] It comprises six to ten producing districts, most of which are located in hilly Tertiary rock areas at some distance back from the coast. The Akita Field was developed much later than the Niigata Field to the south. Although the first trial borings were made in 1902, active work did not begin until about 1914.[18]

The Niigata oil belt, in Niigata Prefecture, was one of the earliest to be developed. It extends some two hundred miles north-south along the Japan Sea coast and is fifty to sixty kilometers wide. Some of the oil derricks are on the coastal alluvial plains and sand dunes, but more of

[16] *Japan-Manchukuo Year Book, 1940,* p. 358.

[17] Yoshinosuki Chitani, "Petroleum Resources of Japan," in *Transactions of Sectional Meeting, World Power Conference,* Tokyo, 1929, 1:436. See also William Harvey Emmons, *Geology of Petroleum,* 2d ed. (New York, 1931), 702–705.

[18] Chitani, *op. cit.,* 436–437. Details concerning the individual districts are given on pages 437 and 438.

TABLE 44.—PRODUCTION AND IMPORTATION OF CRUDE OIL AND HEAVY OIL
(in hundred-thousand gallons; 42 gallons = 1 barrel)

| YEAR | DOMESTIC CRUDE PRODUCTION | IMPORTS | | | | | | | TOTAL SUPPLY |
		Man-churia	British Borneo	Nether-lands East Indies	Russia	United States	Others	Total Imports	
1926	713							1,179	1,892
1927	691							1,627	2,318
1928	772							3,806	4,578
1929	822							4,198	5,020
1930	835							4,264	5,099
1931	808							4,536	5,334
1932	670							5,687	6,357
1933	596	149	422	627	875	3,367	689	6,130	6,726
1934	750	130	388	705	710	4,903	603	7,440	8,190
1935	927	141	492	1,069	10	6,897	579	9,187	10,114
1936	1,032	192	842	1,344	—	7,605	353	10,336	11,368
1937	1,045								
1938	1,074*								
1939	1,127*								
1940	1,108*								
1941	1,116*								

Percentage Distribution of Imports from Each Country

1933		2.4	6.9	10.2	14.3	54.9	11.3		
1934		1.8	5.2	9.5	9.5	65.9	8.1		
1935		1.5	5.4	11.6	0.1	75.1	6.3		
1936		1.9	8.1	13.0	—	73.6	3.4		

Source: Schumpeter et al., 267; The Mineral Industry during 1941, edited by G. A. Roush (McGraw-Hill Book Co., New York, 1942), 408.
* Estimates.

TABLE 45.—PRODUCTION OF OIL FIELDS IN JAPAN PROPER
(in thousands of koku; 1 koku = 1.136 barrels)

Oil Field	1932	1936	Percentage of Total Production
Akita.	596.5	1583.9	73.1
Niigata	815.0	514.8	23.8
Hokkaido (and others)	93.7	67.1	3.1
Total	1505.2	2165.8	100.0

Source: Japan-Manchukuo Year Book, 1940, p. 358.

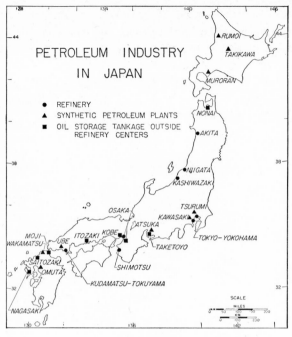

FIG. 44

them are in the hilly districts back of the plains.[19]

Least important is the Hokkaido Field. Since 1933, while the total oil production of the country has been rapidly increasing, Hokkaido's output has declined. In 1936 it represented only 3.1 per cent of the total output. Only two districts, the Ishikari and the Iburi, yielded significant amounts of crude oil in 1935. Ishikari Field is situated in a hilly tract about eight kilometers northeast of the town of Ishikari and nearly thirty kilometers north and slightly east of Sapporo. Iburi is situated some sixty kilometers south and east of Sapporo and about ten kilometers inland from the coast. Producing centers in Hokkaido other than these two are few and very unimportant.

OIL REFINING AND SYNTHETIC OIL PRODUCTION

Japanese crude petroleum, domestic and imported, is refined in a number of plants, many of which are capable of refining only a few thousand barrels a year. At the close of 1932 there were sixty-three refineries in Japan, only twenty of which had an annual capacity of more than 70,000 barrels.[20] Until about 1930 the petroleum industry was dominated by foreign firms importing refined products, but from 1928 on expansion of the refinery industry was so rapid that by 1935 from 40 to 45 per cent of the nation's total oil consumption was domestically refined.[21] In that year Japanese refineries supplied 50 per cent of the nation's gasoline requirements, 50 per cent of the kerosene, 94 per cent of the lubricating oil, and 12.5 per cent of the fuel oil.[22] Government control of the oil industry since

[19] *Ibid.*, 438–443. See also Emmons, *op. cit.*, 698–702.
[20] Bradley and Smith, *op. cit.*, 11–12.   [21] *Ibid.*, 11.
[22] "Petroleum in the Far East," in U. S. Bureau of Mines, *Supplement to International Petroleum Trade,* April 27, 1937, p. 5.

TABLE 46.—PRODUCTION OF IMPORTANT PETROLEUM DISTRICTS IN JAPAN PROPER, 1935
(districts producing over 1,000 kiloliters of crude oil)

MINE		CRUDE OIL		NATURAL GAS	
Name	Location	Quantity in Kiloliters	Value in Yen	Quantity in Cubic Meters	Value in Yen
Ishikari	Ishikari, Hokkaido	4,827	154,467	833,000	11,578
Atsuma	Iburi, Hokkaido	8,011	240,316	1,129,000	15,694
Innai	Akita	55,328	1,825,818	209,300	3,348
Yabase	Akita	43,353	1,387,280	2,832,100	45,313
Yuri	Akita	7,213	238,012		
Nakano-Oguni	Akita	40,772	1,345,466		
Asaki-Innai	Akita	14,375	474,385		
Omonogawa	Akita	9,164	357,396		
Omonogawa	Akita	2,836	111,669		
Omonogawa	Akita	1,959	76,413		
Dai-Nippon-Oguni	Akita	3,268	107,841		
Ogura-Toyokawa	Akita	2,293	66,497	16,700	267
Niitsu	Niigata	30,071	1,082,183	2,130,800	40,486
Kariba	Niigata	16,123	644,912	14,406,000	244,902
Nishiyama	Niigata	16,137	645,488	6,169,600	104,882
Higashiyama	Niigata	12,165	486,582	110,200	1,983
Takamachi	Niigata	7,756	310,228	4,388,700	74,608
Omo	Niigata	8,456	338,228	1,716,400	30,895
Kanatsu	Niigata	7,733	267,762		
Betsuyama	Niigata	3,304	132,170	1,125,800	19,138
Maki	Niigata	1,185	54,524	17,400	417

Source: *The Mining Industry of Japan, 1935* (Japan Bureau of Mines, Tokyo), 51–55.

1934 has resulted in still further expansion of the domestic capacity; by 1939 a much larger percentage of the country's oil consumption was domestically refined than in 1935. The plants are widely scattered for both industrial and strategic reasons.[23] Some are located in the vicinity of the domestic oil fields, notably at Akita, Niigata, and Kashiwazaki in northwestern Honshu (Fig. 44). More of them, however, are in port cities where they depend upon imported crude oil. The greatest single refinery center is in the Tokyo-Yokohama region, which is estimated to have 40–45 per cent of the nation's crude refinery capacity and still higher percentages of the cracking and the octane capacity. Other important refinery centers are those at Osaka, Tokuyama, Kudamatsu, and Shimotsu (south of Wakayama), all located on the borderlands of the Inland Sea. Outside of Japan Proper important refineries have been in operation at Dairen in Kwantung Leased Territory and in Korea.

Experimental manufacture of synthetic gasoline from coal was started in Japan, Korea, and Manchuria as early as 1936, but production on a com-

[23] R. Reinhard, "Öl im Pazific," in *Geographische Zeitschrift*, 48 (1942):85. See also "Die Japanische Mineralölwirtschaft," in *Wirtschaft und Statistik*, April, 1941, pp. 138–142.

mercial scale did not begin until three years later. The project is obviously a military measure, for pure synthetic gasoline is considerably higher priced than the natural product. The first plants built were small, but after the experimental stage had been passed they were rapidly expanded, and since 1937 several larger plants have been erected. In 1940 the Japanese were operating eleven synthetic gasoline plants and expected to have eight more in operation in 1941.[24] Like the refineries, they have been widely scattered throughout Japan Proper, Korea, and Manchuria. German and American authorities estimate that in 1941 some 6 million barrels of synthetic gasoline were being produced annually in the empire.[25] What is probably the largest plant is located at Omuta in north-

TABLE 47.—IMPORTS OF OIL INTO JAPAN BY COUNTRIES OF ORIGIN, 1936*
(quantity in kiloliters, value in thousands of yen)

| COUNTRY | CRUDE AND HEAVY OIL | | REFINED PRODUCTS | | TOTAL, INCLUDING OTHERS |
	Quantity	Value	Quantity	Value	Value
Manchuria	72,520 (1.8%)	1,692	—	—	1,692
British Borneo	318,679 (8.1%)	9,491	199	33	9,527
Dutch East Indies	508,822 (13.0%)	15,501	482,702 (66%)	27,991	43,497
Soviet Russia	—	—	25,849 (3.1%)	1,367	1,367
United States	2,878,746 (73.6%)	99,348	164,757 (22.5%)	9,992	109,340
Total, including others	3,912,377 (3.5%)	129,688	730,660	42,804	182,769

Source: *Japan-Manchukuo Year Book*, 1940, p. 359.
* There were additional imports of crude oil for the use of the Imperial Navy and large quantities of refined products which are not included.

western Kyushu, adjacent to the Miike Coal Field. Others are located at Wakamatsu, the coal-shipping port of North Kyushu; at Ube, in the coal field of the same name; at Atsuta just to the east of Nagoya, where lignite is available; at Kawasaki and Tsurumi near Tokyo; at three sites in Hokkaido, one of which is also the iron and steel center of Muroran. Synthetic plants belonging to the Imperial Army and Navy are located at a number of other places in southwestern Japan. Outside of Japan Proper plants have been established in Karafuto and Korea.

Imports of Petroleum.—The only colonial source of petroleum to meet the non-government requirements of Japan Proper is Formosa, which produces an insignificant amount. In 1936 fully 90 per cent of the total requirements of crude oil were supplied by outside sources (see Table 47). All these importations came from foreign countries and their do-

[24] Louis E. Frechtling, "Japan's Oil Supplies," in *Amerasia*, 5:200 (July, 1941).
[25] *Ibid.*, 200.

minions except a scant 2 per cent produced from shale in Manchuria, a unit of the controlled Yen-Bloc. Nearly 74 per cent of the imported crude oil came from the United States, 13 per cent from the Netherlands Indies, and 8 per cent from British Borneo. Of the refined petroleum products imported, on the other hand, the United States supplied only 22.5 per cent and the Netherlands Indies 66 per cent. The government's policy of expanding Japan's petroleum-refining capacity for strategic reasons has tended to increase importations of crude and heavy oil more rapidly than the refined products. Thus while in the years 1927 to 1931 the value of crude oil and of refined oil imports was about equal, by 1936 five times as much crude oil as refined oil was being imported, the value of which was two and a half times as great.

Throughout the decade of the thirties imports of petroleum increased rapidly; between 1931 and 1936 the volume of crude and heavy oil imports rose 228 per cent and that of refined products about 61 per cent. A portion of this increase was undoubtedly consumed in the country's rapidly expanding industrial structure, but much of it was put in storage in anticipation of a national emergency. Large storage tanks were located in at least ten different centers in Japan Proper, more than one-third of the total capacity being centered in the Tokyo-Yokohama area. Other large oil storage facilities were located at refinery centers. Although no official statistics have been published in Japan since 1936, it seems probable that these increased imports came largely from the United States, where petroleum products were selling at a low price during the depression years. If this is a correct assumption, American export statistics would be a fair guide to Japanese imports. During the three years 1935–36 to 1938–39 petroleum exports from the United States to Japan increased about 30 per cent, which suggests still further expansion of Japanese refinery and storage facilities after 1936.

Hydroelectric Power

Two physical features of Japan, the predominance of hill and mountain land and the abundance of precipitation, are responsible for her large potential waterpower. On the basis of a six-months' flow the potential waterpower of Japan's rivers is estimated at 10.9 million kilowatts. Slightly less than half this amount (5.1 million kw.) can be depended upon at the minimum flow. At the end of 1936 the waterpower actually developed amounted to 4.8 million kilowatts, or about 45 per cent of the six-months' minimum potential.[26] Next to the United States and Canada, Japan was in

[26] Shigemi Shimogaichi, "Power Generation and Transmission in Japan," in *Electrotechnical Journal* (Tokyo), vol. 1 (1937), no. 1, pp. 4–5.

1937 the world's largest producer of hydroelectric power. Electrical output had been expanding rapidly for some years, as had other production; in 1936 the kilowatt capacity was about five and a half times what it had been in 1920. Between 1930 and 1937 alone the output of electric power increased 75 per cent (Fig. 45). In 1936 publication of official statistics on power plants was discontinued, but the fact that at the end of that

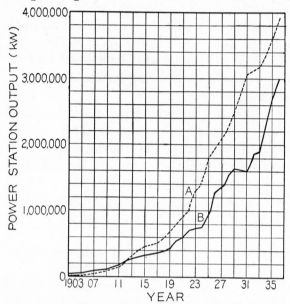

year there was under construction a 45 per cent increase in hydroelectric capacity suggests that it was still being expanded at a rapid rate.[27]

The total consumption of electric power in Japan in 1937 was 26.6 million kilowatt hours, 82 per cent of which was hydroelectric and 8 per cent thermoelectric.[28] This relationship is the reverse of that in the United States, Germany, and Great Britain, where thermoelectric development greatly predominates. The explanation lies in the fact that coal is less abundant and more expensive in Japan, and that waterpower can be so cheaply generated. In 1936 the thermoelectric stations consumed from 6 to 7 per cent of the total coal used in Japan.

FIG. 45. Growth of electric power output in Japan. A: Hydroelectric; B: Steam power. After S. Shimogaichi.

The volume of flow of the short but vigorous Japanese rivers varies considerably, periodically with the seasons and nonperiodically with spells of drought and extreme rainfall. For the country as a whole, May, June, September, and October are the months of maximum flow and available waterpower; January, February, and August are the periods of greatest deficiency. To provide for effective use of waterpower resources in the face of the variable stream flow, a number of regulating ponds and reservoirs have been established in recent years. There are at least sixteen of these, each of which has an effective storage capacity of over a million cubic meters and a total storage capacity estimated at 530 million cubic

[27] *Far East Year Book*, 1941, p. 385.   [28] *Ibid.*, 387.

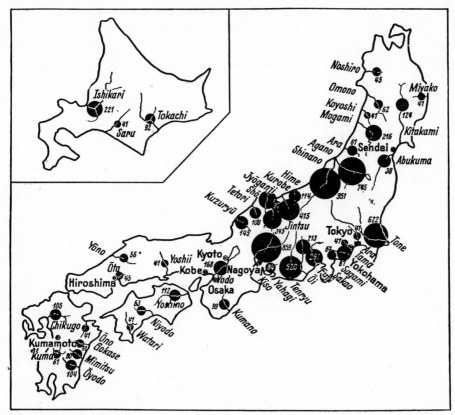

Fig. 46. Waterpower reserves of main rivers (in thousands of kw.). After Rosinski.

meters.[29] To further increase the efficient use of electric power, steam electric plants have been installed to cover the deficiency of hydroelectric power at low-water seasons and thereby facilitate the efficient utilization of the six-months' or three-months' flow. Except for certain plants in Kyushu, where coal is relatively abundant, the steam or thermoelectric establishments in Japan are auxiliary to the hydroelectric plants or are utilized as peakload stations.

Size and Distribution of Plants.—The characteristic river of Nippon has a small drainage basin and small volume, and is short and swift. Decentralization of power plants is therefore a natural result. As of December, 1937, there were 1,388 hydroelectric power generating plants in Japan, 1,081 of which had a capacity of less than 3,000 kilowatts (Fig. 47).[30] In the same year it was reported that there were 90 plants on the Shinano River alone, 80 on the Kiso, 69 on the Tone, and 52 on the Fuji.[31]

[29] Shimogaichi, *op. cit.*, 4.   [30] *Far East Year Book*, 1941, p. 385.   [31] *Ibid.*, 385.

TABLE 48.—CAPACITY OF HYDRO-POWER GENERATION PLANTS CLASSIFIED BY PRINCIPAL
RIVERS, AS OF DECEMBER, 1937

(in kilowatts)

River	No. of Stations	Maximum Capacity	Normal Maximum Capacity	Normal Capacity	Special Capacity
Kwanto*					
Tone	69	327,026	258,601	174,648	99,774
Sagami	22	97,274	85,027	63,940	11,307
Sakao	10	44,990	39,696	26,199	5,177
Fuji	52	93,608	64,932	59,002	28,466
Oi	6	127,830	73,667	41,576	24,247
Chubu†					
Tenryu	35	123,856	56,381	84,466	67,090
Yahagi	31	73,440	33,719	44,839	36,201
Kiso	80	398,008	156,865	216,425	200,113
Kinki‡					
Kumano	12	28,633	16,375	9,625	19,008
Hidaka	6	11,600	6,165	6,165	5,435
Yodo	37	105,867	65,721	65,721	40,146
Shin-Etsu§					
Agano	37	282,515	246,945	135,745	83,530
Shinano	90	333,401	238,381	158,633	149,258
Seki	16	76,038	51,109	44,964	24,014
Hime	9	55,849	29,829	25,999	28,990
Hokuroku**					
Kurobe	8	175,210	61,450	61,450	113,760
Jyoganji	10	89,000	47,100	36,600	28,000
Jintsu	35	116,212	49,387	48,207	67,245
Sho	6	137,889	100,439	43,139	94,750
Tedori	16	42,960	27,360	26,740	16,220
Chugoku††					
Yoshii	7	21,733	18,273	10,103	4,760
Ota	6	33,415	27,215	20,125	6,600
Tohoku‡‡					
Kitakami	24	26,162	17,496	17,496	8,666
Abukuma	34	32,093	23,957	21,532	9,371
Natsui	12	18,176	14,384	12,074	4,322
Noshiro	14	15,411	10,928	10,928	4,483
Mogami	20	32,209	19,725	16,085	15,094
Shikoku					
Yoshino	18	53,233	26,410	21,760	30,313
Niyodo	12	34,475	21,816	15,598	17,601
Kyushu					
Gokase	12	35,505	15,675	14,475	21,030
Oita	10	17,730	15,042	15,042	2,688
Oyodo	9	49,962	36,672	25,792	24,170

Source: *Far East Year Book*, 1941, pp. 384–385.
* Tokyo, Kanagawa, Saitama, Gumma, Chiba, Ibaraki, Tochigi, Shizuoka, Yamanashi prefectures.
† Aichi, Miye, and Gifu prefectures.
‡ Osaka, Kyoto, Hyogo, Nara, Shiga, Wakayama prefectures.
§ Nagano and Niigata prefectures.   ** Fukui, Ishikawa, and Toyama prefectures.
†† Hiroshima, Tottori, Shimane, Okayama, and Yamaguchi prefectures.
‡‡ Miyagi, Fukushima, Iwate, Aomori, Yamagata, and Akita prefectures.

TABLE 48.—*continued*

River	No. of Stations	Maximum Capacity	Normal Maximum Capacity	Normal Capacity	Special Capacity
Kyushu (*continued*)					
Sennai	7	30,850	17,990	17,990	12,860
Tama	13	23,153	11,447	9,847	12,606
Shira	4	25,200	18,800	18,800	6,400
Chikugo	18	70,474	42,435	31,635	24,989
Hokkaido					
Akan	4	15,620	11,380	11,380	4,240
Shiribetsu	5	15,285	7,595	7,595	7,690
Ishikari	21	88,299	59,937	42,870	34,229
Total, including others	1,113	3,885,466	2,493,298	1,843,949	1,653,417

TABLE 49.—HYDROELECTRIC POWER STATIONS CLASSIFIED BY CAPACITY, 1937

Capacity in Kilowatts	No. of Stations	Capacity in Kilowatts	No. of Stations
Less than 100	265	7,000– 9,999	30
100– 499	300	10,000–14,999	36
500– 999	198	15,000–19,999	15
1,000–2,999	318	20,000–29,999	23
3,000–4,999	85	Over 30,000	21
5,000–6,999	67	Total	1388*

Source: *Far East Year Book*, 1941, p. 385.   * The sum of the figures here given is 1,358.

Only 95 of the nearly 1,400 plants had a rating of 10,000 kilowatts or more, but the total output of these larger stations was approximately 57 per cent of the total.[32] A great majority of the large stations are concentrated in the central part of Honshu, the broadest and most mountainous section, where rivers are longest and have the greatest volume (Figs. 46, 48). This region of maximum hydroelectric generation and consumption is in relatively close proximity to three of the four greatest industrial nodes of the country: Tokyo-Yokohama, Osaka-Kobe-Kyoto, and Nagoya. It may be divided into two principal zones, separated by the Japanese Alps and the Tenryu River: an eastern zone whose center is in the *Kei-hin* district (Tokyo-Yokohama) and a western zone with two centers, *Kei-han* (Osaka-Kobe-Kyoto) and *Chukyo* (Nagoya). These three districts of *Kei-hin, Kei-han,* and *Chukyo* are the largest load centers of Japan. Fig. 48 shows the location of 14 of the largest hydroelectric and 8 of the largest steam-power stations in central Honshu. The latter are located in the larger coastal cities, where demands for power are greatest.

Uses of Electric Power in Japan.—Of the electric power produced in

[32] *Ibid.*, 384.

FIG. 47. A representative small-size hydro-electric plant of Japan. Most of the rivers of Nippon are too small to permit of large plants.

Japan in 1936, about 55 per cent was consumed by industry, and most of the remainder was used in electric lighting.[33] The chemical industry was by far the largest consumer (40 per cent), and next in order are the metals, textiles, and mining industries.[34] Probably no country in the world has a higher percentage of its homes wired for electric lighting than does Japan, despite the fact that 40 per cent of its population is composed of low-income farmers and fishermen living in little rural villages. Electric lighting is available in all the eleven thousand and more towns and villages of Japan Proper except about two hundred small villages in the remotest districts and islets.[35]

Iron Ore

Although Japan is the largest producer and consumer of iron and steel in the Far East, her reserves of iron ore are utterly inadequate to supply her metallurgical industries. Moreover, it is unlikely that the country has any significant undiscovered deposits, for geologists have made a detailed search. Even in the crisis of World War I no finds were made that were significant enough to survive after the war boom.[36] Viewed only from the economic standpoint, a deficiency of an important resource which can be transported is not necessarily alarming, but on strategic grounds there is reason for apprehension. In 1911 the reserves of workable iron ore in Japan Proper were estimated by the director of the Imperial Geological Survey at about 60 million tons.[37] Of this some 56 million tons were classed as good ore, containing 50–60 per cent iron, the remainder as poor

[33] *Japan Year Book*, 1939–40, pp. 500–502.
[34] *Ibid.*, 501.   [35] *Ibid.*, 502.
[36] F. R. Tegengren, "The Iron Ores and Iron Industry of China," Part I, in *Memoirs of the Geological Survey of China*, Series A, No. 2, 1921–1923 (Peking, 1924), 407.
[37] Kinosuke Inouye, "The Iron Ore Supply of Japan," in *The Iron Resources of the World* (International Geological Congress, Sweden, 1910), 1:933.

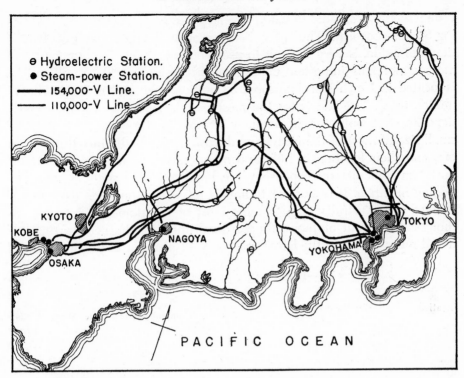

FIG. 48. Principal electric power stations and transmission lines in central Honshu. After S. Shimogaichi.

ore averaging some 30 per cent metallic iron.[38] Later estimates have not materially increased these figures. In 1921 Tegengren estimated the total reserves of Japan Proper at 80 million tons, 35 million tons of which were in the Kamaishi deposit of northeastern Honshu.[39] Kuhn's[40] estimate of 1926 placed Japan's iron ore reserves at 81 million tons, 35 million tons of which are 60 per cent magnetite in the Kamaishi deposits. A summary of his findings follows:

1. Magnetite at Kamaishi averaging 60 per cent iron . . . . 35,000,000 T.
2. Magnetite outside Kamaishi district . . . . 6,000,000 T.
3. Red hematite averaging 35–53 per cent iron . . . . 30,000,000 T.
4. Brown ore averaging 53–62 per cent iron . . . . 10,000,000 T.

Total . . . . 81,000,000 T.

In 1931 it was estimated that Japan Proper had about 40 million tons of workable ore, an additional 40 million tons of low-grade magnetite not

[38] *Ibid.*, 932–933.   [39] Tegengren, *op. cit.*, 407–408.
[40] Olin R. Kuhn, "World Iron-Ore Resources Now Exceed 57,000,000,000 Tons," in *Engineering and Mining Journal*, 122:89 (July 17, 1926).

commercially profitable to work, and large deposits of iron sand containing 30 per cent iron. The latter, because of its low grade and content of titanium oxide, is very difficult to use economically.[41] The larger part of the commercially important deposits of this reserve of 80–85 million tons is located in North Honshu (about 53 million tons) and in Hokkaido (11 million tons). The rest is for the most part in small, widely distributed deposits. Not only the inadequacy of the total reserve but also the small size of most of the individual deposits, their badly mixed grades of ore, and their location in hilly and mountainous regions, making transportation difficult and expensive, are handicaps to large-scale iron ore mining in Japan. It is cheaper to import ore even from such distances as Malaya and Australia than to mine most of the domestic deposits. Although the output of Japan Proper quadrupled in the decade 1926–36, it still represented, in the latter year, only 13 per cent of the ore smelted.

TABLE 50.—IRON ORE RESERVES IN JAPAN PROPER

Location	Prefecture	Kind of Ore	Reserve in Thousands of Tons	Percentage Content of Metallic Iron
Futochonnai	Hokkaido	Hematite	730	
Sorachi	Hokkaido		488	
Horobetsu	Hokkaido		1,641	
Kuchan	Hokkaido		———	52
Abuta	Hokkaido		8,386	56
Kamaishi	Iwate	Magnetite	47,428	62–64
Sennin	Iwate	Hematite	614	
Kesen	Iwate	Magnetite	563	
Ishikawa	Fukushima	Magnetite	1,250	
Akatani	Niigata	Hematite	2,396	
Awagadake	Niigata	Hematite	936	
Nakakosaka	Gumma	Magnetite	570	
Dorogawa	Nara	Magnetite	170	
Kawarada	Hyogo	Magnetite	231	
Kashino	Okayama	Magnetite	206	

Source: *Vierteljahrshefte zur Statistik des Deutschen Reichs*, 50 (1941), Heft 1, p. 84.

As compared with the reserves of the United States, then, those of Japan are pitifully small. In 1940 American production was nearly 75 million metric tons, an output equivalent to Japan's total reserves. The necessity of importing ore from a great distance is not, however, too serious a handicap to the development of an iron and steel industry. Iron

[41] William S. Dowd, *Economic and Trade Notes*, No. 232 (MS), dated Tokyo, Japan, May 21, 1931 (U. S. Bureau of Foreign and Domestic Commerce). See also J. H. Ehlers, *Raw Materials Entering into the Japanese Iron and Steel Industry* (U. S. Bureau of Foreign and Domestic Commerce, *Trade Information Bulletin*, No. 573. 1928).

can be hauled largely by water from southeastern Asia, at a cost no higher than the shorter rail hauls in Western countries.

NATURE AND ORIGIN OF JAPANESE IRON ORE

The most important iron ore deposits of Japan are found along the contact metamorphic zones associated with eruptive rocks. Such ore is usually magnetite or hematite, and much of it is of 60 per cent quality, sometimes even higher. The iron of Kamaishi, the most important iron ore body of Japan, is of this contact type (Fig. 42). Limonite ores resulting from chemical precipitation rank next in importance. The principal region producing limonite bog ore is in southwestern Hokkaido.

Detrital deposits of iron sands are widespread. In Chugoku in southwestern Honshu the iron sands have been formed by disintegration of granite, diorite, and basic volcanic rocks. There are also large deposits of iron sand in the diluvial terraces and beach sands. These ancient beach deposits containing iron exist in parts of southwestern Hokkaido, particularly along the shores of Volcano Bay, and near Kuji on the Pacific coast of Iwate Prefecture in northeastern Honshu. The Kuji iron sands occur in terraces at elevations of 500 to 1,000 feet. Their total reserves are estimated at 150 million to a billion tons, but the recoverable amounts are unknown.[42] The sands contain both magnetite and limonite particles, and samplings reveal that the total metallic iron content ranges from 23 to 60 per cent. The ore thus far mined has averaged 35–40 per cent metallic iron. A content of titanium oxide up to 12 per cent creates a smelting problem which apparently has not been solved, at least economically, for despite several attempts to utilize these iron sands in the steel and iron industry, no important use seems to have been made of the resource, at least before the present war. They may possibly furnish an emergency supply at this critical time when economy is secondary to other conditions.[43]

Production of Iron Ore.—In 1936 production of iron ore in Japan Proper was only 620,400 metric tons, or 13 per cent of the total consumed. At that, it was three times the amount produced five years earlier—obviously the spurt in iron and steel production had its effect on domestic iron mining also. With Korea's contribution of 243,000 tons, or 6 per cent of Japan's consumption, domestic production plus imports from colonies accounted for 19 per cent of that year's requirements. The remaining 81

---

[42] Ehlers, *op. cit.*, 8–9.

[43] For a good summary of the possibilities of utilizing Japanese iron sands see J. H. Ehlers, *op. cit.*, 18–22.

per cent was imported chiefly from British Malaya, China, the Philippines, and Australia (Table 51).

In 1936, the last year for which figures are available, Japan produced about 620,400 tons of iron ore (Table 51). Nearly sixty per cent of this

TABLE 51.—JAPAN'S IRON ORE SUPPLIES
(in thousands of metric tons)

Region	1932	1933	1934	1935	1936
JAPAN PROPER					
Total domestic production.	226.7	320.7	431.7	515.9	620.4
Kamaishi and Sennin mines (Iwate) . . .	139.6	231.1	266.6	323.7	369.5
Kutchan Mine (Hokkaido)	51.9	83.1	111.0	147.0	196.1
Abuta Mine (Hokkaido)	27.8	16.7	13.4	10.6	7.5
Nakadoya Mine (Hokkaido).	7.4	7.8	29.8	16.2	26.3
Horomoe Mine (Hokkaido)	—	—	10.9	14.0	4.9
Ohinata Mine (Nagano) and others. . . .	—	—	—	4.4	16.0
Total imports	1,634.0	1,778.9	2,312.4	3,646.2	4,022.7
Korea	151.6	255.3	180.6	242.2	242.7
From foreign countries	1,482.4	1,523.6	2,131.8	3,404.0	3,780.0
Manchuria and Kwantung	6.2	0.2	3.3	0.1	0.1
China.	557.1	573.1	825.5	1,261.8	1,251.9
British Malaya	877.9	927.2	1,205.9	1,474.3	1,691.4
Philippines	—	—	7.3	290.9	570.2
Indo-China	—	—	—	—	2.4
British India	0.1	0.5	6.5	12.5	25.8
Australia	21.0	20.8	81.6	356.2	214.6
Exports to the colonies	4.0	6.0	6.0	6.0	—
Consumption	1,856.7	2,093.6	2,738.1	4,156.1	4,643.1
Percentage ratio production to consumption	12.2	15.3	15.8	12.4	13.4
KOREA					
Production	376.4	522.6	570.5	598.1	629.1
Exports.	151.6	255.3	180.6	242.2	242.7
Consumed at home	224.8	267.3	390.0	355.9	386.4
GREATER JAPAN					
Production	603.1	843.3	1,002.2	1,114.0	1,249.5
Consumption	2,085.5	2,366.9	3,134.0	4,518.0	5,029.5
Percentage ratio production to consumption	28.9	35.6	32.0	24.7	24.8
Iron sand production	4.5	1.1	2.3	5.9	4.3
Value of imports from foreign countries (in millions of yen).	11.9	12.8	19.4	34.5	40.0

Source: *Vierteljahrshefte zur Statistik des Deutschen Reichs*, 50 (1941), Heft 1, p. 85.

domestic supply came from the Kamaishi and Sennin mines in Iwate Prefecture in northeastern Honshu (Figs. 42, 49). Kamaishi is located about twenty kilometers inland from the port of Kamaishi, and Sennin is somewhat farther to the west (Fig. 42). The ore is of a high grade, averaging about 60–64 per cent metallic iron. Kamaishi ore is magnetite, and that from Sennin is micaeous iron. Phosphorus is present in small quantities. These ores are consumed locally in the blast furnaces at Ka-maishi. The only other large iron ore producer in Japan Proper is the Kutchan Mine in Iburi Province, Hokkaido, which in 1936 contributed 31 per cent of the domestic production. The product of this mine, which is limonite of 45–55 per cent metallic iron, is used in the furnaces at Muroran on the southwestern coast of Hokkaido. South of Kutchan and

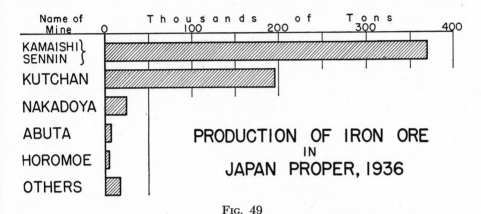

FIG. 49

close to Muroran are three other rather insignificant Hokkaido mines. The ore, which has a fairly high iron content, is limonite bog ore derived from ferruginous springs. A similar unimportant mine is the Ohinata in Nagano Prefecture. A number of other small iron deposits scattered throughout the country are unprofitable in normal times, but may have been put into production during the present emergency.

It is estimated that in 1941 Japan had a total supply of about 10 million metric tons of iron ore. Four million tons of this was produced in Japan Proper; 2 million tons came from Korea, more than a million tons from the Tayeh mines in the Yangtze Valley of China, another million from the Philippines, and 2 million from Malaya.[44]

Other Minerals

Next to coal, gold was the most important mineral produced in Japan in the mid-thirties. In the face of the necessity of balancing international accounts, the search for gold was greatly stimulated, with the result that in 1936 about twice as much was mined as in 1932, the value of which (75 million yen) was treble that of the 1932 product. Mining operations are widely scattered throughout the country, being most concentrated in

[44] *Vierteljahrshefte zur Statistik des Deutschen Reichs*, 50 (1941), Heft 1, p. 88.

northern Honshu and southern Kyushu. The gold ore is commonly found in association with copper and silver ores, and such important copper mines as Hitachi, Kosaka, and Saganoseki are also some of the largest gold producers.

Under normal conditions copper ranks next to coal in value, and until recently Japan has been an exporter of the metal; even as late as 1932 her net exports of copper amounted to about 21,000 tons. Thereafter, however, as the demands of the munitions and electric industries mounted, she became a net importer; in 1936 only 65.6 per cent of the amount consumed was produced domestically. Despite an increase of 135 per cent in consumption between 1932 and 1936, the domestic output of copper remained nearly static, fluctuating between 70,000 tons and an approximate 78,000 tons in 1936. This has been due not to depletion of reserves, for Japan has enough copper to meet her requirements, but to the high cost of mining the low-grade domestic ores. Ninety per cent of the imports in 1936 were from the United States. Eleven widely distributed mines produced 98 per cent of the country's copper output in 1938, and 83 per cent came from six mines (Fig. 42). The names, locations, and 1936 production of the important mines are shown in Table 52.

TABLE 52.—COPPER PRODUCTION FOR IMPORTANT MINES IN JAPAN, 1936

Name and Location of Mine	Copper (metric tons)	Gold kg.	Silver kg.
Ashio, Tochigi	12,762	227	16,454
Besshi, Ehime	11,991	786	16,821
Saganoseki, Oita	10,948	4,712	31,826
Kosaka, Akita	8,679	1,231	28,118
Hitachi, Ibaraki	10,790	3,969	41,922
Ikuno, Hyogo	8,461	1,636	32,288
Osarizawa, Akita	4,888	241	3,815
Hassei, Akita	2,890	305	11,120
Arakawa, Akita	978		
Ogoya, Ishikawa	1,698		
Chigirishima, Ishikawa	2,144	90	2,490
Other mines	1,744		
Total	77,973		

Source: *Japan-Manchukuo Year Book*, 1940, pp. 350–351.

Next to coal, gold, and copper, which in 1936 represented 76 per cent of the total value of all mineral output, the minerals produced in Japan, in order of importance, are iron pyrites, crude petroleum, silver, zinc, sulphur, and tin. Japan is self-sufficient with respect to iron pyrites and has an excess of sulphur which enables her to export half or more of the output in normal times. For all other minerals, however, she is more or less dependent on outside sources, most of them foreign.

Of the 104,389 tons of lead utilized in 1936 only 8,883 tons, or 8.5 per cent, were domestically produced. Imports came largely from Canada (43,476 tons), Mexico (39,043 tons), and British India (13,047 tons).[45] The most important Japanese lead mines are the Kamioka mines in Gifu Prefecture, central Honshu (Fig. 50).[46]

Of the nation's zinc requirements in 1936 (100,840 tons) only about 38.7 per cent or 39,066 tons came from domestic mines, notably the Kamioka mines in Gifu Prefecture, Ikuno in Hyogo Prefecture, and Sasu near Nagasaki.[47] Imported zinc and zinc ore came chiefly from Canada, Australia, Great Britain, British India, and Mexico. Local and imported ores are smelted at Miike, Hiroshima, and Takata.[48]

With respect to tin Japan was only 28.8 per cent self-sufficient in 1936, domestic production totaling 1,870 tons, of which 80 per cent was produced at the Akebono mines in Hyogo Prefecture (Fig. 50).[49] Most of the imported tin is purchased from Malaya.

Consumption of manganese in Japan increased markedly after 1932 as the nation embarked upon active preparations for war. From only 26,242 tons in 1932 domestic production increased to 67,753 tons in 1936,[50] most of which was derived from a number of small deposits in the vicinity of Kyoto (Fig. 50). Not only has domestic production of manganese increased but imports also have risen at approximately the same rate. Thus the percentage of self-sufficiency remained the same, 27–30 per cent.

Domestic chrome production nearly meets the nation's demands, although some is imported from New Caledonia. Nickel has only recently been mined in Japan, but with the greatly increased demands of the war industries, the government has strongly subsidized explorations for, and production of, this strategic metal. The small domestic production, amounting to only 350–400 tons, came from the Oya mines in Gumma Prefecture (Fig. 50).[51] A report issued in 1940 stated that a deposit of nickel containing 10 million tons of the ore had been discovered near Fukui on the peninsula of Oshima.[52] Plans were made by several Japanese companies to produce 16,000 tons of the metal a year.[53]

---

[45] "Kohle und Metalle im Yenblock-Gebiet," in *Vierteljahrshefte zur Statistik des Deutschen Reichs,* 50 (1941), Heft I, pl. 90; *Far East Year Book,* 1941, pp. 350–351. [46] *Ibid.* [47] *Ibid.* [48] *Ibid.* [49] *Japan-Manchukuo Year Book,* 1940, p. 352. [50] *Far East Year Book,* 1941, pp. 350–351. [51] "Kohle und Metalle im Yenblock-Gebiet," *op. cit.,* 91. [52] *Ibid.* [53] *Ibid.*

TABLE 53.—PRODUCTION OF MINERALS IN JAPAN PROPER

Kind of Ore	Unit	1934		1935		1936	
		Quantity	Value in Yen	Quantity	Value in Yen	Quantity	Value in Yen
Gold	Gramme	15,094,094	44,906,708	18,293,869	56,234,439	22,235,000	74,828,000
Gold dust	Gramme	52,491	134,895	27,447	75,262	—	—
Platinum dust	Gramme	3,678	20,251	1,575	9,980	—	—
Silver	Gramme	217,254,393	11,039,296	256,004,834	17,917,084	303,753,000	15,172,000
Silverdust	Gramme	—	—	—		—	—
Copper	Kg.	67,002,270	46,746,330	70,317,043	52,152,075	77,973,000	66,617,000
Lead	Kg.	7,039,311	1,415,177	7,070,361	1,774,996	8,883,000	2,691,000
Bismuth	Kg.	50,354	376,062	51,980	318,793	—	—
Tin	Kg.	1,218,216	4,094,874	2,068,839	7,872,479	1,871,000	6,377,000
Tindust	Kg.	500	1,975	241	499,901	—	—
Tin ore	Metric Ton	903	2,093,849	173	40,709	—	—
Antimony sulphide	Kg.	—	—	—		—	—
Antimony ore	Kg.	106	15,349	5,089	27,555	—	—
Mercury	Metric Ton	6,772	32,639	3,888,710	1,318,678	—	—
Zinc	Metric Ton	32,145,458	9,516,702	370,689	17,540,993	39,066	12,439,000
Iron pyrites	Metric Ton	1,090,454	10,733,989	35,969	1,381,480	1,750,914	19,663,000
Chromite	Metric Ton	27,070	993,550	71,659	1,370,671	—	—
Manganese ore	Metric Ton	10,637	336,366	89	97,577	—	—
Dioxide metal	Metric Ton	46,528	572,524	6,435	13,357	—	—
Scheelite ore	Metric Ton	65	82,381	2,889,144	461,226	—	—
Phosphate rock	Metric Ton	56,500	626,765	1,201	78,325	—	—
Graphite	Metric Ton	969	48,931	108,526	568,600	—	—
Coal	Metric Ton	35,924,989	245,555,471	37,762,491	270,177,016	41,803,000	305,537,000
Lignite	Metric Ton	124,356	614,283			—	—
Crude petroleum	Bbl.	2,838,630	9,429,848	3,509,568	11,985,514	3,907,000	15,529,000
Sulphur	Metric Ton	135,412	9,018,901	164,945	10,244,145	198,237	11,911,000
Sulphur ore	Metric Ton	4,782	53,394	165,867	1,684,238	—	—

Source: *Japan Year Book*, 1939–40, p. 456.

114

TABLE 54.—DEMAND AND SUPPLY OF PRINCIPAL MINERALS IN JAPAN PROPER

Mineral	Output Metric Tons	Import Metric Tons	Export Metric Tons	Demand Metric Tons	Percentage of Output against Demand
Copper					
1932	71,877	1,967	23,122	50,722	141.7
1934	67,002	51,368	12,622	105,749	63.4
1936	77,973	53,330	12,427	118,876	65.6
Lead					
1932	6,415	55,954	518	61,850	10.4
1934	7,039	95,114	2,082	100,071	7.0
1936	8,883	97,822	2,317	104,389	8.5
Tin					
1932	1,002	3,807	—	4,451	21.6
1934	1,218	4,063	—	5,281	23.1
1936	1,870	4,624	—	6,494	28.8
Zinc					
1932	27,043	26,572	—	53,615	50.4
1934	32,145	33,208	—	65,354	49.2
1936	39,066	61,774	—	100,840	38.7
Iron pyrite					
1932	726,673	—	—	726,673	100.0
1934	1,090,484	—	—	1,090,484	100.0
1936	1,750,914	—	—	1,750,914	100.0
Sulphur					
1932	84,530	—	25,998	58,532	144.4
1934	135,412	—	45,650	89,762	150.9
1936	198,237	—	71,870	126,367	156.9
Manganese					
1932	26,242	72,073	3,444	94,871	27.7
1934	57,165	147,354	4,618	199,901	28.6
1936	67,753	—	5,725	236,700 (1935)	30.0 (1935)
Nickel					
1932	—	1,844	—	—	—
1934	—	2,638	—	—	—
1936	—	2,578	—	—	—
Platinum (in Kg.)					
1932	8.2	344.4	—	352.7	2.3
1934	3.6	1,211.7	—	1,215.3	0.3
1936	8.8	756.3	—	757.4	1.2
Mercury (in Kg.)					
1932	2.4	340.8	—	343.2	0.7
1934	6.7	498.0	—	504.7	1.3
1936	14.7	512.4	—	527.1	2.8
Antimony (in Kg.)					
1932	67	2,051.1	61.4	2,056.7	3.3
1934	106	2,574.6	50.4	2,630.2	3.9
1936	460	3,603.9	81.6	3,982.3	4.9

Source: *Far East Year Book*, 1941, pp. 350–351; "Kohle und Metalle im Yenblock-Gebiet," in *Vierteljahrshefte zur Statistik des Deutschen Reichs*, 50 (1941), Heft 1, 79–92.

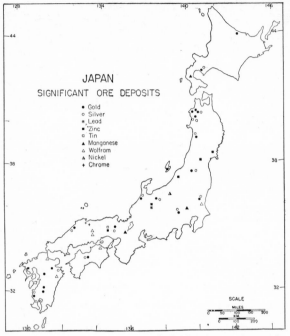

JAPAN
SIGNIFICANT ORE DEPOSITS

- • Gold
- o Silver
- ■ Lead
- ■ Zinc
- ◻ Tin
- ▲ Manganese
- △ Wolfram
- ▲ Nickel
- + Chrome

SCALE
MILES

FIG. 50. After map in *Vierteljahrshefte zur Statistik des Deutschen Reichs,* 50 (1941), Heft 1, p. 81.

Only very small quantities of mercury, molybdenum, vanadium, and antimony are available in the homeland. Tungsten, molybdenum, magnesite, and alunite, on the other hand, were supplied chiefly by Japan's colonies and by controlled Manchuria.

Not until 1934 was the first aluminum plant established in Japan, and in that year the output was only 664 tons. Expansion was so rapid, however, that by 1936 production amounted to 6,600 tons and two years later to 18,000 tons.[54]

The annual capacity of the plants in operation in 1940 or thereabouts was about 30,000 tons.[55] Despite this marked expansion, domestic production in 1938 met only about half the country's needs. In 1936 aluminum was imported chiefly from Canada and Switzerland.

The main sources of bauxite ore in the Japanese Empire are (1) Palau in the Mandated Islands, which supplied between 20,000 and 30,000 tons in 1938 and was expected to supply 100,000 tons shortly thereafter, and (2) an undisclosed source in northern Korea on the upper course of the Yalu River.[56] These two sources of bauxite did not, however, meet the needs of the expanding Japanese aluminum industry, and it was necessary to import additional quantities from the Netherlands Indies and Malaya.

From this review it is clear that Japan Proper is poor in most mineral resources except coal, gold, copper, and sulphur. Moreover, the Imperial possessions do not greatly ameliorate the situation. For a country determined to play the game of power politics, which entails a powerful army and navy, Japan's mineral resources are fatally weak. To the controlling military and industrial cliques an expanded empire has seemed

[54] *Ibid.*   [55] *Ibid.*   [56] *Ibid.*

the obvious solution. With political and economic control over eastern and southeastern Asia many of Japan's critical mineral deficiencies would be corrected. With respect to coal, petroleum, iron ore, manganese, tin, and aluminum ore Japan would be independent of other sources. Thus it is a prospective empire with immense potentialities in mineral and other resources that Nippon has set out to conquer.

SELECTED REFERENCES

GENERAL

BAIN, H. FOSTER. *Ores and Industry of the Far East,* 2d ed. Council on Foreign Relations, Inc., New York, 1933.

BRADLEY, JOHN R., and DONALD W. SMITH. *Fuel and Power in Japan.* United States Department of Commerce, *Trade Information Bulletin,* No. 821, Washington, D.C., 1935.

"Kohle und Metalle im Yenblock-Gebiet." *Vierteljahrshefte zur Statistik des Deutschen Reichs,* 50 (1941), Heft 1, pp. 79–92.

Mining Industry of Japan, 1935. Mining Bureau, Department of Commerce and Industry, Tokyo, 1935.

Mineral Resources of Japan. Bureau of Mines, United States Department of the Interior, *Foreign Minerals Survey,* Vol. 2, No. 5 (October, 1945).

SCHUMPETER, E. B., editor. *The Industrialization of Japan and Manchukuo, 1930–1940,* 237–241, 362–474. The Macmillan Co. New York, 1940.

SMITH, GUY-HAROLD, and DOROTHY GOOD. *Japan: A Geographical View. Special Publication,* No. 28, American Geographical Society, New York, 1943.

COAL

INOUYE, KINOSUKE. "The Coal Resources of Japan." International Geological Congress, *The Coal Resources of the World,* 1:279–348, with atlas. Toronto, 1913.

WATANABE, KYUKICHI. "Coal Resources of Japan." *Transactions of the Sectional Meeting, World Power Conference,* Tokyo, 1929, pp. 307–317.

———. "Coal Resources of Japan." *Proceedings of the Fifth Pacific Science Congress,* Toronto, 1933, 2:1491–1495.

PETROLEUM

CHITANI, YOSHINOSUKE. "Petroleum Resources of Japan." *Transactions of the Sectional Meeting, World Power Conference,* Tokyo, 1929, pp. 433–447.

"Die Japanische Mineralölwirtschaft." *Wirtschaft und Statistik,* April, 1941, pp. 138–148.

EMMONS, W. H. *The Geology of Petroleum,* 2d ed., 696–706. McGraw-Hill Book Co., New York, 1931.

FRECTLING, LOUIS E. "Japan's Oil Supplies." *Amerasia,* 5:197–201 (July, 1941).

REINHARD, R. "Öl im Pazifik." *Geographische Zeitschrift,* 48 (1942): 81–92.

HYDROELECTRIC POWER

BRADLEY, JOHN R., and DONALD W. SMITH. *Fuel and Power in Japan.* Bureau of Foreign and Domestic Commerce, *Trade Information Bulletin,* No. 821, pp. 12–20. Washington, D.C., 1935.

Obama, Toshiye. "Our Electric Industry." *Contemporary Japan* (Tokyo), 9:576–585 (May, 1940).

Shimogaichi, Shigemi. "Power Generation and Transmission in Japan." *Electrotechnical Journal* (Tokyo), 1:4–11 (June, 1937).

Iron Ore

Ehlers, J. H. *Raw Materials Entering into the Japanese Iron and Steel Industry.* United States Department of Commerce, *Trade Information Bulletin*, No. 573. 1928.

Inouye, Kinosuke. "The Iron Ore Supply of Japan." International Geological Congress (Sweden), *The Iron Ore Resources of the World*, 2:927–969. 1910.

Kuhn, Olin R. "World Iron Ore Resources Now Exceed 57,000,000,000 Tons." *Engineering and Mining Journal*, 122:84–93 (July 17, 1926).

PART TWO

The Country as a Whole: Cultural Features

CHAPTER V

Population and Culture

O CCUPIED by a civilized people for more than a millennium and a half, the land of Japan bears the indelible imprint of long tenure, not merely in its purely man-made features but in altered natural ones as well. "Japan is a country where the stones show human finger prints; where the pressure of men on the earth has worn through to the iron rock."[1] The crowding of many men on little land is a dominant feature of Nippon, and the works of their hands are ultra-conspicuous.

The present cultural scene is an incongruous one in many respects. Upon a base composed of feudal Oriental forms there has been hastily and unconformably superimposed the elements of a modern, Occidental machine-age civilization. So recent has been Nippon's emergence from a state of Oriental feudalism that except in the downtown sections of a few of the great cities the ancient and indigenous features still prevail. Westernism is largely a façade, and a genuine amalgam is lacking. The West has assumed that Japan's new industrial and commercial wealth has meant a close approximation to Western standards and forms, but the West has been wrong. The few broad boulevards of the metropolis feed directly into damp alleys flanked with wood-and-paper combination shops and residences. Outside the city these same boulevards terminate abruptly in narrow, pitted country roads where the traffic is predominantly slow-moving man- or animal-powered vehicles. Among the rural people the ways and standards of living are not much different from those of their grandparents living under the feudal rule of the Tokugawa shoguns.

❊   ❊   ❊   ❊   ❊

Racial and Cultural Origins[2]

The exact origins of the Japanese people are much in dispute, but it is agreed that they are a mixture of several racial strains. Basically, both in race and in fundamentals of culture, they are of Mongoloid stock drawn

[1] *Fortune*, September, 1936.
[2] Carl Whiting Bishop, "The Historical Geography of Early Japan," in the *Geo-*

121

in prehistoric times from the eastern and southeastern fringes of Asia and the adjacent islands. It is probable that one of their principal routes of migration traversed the Korean peninsula and the narrow Tsushima Straits. From the south, probably by way of the Ryukyu Islands, came Proto-Malayan and Polynesian strains. These were the Yamato people. The wavy hair of some modern Japanese reflects this strong southern racial element, and the frizzly hair of the occasional individual points to a small but definite strain of Negrito in southernmost Japan. Superimposed upon this base derived from the ancient inhabitants of the Asiatic coastlands and islands was a later migration of blood and culture, largely from Korea and North China, which began to reach Japan about the beginning of the Christian era and which affected chiefly the ruling classes of Japan. And, finally, the last major element that entered into the compounding of the present Japanese people was the Ainu group, the aboriginal inhabitants of the Japanese islands at the time of the earliest Mongoloid invasions. The Japanese Archipelago, fringing the shores of eastern Asia, with its face toward an immense continent peopled by diverse elements and its back toward a great ocean, might be described as a dead-end street into which immigrants moved as they were impelled by fear, hunger, or sheer love of adventure; and where, because they could go no further east, they were forced to amalgamate or perish. The southern oceanic element dominates over the strain brought from the continent, the racial ratios being approximately as follows: Malayan-Mongolian, 60 per cent; Chinese-Mongolian-Tungusian, 30 per cent; Ainu-Palaeoasiatic, 10 per cent.[3] This preponderance of southern strains has far-reaching effects, for the whole mode of Japanese living—dwellings, clothes, and food—is closely adjusted to a rainy tropical or subtropical climate.

The modern Japanese, evolved from an extensive racial mixture, are relatively uniform in physical traits, although there is of course some diversity among individuals. The representative male of Nippon is short of stature, with legs short in relation to trunk; he has little, if any, body hair, and his beard is light; his skin is tan, and his hair is black and usually straight, although occasionally wavy; his eyes are dark, and of frequent occurrence is the epicanthic fold of the characteristic Mongoloid eye. Since both Japanese and Chinese are predominantly of Mongoloid strain,

graphical Review, 13 (1923): 40-63; G. G. Sansom, Japan: A Short Cultural History (D. Appleton-Century Co., New York, 1938), 3-20; John Embree, "The Japanese," in War Background Studies (Smithsonian Institution, Washington, D.C., 1943), 5–8.

[3] Gustave Fochler-Hauke, Der Ferne Osten: Macht- und Wirtschaftskampf in Ostasien (Leipzig, 1936), 23.

one cannot identify individuals of these countries on the basis of physical traits alone. On the average, however, Japanese are likely to have shorter legs, wavier hair, and a somewhat heavier beard.

The aboriginal Ainu, ancestors of the present Ainu of Hokkaido, are believed to represent a very ancient Caucasoid stock from eastern Asia. In physical appearance they differed markedly from the typical modern Japanese, having heavy beards and hairy chests. Before the Mongoloid invasions they occupied the entire archipelago, as is evidenced by the survival, throughout Japan, of place names which are Ainu in derivation. But after the entrance of the Mongoloid peoples into Kyushu they were gradually pushed back, through centuries of hard fighting, to the north and east. Cut off as they were, they retained a cruder civilization, including primitive stone weapons, and hence were no match for the invaders; eventually they were overcome throughout Honshu. Their splendid fighting qualities were inherited by the former *samurai* or feudal warrior class, which was in large part descended from the Ainu who were incorporated into the Japanese armies of the eighth and ninth centuries. Today the Ainu still exist as a distinct ethnic unit in Hokkaido, and there are still a surprising number of pure Ainu types in the isolated mountain regions of Japan. By and large, however, it is only the occasional man of Nippon with ruddy complexion and hairy chest whose physical appearance betrays this racial strain.

By the close of the seventh century the Ainu had been pushed northeastward of a line running from about latitude 39° on the Japan Sea side to latitude 37° on the east.[4] At about this time the Yamato invaders moved their seat of government from Kyushu to Nara in central Japan in the vicinity of the Biwa Depression in order to be nearer the fighting frontier. Early in the eighth century, which is the beginning of the earlier historic period as described in the oldest Japanese records, the *Kojiki* and the *Nihongi,*[5] Japan appears to have had a culture consisting of littoral and riverine communities engaged in agriculture, hunting, and fishing. Throughout this early period most elements of their civilization—written language, religion, land system, government, the arts and crafts—were borrowed from Korea and China. Thus it came to pass that much of the foundation of Japanese civilization was derived from the mainland of Asia.

[4] Bishop, *op. cit.*, 60.
[5] *The Kojiki,* translated by B. H. Chamberlain and published by J. L. Thompson (Kobe, 1932), was written in 712 A. D. The *Nihongi* has been translated by W. G. Aston and published by Kegan Paul, Trench and Trubner & Co., Ltd. (London, 1924).

The Tokugawa or Late Feudal Period

It is outside the scope of this book to trace the history of Japan down through the centuries. Nevertheless an understanding of modern Japan requires some knowledge of the period of internal peace and cultural unification which just preceded the modern era and which had such a great influence on the culture of contemporary Japan.

This period coincided with the two and a half centuries of Tokugawa rule (1615–1860). It was an era of feudal military dictatorship under princes whose chief ambition was to preserve the existing military form of government, maintain peace and order, and prevent as far as possible any social changes. The sacred puppet Emperor, largely without power, was maintained as the nominal head of the State and housed in the Imperial Palace at Kyoto. Actual power was in the hands of the Tokugawa princes or *shoguns,* who ruled from the real center of government in what was then called Yedo, now Tokyo. Society and government were organized along feudal lines. The country was divided into scores of small isolated, self-sufficient feudal fiefs. Each of these was ruled over by a military lord called a *daimyo,* who lived in feudal fashion in moat- and wall-encircled castles and was surrounded by large retinues of professional soldiers called *samurai.* The predominantly farming population paid taxes and owed allegiance to the daimyo and was under the control of his samurai. The Tokugawa shoguns were merely the most powerful of the daimyo, who because of their greater wealth and power were able to exercise wider influence. As a safeguard against revolution every daimyo was required to spend a part of each year in Tokyo, and when in residence at his local capital was obliged to leave his family in Tokyo as hostages. To prevent monopoly of power the responsibilities of high government officials were divided and rotated. The virtues promulgated were filial piety, loyalty to one's superiors, frugality, industry, physical endurance, and willingness to sacrifice one's self for the sake of the State, the same Spartan virtues which modern Japan exalts. *Bushido,* or the way of the warrior, representing the code of chivalry of the feudal samurai, is still extolled as the model for Japanese youth. To forestall political disloyalties a system of government secret police was maintained, forerunner of the contemporary internal espionage system. The people were required to obey the will of the authorities implicitly, even as they are expected to do today. The unquestioning faith of the modern Japanese in his government is a revelation to an American.

Feudal society under the Tokugawas was rigidly stratified, the shoguns and daimyo constituting the upper stratum. Next below them was the military caste of swashbuckling samurai, then the farmers and artisans, and at a still lower level the merchant caste. In an effort to keep Japan sealed against foreign influence, missionaries were expelled, and the only foreign trade permitted was a government-controlled trickle through the Dutch merchants at Nagasaki. The building of ocean-going ships was prohibited, and Japanese were forbidden to leave the country. In this way Japan cut herself off from the Occident at the very time that Western European countries and the United States were surging ahead in industry and trade and expanding their colonial territories. Even as late as 1850 the population of Japan was less than half what it is today, having remained nearly stationary for over a century. Internal as well as foreign trade was negligible; railroads were unknown, and the country possessed not a single ship that could cross an open ocean. Agriculture was primitive, and industry was exclusively handicraft; even silk production was insufficient to meet the home demands. Large cities were few; Hokkaido was virtually an empty wilderness. Thus within the memory of persons still living, Japan was a feudal country whose political, social, and economic organization was cast in the molds of thirteenth-century France and England.

But long before Commodore Peary in 1853 forcibly induced Japan to abandon her seclusion, the feudal system was crumbling. The increasing importance of the merchant class and its trading economy spelled doom to Japan's self-sufficiency, which was based entirely on her agriculture. In 1867 the Shogunate fell, and two years later the Emperor Meiji was restored to power. Modern Japan thus covers a period of only three-quarters of a century. With meteoric rapidity she has emerged as a world power and transformed herself from an impotent feudal nation of peasant farmers to an economic and military power of first rank. Within a human lifetime she has imported an industrial and commercial civilization and adapted it to her own needs, telescoping what would normally be several centuries of development into a couple of generations. Unfortunately this headlong rush into Occidental capitalism was inspired by the uneasy realization that Japan was much weaker than the Great Powers around the Atlantic Basin. Hence the ousting of the Tokugawas and the restoration of the Emperor was merely a symbol rather than a really far-reaching change so far as the majority of the Japanese were concerned. The Emperor was still a puppet ruler, and society was still organized in the interests of a small minority; one group of aristocrats simply replaced another. In recent decades the ruling group has been the army, the capitalists, and the bureaucrats. For a large majority of the Japanese people, food, clothing, and housing are still much as they were three-quarters of a century ago.

In the realm of the mind and spirit the recent emergence of Japan from feudalism is even more significant. The God-Emperor medievalism which demands of seventy-three million people that they accord to a mortal man the homage due a God; their docile submission to regimentation and dictatorship, comparable only to the behavior of a swarm of bees; the degree to which the samurai or warrior tradition still dominates the country and holds its soul in subjugation; the political power of the army in addition to its military power; the acceptance of an ethical code that perpetuates the feudal compulsions of unlimited self-sacrifice, exalts the community over the individual, and officials over law—all these and other elements of its culture and mores testify that Japan is unique among the Great Powers, a nation that has one foot in the modern era and the other shackled to feudal philosophies and ideals.

Population Numbers

Reliable statistics for natality, mortality, and rate of population increases in Japan date from 1920, the year of the first real census. Earlier vital statistics are so inadequate and contain so many inconsistencies that they must be used with great care and with many more qualifications.[6] From the best information available it would appear that the Japanese population remained nearly constant at twenty-eight to thirty millions in the century and a half prior to the Restoration in 1868.[7] Considering how small the area of arable land was, thirty million was a large population for the time, the density per unit of arable land being higher than it is in Italy and Germany today. In view of the inefficient and exploitative feudal agricultural economy prevailing in Japan under the Tokugawas, which required the farmers to support a large parasitic leisure class of nobles, samurai, and their subordinates, it was probably as large a population as the country could maintain. The static population was therefore largely of economic origin. The wretched life of the peasant farmers led some of them to migrate to towns, and others to become vagrants. Famine,

[6] E. B. Schumpeter, ed., *et al.*, *The Industrialization of Japan and Manchukuo, 1930–1940* (New York, 1940), 41–115; Ryoichi Ishii, *Population Pressure and Economic Life in Japan* (London, 1937); E. F. Penrose, *Population Theories and Their Application* (Stanford University, California, 1934); Grzegorz Frumkin, "Japan's Demographic Expansion in the Light of Statistical Analysis," in the *Sociological Review*, 30 (1938): 1–28.

[7] Schumpeter, *op. cit.*, 48–50.

TABLE 55a.—TOTAL POPULATION OF JAPAN PROPER, 1872–1940

Year	Estimated Population	Crude Birth Rate	Crude Death Rate	Natural Increase*	Gross Increase	Percentage Rate of Growth
			Per 1,000 Population			
1872	34,806,000	—	—	—		
1873	34,985,000	24.1	19.6	—		
1878	36,166,000	24.5	16.9	12.4		
1883	37,569,000	26.8	18.1	9.2		
1888	39,029,000	29.6	19.0	11.3		
1893	40,860,000	28.5	22.7	8.8		
1898	42,886,000	31.3	20.4	11.2		
1903	45,546,000	32.0	20.0	13.2		
1908	47,965,000	33.7	20.9	11.9		
1913	51,305,000	33.2	19.4	14.8		
1918	54,739,000	32.2	26.8	12.1		
	Census		Census		Census	Census
1920	55,963,000	36.2	25.4	—		
1925	59,737,000	34.9	20.3	12.6	3,773,769	6.7
1930	64,450,000	32.4	18.2	14.6	4,713,183	7.9
1935	69,254,000	31.6	16.7	13.9	4,804,143	7.5
1940	73,114,308	—	—	—	3,860,160	5.6

Source: Compiled from Schumpeter, *op. cit.*, and Ishii, *Population Pressure and Economic Life in Japan.* Data for 1940 from the *Commercial Intelligence Journal*, 65: 42 (July 12, 1941).
* Not annual figures, but for five-year periods ending in the years given.

TABLE 55b.—JAPAN PROPER: GROWTH OF POPULATION IN PERIOD 1935–40
(in thousands)

Year	Population*	Deaths	Births	Excess of Births	Death Rate	Birth Rate	Rate of Increase
1935	69,254	1,162	2,191	1,029	16.8	31.6	14.8
1936	70,258	1,230	2,102	872	17.5	29.9	12.4
1937	71,253	1,208	2,181	973	17.0	30.7	13.7
1938	72,223	1,260	1,928	668	17.5	26.7	9.2
1939	72,520						
1940	73,114						

Source: Data for the years 1935 and 1940 are from the Japanese Census. The data for intervening years are estimates by the Japanese Bureau of Statistics and consequently are not strictly comparable with the census data. Compiled from *Statistical Year Book of the League of Nations*, 1940–41, and the *Japan-Manchukuo Year Book*, 1940.
* As of October 1, 1935–39; as of December 31, 1940.

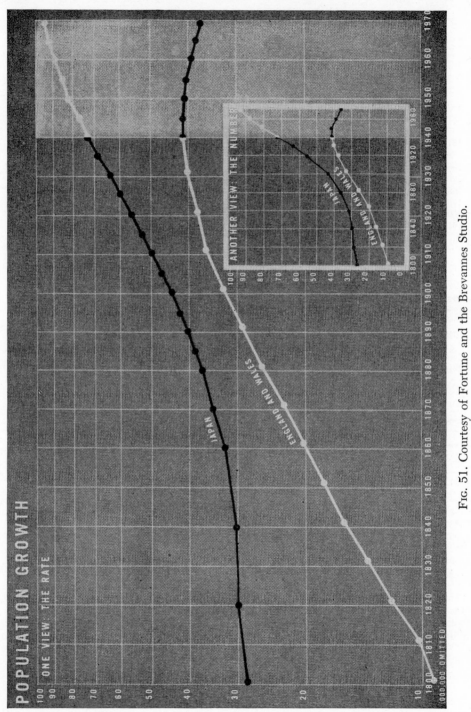

Fig. 51. Courtesy of Fortune and the Brevannes Studio.

epidemics, and natural disasters took a large toll of human life, and abortion and infanticide were practiced in all social classes. "The Tokugawa period gave to modern Japan the tradition of population control and the small family system, plus folk memories of abortion and infanticide as acceptable controls of family size. Even more, it consolidated the political-economic system and unified the cultural values that have been the major barriers to the diffusion of Western patterns of fertility and mortality control." [8]

The Meiji Restoration in 1868 inaugurated a steady and spectacular growth in population which has continued almost to the present day. By 1872, when the first estimate for Japan Proper was made, the population had increased to almost thirty-five million, and by 1918 to almost fifty-five million (see Table 55). The census of 1920, the first reasonably accurate count, gives the population as 55,963,000, that of 1940 as 73,114,000.[9] The two outstanding features of Japan's population are (1) the rapid increase in total numbers and (2) the continuous migration, particularly of young people, from rural areas to the cities. In the decade 1925–35 the average annual increase in the population of Japan Proper was not far from a million, which is greater than that for the United States, or for all of northern and western Europe, where the population is from two to three times as great. This is a rapid rate of increase, but it is not abnormal, for it corresponds to that in the Western world fifty to seventy-five years ago. The present high fertility of Japan was matched by an equally high fertility in Occidental countries over a large part of the nineteenth century, during the first three-quarters of which Nippon's population was nearly static. It required sixty years for Japan to double its nearly static Tokugawa population, but this same feat was accomplished by the United States in about half the time during the expansionist period after the Civil War. In the sixty-year period 1811–71 the population of England and Wales increased 125 per cent. With a time lag of about half a century, Japan is duplicating the population history of western Europe and the United States. The only reason that its large numerical increases are so conspicuous is that they come at a time when population growth in many Western countries has begun to level off (Fig. 51). The intercensal increase in population was

[8] Irene Taeuber and Edwin G. Beal, "The Dynamics of Population in Japan: A Preliminary Report," in the *Milbank Memorial Fund Quarterly*, 22 (1944): 222–235.

[9] Some official publications give the population of Japan as 2 and 3 millions higher than the census figures in Table 55. This results from the fact that a number of government agencies collect and publish statistics independently of one another. Thus the General Statistical Bureau of the Imperial Cabinet gave the population in 1935 as 71,968,416. On this basis the population of 1940 would probably be about 75 million.

6.7 per cent in 1920–25, 7.9 per cent in 1925–30, 7.5 per cent in 1930–35, and 5.6 per cent in 1935–40. The quinquennium 1930–35 saw a maximum absolute increase of 4.8 millions, which declined to 3.9 millions in the next five-year intercensal period.

The large annual increment to Japan's already very large and dense population, together with such impedimenta to trade as high tariffs, empire preference, quotas, and exchange restrictions, which became increasingly prevalent during the past decade, made it more and more difficult for resource-poor Japan to exchange her manufactures for raw materials on the world markets. In the face of this situation the military and nationalist elements in Japan found it easy to convince themselves that economic and strategic security required control of southeastern Asia, which could be developed both as a market for manufactures and as a source of raw materials and food. This was the theme of the propaganda disseminated to prepare the country for the present war.

The crude birth rate for Japan for about forty years prior to 1935 was between 30 and 36 per 1,000 population. This is about double the crude birth rate of northern and western Europe and of the United States during the past decade. Since 1930 when the rate reached its all-time high of 36.2, it has declined steadily; in 1935 it was 31.6, and in 1938, 27.0. More refined measurements clearly establish the fact that fertility in Japan began a definite downward trend as early as about 1920. The number of births per 1,000 women in the reproductive period of life decreased from 169.4 in 1920 to 142.6 in 1935. Penrose attributes this partly to the increasingly widespread practice of birth control by the rapidly expanding urban population, which recognized the handicap of large families in city living.[10]

But despite this decline in reproduction rates for nearly all ages of mothers, there has been no commensurate reduction in the annual increment of population; on the contrary, it actually increased somewhat between 1920 and 1935. The reason is that mortality rates have declined more rapidly than the birth rate. Thus the crude death rate in Japan declined from 26.8 in 1918 and 25.4 in 1920 to 16.7 in 1935. Infant mortality especially showed a rapid decline: from 166 deaths under age one per 1,000 live births in 1920 to 106 in 1937. Nevertheless the mortality figures of Japan are still 4 to 6 per 1,000 higher than in northern and western Europe.

It is, then, Japan's Oriental birth rate and Occidental death rate that produced, until about 1935 or a little later, an annual net increase in population of almost a million despite a falling reproduction rate. If the war

[10] Penrose, *op. cit.*, 104–105.

in China, and thereafter World War II, had not interrupted normal living in Japan, mortality rates would probably have continued to decline, but it is dubious whether they could have kept pace with the decline in reproduction rates. Ultimately the net rate of population increase would have begun to fall. Until 1935 the annual rate of population increase actually mounted; in the period 1930–35 it rose to 1.5 per cent. During the next five years, however, it declined to 1.1 per cent. Thus the problem created by a rapid increase in population would slowly have disappeared. Nevertheless the age distribution of the Japanese population, characterized by a large proportion of young people, indicates that rapid growth is possible for some time to come (Fig. 52). In this respect Japan resembles

PERCENT OF TOTAL POPULATION OF JAPAN
IN DIFFERENT AGE GROUPS, 1936.

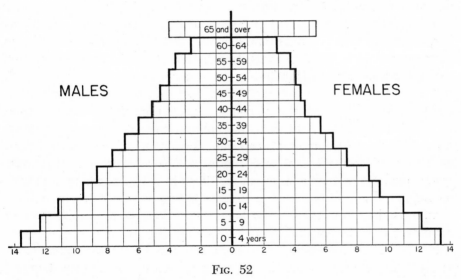

FIG. 52

eastern Europe and Soviet Russia more than western and northern Europe, where the percentages of mature and older people are greater. In 1935 almost 40 per cent of Nippon's population was under fifteen years of age, as compared with 22 per cent in the British Isles, 24 per cent in western and central Europe, and about 25 per cent in the United States. Only 7.8 per cent of Japan's population is between the ages of fifty and fifty-nine, as compared with nearly 10 per cent in the United States and over 11 per cent in France. With such an age distribution Japan may not feel the full effects of declining fertility for several decades. Before the outbreak of the Sino-Japanese War in 1937 it was estimated that the population of Nippon would reach 80 million by 1950 and 105 million by 1970.[11] Dr. Ueda, however, concluded that it could never reach 100 million (Fig. 51). Under present conditions all such prophecies are of course meaningless, for no one knows what the conditions will be in Japan after this war.

Since the outbreak of the Sino-Japanese War in 1937 population growth has been abnormal. Statistics on births, deaths, and marriages have not been published since 1939, but the figures for 1938 reveal that certain trends had begun to accelerate. In that year as compared with 1937 there was an increase in total deaths and a sharp decline in births, and hence a sharp decline in the excess of births over deaths. In 1938 the crude birth rate (26.7 per 1,000) was the lowest it had been in many decades, and the population increase (9.3 per 1,000) was about 33 per cent less than in the previous year. In the fourth quarter of 1938 there were 20 per cent fewer births than in the same period of 1937. Even if the rate declined no further, the total births in 1939 would have fallen to about 1,750,000, the lowest figure since 1920.[12] As reckoned from October to October the net population growth of 970,000 in the 1937–38 period would have declined to 653,000 in 1938–39 and to 239,000 in 1939–40.[13] It may have become nearly static by 1940. All this of course reflects the military mobilization for the Sino-Japanese conflict and the emigration of civilian war workers to the industrial centers of Manchuria, Korea, and China, which is attended by increasing separation of the sexes. The rise in mortality in 1938 seems to indicate a decline in Japan's national health as a result of the war in China and the exertion being made for the more serious conflict to follow. Since 1940 the situation has been aggravated by the much greater manpower mobilization, the higher mortality due to military casualties, and the weakened resistance to disease induced by the decreased food supply, the crowded conditions in industrial cities, and the shortage of domestic fuel.

Strangely enough, the decline in the birth rate and more recently in the rate of population growth have alarmed official circles. In January, 1941, the Japanese Cabinet approved a plan for increasing Japan's population to a hundred million by 1960. The stated objectives of the plan are

---

[11] For a discussion of the various estimates of Japan's future population see Ryoichi Ishii, *Population Pressure and Economic Life in Japan* (London, 1937), 126–139. See also *Population Index*, 7:264–267 (October, 1941).

[12] Kurt Block, "Japan's Population Problem Reversed," in the *Far Eastern Survey*, 10:11 (January 29, 1941).

[13] *Population Index*, 7:264 (October, 1941).

(1) to maintain a perpetual increase; (2) to outrank other nations in the quality and rate of the natural increase; (3) to supply the military and industrial manpower required by the State; and (4) so to distribute the population as to maintain Japan's leadership in Asia.[14] To make it easier for young people to marry early and have large families the plan provides for (1) preferential rights of large families with respect to daily necessities; (2) marriage loans, the principal of which shall be reduced 20 per cent upon the birth of each child; (3) reduction of taxes for large families; (4) health measures to reduce infant mortality; (5) honors and rewards to parents of large families, to be paid from funds created by (6) the taxation of bachelors; (7) establishment of marriage agencies; and (8) the restriction or prohibition of birth control.[15]

It seems somewhat incongruous for a nation which proclaims its need for more room because of its large population, and which justifies its territorial robberies in eastern Asia on that ground, to encourage reproduction by offering bonuses and bribes. Obviously Japanese leaders are more impressed with the military handicap of a numerically inferior population than with the probable benefits of a reduced population. At one time the Japanese government cited the country's population density as reason for her economic dilemma, hoping to gain sympathy for the solutions she contemplated. But as a greatly expanded empire began to take form in southeastern Asia, the increasingly army-dominated government saw the need for greater manpower and likewise the opportunities for migration into the tropical lands to the south.[16] Recent Japanese literature tends to identify declining fertility with national decadence and to urge the bearing of babies in terms of duty to race and State, stressing the historic destiny of the Japanese nation rather than the economic and social welfare of the individual.[17]

A second striking feature of Japan's population growth since 1920, which has in it the seeds of a declining birth rate, is the differential rate of increase between the rural and the urban population (Fig. 53). In the two decades 1920–40 the number of people residing in communities of more than 10,000 doubled, whereas the rural population declined by about 1,400,000. In general both the farm population per se and the rural popu-

[14] *New York Times*, January 23, 1941, as quoted in *Population Index*, 7:264 (October, 1941).

[15] *Population Index*, 7:264 (October, 1941). See also the *Statistical Bulletin* of the Metropolitan Life Insurance Company, 22:1–3 (December, 1941).

[16] Kayo Noma, "Japanese Capacity for Colonizing the Tropics," in *Contemporary Japan,* 10:400–405 (March, 1941). See also *Contemporary Japan,* 10:816–819 (June, 1941).

[17] "Japan's Population Policy," in *Population Index,* 7:264–267 (October, 1941).

lation as a whole (those living in communities of less than 10,000) have remained nearly stationary. But whereas two decades ago the rural population constituted 68 per cent of the total population and the urban population 32 per cent, the respective proportions are now about 50 and 50 per cent. In the five years 1930–35 the total increase in Japan's population was

GROWTH OF POPULATION IN JAPAN PROPER

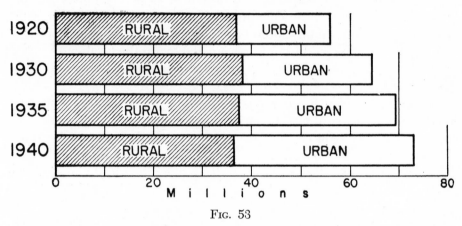

FIG. 53

4,804,000, of which 3,217,000 or 67 per cent took place in the cities; in the three years 1935–38 the estimated increase in total population was 2,969,000, but with an increase of 3,291,000 in the cities.[18] Since the total population living outside of incorporated communities of 30,000 or more has remained at about 45 million from 1920 to 1940, the entire national increase of 17,200,000 was absorbed by the cities,[19] chiefly cities of over 100,000. All this reflects the increasing importance of industry and trade in Japan's economy, and suggests that agricultural expansion and intensification has reached a ceiling. (The regional aspects of the urban growth are dealt with in the following topic on internal migrations.)

Population Movements within Japan.—The rapid increase in population has been very unequally distributed over the country, some sections growing with astonishing speed, others declining, and still others undergoing intermediate rates of change.[20] Between 1920 and 1935 population de-

[18] R. E. M. Cameron, "Urban Population Problem in Japan," in *Contemporary Japan*, 9:279–283 (March, 1940).

[19] "Population Redistribution and Urbanization in Japan," in *Population Index*, 9:73–77 (April, 1943).

[20] A number of studies of population movement in Japan and the growth ratios of various parts of the country have been made and the comments here are a summary of these studies. See Syuzi Inoue, "A Morphometric Analysis of the Movement of Population in Japan" (in Japanese with English summary), in the *Geographical*

clined principally in the remote hilly and mountainous areas south and west of a line joining Tokyo and Niigata, the chief areas being (1) in the hill lands of the Kinki district at the eastern end of the Inland Sea; (2) much of the extreme southwestern part of Honshu in what is known as Chugoku; (3) mountainous central Shikoku; and (4) the Hokuroku region

TABLE 56.—GROWTH OF URBAN AND RURAL POPULATIONS IN JAPAN PROPER

Year	Total Population	Urban Population	Percentage of Total	Rural Population	Percentage of Total
1920	55,900,000	18,000,000	32.2	37,900,000	67.8
1930	64,450,000	26,300,000	40.8	38,150,000	59.2
1935	69,300,000	31,750,000	45.9	37,550,000	54.1
1940	73,114,000	36,627,000	50.1	36,487,000	49.9

Source: *Japan Year Book*, 1926, p. 52; 1940–41, p. 47; *Toshi Mondai*, vol. 32, pp. 1148–1167, as translated by Shannon McCune.

facing the Japan Sea between latitudes 36° and 38°.[21] Despite the high birth rates of the peoples in these districts of rugged terrain, emigration exceeds births because the opportunities for earning a livelihood are so limited. In only two large non-urban regions, northern Honshu and Hokkaido, did population increase during the fifteen-year period at a rate higher than that for the country as a whole (23.8 per cent), although there are numerous isolated patches in other districts, particularly central Honshu and southern Shikoku, of which the same may be said. Exclusive of the districts with great cities, it is southwestern Japan that has had the slowest rates of increase; for the part of the country north of the latitude of Tokyo they have been somewhat higher (Fig. 54).

Much the larger part of the higher than average rate of population increase, however, was localized in the four important industrial nodes of southwestern Japan, the *Keihin* or Tokyo-Yokohama center, the *Han-shin* or Osaka-Kobe-Kyoto center, the head of Ise Bay around Nagoya, and the North Kyushu node of heavy industry. Between 1920 and 1940 only ten prefectures[22] grew at a rate higher than the national average, and these

Review of Japan (Chirigaku Hyron), 10 (1934):1–26, 127–153 (with colored map); H. Tanakadate, "Regional Analysis of the Distribution of Population in the Main Land of Japan," in *Comptes Rendus du Congrès International de Géographie*, Amsterdam, 1938, vol. 2, sec. A, pp. 151–167; T. Odanti, "Regional Movements of Population in Japan," *ibid.*, vol. 2, sec. IIIa, pp. 41–50; George Kiss, notes to accompany a map of population changes in Japan, in American Geographical Society, *Special Publication*, No. 28, pp. 50–51; "Population Redistribution and Urbanization in Japan," in *Population Index*, 9:73–77 (April, 1943).

[21] Kiss, *op. cit.*, 51.

[22] Hokkaido; Aomori and Miyagi prefectures in northern Honshu; Tokyo and

ten accounted for more than two-thirds of the nation's total increase; two prefectures alone, Tokyo and Osaka, were credited with more than one-third. The prefectures containing the six great cities with a million or more population had 13.3 million people in 1920 or 24 per cent of the nation's population and 22.5 million or 31 per cent in 1940. The prefectures of Tokyo and Osaka alone gained 6 million during the two decades, which increased their percentage of the total population from 11 to 17. By 1940 nearly one-fifth (19.67 per cent) of the Japanese were concentrated in the six largest cities, all situated within the three important industrial nodes. Here in an Oriental country there has been in progress a migration of the younger people from the farm areas into the industrial cities that duplicates the population changes that accompanied industrialization in the United States and western Europe; only in Nippon the movement has been more rapid. The rapidity of the rural-urban migration is revealed in the fact that in the single decade 1930–40 the proportion of people living in Japan's large cities increased as much as it did in the United States in the four decades after 1900.[23] This gravitation toward the urban centers seems natural in view of the rapid expansion of industry and foreign trade. The greater than average rate of increase in Hokkaido's population also seems warranted in view of the opportunities offered by that semi-frontier island. More difficult to justify is the higher than average increase in northeastern Honshu, a region largely without industry and one of the most impoverished sections of Japan. The largest migration to the cities has been from the more prosperous agricultural districts of commercial agriculture in southwestern Japan, which themselves offer the greatest economic opportunities, while population continues to pile up on the poor areas characterized by subsistence agriculture. This parallels the situation in the United States.[24]

Significant as is the internal migration and the resulting redistribution of population which has been analyzed above, it should not be inferred that the population of Japan is a constantly or widely shifting one, for that is not the case. In 1930, for example, 83 per cent of the people were living in the prefecture of birth, a larger proportion than anywhere in the United States except a few states in the Old South.[25] Only in Hokkaido and the industrialized prefectures of Tokyo, Kanagawa, Kyoto, and Osaka were

---

Kanagawa in the central Kwanto region; Kyoto, Osaka, and Hyogo in Kinki; and Fukuoka in northern Kyushu. See Fig. 54 for the location of prefectures.

[23] "Japan's Population Policy," in *Population Index*, 7:264-267 (October, 1941).

[24] Taeuber and Beal, *op. cit.*

[25] "Japan's Population Policy," in *Population Index*, 7:265 (October, 1941).

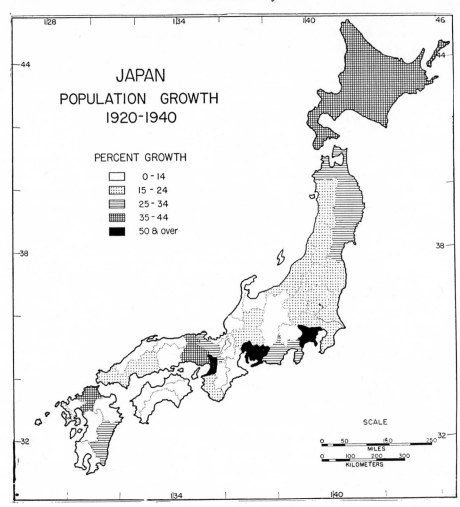

JAPAN
POPULATION GROWTH
1920-1940

PERCENT GROWTH

☐ 0 - 14
▦ 15 - 24
▤ 25 - 34
▦ 35 - 44
■ 50 & over

SCALE

FIG. 54. Rates of growth were most rapid in the urban industrial prefectures, in Hokkaido, and in the extreme northern part of Honshu.

more than 30 per cent of the inhabitants natives of other prefectures. Even the fact that in four-fifths of the prefectures emigration has exceeded immigration does not invalidate the statement that in general the Japanese population has been a stable one, for the loss has been due largely to a one-way migration, chiefly of younger people from the agricultural areas to the great industrial centers; there has been little compensating inmigration from other prefectures.

In general the internal migration after 1935 was similar to that which took place in the fifteen years preceding. Of greatest significance are the absolute population declines which 14 of the 47 prefectures suffered. This represents an accelerated movement away from the agricultural areas. But there is evidence also that the trend toward concentration of population in the great cities was losing momentum, and that the cities of less than 300,000 were receiving a greater share of the total urban increase.[26] This may have been a result of the war rather than a normal trend, however. Many satellite towns and cities of the great metropolises grew at a relatively faster rate than the mother city itself, and there was also a proliferation of new industrial towns. For example, Kawasaki, a shipbuilding center near Tokyo grew from 104,000 to 301,000 in the five-year period, and Yokosuka, a naval base, from 110,000 to 193,000. The Kwanto cluster of cities numbered thirteen in 1930; in 1940 there were twenty-eight whose population exceeded 25,000. Those industrial urban areas in which there was a marked concentration of new war industries, such as North Kyushu, the Kwanto district, and the Nagoya area at the head of Ise Bay, grew much more rapidly than those not so stimulated by war preparations. The great Kinki urban area, for example, lagged well behind Kwanto in population increase during the decade of the thirties, whereas the eight principal cities of Fukuoka Prefecture in northern Kyushu, the nation's principal focus of heavy industry, expanded 46 per cent. This transformation has far-reaching effects, economic and political, on the Japanese population.[27] Not the least of these are the effects upon health and sanitation conditions and upon birth and mortality rates. They have already been significant and are likely to become more marked.

Population Density and Distribution Patterns

Density of Population.—In 1940 Japan Proper had a population density of about 500 per square mile. This was more than eleven times the density of the United States (Fig. 56). In only two European countries, Belgium and Holland, does population density markedly exceed Japan's, and in Great Britain it is slightly higher than in Japan, but none of these depend upon agriculture to the same extent as Nippon. Of the Asiatic countries only Java has a greater population density.

But even this high figure of about 500 per square mile is an understatement of real density because so little of the country is closely settled, owing to the prevalence of hill land and mountain. Only 20 per cent of the total area is classed as potentially cultivable, and only 16 per cent is ac-

[26] *Ibid.*, 74.

[27] R. E. M. Cameron, "Urban Population Problem in Japan," in *Contemporary Japan*, 9:279–283 (March, 1940).

tually under cultivation. This does not mean that the hill and mountain land is without resource value and incapable of supporting human life; merely that its potentialities are much less than those of the lowlands. If we substitute cultivated area for total area in the denominator of the ratio, we arrive at the almost unbelievable figure of about 1,200 per square kilometer or more than 3,000 per square mile (Fig. 56). In no other country are human beings crowded together so thickly on the cultivated land. Even in Great Britain, a highly industrialized country, the arable-land density is much lower. In Japan about 42 per cent of the population is still engaged in agriculture. Even if the agricultural population alone is considered, the density is still 1,200 to 1,300 per square mile, which is one of the highest anywhere on earth.

TABLE 57.—POPULATION DENSITY OF VARIOUS COUNTRIES

Country	Density per Square Mile	Country	Density per Square Mile
Japan Proper	501	Belgium	712
United States	44	Java and Madura	818
The Netherlands	687	China (17 inner provinces)	324
Great Britain	545	Philippines	140
Germany	441	Australia	2.3
Italy	359		

TABLE 58.—DENSITY OF POPULATION PER SQUARE KILOMETER OF CULTIVATED LAND

Country	Cultivated Land Density per Sq. Km.	Country	Cultivated Land Density per Sq. Km.[†]
Germany (1939)*	339	USSR (1934)	71
France (1938)	185	Japan Proper (1940)	1,199
Great Britain and Northern Ireland (1938)	913	British India (1931)	321
		United States (1939)	92
Italy (1937)	284	Australia (1937–38)	52

Source: Shiroshi Nasu, *Aspects of Japanese Agriculture*, 2.
* Includes Saar and Australia.   † 1 square mile = 2.59 square kilometers.

There is no question that Japan's chief national problem is that of supporting this unusually dense and rapidly increasing population in a small territory poor in essential resources. Still one hesitates to say that Japan is actually overpopulated. The fact that, until recently at least, the per capita income has been slowly rising would suggest that she has not yet reached that point. On the other hand, if there were fewer people in Japan, more of them could live better, provided the national income were well distributed. Population density is not an absolute, but a relative measure; the ratio of people per square mile of gross area or even of cultivated land must be considered in the light of other factors. Thus in Japan much of the rough non-arable land must be regarded as productive, since it yields timber and other forest products, and more of it could doubtless be used for growing tree crops of nuts and fruits. Another source of great wealth

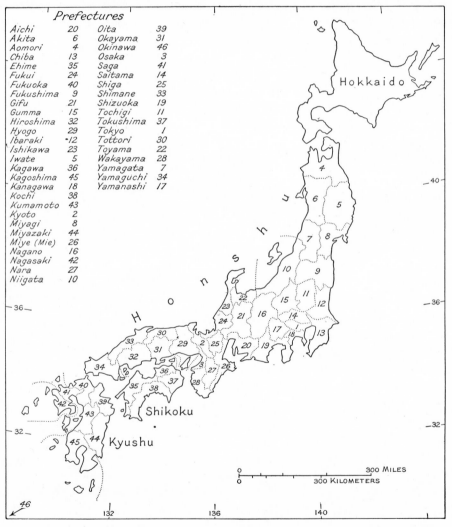

Prefectures

Aichi	20	Oita	39
Akita	6	Okayama	31
Aomori	4	Okinawa	46
Chiba	13	Osaka	3
Ehime	35	Saga	41
Fukui	24	Saitama	14
Fukuoka	40	Shiga	25
Fukushima	9	Shimane	33
Gifu	21	Shizuoka	19
Gumma	15	Tochigi	11
Hiroshima	32	Tokushima	37
Hyogo	29	Tokyo	1
Ibaraki	•12	Tottori	30
Ishikawa	23	Toyama	22
Iwate	5	Wakayama	28
Kagawa	36	Yamagata	7
Kagoshima	45	Yamaguchi	34
Kanagawa	18	Yamanashi	17
Kochi	38		
Kumamoto	43		
Kyoto	2		
Miyagi	8		
Miyazaki	44		
Miye (Mie)	26		
Nagano	16		
Nagasaki	42		
Nara	27		
Niigata	10		

Hokkaido

Shikoku

Kyushu

300 Miles
300 Kilometers

FIG. 55. Map by the American Geographical Society, New York.

are the extensive and very productive fishing grounds in the vicinity of Nippon. And one cannot refrain from remarking that the country's limited resources were well known to the Japanese long before they had increased to seventy-three million. Yet the government has taken pride in the high birth rate and lately has adopted measures to halt its decline. That decline may presage a return to the population stability which characterized the pre-Meiji period; in any case the dangers of overpopulation seemed less serious in 1940 than a decade earlier.

The population problem of Japan has of course been greatly aggravated by the maintenance of national policies inconsistent with the country's scarcity of resources. A nation that spends so much of its national income on armaments will naturally have less capital to spend on developing its resources; yet Japan insists she must rob her neighbors to obtain new resources. Clearly it is an anomaly that it should be the fascist military nations which urge high birth rates and large families. The whole economy of Japan is designed to benefit a few already wealthy groups and to build an invincible military power.[28] Few of the benefits of modern capitalism have filtered down to the large mass of the population. Industrialization has been promoted for the purpose of producing certain goods that could be exchanged abroad for oil, steel, armaments, etc. The market at home for manufactured goods has remained small because of the low income of the working people. The poverty so prevalent in Japan, then, is not wholly attributable to overpopulation of the land, but partly also to the fact that industrialization has been fostered to amass strength for the preservation of the State rather than to improve the lot of the people. Japan as a small, resource-poor country, lacking a large and profitable colonial empire, is dubiously equipped by nature for a place among the first-class powers, and it is doubtful whether she can afford both military pre-eminence and a high standard of living for her population. Up to the present time, unfortunately, she has sought to become a great military power, to the serious detriment of her people's welfare. It may be suggested, however, that it is only in a world in which economic nationalism, empire preference, high tariffs, and other forms of trade restriction are less prevalent that a peaceful, non-aggressive Japan can be reasonably prosperous and satisfied.

Solutions.—Much has been written both by the Japanese themselves and

[28] Roswell G. Townsend, "Is There a Japanese Population Problem?" in *Amerasia,* 3:135–139 (May, 1939). See also Freda Utley, "Population and Conquest," in *Pacific Affairs,* 10:16–29 (March, 1937), and F. A. Roger, "Japanese Emigration and Japan's 'Population Pressure,'" in *Pacific Affairs,* 14:300–321 (September, 1941).

by foreigners on this problem of population. The solutions that have been suggested may be summarized as follows:[29]

1. Negative solutions:

a. Reduction of the biological rate of increase through limitation of the birth rate or an increase in the mortality rate.

b. Emigration to foreign soil.

2. Positive suggestions:

a. Increase in agricultural productivity at home by various means, including the reclamation of additional land for agriculture and the modernization of agricultural techniques. It has been estimated that 6 million acres can be reclaimed; part of this is land now used for dike boundaries between paddy fields and for pathways, which could be eliminated if the tiny fields were consolidated. The cost of reclamation would be so high, however, as to make much of it unprofitable.

b. The acquisition and ultimate colonization of some new and relatively empty lands in the western Pacific.

c. Further industrialization of the country on the basis of (1) sale in a much larger home market and (2) sale in foreign markets, some of those in close proximity to be under Japanese political control.

These proposals cannot be discussed in detail here. Some of them will be treated at greater length in later discussions on population migration, agriculture, industry, and foreign trade. The first negative solution, reduction of the biological rate of increase, has been touched upon in the earlier part of this chapter. It seems fairly certain that the rapid increase in Japanese population has been temporarily halted, and there is reason to believe that the rate will never again be as high as it was before 1938. The declining birth rate of the past few decades, which has aroused such alarm as to prompt corrective legislation, is probably a normal trend that will be accelerated in the postwar period.

Distribution Patterns.—Almost any map showing population distribution in Japan, but especially Ishibashi's,[30] which expresses density ratios for small political subdivisions (*gun*) by means of colors, reveals that for the country as a whole—disregarding for the moment the local variations between hill land and lowlands—population density decreases progressively north of about latitude 37°. Thus, whereas most of the prefectures

[29] Albrecht Haushofer, "Kulturboden und Volksdruck in Japan," in *Zeitschrift der Gesellschaft für Erdkunde zu Berlin*, 1938, p. 32; Ishii, *op. cit.*, 188–248.

[30] The two outstanding population maps of Japan are by:

1. K. Tanaka and K. Yamamoto: A dot map of Japan Proper exclusive of Hokkaido. Scale 1:1,000,000. Data for 1925. Five sheets.

2. G. Ishibashi and T. Ono: Densities per square kilometer by small political

in central and southwestern Japan averaged 150–400 persons per square kilometer in 1940, Hokkaido had an average of only 37, and the three northern provinces of Honshu (Aomori, Akita, Iwate) only 89 persons per square kilometer. These differences are associated with differences in the proportions of rough land and plain, and with the presence or absence of large cities. In all of northern Honshu and Hokkaido the average population density was well below that for the whole country, which in 1940 was 194 per square kilometer or 501 per square mile.

If cultivated land is substituted for total area, in order to eliminate the effects of relief in the several prefectures, the same decrease of density northward is evident. If the population density per unit of cultivated land in the southwestern prefectures (lacking large cities) is taken as 100, southern Tohoku in latitudes 37° or 38° has an index of 65–80, northern Tohoku 45–65, and Hokkaido 25–35. This progressive decrease of population north of about latitude 37° reflects, for one thing, increasing remoteness from the economic and political heart of Japan. Even more it reflects the increasing severity of climate, which makes living conditions harder and land less productive, particularly for a people strongly bound to subtropical agriculture and housing. Rice declines in yield, winter cropping becomes much more precarious and is entirely absent over large parts of Japan's northland, and such commercial crops as tea, citrus, and mulberry are either absent or less important. Table 59, which shows farm production and farm population per tan (1 tan = 0.245 acres) in large regional subdivisions, reveals that it is in Hokkaido that ratios are lowest and most out of line with the normal for Old Japan, and that Tohoku, comprising the northernmost six prefectures of Honshu, is next lowest. The most important boundary separating regions of widely differing population density is the Straits of Tsugaru between Hokkaido and Old Japan. Tohoku or northern Honshu in population density and in many other ways has char-

---

subdivisions, are shown in color for the entire Japanese Empire. Scale 1:1,000,000. Data for 1920.

See also:

3. H. Tanakadate and others: Distribution of Population in Northeast Japan. Scale 1:800,000. Densities per square kilometer for smallest political subdivisions (villages). Sendai, 1926.

4. L. Mecking: Japan's Siedlungsräume, *Mitt. der Geog. Gesellschaft in München*, 24 (1931): 193–210. Map based upon Tanaka's and Yamamoto's map.

5. Map of Density of Population in Japan. Institute for the Research of Population Problems, 1934. Text in Japanese and English. Three colored maps: Map I, Density of Population by Villages; Map II, Density of Population for Cultivated Area in Villages; Map III, Density of Population in Cities Grouped by Prefectures and in Towns Grouped by Prefectures and Districts. 1930 data.

6. Francis Ruellan, *La Production du Riz au Japon* (Paris, 1938).

acteristics that are intermediate or transitional between subtropical Japan lying south and west of Tokyo, and the real northland of Hokkaido.

South of latitude 37° population is markedly concentrated along the Pacific side of the country in an irregular zone extending south from the Tokyo Plain along the Pacific coast (excluding Kii Peninsula) to Osaka and including both shores of the Inland Sea and northwestern Kyushu (back end paper). This was one of the first sections settled, and is the most urban and industrial part of modern Japan. It contains both the nation's

TABLE 59.—FARM PRODUCTION AND FARM POPULATION PER TAN
(1 tan = .245 acres)

Region	Farm Production per Tan, 1934 (in yen)	Farm Population per Tan, 1930	Region	Farm Production per Tan, 1934 (in yen)	Farm Population per Tan, 1930
Hokkaido	12.55	0.107	Tokai	52.63	0.562
Tohoku	25.96	0.415	Kinki	64.23	0.611
Kwanto	43.15	0.483	Chugoku	54.78	0.556
Hokuroku	42.08	0.471	Shikoku	54.61	0.638
Tosan	43.27	0.598	Kyushu	49.04	0.510

Source: Nasu, *Aspects of Japanese Agriculture*, 115. See Fig. 204 for the locations of the several regions.

ancient and modern capitals and the modern centers of business and commerce. Here large alluvial plains face on the quiet waters of spacious bays, where great industrial port cities have developed. The whole region is easily accessible, for its deeply indented coastline borders protected waters that offer numerous havens for boats. At its western end is the nation's most utilized coal field, one of the largest in the country. All six of Nippon's great metropolitan centers of more than 950,000 population, five of them occupying tidewater locations, are included within this populous belt, as are twenty-six of the other thirty-eight cities of more than 100,000 inhabitants.

In a region as complicated in relief as Japan it is almost inevitable that the population pattern should be a very discontinuous, fragmented, or clotted one (back end paper). The compact settlement clusters are almost coincident in both size and shape with alluvium-floored lowlands.[31] Very sharp, almost knife-edge boundaries frequently separate densely populated areas from almost uninhabited ones. Indeed, it is almost possible to reconstruct the relief pattern of Japan from a detailed population map. Here and there smooth ash uplands and low, much-dissected Tertiary

[31] Ludwig Mecking, "Japans Siedlungsräume," *op. cit.*, 204–208.

areas are also fairly well settled. This coincidence of the plains of river aggradation with areas of settlement makes for a decided peripheral or seaboard concentration of population, since most of Nippon's lowlands are delta-plains (back end paper). Hence it is not surprising that the Japanese are closely bound to the sea. The coincidence of alluvial areas with population is perhaps more pronounced in Nippon than in most parts of the world because of the Japanese farmers' determination to grow irrigated rice. In the hill lands it results in a close correspondence between population and drainage lines.

Like the Chinese, the Japanese tend to overcrowd the best lands and neglect the possibilities of the less fertile and more isolated upland areas. In part this may reflect their gregarious nature and their dislike for frontier isolation. A more important factor is the inability of a farmer, under conditions of spade agriculture, to obtain a living from any but the best land. The United States Department of Agriculture has estimated that it takes about fifteen man-days to spade an acre of land by hand; hence the farmer who lacks draft animals and machinery and thus must depend altogether on his own labor can cultivate no more than an acre or two of ground. Even those more fortunate Japanese who own an ox or a horse can plow only a few acres at most. Inasmuch as it takes just as long to spade, plant, and cultivate poor land as good land, the Oriental farmer must apply his labor on the most productive soil if he is to keep his family from starvation. In the United States the farm area is increased as the productivity of the land declines;

FIG. 56. Courtesy of Fortune and Brevannes Studio.

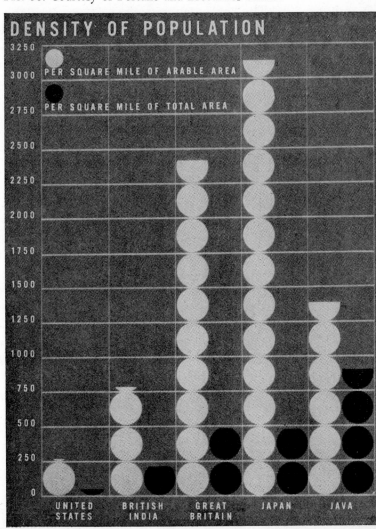

DENSITY OF POPULATION

PER SQUARE MILE OF ARABLE AREA

PER SQUARE MILE OF TOTAL AREA

3250 · 3000 · 2750 · 2500 · 2250 · 2000 · 1750 · 1500 · 1250 · 1000 · 750 · 500 · 250 · 0

UNITED STATES · BRITISH INDIA · GREAT BRITAIN · JAPAN · JAVA

increasingly extensive methods are possible through the use of more animal or motor power and labor-saving machinery. But this adaptation the Japanese peasant farmer, almost devoid of capital, cannot make.

Japanese Migration and Colonization[32]

Among the proposals for meeting Japan's population problem which were noted above was that of emigration. Between 1638 and 1868, the two centuries that witnessed the establishment of the empires of the European powers and the migration overseas of large streams of Europeans, Japan was a hermit nation bent upon preventing not only the ingress of outside influence but the egress of its own subjects. In recent years, however, the Japanese government has sponsored and subsidized emigration, either to Japanese colonies or to foreign lands where Japanese immigrants are welcome. In doing so it has had two objectives: to ease the mounting pressure of population, and to promote its imperialistic policies by extending and consolidating the military and economic strength of Japan.

The first Japanese emigrants were contract laborers who, beginning in 1885, settled in Hawaii, the United States, and Canada. After immigration into the United States was limited, about the turn of the century, and eventually stopped entirely by 1924, the Japanese began to migrate to South America, more especially to Brazil, and to the mainland of Asia and the tropical islands off its southeastern shores. From 1918 to 1936 the number of Japanese authorized to emigrate annually ranged from a low of 8,825 in 1923 to a high of 28,087 in 1934. In at least six of these years the number of returning emigrants exceeded the number leaving. Thus Japanese emigration has been at best a feeble movement. One reason is that the Japanese are poor colonizers and do not like to emigrate, especially to a severe continental climate. Dr. Ishii believes that the long period of isolation in the Tokugawa era, during which overseas activity was suppressed, had a devitalizing effect upon Japanese colonizing ambitions. Then, too, many of the areas they would regard as attractive have been closed to them. The few colonies they established during the last three or four decades had become densely populated by peoples of lower standards of living.[33] Some writers stress the southern origins of the Japanese as a factor impairing their capacity to colonize cold climates.[34]

[32] Karl J. Pelzer, "Japanese Migration and Colonization," Chapter VII, pp. 155–194, in *Limits of Land Settlement*, edited by Isaiah Bowman (New York, 1937); Roger, *op. cit.*; Schumpeter, *op. cit.*, 66–72.

[33] Pelzer, *op. cit.*, 31.

[34] K. Haushofer, *Japans Werdegang als Weltmacht und Empire* (Berlin, 1933), 63;

Certainly many elements of their culture—their dwellings, clothing, diet, agricultural crops, etc.—are so acclimated to the subtropics that they must make serious readjustments when they move into regions with so severe a climate as Manchuria, Hokkaido, and Karafuto. The Japanese farmer offers much less resistance to southward migration, though at best he is unenthusiastic.

Within the Japanese Empire itself and its "sphere of influence" the possibilities for colonization have not been great. In 1940 Hokkaido had a population of about 3.3 million, a large part of which represented migration from Old Japan. But virtually all the valuable agricultural land has now been settled; all that remains is a modest amount of the poorer land.[35] Hence further migration to Hokkaido will be slow. Karafuto or southern Sakhalin is even less suitable for Japanese agriculturists, for its 300,000 inhabitants are largely engaged in such extractive occupations as fishing, mining, and logging. Korea, or Chosen, is already thickly populated (24.3 million in 1940), having a density of 286 per square mile, and 1,451 per square mile of crop area. Moreover, since the Koreans have a lower standard of living, the Japanese agriculturist cannot compete in the same area. The business and professional occupations offer somewhat better opportunities, so most of the few hundred thousand Japanese in Korea are in the cities and towns. In Formosa the density of population, higher than in Korea, has discouraged agricultural settlement by the Japanese. In the Pacific Mandated Islands Japanese population has increased rapidly, from 3,671 in 1920 to 70,141 in 1938; many of these are tenant farmers working sugar-cane plantations. Japanese authorities estimate that a total of 100,000 farmers and a considerable number of tradesmen and fishermen can be accommodated in the islands.

Manchuria, more than any other region within Japan's "sphere," has been regarded as a promising field for agricultural colonization. But as late as 1930, despite the ambitious schemes which authorities and organizations had been fostering for nearly a quarter century, there were only 743 Japanese farm families in Manchuria. After the creation of the puppet state of Manchukuo, when it was made legal for the Japanese to own land in Manchuria outside the Kwantung Leased Territory and the South Manchurian Railway Zone, immigration increased. Between 1932 and the spring of 1937, 2,367 Japanese families (4,245 individuals) were settled on the land in Manchuria and continued to remain there. This

K. Sapper, "Akklimatization und Rasse," in *Zeitschrift für Rassenkunde und ihre Nachbargebiete*, 3 (1936): 235.

[35] Alfons Scheinpflug, "Die japanische Kolonisation in Hokkaido," in *Mitteilungen der Gesellschaft für Erdkunde zu Leipzig*, 53 (1935), 1–63.

TABLE 60.—JAPANESE EMIGRATION TO FOREIGN COUNTRIES, 1918–36

Year	No. of Japanese Authorized to Emigrate	No. of Returning Emigrants	No. of Japanese Residents Abroad*	No. of Foreigners Resident in Japan†
1918	23,574	12,584		19,500
1919	18,244	18,114	584,303	20,242
1920	13,541	20,376	667,442	22,595
1921	12,944	18,755	631,343	23,400
1922	12,879	14,912	590,168	24,932
1923	8,825	10,784	581,652	18,761
1924	13,098	12,579	594,680	24,122
1925	10,696	13,918	625,430	28,279
1926	16,184	14,549	640,099	31,140
1927	18,041	14,735	674,522	32,917
1928	19,850	15,004	717,529	34,917
1929	25,704	14,073	759,439	38,829
1930	21,829	15,432	755,209	40,290
1931	10,384	12,965	635,227	28,317
1932	19,033	13,170	672,266	26,885
1933	27,317	14,141	749,158	29,268
1934	28,087	———	872,807	32,641
1935	10,813	———	689,818‡	38,475
1936	11,119	———	997,115	40,865

Source: Schumpeter *et al.*, *The Industrialization of Japan and Manchukuo, 1930–1940*, 79.
* Before 1930 this column included Japanese in Kwantung Leased Territory and the South Manchurian Railway Zone, but not thereafter.
† Does not include foreigners in the consular and diplomatic service.
‡ Although this figure appears in several Japanese sources, there are many reasons for believing it to be incomplete. There is no reasonable explanation of the sudden drop in 1935 and the equally sudden rise in 1936.

TABLE 61.—NUMBER OF NEW EMIGRANTS TO VARIOUS COUNTRIES, 1930–36

Year	Brazil	Philippines	Peru	Canada	USSR	Malay States	Dutch East Indies	Argentina	Mexico	Australia	Total, Including Others
1930	13,741	2,685	831	137	1,512	835	558	489	434	75	21,828
1931	5,565	1,109	299	106	1,238	549	447	362	283	34	10,384
1932	15,108	746	369	98	1,096	356	533	239	149	101	19,028
1933	23,299	941	480	91	1,095	322	468	135	85	59	27,317
1934	22,960	1,544	473	105	1,320	598	356	112	80	105	28,087
1935	5,745	1,802	814	57	322	583	389	201	53	92	10,813
1936	5,357	2,891	593	82	297	534	145	349	62	223	11,119

Source: *Japan-Manchukuo Year Book*, 1940, p. 54.

movement was subsidized by cash and services. In addition there was a free non-subsidized immigration of 2,150 people.[36] Most of the settlers were young army reservists between the ages of twenty-two and thirty, and many were unmarried. Obviously the plan was to create military farm colonies along the northern and eastern frontier of Manchuria. North

[36] Schumpeter, *op. cit.*, p. 68.

Manchuria is one of the few areas in eastern and southern Asia in which much good agricultural land is still unsettled; it is estimated that from 40 to 50 million acres are still available. But the climate of this region, where the frost-free season is only 120 days or less and where average January temperatures are below zero, is more severe than most Japanese farmers care to endure, and many discouraged colonists have returned to the homeland. Beginning in 1937 the government put into operation a project for settling a million Japanese farm families or 5 million persons in Manchuria during a twenty-year period.[37] Part of this immigration was to be subsidized, the rest was free. As a result of the Sino-Japanese War the project was somewhat reduced in the second year, but by early 1939 some 50,000 Japanese had already migrated to Manchuria.[38]

After 1934 Japanese emigration to foreign countries dropped off sharply; in 1935 and 1936 it was less than half as great as it had been in the two years preceding (Table 61). By far the largest exodus was to Brazil, though the Philippines, Soviet Russia, Peru, the Malay States, the Dutch East Indies, and Argentina also received substantial numbers. The migration to Brazil reached a maximum of 23,299 in 1933, and in 1934 it was almost as large. Thereafter, as a result of restrictions imposed by the Brazilian government, the numbers were greatly reduced. In 1937 there were 197,733 Japanese residents in Brazil.

Despite the government's encouragement to emigration, the number of Japanese in foreign countries is still less than a million, and the total number of Japanese outside of Japan Proper is only from 1.8 to 1.9 million. If Japan could retain and consolidate as a part of her empire the regions of tropical South Asia recently acquired by conquest, she would have at her disposal large areas and extensive resources still virtually undeveloped: in Burma, Thailand, French Indo-China, Malaya, the Dutch East Indies outside of Java, New Guinea, and other islands in its general neighborhood. It is these tropical regions that Japan hoped to conquer and make available to her people. Even after Japan is defeated and stripped of the fruits of conquest, there are good arguments for permitting Japanese farmers to settle in these undeveloped lands of tropical South Asia, provided of course they come purely as homeseekers and not with the backing of an imperialistic government.

[37] *Ibid.*, 68–70.   [38] *Ibid.*, 69.

SELECTED REFERENCES

BLOCK, KURT. "Japan's Population Problem Reversed." *Far Eastern Survey*, 10:10–11 (January 29, 1941).

CROCKER, W. R. *The Japanese Population Problem.* George Allen and Unwin Ltd., London, 1932.

FRUMKIN, GRZEGORZ. "Japan's Demographic Expansion in the Light of Statistical Analyses." *Sociological Review*, 30:1–28 (January, 1938).

HAUSHOFER, ALBRECHT. "Kulturboden und Volksdruck in Japan." *Zeitschrift der Gesellschaft für Erdkunde zu Berlin*, vol. 1–2, pp. 26–36 (March, 1938).

ISHII, RYOICHI. *Population Pressure and Economic Life in Japan.* P. S. King and Son, Ltd., London, 1937.

"Japan's Population Policy." *Population Index*, 7:264–267 (October, 1941).

KISS, GEORGE. *Le Probleme de la population au Japon.* Paris, 1936.

MECKING, LUDWIG. "Japans Siedlungsräume." *Mitteilungen der Geographischen Gesellschaft in München*, 24 (1931): 193–210.

PELZER, KARL. "Japanese Migration and Colonization." Chapter VII in *Limits of Land Settlement*, edited by Isaiah Bowman. Council on Foreign Relations, New York, 1937.

————. *Population and Land Utilization*, 28–32. Institute of Pacific Relations, New York, 1941.

PENROSE, E. F. *Population Theories and Their Application with Special Reference to Japan.* Food Research Institute, Stanford University, California, 1934.

"Population Redistribution and Urbanization in Japan." *Population Index*, 9:73–77 (April, 1943).

REIKICHI, KOJIMA. "The Population of the Prefectures and the Cities of Japan in Most Recent Times (Based upon the Results of the 1940 Census)." Translated by Edwin G. Beal, Jr. *The Far Eastern Quarterly*, 3:313–361 (August, 1944).

ROGER, F. A. "Japanese Emigration and Japan's 'Population Pressure.'" *Pacific Affairs*, 14:300–321 (September, 1941).

SCHUMPETER, E. B., ed., et al. *The Industrialization of Japan and Manchukuo, 1930–1940*, 41–115. The Macmillan Co., New York, 1940.

SCHWIND, MARTIN. "Der Japanische Bevölkerungszuwachs in Rückgang." *Ostasiatische Rundschau*, 22:216–220 (October, 1941).

STEINER, JESSE F. "Population Trends in Japan." *American Sociological Review*, 9:36–40 (February, 1944).

TAEUBER, IRENE B., AND EDWIN G. BEAL. "The Dynamics of Population in Japan: A Preliminary Report." *Milbank Memorial Fund Quarterly*, 22 (1944): 222–235.

TANAKADATE, H. "Regional Analysis of the Distribution of Population in the Main Land of Japan." *Comptes Rendus du Congrès International de Géographie*, Amsterdam, 1938, vol. 2, sec. A, pp. 151–167.

TOWNSEND, ROSWELL G. "Is There a Japanese Population Problem?" *Amerasia*, 3:135–139 (May, 1939).

UTLEY, FREDA. "Population and Conquest." *Pacific Affairs*, 10:16–29 (March, 1937).

UYEDA, TEIJIRO. "The Growth of Population and Occupational Changes in Japan." *Japanese Council Papers*, No. 2. Institute of Pacific Relations, Tokyo, 1936.

CHAPTER VI

Settlements and Houses

SETTLEMENTS

BY THE term *settlement type* as used in this book is meant the characteristic colonization or occupance unit. These units range in size and function from the simple isolated farmstead to the great metropolis like Tokyo. In all cases, however, the term settlement unit designates an organized colony of human beings together with their houses and other buildings and the paths and streets over which they travel.

On the basis of form and function, two principal subdivisions of world settlements are recognized: (1) the dispersed type, in which the isolated one-family residence unit is the distinctive nucleus, as it is on an American farmstead, for example, and (2) the agglomerated or cluster type, in which there is a more or less compact grouping of several or many residences together with buildings serving other purposes. According to its size and the complexity of its functions, an agglomerated settlement is designated a hamlet, village, town, or city. Whatever its size, the two most conspicuous features are always the house and the street. In the United States and some other parts of the world dispersed settlement is almost synonymous with rural or agricultural population, but that is far from being true in Europe and Asia, where it is common for farmers to live in compact villages.

Rural Dispersed Settlement

In accordance with the prevailing village pattern of agricultural settlement in southeastern Asia, Japan's rural sections are characterized by cluster settlements, the isolated farm dwelling being characteristic only of certain type locations and regions (Fig. 57). This tendency toward agglomeration is most marked in the lowlands, where irrigated rice is the principal crop, and along coasts where fishing is important.[1] The most important regional exception to the prevailing pattern of rural cluster

[1] Robert Burnett Hall, "A Map of Settlement Agglomeration and Dispersion in Japan," in *Papers of the Michigan Academy of Science, Arts, and Letters*, 22 (1936): 365–367.

settlement is Hokkaido. In that northland region of recent colonization, where land is more abundant and farms are larger and in one continuous plat rather than in small scattered parcels, it is much more difficult for farmers to live in villages.

The second major exception to the cluster type of rural settlement is the mountain and hill land. This is not to say that there is a lack of agricultural villages in the hilly interior, but only that the isolated farmstead is much more prevalent than on the lowlands. Such an association of dispersed farm settlement with rough lands is characteristic not only of Japan but of parts of Europe as well. A number of European geographers have noted this relationship in Switzerland, Germany, southwestern Poland, Austria, Hungary, and Slovakia. The explanation may be found in part in the physical character of hill land, the whole aspect of which leads to a diffusion of resources—arable land, water, and natural sites with pleasant exposures. In regions of dissection and abundant slope the scattered fragments of cultivable land are often too small to support more than a few separate farmsteads, and the inhabitants must depend on other resources, such as woodland and pasture, which require larger holdings. In Japan dispersion is particularly marked in the hill lands of Chugoku in southwestern Honshu, and in certain strongly dissected Tertiary rock areas.

Besides the two areas described above as regions of dispersed settlement, the following are noteworthy: (1) ash and diluvial uplands where agricultural settlement is more recent and farms larger; (2) certain steeply inclined delta-fans, such as those of the Oi River in Shizuoka Prefecture and those of a number of rivers forming the Toyama Piedmont and the Hinokawa Plain on the Japan Sea side of the country; and (3) the recently reclaimed land along the outer margins of some advancing deltas. Certainly in some, if not most, of these cases the dispersed settlement is associated with recency of occupation. On the steep alluvial fans the dispersion seems to be associated with a retarded settlement due to the frequency and violence of floods. These inundations led to the construction of individual elevated dry sites for the farmsteads.[2]

More common, I believe, than one would gather from the usual descriptions is a semi-dispersed or amorphous type of Japanese rural settlement which is intermediate between the compact village and the isolated farmstead. In these loose agglomerations a definite street pattern may be lack-

[2] O. K. Kodera and H. Iwamoto, "On the Scattered Settlements (Strendorf) on the Alluvial Fan of Ooi-gawa River" (in Japanese with English summary), in the *Geographical Review of Japan*, 15 (1939): 686–710, 760–783.

ing, the straggling residences separated by small fields being connected
only by winding foot or cart paths.

Rural Agglomerated Settlements

Statistical volumes on Japan and some of the literature on Japanese
settlements frequently fail to make clear in their discussions of villages and
towns whether reference is to bona fide geographic and social settlement
units or to political subdivisions. It is the same ambiguity which in this
country surrounds the word *town,* which may refer either to an administrative area or to a relatively compact geographic and social settlement, intermediate in size and importance between village and city. In Japan the
country is divided into forty-six administrative districts or *prefectures,*

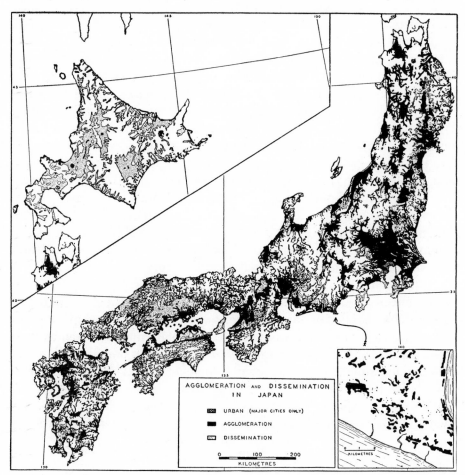

AGGLOMERATION AND DISSEMINATION
IN JAPAN

URBAN (MAJOR CITIES ONLY)

AGGLOMERATION

DISSEMINATION

FIG. 57. Map by Robert B. Hall.

three of which are urban prefectures. These are subdivided into 627 *gun*, comparable to our counties, except that since 1926 they have served no political function, though they continue to be important social, economic, and geographic units. Agricultural and business organizations are developed on a *gun* basis, and local customs often coincide with *gun* boundaries. The Japanese take great pride in belonging to a particular *gun*. Since the abolition of the *gun* as a political unit the subdivisions of the prefecture are the *mura*, the *machi*, and the *shi*.[3] The common translation of *mura* is "village" and of *machi* "town," but these are somewhat misleading terms, for they refer not to clustered settlements but to small administrative areas. Perhaps there would be less confusion if the word *mura* were translated "township." A *mura* may have within it several small house clusters, which are the rural hamlets and villages. These are called *buraku*. The *machi* differs from the *mura* in that it contains at least one settlement cluster large enough to be incorporated, and it may have a number of unincorporated rural *buraku* as well. To my knowledge, there is no source that indicates the number and distribution of bona fide compact settlements, i.e., the rural hamlets and villages (*buraku*, not *mura*), and of the larger incorporated cluster settlements which we designate as towns (not *machi*).[4] When, for example, statistical volumes state that in 1935 Japan had 6,564 towns with a population of 2,000 to 5,000, they mean towns as administrative units (*machi*) and not settlement units. *Shi* is the city administrative unit and the name is applied to settlements of more than 25,000 to 30,000 inhabitants which have municipal governments. The *mura*, in contrast to the *machi* and *shi*, is a rural administrative unit; each *mura* has a common headman, administrative office, school, and Shinto shrine. Each *buraku* community, which is the rural social, economic, and geographic unit, has its own head, and its citizens handle cooperatively such matters as funerals, festivals, road and bridge building and repairing, etc.

The most elemental form of rural agglomerated settlement is the unincorporated hamlet or farm village. Suye Mura, a township in south-central Kyushu, which has been studied in detail, may be taken as fairly representative.[5] It has a total area of 6.5 square miles and a population of 1,663, comprising 285 households. Within Suye Mura there are 17 separate household clusters or *buraku*. Each of these hamlets or small villages, containing on the average between 15 and 20 households, has a name of its own and is recognized as a distinct settlement. Each *buraku* has one or

[3] There were on April 1, 1937, 141 *shi* or cities, 1707 *machi* or towns, and 9,568 *mura* or villages in Japan Proper.

[4] John F. Embree, *Suye Mura: A Japanese Village* (Chicago, 1939), 12–35.   [5] *Ibid.*

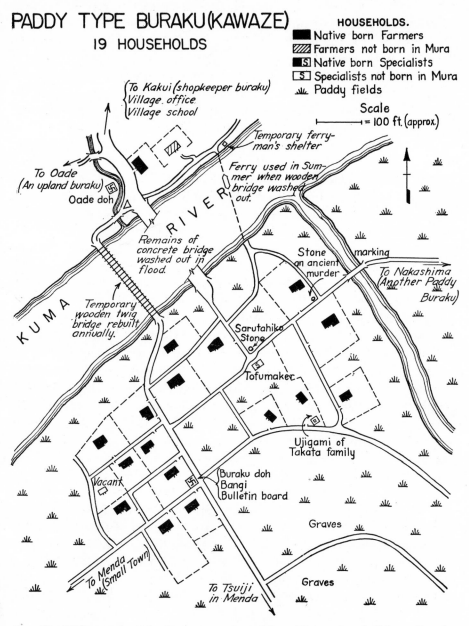

PADDY TYPE BURAKU(KAWAZE)
19 HOUSEHOLDS

HOUSEHOLDS.
■ Native born Farmers
▨ Farmers not born in Mura
■S Native born Specialists
□S Specialists not born in Mura
⊥⊥ Paddy fields

Scale
⊢————⊣ = 100 ft. (approx.)

To Kakui (shopkeeper buraku)
Village office
Village school

Temporary ferry-
man's shelter

Ferry used in Sum-
mer when wooden
bridge washed
out.

To Oade
(An upland buraku)
Oade doh

RIVER

Remains of
concrete bridge
washed out in
flood.

Stone marking
an ancient
murder

To Nakashima
(Another Paddy
Buraku)

KUMA

Temporary
wooden twig
bridge rebuilt
annually.

Sarutahiko
Stone

Tofumaker

Ujigami of
Takata family

Vacant

Buraku doh
Bangi
Bulletin board

Graves

To Menda
(Small Town)

To Tsuiji
in Menda

Graves

FIG. 58. After map by John Embree, in *Suye Mura* (University of Chicago Press).

155

more headmen called *nushidōri,* who are elected by the responsible heads of households in the hamlet, each house having but one vote. To the *nushidōri,* who is the caretaker of *buraku* affairs, fall such duties as the supervision of funeral preparations, the announcing of holidays and *buraku* meetings, the care of hamlet property, and the supervision of road and bridge repairing. Each *buraku* has a shelter house, called a *do,* which houses some Buddhist deity; here the children play in the daytime, and pilgrims, beggars, and itinerant workmen find shelter. Good-natured rivalry exists between the several *buraku* and there is inter-hamlet competition at *mura* parties and festivals.

Individual *buraku* in Suye Mura vary considerably in character. Those in the midst of bountiful rice fields on the plain are more prosperous, their households are larger, and the people have common political interests and close social and blood ties. Most of them have resided there since early times, hence intermarriage is common. The paddy *buraku* are relatively compact settlements with rectangular street patterns and houses fairly close together (Fig. 58). Other *buraku* are situated on the upland diluvial terraces and in the foothills where unirrigated crops prevail because the land is unsuited for paddy rice. Because of the irregular terrain the houses of these upland *buraku* are rather scattered, and the lanes and paths that connect them are winding, so that the settlement lacks compactness (Fig. 59). Much the larger part of the population of Suye's hamlets are farmers, but at least two of them have a considerable number of shopkeepers. Such shopkeepers' *buraku* are influenced in their functional development by the fact that they are located on the chief thoroughfare, the prefectural road (Fig. 60). The shops of various kinds front directly on the highway, whereas the farmers' houses are usually off the main highway and irregularly arranged. In those shopkeepers' hamlets where both farmers and merchants are well represented there is much less social cohesion than in the farmers' *buraku,* and the divergent interests of the inhabitants lead to numerous quarrels. Many of the inhabitants of the shopkeepers' *buraku* are relative newcomers to Suye Mura. The mountain *buraku* are more poverty-stricken than the others, and their citizens are regarded as cruder and more ignorant.

Although the above description applies specifically to a small portion of the Hitoyoshi Basin in south-central Kyushu, it is fairly representative of small agricultural settlements throughout much of Old Japan. By far the larger part of Japan's 5.5 million farm families, which comprise some 27 million people, live in hamlets and small villages of a few score or a few hundred inhabitants like the seventeen communities in Suye Mura. The

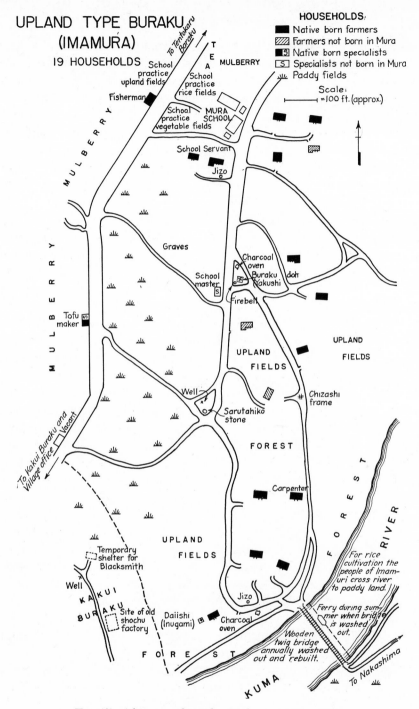

UPLAND TYPE BURAKU
(IMAMURA)
19 HOUSEHOLDS

HOUSEHOLDS:
■ Native born farmers
▨ Farmers not born in Mura
🅑 Native born specialists
Ⓢ Specialists not born in Mura
⩗ Paddy fields

Scale:
⊢———⊣ =100 ft. (approx.)

To Tentokaru Buraku
TEA
MULBERRY

School practice upland fields
School practice rice fields
Fisherman
School practice vegetable fields
MURA SCHOOL

MULBERRY

School Servant
Jizo

MULBERRY

Graves
Charcoal oven
Buraku Nakushi doh
School master Ⓢ
Firebell

Tofu maker Ⓢ

UPLAND FIELDS
UPLAND FIELDS

Well
Chizashi frame
Sarutahiko stone

FOREST

To Kakui Buraku and Village office
Vacant

FOREST
RIVER

Carpenter

Temporary shelter for Blacksmith

UPLAND FIELDS

For rice cultivation the people of Imamuri cross river to paddy land.

Well
KAKUI BURAKU

Site of old shochu factory

Daiishi (Inugami)

Jizo
Charcoal oven

Ferry during summer when bridge is washed out.
Wooden twig bridge annually washed out and rebuilt.

FOREST

KUMA
To Nakashima

FIG. 59. After map by John Embree, in *Suye Mura*
(University of Chicago Press).

157

dimensions of these little settlements range from a few hundred feet up to 2,000 or more. In general they are less compact than the larger towns, and the houses may be separated by small plots of rice and unirrigated garden crops. Some of them, lacking a well defined street pattern, give the impression of semi-dispersion.

Living standards in the thousands of farming villages and hamlets in Japan are almost unbelievably frugal; the rural folk have learned to get along on less than most peoples. The pressure of many men on little land has forced the peasant farmer to keep alive on the very cheese rind of

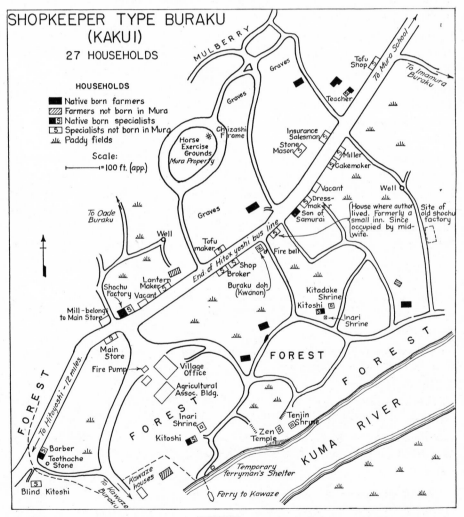

FIG. 60. After map by John Embree, in *Suye Mura* (University of Chicago Press).

existence. The whole atmosphere is one of careful and never-ending thrift. They are denied all the luxuries and most of the comforts of life. Their Spartan philosophy, as it was expressed by one model Japanese farmer to an American traveler, is to "Rise early; work late; raise everything you need yourself; buy no city luxuries; bow to the Imperial Palace twice a day; attend services in the temples regularly."[6]

This nearly universal frugality is made endurable by the close communal life of the *buraku*, for the latter is a social unit to a degree unknown in American settlements. Also to an extent unknown in the West trade is in the form of barter, and relatively little cash is required. Probably two-thirds of the expenditures of a village family are in kind and only one-third in money. The rice-money economy of the feudal period still prevails to a great extent. Most of the commodities needed are produced either in the home or by local craftsmen. The *buraku* residents build their own houses, make their own mats, baskets, tools, and charcoal, and clean their own rice. The villagers work and play, sorrow and rejoice together. The result is a closely integrated and interdependent life which is attractive and warm despite the incredible meagerness of material things (Fig. 61).[7] This willing frugality of living on the part of Japan's large agricultural population is one of the country's greatest assets in its industrial competition with the Occident. It keeps industrial wages low and thus permits the Japanese manufacturer to compete on a more even footing with nations having superior natural resources. It is the successful meager living of the large farming group in Japan that sets the standard for the country as a whole.

The Towns

The market towns are distinguished by size and by functional and structural differences from the typical rural *buraku*, although the line of demarcation is certainly not sharp. Characteristically the towns are larger communities, with a few thousand rather than a few score or a few hundred people. Moreover, non-farmers constitute a much larger proportion of the total population than in most rural *buraku*, for the town functions as the shopping center for the rural areas. Thus shops are prominent features of the towns. The town buys its food and raw materials from the nearby *buraku* and in return sells to the residents of the farm hamlets processed goods such as hardware, dry goods, implements and tools, and some foods and drink. Peddlers from the towns vending various kinds of

[6] W. H. Chamberlain, "Japan's Farm Crisis," in *Asia*, 36:370 (June, 1936).
[7] One of the best descriptions of this Japanese community life appeared in *Fortune*, September, 1936, p. 87 ff. See also Embree, *Suye Mura*.

wares make regular trips through the farm villages. In the towns also are the restaurants with their *geisha* entertainers, where men from the hamlets may seek merriment. These larger settlements, to be sure, are not without farm dwellings; in some of them farm families make up a considerable part of the population, but usually they are in the minority. More commonly than the *buraku* the towns are located on railway lines or on main highways, which give them direct access to bus transportation. They contain the post-offices from which mail is distributed to the rural areas.

Although differences between towns are not lacking, a foreigner will note that they have many features in common. In the larger and more compact ones the absence of shade trees is conspicuous. In general they lack brightness and color, the closely set unpainted houses being monotonously alike, especially where tile roofs prevail. No church spires relieve their even skylines. Grass is absent. At night they are ablaze with light, for recent years have seen an almost complete electrification of Japan. Because of its narrower streets and the closer spacing of its dwellings, the compact town of Nippon occupies less space than one of the same population in the United States; often its structures abut against one another as they do in our commercial districts (Fig. 62). Most towns have no distinct and compact commercial core and residential district. Many of the streets serve both functions, the dwelling being used also

FIG. 61. Residents of a *buraku* (farm village) cleaning the prefectural road. Note the narrowness of the road. Photograph by John Embree.

as the shop; the latter occupies the street side and the family lives in the back or second-story rooms. Normally each shop specializes in a single type of product—fish, eggs, hardware, paper, liquor, cloth, etc. By means of sliding doors the entire front of the little store can be thrown open to the street,

FIG. 62. Main street of a town in Niigata Prefecture. Photograph by Herman R. Friis.

and its stock of wares displayed to the passer-by (Fig. 63). The narrow streets appear to be always crowded; pedestrians, bicycles, human- and animal-drawn carts, and playing youngsters all jostle one another. Sidewalks are rare; pedestrians use the street, which is usually macadamed but not smooth. Open drains or gutters carrying drainage or refuse water (not sewage) from the residences line both sides of the street. Local dug wells commonly provide the homes with water.

Settlement Locations and Sites.—In the mountains, because of the very obvious advantage of transportation facilities, villages and towns occupy the valley floors. These sites are also the only patches of near-level alluvium, where water is available for irrigation and the precious rice crop can be readily cultivated. If the lowest part of the valley floor is subject

FIG. 63. Typical small open-front shop in a Japanese town or city.

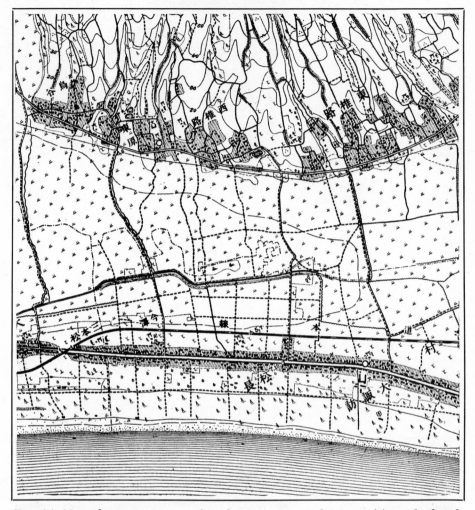

Fig. 64. Note the concentration of settlements on two dry sites: (1) on the beach ridge near the sea and (2) along the lower margins of the volcanic cone at the top of the map. Rice occupies the wet lagoon plain between the volcanic slopes and the beach ridge. Section of Japanese army topographic sheet for eastern Shizuoka Prefecture. Scale 1:25,000.

to serious inundation, an adjacent terrace bench or the slopes of an alluvial fan may furnish a better site.

Many of the less extensive diluvial terraces, especially those that are considerably elevated and separated from the alluvial plain by abrupt slopes, have few villages, their cultivated lands being worked by agriculturists residing on the alluvial plain below. Where they are of considerable area, as on the Tokyo Plain, or less elevated, villages may be relatively numerous on the diluvial uplands as well. Both on the terraces and in the mountains dispersed settlement tends to be more common.

Very definitely, however, rural villages and towns are concentrated on the plains of recent alluvium. If the lowland is not too wet or subject to serious inundation, villages dot its surface at sufficiently frequent intervals to enable the farmer to reach his scattered plots of land without traveling excessive distances. To such settlements, surrounded as they are by inundated rice fields, the road takes on the importance of a bridge and may largely determine the shape of the settlement. Besides those settlements widely distributed over a plain and associated with roads in both cause and effect relationships, there are others which occupy typically strategic sites. These are usually on elevations or dry sites, which have the dual advantage of saving the settlement from occasional inundation and of providing superior locations for transportation lines, rail and highway. Three types of such elevated dry sites, on or adjacent to the paddy-covered lowlands are the (1) beach ridges paralleling the coast, (2) river levees, either present or relict, and (3) the contact zone between the wet alluvium and the hardrock foothills and diluvial terraces (Fig. 64). The first and third types not only provide dry points in an otherwise wet plain, but have the additional advantage of being adjacent to both rice land and dry-crop land, both of which the farmer finds it desirable to cultivate. The beach-ridge location has a further advantage in its proximity to the ocean, and its settlements are frequently combination agricultural-fishing villages, and often local ports as well.

Settlement Forms of Villages and Towns.—No general summary of the various Japanese settlement types and their distribution is yet available in Occidental languages, although some forms have been described for certain parts of Japan.[8] One of the most widespread village types is the *strassendorf*, or an approximation of it, whose linear dimension greatly exceeds its width.[9] Not infrequently it is a single row of houses extending for a mile or more along either side of a main road (Fig. 64). Some of the longest villages of this type are located along a highway paralleling a narrow strip of coast between the mountains and the sea. Where this form occurs on a low plain in the midst of inundated rice fields, or on a well drained diluvial upland, the road alone may be the cause of its shape. But many such shoestring settlements, perhaps a majority of them, occupy elevated dry

[8] R. B. Hall, "Some Rural Settlement Forms in Japan," in the *Geographical Review*, January, 1931.
[9] H. Sato, "Distribution of the 'Strassendorf'" (in Japanese), in the *Geographical Review of Japan*, July, 1930 ("Essays in Memory of Dr. N. Yamasaki"), 6:550–557.

sites such as beach ridges and levee tops, where the landform itself in conjunction with the highway along its crest is responsible for its elongation. Most villages occupying such elevated sites are bordered on either side by strips of dry fields.

Another common settlement form is the compact village or *haufendorf*, which often has a checkerboard street pattern. In some parts of Japan the nuclei of such settlements have grown up within walls and moats, most of which have disappeared as expansion has taken place (Fig. 66). Other *haufendorf* settlements are simply nodal developments at intersections of local travel routes. Such compact villages are particularly suited to paddy areas where cooperative effort is required.

Regional Settlement Types

Hall has described the rural settlement forms in a number of widely separated localities in Japan (Fig. 65).[10] The *Yamato* type characterizes the plains of the Kinki district at the eastern end of the Inland Sea, including the Yamato or Nara Basin and parts of adjacent Kyoto, Biwa, and Osaka plains. In this section the rural population lives in small, compact agglomerations, rectangular in form and of relatively uniform size and distribution (Fig. 66). There is also a well developed rectangular system of streets. In the Yamato Basin rural villages range in size from a minimum of 20 houses to a maximum of 80, the majority having about 60. These farm hamlets and villages are spaced about one kilometer apart on the average. Their compactness and rectangularity is determined in part by the fact that they developed within an encompassing hedge and moat. All the walls have practically disappeared, but the moats, in various stages of deterioration, are still conspicuous, although they no longer serve as a protection against attack. The individual farmstead of the Yamato settlement differs from occupance units in other parts of Japan. The whole unit is oblong in shape, and within its wall are enclosed the house, sheds, stable, drying yard, and garden. The compactness of the village, making the fire hazard serious, has led to the abandonment of thatch for roofing and the substitution of tile or galvanized iron. Three to five rooms constitute the ordinary house. There is a maximum of seclusion both in the village itself and in each individual occupance unit. Looking at the village from the outside one sees through the encompassing hedge chiefly the bare walls of sheds and outbuildings. Passing along the narrow streets inside the village one sees only the continuous walls of the individual farm-

[10] Hall, *ibid.* See also Robert B. Hall, "Cities, Villages and Houses of Japan," in the *Michigan Alumnus Quarterly Review,* 40:138--149 (July, 1934).

steads with their closed and locked gates. The whole atmosphere is one of lifelessness.

The *Satsuma* type of rural settlement is characteristic of southern Kyushu south of the Kuma-Kii mountain land. The region comprises an extensive ash plateau into which the rivers have cut shallow, steep-walled, flat-bottomed gorges. The settlements are chiefly on the floors of the valleys, where there is some protection from the typhoon winds, to which this region is particularly subject (Fig. 280). The center of the settlement is the walled village, which in pre-Restoration days was the fortified quarters of the samurai. In the older sections of the town the houses are of fine urban quality. Along the main highway outside the old sections is the concentration of shops. The houses of the *buraku* farm families are crude thatched huts of very light construction, which greatly resemble tropical houses (Fig. 79). They are often separated from one another by gardens or even fields, but are nevertheless connected by winding trails. Compactness is generally lacking (Fig. 67). A heavy semi-tropical vegetation, part of it bamboo, encloses the houses and overhangs the trails.

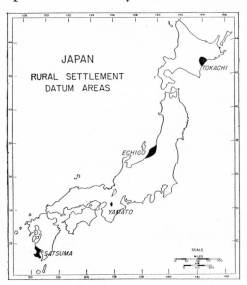

Fig. 65. Map after Robert B. Hall.

The *Echigo* type of settlement is especially characteristic of the complex delta-plains of the Shinano and other rivers in Niigata Prefecture, facing the Sea of Japan. Here on this poorly drained plain in a region of abundant snows and great floods it is the elevated dry sites, such as levee crests, beach ridges, and dunes, which have attracted settlements. Because of the linear dimensions of these sites the settlements are prevailingly of the *strassendorf* or shoestring type (Fig. 68). Usually the elevated site is the location of a highway, along either side of which the houses are strung out, sometimes presenting an almost unbroken front for several miles. Dry fields usually lie back of the houses. The typical house is an oblong, the narrow front facing the street. The living quarters are toward the front or street end, and the sheds and outhouses to the rear, but continuous with the living quarters. The snowy, windy winters have resulted in a particularly sturdy construction, and the roofs of shingles are sometimes weighted down by heavy boulders.

The *Tokachi* type of settlement is representative of the Hokkaido lowlands. Here widely separated isolated farmsteads are strung out along the rectangular system of highways that is a distinguishing feature of Hokkaido (Fig. 69). Relatively large barns and other detached out-buildings are characteristic. Houses are multiple in type, reflecting a variety of influences. In general house construction is somewhat sturdier here than

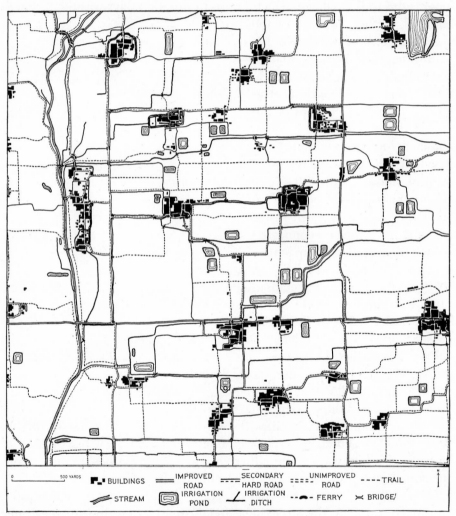

FIG. 66. The compact type of farm village. A section of the Yamato Basin in Nara Prefecture. Note the rectangularity of all forms, indicating *handen* influence. Map from the *Geographical Review*, published by the American Geographical Society, New York.

in subtropical Japan, but the contrasts are not as great as one might expect. Heating by stoves is common, so while chimneys are lacking there is the ubiquitous stovepipe projecting above the roof line.

Urban Communities[11]

Throughout the greater part of its history Japan has been decidedly a nation of rural people, and cities have therefore not been numerous. It is only since the Restoration, and particularly in recent decades, that the rapid expansion of industry and foreign trade has stimulated the growth of cities. For thirty years or more the farm population has varied little;

TABLE 62.—NUMBER AND RATE OF GROWTH OF VARIOUS-SIZED CITIES

Size of City	Number	Average Rate of Growth by Five-Year Periods, 1920–35	Average Rate of Growth, 1935–40
Japan Proper		7.4	5.6
Over 900,000	6	18.6	12.5
500,000–900,000.	0	—	—
350,000–500,000.	0	—	—
200,000–350,000.	12	16.5	10.2
100,000–200,000.	29	13.1	10.8
50,000–100,000.	57	12.6	5.9
Under 50,000	78	9.7	6.1
Total	182		

Source: *Toshi Mondai*, as quoted by Shannon McCune in "Recent Growth of Japanese Cities," in the *Geographical Review*, 32: 164–165 (January, 1942).

between 1920 and 1940 it actually declined by more than a million. Hence all the population increase of recent decades has gone into the cities. Between 1927 and 1940 the number of municipalities in Japan Proper increased from 101 to 182.[12]

ORIGINS OF JAPANESE CITIES

Despite the remarkable growth of urban population in recent years it appears that only a few large cities owe their existence to the needs of the modern era. Chief among them are the great deepwater ports of Kobe and Yokohama, the new urban centers of semi-frontier Hokkaido, and the industrial port cities of North Kyushu. Others, like Osaka, Nagoya, and Sakai, ancient in origin and fame, have been greatly expanded and

[11] In portions of this discussion I have drawn freely from Ludwig Mecking's "Japanische Stadtlandschaften," in *Stadtlandschaften der Erde*, edited by Siegfried Passarge (Hamburg, 1930), 109–123.

[12] In all of them the population was 25,000 or more. Two of the 182 cities are in Okinawa Prefecture, which includes the islands south of Kyushu.

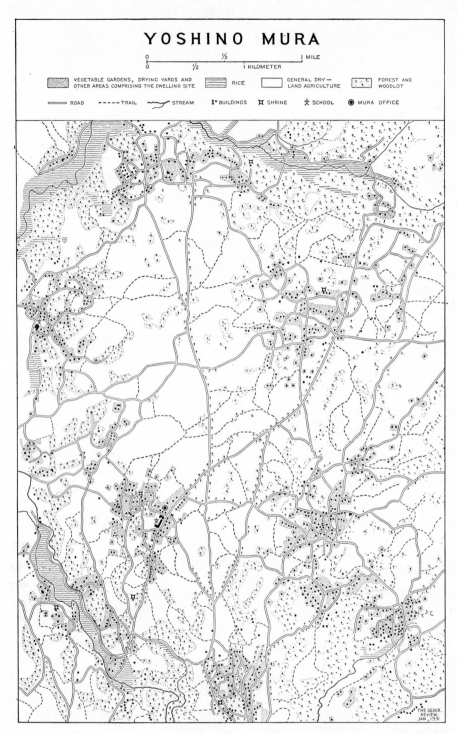

Fig. 67. Settlements on the ash plateau of southern Kyushu, where unirrigated agriculture predominates. Compactness in settlements is lacking. Map from the *Geographical Review*, published by the American Geographical Society.

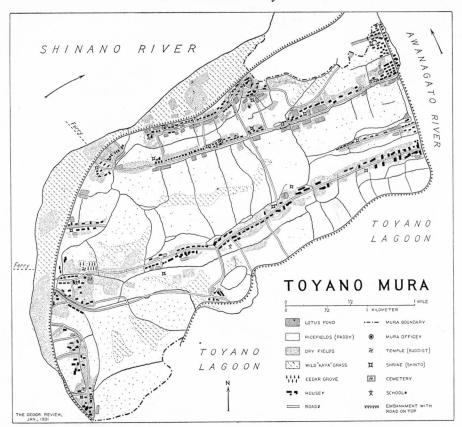

FIG. 68. Elongated shoestring settlements occupying the crests of old dunes, Echigo Plain, Niigata Prefecture. Map from the *Geographical Review,* published by the American Geographical Society, New York.

altered during the modern era of rapid industrial and commercial growth. But the fact remains that by far the greatest number of Japan's modern cities had their origin during the long feudal era, more particularly during its latter part, the Tokugawa Period (1615–1867), when a strong central-ized authority and associated internal peace combined to foster the development of urban centers with many standardized features.

Takekoshi[13] in his economic history of Japan indicates four principal types of city origin in feudal Nippon: (1) castle towns, which were the provincial capitals; (2) temple and shrine towns, which were the pilgrim-age centers for thousands of worshippers who required goods and services; (3) critical post stations containing numerous inns, located along impor-tant highways and hence offering special market advantages; and (4) the

[13] Yosoburo Takekoshi, *The Economic History of the Civilization of Japan* (New York, 1930), 243–245, 358.

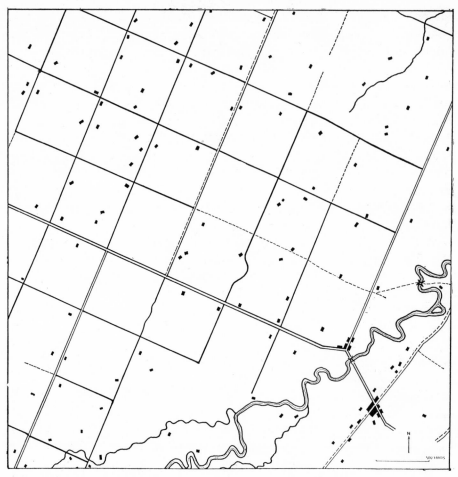

Fig. 69. Rectangular road pattern and dispersed farmsteads on the Tokachi Plain in Hokkaido. Map from the *Geographical Review,* published by the American Geographical Society, New York.

free ports and markets, which were not under the control of any feudal lord or group of priests, but were ruled exclusively by the merchants who inhabited them.

Castle Towns.—The data available do not permit a statement of the exact number of cities having a given origin. Certainly the castle towns and the post-road towns greatly outnumbered the others, but in many instances a city served more than one function. Thus many of the post stations were also castle towns. Throughout the Tokugawa period Japan was divided into a large number of principalities or fiefs of various sizes, which were ruled over by local sovereigns or *daimyos.* Such a feudal type of political organization involving many semi-independent states was

favorable to the growth of towns. The centripetal force acting to concentrate population was the castle-housed daimyo surrounded by the
homes and families of a large group of professional warriors, the *samurai*.
Such centers offered at least three advantages: they had superior market
facilities; they furnished a measure of protection in periods of internecine
warfare; and they offered opportunities for amusement and entertainment
that the country village did not. Thus most of the first large towns in
Japan had their origin as strategic political-economic centers of small
semi-independent feudal states. Artisans and traders flocked to these
daimyo towns and not infrequently a center specialized to such an extent
in a particular feature of trade or manufacture as to acquire national fame.
So firmly established did these specializations become that some of them
have persisted to the present time.

When Shogun Hideyoshi's land survey was made in the last decade of
the sixteenth century there were 160 fiefs, most of which had one or more
castles and castle towns. At the time the Tokugawa shoguns were estab-
lishing their capital at Yedo (Tokyo) a quarter of a century later, there
were 197 feudal lords, all except two of whom possessed definite fiefs.[14]
Sometimes a fief had more than one castle, the principal one being occupied by the daimyo and secondary ones by a son or other relatives. It
would not, therefore, seem unlikely that in the neighborhood of 200 of
the modern towns and cities of Japan have castle sites as nuclei.

At first the daimyo castle was a simple frame structure surrounded by
turf-covered earthen embankments in the form of steps or terraces, protected and made more durable by wooden piles. No radical departures
from this simple type of structure were made until after the introduction
of European firearms. The first castle having definite European earmarks
was constructed under Portuguese direction in 1575. It was at this time
that heavy flared walls of cut stone, usually andesite or granite, pierced
by several protected gates, began to supplant earthen terraces and embankments, and encircling moats were added as a further measure of
defense. The residential unit, however, still remained a frame structure,
Japanese in type and appearance. These extensive wall- and moat-encom-
passed grounds with their prominent castles, quite disproportionate to
other Japanese structures in size and massiveness, were and still are conspicuous and attractive features in the otherwise somewhat drab and
crowded cities (Figs. 70, 74). They have been the cores around which
accretion has taken place. Today the extensive grounds of these feudal
relics are commonly occupied by military barracks and schools, for they
provide an environment in which both children and soldiers may absorb

[14] *Ibid.*, 418–419, 527–534.

Fig. 70. The outer wall and moat of daimyo castle grounds, city of Shizuoka. The moat is now used for rice fields.

the spirit of Japan's chivalrous past when daimyo princes and their samurai warriors ruled Nippon. Few, if any, of the original residences remain, for numerous fires have razed the wooden structures repeatedly.

Ordinarily the daimyo's castle was so located as to command an important productive area, which in Japan means an alluvial plain. Moreover, the encircling moats had to be filled with water, and usually this was possible only where the groundwater was near the surface, as it is on the plains. On the other hand, to increase its conspicuousness, facilitate its defense, and make it more impressive, the castle was usually on an elevated site. Sometimes these sites were outliers or spurs of hardrock, more often they were the edges of diluvial terraces. Proximity to the seacoast was also considered of some importance, since in time of war it made more certain an uninterrupted supply of salt evaporated from ocean water.

Beyond the outer walls and moats of the nuclear castle and along the principal highways leading to the castle were concentrated the shops of the expanding town. To make defense easier the streets of castle towns were laid out with numerous offsets, hence sharp angles and jogs were characteristic. The result was a street pattern of great irregularity and complexity. The samurai, representing the highest of the several social classes, occupied the best residential areas.

Temple and Shrine Towns.—Somewhat comparable to the daimyo castle as a lodestone attracting population were certain important shrines and temples. To these holy spots came pilgrims by the thousands, even as they visit modern Nara to the number of three million a year. Since these pilgrims had money to spend for services and goods, inns, shops, theaters, and a variety of service establishments catering to their needs sprang up along roads leading to the holy places. Like the castles, the shrines and temples were large and were set in spacious grounds, and hence they were the conspicuous features of towns or cities where they existed. They did not, however, commonly occupy conspicuous elevated sites, and more often they were located on the peripheries rather than at the centers of their service towns. Only eight great Shinto shrines and eight similarly important Buddhist temples were recognized by the Tokugawa Shogunate,[15] but there were many more of lesser importance. It seems likely, therefore, that while no great number of feudal towns or cities owed their origin and development principally to a temple or shrine, there were many in whose development these holy places played an auxiliary role. At the time of the Restoration in 1868 several hundred shrines and temples of national fame were listed in contemporary pilgrims' guides.[16]

Commercial and Post-Road Towns.—Along the great network of gravel highways built by the shoguns and covering Japan from northernmost Honshu to southern Kyushu, post-towns were established at more or less regular intervals. Their function was to vend services and goods to the travelers. Horse stables, teahouses, inns, pleasure houses, porter depots, shops, and open market places—these were some of the distinguishing features. Since more than eighteen hundred of these post-road stations were in existence at the time of the Restoration, it is probable that a great majority of today's towns and cities owe their origin, in part at least, to their position on the post-roads.[17] By far the greater number of the castle towns were also stations on the main highways and thus profited from both functions. Although to some extent all the post-road and castle towns also performed market functions, some of them, by reason of particularly favorable locations at the intersection of highways, at river crossings, etc., were especially significant for this service. Certain free ports also came into existence and flourished as a result of the services they rendered in connection with water-borne commerce. These were never numerous, however, the total being only ten in the year 1500.[18]

[15] *Ibid.*, 418–419, 527–534.

[16] Robert B. Hall, "The Cities of Japan: Notes on Distribution and Inherited Forms," in the *Annals of the Association of American Geographers*, 24:175–200 (December, 1934).

[17] *Ibid.*, 196.

[18] Takekoshi, *op. cit.*, 373.

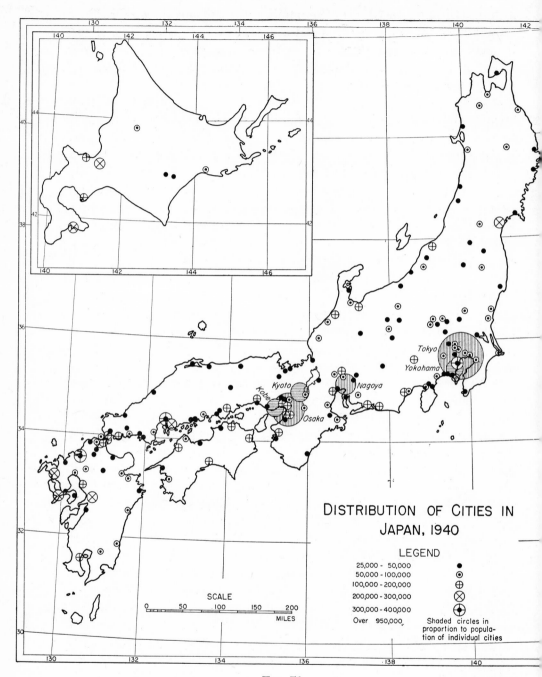

DISTRIBUTION OF CITIES IN
JAPAN, 1940

LEGEND

25,000 - 50,000	●
50,000 - 100,000	⊙
100,000 - 200,000	⊕
200,000 - 300,000	⊗
300,000 - 400,000	⊕
Over 950,000	

Shaded circles in
proportion to popula-
tion of individual cities

SCALE

0   50   100   150   200
MILES

Fig. 71

174

DISTRIBUTION AND LOCATION

Of the 180 cities[19] in Japan Proper whose population exceeded 25,000 in 1940, only 8 are in Hokkaido, the northern island, and 24 in Ou or northern Honshu; the remaining 148, or 83 per cent, are in old subtropical Japan south of latitude 37° (Fig. 71). This latitudinal distribution, with increasing density of total population and, even more markedly, of cities, toward the south, reflects not only the unsuitability of the Japanese mode of living to the more severe northern climates, but also an increasing distance from ancient and modern economic and political centers.

In that part of old subtropical Japan south of parallel 37° there is a marked concentration of cities in a much elongated belt between Kwanto on the north and northern Kyushu on the south. This includes northern Kyushu, the Inland Sea borderlands, and the Pacific littoral from the eastern end of the Inland Sea to Kwanto. Of the 148 cities in subtropical Japan whose population exceeds 25,000, over 110, or roughly 75 per cent, are located within this belt. This concentration is not due to any single advantage, although the region benefits from easy accessibility by water, and there are historical antecedents which are partly responsible. Within this much elongated urbanized belt are three striking clusters of cities coinciding with three of the largest plains of Nippon at the heads of three similarly long and extensive bays (Fig. 71). The greatest single cluster of cities, a total of 28, including Tokyo and Yokohama, two of Japan's six great metropolises, is on Nippon's largest plain, Kwanto. Second in rank is the cluster of 14 cities in the Kinki region, occupying the Settsu Plain at the eastern end of the Inland Sea. In this cluster are Osaka, Kobe, and Kyoto, three more of the six metropolises. Thirteen cities, among them Nagoya with over 1.3 million inhabitants, are grouped on the lowlands surrounding Ise Bay. Included in these three clusters, all associated with deep tectonic indentations and bay-head plains of some magnitude, are Japan's six cities of more than 950,000 inhabitants, her three greatest ports, and three of her four principal industrial nodes.

Of the 180 cities under consideration, 161 or nearly 90 per cent are located on littoral plains of aggradation, and 60 to 70 per cent have tide-water locations. This peripheral concentration of population reflects not only the coastal nature of most Japanese lowlands but the great dependence, especially in the pre-railroad era, on water-borne commerce. Interior cities are comparatively few. Only 19, located in interior basins having no sea frontage, are genuinely inland; 6 of them are in the

[19] Two small cities located in the islands south of Kyushu are excluded in this discussion.

meridional tectonic depressions of northern Honshu, and 6 are in local basins of that great traverse fracture zone in central Honshu known as the Fossa Magna. Most of these are strategically located on intercoastal land routes, formerly highways, now railways.

The sites of most urban centers are portions of low alluvial or diluvial plains where, because of the flatness of site and the squat buildings, it is nearly impossible to get a panoramic or bird's-eye view of a settlement. Of the 47 cities whose population exceeded 100,000 in 1940, all but a few were nearly exclusively on flattish littoral-plain sites. In contrast with conditions along the Mediterranean and Cornish coasts, where picturesque towns cling to the sides of declivities, most Japanese settlements occupy flattish sites, and only a few, like Nagasaki, Hakodate, and Kobe, spread up the slopes. A number of cities, like Tokyo and Yokohama, have two distinct levels of occupance, the flattish tops of the diluvial terraces and the lower alluvial and coastal plains, but the difference in elevation is seldom great.

Morphology.—On the basis of size, functions, and general morphology two large groups of Japanese cities may be distinguished. The first comprises the six great metropolises or "national cities"—Tokyo, Osaka,

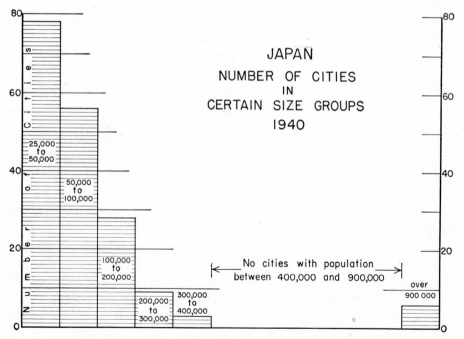

Fig. 72

Nagoya, Kobe, Kyoto, and Yokohama—having more than local hinterlands, a population exceeding 950,000, and a definite foreign aspect,
especially throughout the business and industrial sections. Contrasting
with these are scores of other cities that are essentially Japanese in their
features and appear to be cast in much the same mold. Between the six
large cities and the several score smaller ones, there is a wide gap (Fig.
72). Except for the six metropolises there are no cities having a population

FIG. 73. The typically even skyline of a Japanese city. From Edward S.
Morse, *Japanese Homes and Their Surroundings*.

as large as 400,000. Only three have as many as 300,000 and only nine
others as many as 200,000. It would almost seem as though the small local
hinterlands of Japan cannot support indigenous cities of more than
200,000 or 300,000 people. Larger cities require a national and international hinterland, and only six are so supported.

The Indigenous Cities.—The indigenous Japanese city of 25,000 to
350,000 people has many features in common with the much more numerous market towns, though their populations include fewer farm families. As a group they are characteristically local business centers and
ports, almost invariably situated on a railroad, and serve a restricted
tributary area much as they did during the feudal period. Mecking comments on their functional similarity to the towns of feudal Germany.
Not only the occupied sites, but the skylines also are flattish. As in the
towns, there is a dead levelness about the sea of somber slate-colored
tile roofs and unpainted frame buildings that is absent in even small
American cities (Fig. 73). Water towers, church spires, and tall substantial buildings of brick and stone are usually lacking. There are few trees.
The structures are flimsy, unpainted, and weather-stained, and one misses
the color supplied by the painted residences or the building materials in
an American city. Two features are often conspicuous because their
height or mass breaks the monotony of the skyline; one is the daimyo
castle, with its extensive wall- and moat-encircled grounds containing

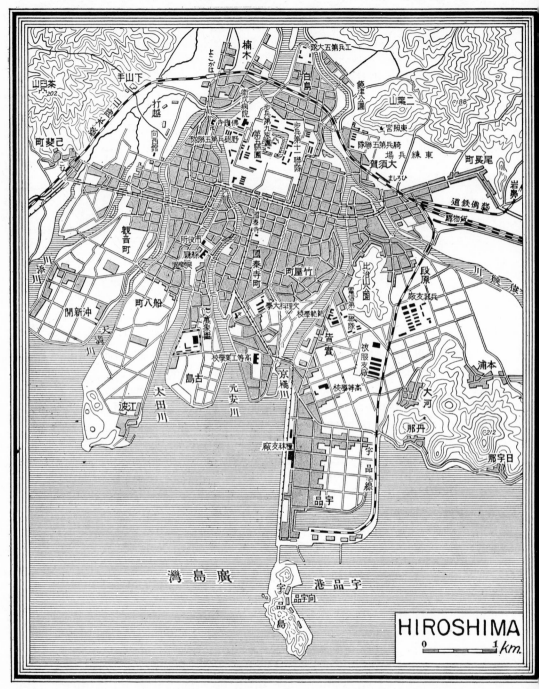

FIG. 74. Hiroshima, a representative "indigenous" city, occupies a flat delta site on the shores of the Inland Sea and is threaded by numerous rivers and canals. The daimyo castle grounds in the north-central part of the city are the core around which accretion has taken place. In this older section the rectangular grid of the streets is well developed. From *Nippon Chiri Taikei*.

178

trees; the other the shrines and temples, the latter usually being gaily painted.[20]

A prevailingly rectangular grid of streets, often with a north-south, east-west orientation, characterized many of the early cities and is still a common feature of the old cores of numerous modern ones (Fig. 74). Two explanations have been offered for this street arrangement. Certainly the low flattish delta sites of most of the cities make such a grid arrangement feasible. This influence of the site is supported by the fact that where Japanese cities are on slopes the rectangular grid disappears or is modified. In these slope towns there is a tendency for one set of streets to follow the contours or the waterfront and the other set to cross them at right angles. The other explanation is that the Chinese, who produced the grid of Imperial Peking, had a widespread influence on Japanese city plans as on so many other things Japanese. Imperial Kyoto and Nara are excellent examples of this Chinese influence. Many of the rural highways, however, are not straight, nor do they follow the cardinal directions; hence, as the city expands and encroaches upon what were once agricultural areas, the street system built upon the original rural highway skeleton frequently loses the grid pattern and becomes confused. Thus in many Japanese cities the original core has a rectangular street arrangement, whereas its newer peripheral section does not (Fig. 74). This is the reverse of the situation in many old American and European cities.

The numerous and recurrent fires which have devastated so many Japanese settlements have permitted frequent and extensive modifications of the original city plans, modifications that are often made with revolutionary rapidity rather than at the slow rate of the evolutionary process. Such drastic changes have been in progress at Tokyo and Yokohama as a result of the earthquake and fire of 1923. Chronic fires and the universal use of wood account for the almost total lack of ancient buildings.[21]

With its narrow surfaced, but unpaved, thoroughfares, its numerous streets with combination residences and small shops, open gutters, and lack of sidewalks, the Japanese city much resembles the market town (Fig. 75). The concentric zoning of functions and building forms so characteristic of American cities is almost altogether lacking. Well defined and

---

[20] See Ludwig Mecking, "Kult und Landschaft in Japan," in *Geographische Anzeiger*, 30 (1929): 137–146, where landscape features are analyzed in relation to the spiritual life of the country.

[21] The frequency of conflagrations is due in large part to the closely spaced, flimsy wooden buildings and the universal use of open fires for heating and cooking. Until recently paper lanterns with candles were the common form of illumination. In some parts of the country fires are associated with earthquakes.

FIG. 75. A narrow, congested street in Nara, an "indigenous" Japanese city. Photograph by Darrell Davis.

compact business sections are rare. Buildings of foreign style are not numerous, and those which do exist are single and isolated; rarely do they form solid blocks. In the exclusively residential sections, where most houses are surrounded by high, forbidding wooden walls, the streets are often very uninteresting (Fig. 81).

Composed as they are of small one-family houses, all much alike and closely spaced, often abutting against one another, it might seem that a Japanese city of a given population should occupy much less space than in the Occident, and perhaps the smaller urban centers do; but it must be remembered that the wider spacing of houses in European and American cities of over 50,000 is offset to a considerable extent by the prevalence of the multi-family apartment house. So uniform in size, spacing, and number of occupants are Japanese houses that it is said one can calculate the population of a city accurately from its dimensions.

Because of their delta locations, Japanese cities are interlaced by numerous rivers and canals (Fig. 76). These are arteries both of trade and commerce and of waste disposal. Factories, warehouses, and heavy-retail establishments tend to be concentrated along their margins, largely because they offer cheap transport services for bulky goods; lighters and sculled barges can bring wares from little tidewater ports to the very

FIG. 76. Numerous canals and rivers intersect Japanese cities, most of which occupy low alluvial sites. These canals of Niigata carry sewage as well as freight. Photograph by Darrell Davis.

doors of the business houses. Most of the canals are unattractive because of the kinds of establishments bordering them and the refuse they carry. A corollary of the network of canals and rivers is the unusual number of bridges in Japanese cities.

On the whole it is the larger indigenous cities that have increased in population most rapidly over the past two decades. In fact, rate of growth is directly proportionate to size; the twelve cities of over 200,000 (exclusive of the metropolises) are increasing most rapidly, and those under 100,000 the least rapidly (see Table 64). In the years 1920–35 small

TABLE 63.—JAPANESE CITIES OF MORE THAN 200,000 POPULATION, EXCLUSIVE OF THE SIX METROPOLISES

City	General Location	1940 Population	Percentage of Increase, 1920–40
Hiroshima	Inland Sea	343,968	63.2
Fukuoka	Northern Kyushu	323,217	59.5
Kawasaki	Between Tokyo and Yokohama	300,777	166.7
Yawata	Northern Kyushu	261,309	98.3
Nagasaki	Western Kyushu	252,630	30.3
Kure	Inland Sea	276,085	48.5
Sendai	Northeastern Honshu	233,630	51.0
Sapporo	Southwestern Hokkaido	222,827	82.6
Shizuoka	Between Yokohama and Nagoya	212,198	63.0
Kumamoto	Central Kyushu	210,038	30.9
Sasebo	Western Kyushu	205,989	70.9
Hakodate	Southern Hokkaido	203,862	33.4

Source: *Toshi Mondai*, 32 (1941): 1148–1167, as translated by Shannon McCune.

TABLE 64.—DISTRIBUTION OF URBAN POPULATION OF JAPAN PROPER ACCORDING TO SIZE OF CITIES, 1920–40
(population in thousands)

Size of Cities	1920	1925	1930	1935	1940
"Great Cities" (over 900,000)					
Population	5,479	6,778	7,605	12,646	14,384
Percentage of total population	9.79	11.35	11.80	18.26	19.67
Over 100,000, including "Great Cities"					
Population	6,754	8,741	11,481	17,518	21,291
Percentage of total population	12.07	14.63	17.81	25.30	29.12
50,000–100,000					
Population	2,105	3,445	4,402	3,685	3,858
Percentage of total population	3.76	5.77	6.83	5.32	5.28
10,000–50,000					
Population	9,177	9,667	10,409	10,549	11,338
Percentage of total population	16.40	16.18	16.15	15.23	15.51

Source: *Toshi Mondai*, 32 (1941): 1148–1167, as translated by Shannon McCune.

cities in the 10,000–50,000 class declined in importance, measured in terms of percentage of the nation's population, and even their total population was nearly stationary. In the next five years the downward trend was reversed, but the increase was small. Cities in the 50,000–100,000 class had a smaller total population in 1940 than in 1920, and they constituted a distinctly smaller percentage of the nation's population. It was the cities of over 100,000 population that increased most remarkably in the quinquennium 1930–35; in that short period their total populations expanded by over 6 million, and their ratio to the nation's total population rose from 17.81 to 25.30 per cent. Five million of the 6 million increase

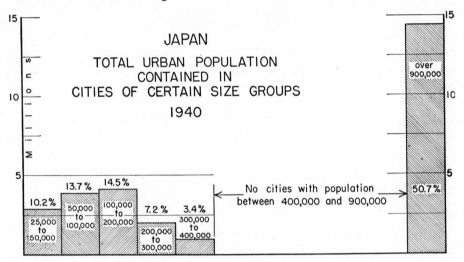

Fig. 77

in the large cities was in the six "great cities," whose ratio to total population rose from 11.80 to 18.26 per cent. In the succeeding quinquennium the absolute as well as the percentage increase in cities over 100,000 was considerably less, and the "great cities" slowed down more rapidly than those in the 100,000–350,000 class. In the five years preceding 1940 it was the latter group of cities that expanded most notably.

The Six Metropolises.[22]—It is only the six great metropolitan centers of more than 950,000 inhabitants that have much more than a local sphere of influence. Their distinctive landscapes are the result not of a different Japanese element but of more complete Westernization of their business, transportation, and manufacturing features. The stamp of foreign influ-

[22] The best treatment of the five great tidewater cities is to be found in Ludwig Mecking's "Japans Häfen," *op. cit.*

ence is most evident in the downtown retail business core. Here there are solid blocks of large, substantial buildings, European in appearance, which are built of brick, stone, and re-enforced concrete (Fig. 78). The greater part of their areas, however, are still distinctly Japanese in appearance. Flimsy Oriental wooden structures, combining the functions of retail shops and residences, front on the surfaced but unpaved thoroughfares. Narrow streets are still the rule, although in the six large cities a number of the business thoroughfares have been widened and paved, and in Tokyo and Yokohama ambitious new city plans are being executed. The composition of the traffic is most cosmopolitan, and numerous taxis, motor

TABLE 65.—GROWTH OF GREAT CITIES OF JAPAN, 1888–1940

Year	Tokyo	Osaka	Nagoya	Kyoto	Yokohama	Kobe
1888	1,313,299	442,658	154,981	275,780	118,947	115,954
1898	1,440,121	821,235	244,145	353,139	193,762	215,780
1908	1,626,103	1,226,647	378,231	442,462	394,303	378,197
1920	2,173,201	1,252,983	429,997	591,323	422,938	608,644
1925	1,995,567	2,114,804	768,558	679,963	405,888	644,212
1930	2,070,913	2,453,573	907,404	765,142	620,306	787,616
1935	5,875,667	2,989,874	1,082,816	1,080,593	704,290	912,179
1940	6,778,804	3,252,340	1,328,084	1,089,726	968,091	967,234
Percentage increase, 1935–40	15.0	8.8	19.6	0.8	21.5	6.0

Source: *Toshi Mondai*, 32 (1941): 1148–1167, as translated by Shannon McCune.

buses, and tram cars contrast strangely with the slow human- and animal-drawn carts and the ubiquitous bicycle.

All six of Japan's great cities are on or near some of the largest of the country's alluvial plains that have collected in the quiet waters at the head of long tectonic bays. Each plain is a major focus of settlement and an important local hinterland. Only one, Kyoto, is not located on tidewater. Three of them compose the nation's triumvirate of greatest foreign-trade ports. All are important rail centers as well. These six cities are focuses of manufacturing in the three greatest industrial nodes of the country and so, with one exception, combine port and manufactural functions.

On the basis of location and function the six great cities may be divided into three groups: 1. The three largest centers, Osaka, Tokyo, and Nagoya, each located at the head of its respective bay on the sea margins of advancing delta-plains, are the business, industrial, and consuming centers of their large local hinterlands. 2. Kobe and Yokohama, the deep-water ports of the adjacent Osaka and Tokyo industrial nodes, are located

FIG. 78. Downtown section of Tokyo. Above, *National Geographic Magazine*. Below, Three Lions, Black S

fifteen to twenty miles down their respective bays, where silting is not marked. The Nagoya, or Nobi, Plain at the head of Ise Bay has no representative in this port group. 3. Kyoto is the only city of the six which is located inland; its principal fame derives from the fact that it was for over a thousand years the nation's capital. Thus from a regional point of view, as shown by the previous analysis, four of Japan's great cities are arranged into two binuclear conurbations, Osaka-Kobe and Tokyo-Yokohama, the members of each group being very similar in respect to location, site, and function.

The phenomenal growth of Japan's six great cities during the decade of the thirties has resulted in a remarkable concentration of the nation's population in them and their environs. In 1940 the "big six" had a combined population of 14.4 million or nearly 20 per cent of the nation's total; with their satellite cities and towns the ratio is almost 25 per cent. But not all of the sextette felt the impact of war preparations with equal intensity. Kyoto, for example, the old capital and a focus of craft industries, had only a very modest population increase—less than one per cent—during the quinquennium 1935–40. Kobe and Osaka, the industrial metropolises of the Kinki region, felt the surge of wartime industrial expansion more keenly, registering population increases of 6 and 8.8 per cent. But even more meteoric was the expansion of the industrial metropolises of the Kwanto and Nobi plains; Tokyo increased 15.0, Yokohama 21.5, and Nagoya 19.6 per cent.

THE JAPANESE HOUSE

The prevailing type of Japanese house was designed for the never-ending summer of the tropics. This would appear to be one of the cultural features that the Japanese inherited from that branch of their stock which moved northward from the tropical islands and coastlands of southeastern Asia. In its present-day modified form it is perfectly adjusted to the long, hot, humid summer of subtropical Japan, which is, to be sure, the dominant season in the populous southwestern part of the country. It is less well adapted, on the other hand, to the chilly, raw winters of the same section, and still less so to northern Honshu and Hokkaido with their continental winter climates. Apparently the philosophy of the Japanese is to endure the discomforts of winter in anticipation of obtaining the fullest enjoyment of the long summer to come. Genuine fortitude is required, however, to carry on normal living throughout the winter in a drafty tropical house in which little or no provision is made for heating the rooms, but only the occupants. It is true that in the mountains and in northern

Japan, where winter temperatures are much lower and the summer period cooler and shorter, the subtropical house has been modified to some extent, but the amazing thing is that so many of its tropical features have been retained.

Japanese rural houses vary greatly in details but in basic elements they are very similar. Simply rectilinear in form, they are small, the three-room structure being the most common, although four- and five-room houses are also numerous (Figs. 79, 80). One story is much more common than two. There is no attic, no cellar, and no continuous foundation.

TABLE 66.—NUMBER OF HOUSES OF VARIOUS SIZES IN JAPAN PROPER, 1930
(12,557,931 housholds investigated)

No. of Rooms	Households	Percentage of Households	No. of Rooms	Households	Percentage of Households
Less than one. . .	6,147	0.04	Six	686,361	5.46
One	1,398,960	11.14	Seven	310,060	2.46
Two.	3,114,387	24.80	Eight	159,105	1.26
Three	2,576,473	20.51	Nine	77,729	0.61
Four.	2,721,291	21.67	Ten	49,667	0.39
Five.	1,382,189	11.00	Eleven or more . .	75,562	0.60

Source: *Japan Yearbook*, 1939–40, p. 48.

Wooden posts resting upon stones serve as the underpinning of the house, the floor of which usually stands one to three feet off the ground. This stilt foundation is suggestive of the tropical house, which is elevated to greater height than in Japan as a precaution against seasonal floods. Since most Japanese farmhouses are in the immediate vicinity of flooded paddy fields, their elevation, permitting free passage of air beneath, prevents excessive dampness. The structure is not anchored to the ground but is weighted down by its heavy roof of thatch or tile. This tends to make the Japanese house topheavy, but enables it to withstand the strong winds.

The average Japanese house is much more cheaply and fragilely constructed than the Occidental. The following quotation from Lafcadio Hearn describes the simple and inexpensive character of the common Japanese dwelling.

Leaving my home in the morning, I observe, as I pass the corner of the next street crossing mine some men setting up bamboo poles on a vacant lot there. Returning after five hours' absence, I find on the same lot the skeleton of a two-story house. Next morning I see the walls are nearly finished already—mud and wattles. By sundown the roof has been completely tiled. On the next morning I observe that the mattings have been put down and the inside plastering has been finished. In five days the house is completed. This of course is a cheap building; a fine one would take much longer to put up and finish. But Japanese cities are for the most part composed of such common buildings. They are as cheap as they are simple.

Unlike the Chinese, who have used brick, clay, and stone, the Japanese have always built their homes of wood, despite the frequent and disastrous fires. This is attributable not only to the easy availability of timber, which has undoubtedly been a factor, but to their artistic preference for wood. They do not paint the outside of their dwellings nor varnish the inside, preferring the gray, velvety appearance that outdoor weathering gives to well-dressed timber and the rich tawny and brown tones that are obtained by hand-rubbing the interior wood. It has been said that the Japanese derive from the natural colors and textures of wood a pleasure that is akin to appreciation of a fine skin.[23] The wooden columns which compose the skeletal framework of the house, supporting the heavy roof, and which are both finishing and construction members, are small by our standards, and complete logs of small diameter are used rather than sawed timbers. Those walls that are stationary are made of several coats of mud plaster into which short rice straw has been mixed for binder. Lathing is split bamboo, woven into a mat and bound together by straw ropes. For a finished surface over the mud plaster a coating of fine sand or clay is often used. White lime plaster is also commonly used for a top coating in some districts, notably along the borderlands of the Inland Sea. Sometimes the mud-plaster wall is overlain with a sheathing of thin boards. Only a portion of the house walls, however, are stationary; the rest, especially that on the south side and portions of some of the others, consist of light wooden sliding panels or screens, set in grooves at top and bottom, which on hot summer days can be folded back, thus throwing open the house to receive every breeze there is. At night the panels are drawn together, ostensibly as a protection against burglars, but actually for the sake of privacy. Translucent paper or panes of glass in the sliding panels permit entrance of light. The light streaming through these panels at night gives the Japanese house the semblance of a huge lantern. Houses are usually open to or face the south, so that they get the full benefit of the south winds of the summer monsoon and of the sun in the cooler season. Often there is a narrow veranda, some three feet wide, on this side, the floor of which is an inch or two below the straw mats of the adjacent living room. Double sliding panels, one forming the outer wall of the

[23] *Fortune*, September, 1936.

veranda, the other the wall of the house proper, are characteristic. There is no better place to relax during the sultry evenings than on such a veranda.

It is often said that the beauty of Japanese houses is in their roofs, whose multiple forms have such pleasing combinations of straight and curved lines. The most common roof material in the rural districts is thatch (straw or reeds). In the mountain villages, roofs of bark and shingles are also common. Thatched roofs are steeply pitched to produce rapid runoff of the heavy rain. The beautiful but ponderous low-hipped roofs of thatch, sometimes two feet thick, or of heavy silver-gray tile, strike one as somewhat out of proportion to the fragile walls that support them. But it is these thatch roofs with their variety of roof forms and ridge tops that are most picturesque. Bright-colored flowers growing on the ridges of the thatch roofs are not unusual. Wide eaves projecting as much as six feet beyond the walls of the house protect the open rooms against the rain and the close-to-vertical summer sun, and at the same time offer little obstruction to the entrance of the more oblique rays of the lower winter sun. They also add grace to the roof and give an air of stability to the house. Grain and vegetables are hung under the wide eaves to dry.

The houses in the market towns and cities do not differ fundamentally from the farmhouse except in details. Because of the greater fire hazard thatch roofs are infrequent, being replaced by tile, galvanized iron, and composition products. In the house of the shopkeeper or craftsman the work or sales room is open to the street, and the residential rooms are behind it or on the second floor. Windows are commonly protected by iron bars or wooden shutters. The rich man's town house is set back from the street and is enclosed by a high frame or shrubbery wall, behind which is the garden, where small bushes, ponds, steppingstones, flower beds, and small trees are attractively arranged (Fig. 81). This garden is an integral part of the high-class city residence, for the walls of the house fronting upon it may be slid open and it then becomes a living wallpaper. The Japanese garden is a work of perspective art in which the spacious panoramas and vistas of nature are compressed to domestic scale.

In an ordinary farmhouse of three or four rooms the kitchen is often dirt-floored. One or more of the others is covered with straw mats called *tatami*, which make necessary the removal of shoes or other footgear outside. The *daidokoro*, next to the kitchen, is the most lived-in room. Near its center is a square firepit, above which hangs an adjustable hook that holds the iron tea kettle, or at mealtime a soup kettle. Usually the kitchen is not under the main roof, but is an appendage to the house proper, with its floor at a lower elevation. The best room, *zashiki*, con-

FIG. 79. A representative house of a middle-class farmer. Note the heavy, steeply sloping roof of thatch. There is no continuous foundation, merely wooden stilts to serve as underpinning and permit circulation of air. Photograph by John Embree.

FIG. 80. Portion of a rural village (*buraku*) in southern Japan. The houses front on the prefectural road. In the foreground are paddy fields replanted to winter cereals (*mugi*). Photograph by John Embree.

FIG. 81. City residences of high quality. Each home is surrounded by a wall, and entrance is through a gate, which is kept locked. Photograph by Asahi.

tains the finest *tatami* and also the *tokonoma,* the honored alcove where family treasures are kept. Special small sleeping rooms called *nema* may also be included, although any or all of the rooms, including the *zashiki,* may be used as bedrooms. Since the floor is used to eat, sit, and sleep on, there is little need for furniture. The walls separating the rooms are simply sliding screens traveling in grooves in floor and ceiling.[24]

The house yard of the farm dwelling plays an important part in the life of the family. In it are a number of different sheds and service units

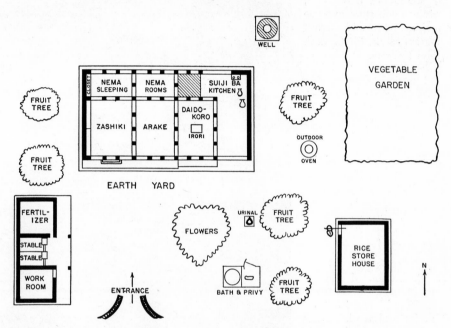

Fig. 82. Representative plan of a house and farmstead. Redrawn from a map by John Embree in *Suye Mura* (University of Chicago Press).

–bathhouse, toilet, woodshed and tool shed, outdoor oven, perhaps a tiny barn, and pens for chickens, rabbits, and pigs (Fig. 82). Some houses also have a fireproof and earthquake-proof *kura,* where the family treasures and heirlooms are safeguarded. In the bare, flat house yard, grain is dried, and various operations such as weaving baskets, reeling silk, and rolling tea leaves are carried on. Usually the yard contains fruit trees, vegetable and flower gardens, and sometimes a fish pond. The size of the yard varies considerably, being smallest in paddy villages. In unusually windy

[24] A good description of the ordinary farmhouse appears in Embree, *Suye Mura,* 89–94.

FIG. 83. The interior of a typical Japanese home. Note the simple rectilinear lines and the small amount of furniture and decorations.

parts of the country, the whole farmstead is protected by windbreaks of trees and bushes.

Economy and simplicity are the keynotes of the Japanese house and furnishings, but the homes are nevertheless attractive and picturesque. Local materials are used almost exclusively in construction, and the village house is usually a product of cooperative labor. Since charcoal braziers take the place of stoves for heating, chimneys and fireplaces are lacking. Glass, paint, plumbing, and builders' hardware scarcely enter at all into the construction costs. The soft interior tones are the result of diffused light through paper windows, the pale green or light straw colors of the reed *tatami* that cover the floors, and the neutral tints of hand-rubbed wood. Floor mats, walls, and frames are harmoniously rectangular in outline, and the angular contours register cleanly, for there is little in the way of decorations and furnishings to detract from the simple recti-linear pattern; there are no rugs, carpets, or curtains, and no chairs, for people kneel or sit upon flat cushions which are stored in closets when not in use (Fig. 83). Tables are used only at mealtime. In its sequence of functions the room of the Japanese house is likewise a model of economy and efficient use of space. Whereas the Occidental house contains separate rooms for different activities, each with its own furniture, a single room of a Japanese house may serve a number of purposes. Furniture and fixtures are reduced to a minimum, beds are blanket rolls which are stored in a closet in the daytime, chairs are lacking, and meals are eaten from trays or small removable tables. Since a man carries on only one activity at a time, it appears wasteful to the Japanese to have numerous rooms, some of which are idle much of the time.[25]

SELECTED REFERENCES

EARLE, FRANCES M. "The Japanese House." *Education*, 63:277–281 (January, 1943).

EMBREE, JOHN F. *Suye Mura: A Japanese Village.* University of Chicago Press, Chicago, 1939.

"Gokkanosho: A Remote Corner of Japan." *Scientific Monthly*, 59:343–355 (November, 1944).

HALL, ROBERT B. "Some Rural Settlement Forms in Japan." *Geographical Review*, 21:93–123 (January, 1931).

Handbuch der Geographischen Wissenschaft: Nordasien, Zentral und Ostasien, 511–514. Akademische Verlagsgesellschaft Athenaion M. B. H., Potsdam, 1937.

HARADA, JIRO. *The Lesson of Japanese Architecture.* Studio Publications Inc., New York, 1936. See especially pp. 45–55.

MECKING, LUDWIG. "Japanischen Stadtlandschaften." Siegfried Passarge, [ed], *Stadtlandschaften der Erde.* Friederichsen, De Gruyter and Co., Hamburg, 1930.

MORSE, EDWARD S. *Japanese Homes and Their Surroundings.* Harper and Brothers, New York, 1904.

NISHIKIORI, HIDEO. *"Togo-Mura: A Village in Northern Japan,"* translation by Toshio Sano with annotations by John Embree. Section of Agricultural Policy, College of Agriculture, Tokyo Imperial University.

ODAUCHI, TSUBIN. "Geographical Study of a Village Community," translation by Toshio Sano. *Geographical Education*, supplement to special number entitled *Collection of Essays on Rural Geography.* 1934.

SCHEIDL, LEOPOLD G. "Die Kulturlandschaft Alt-Japans." *Die Japanisch-Österreichische Gesellschaft*, 29–32. Tokyo, 1937.

TAUT, BRUNO. *Houses and People of Japan.* The Sanseido Co., Ltd., Tokyo, 1936.

WALKER, RALPH. "The Japanese House." *Pencil Points*, 21:332–342. (June, 1940).

[25] Regional variations from the standard type of Japanese house are described in Part III.

CHAPTER VII

Agriculture and Fishing

Agricultural Land

AT THE time of the Meiji Restoration in 1868 nearly 80 per cent of Nippon's total population was engaged in agriculture.[1] Thereafter, as the economy of the country became more diversified, the ratio steadily declined, until in 1939 only about 40 per cent of Japan's families were completely or partially dependent on agriculture for a livelihood. Of the total 13.6 million families in Japan Proper in that year, 5.5 million were engaged in agriculture, of whom 3.7 million were occupied solely with tilling the soil and 1.8 million with supplementary occupations.[2]

As has been said, the steady decline in the ratio of farm population to total population is not the result of a significant decrease in the former, for the number of farming households was substantially the same in 1939 as it had been in 1886, but rather to a rapid increase in the population engaged in commerce, industry, and the professions. At the same time the total amount of cultivated land has increased very slowly. In the thirty-four years from 1905 to 1939 only 241,938 cho (1 cho = 2.45 acres) were added to the nation's cultivated area, an increase of 4.6 per cent. Obviously neither the increase in farm population nor the increase in agricultural land has kept pace with the increase in the population as a whole. Thus while the per capita cultivated area was 0.13 cho or 0.32 acre in 1877, the corresponding figure in 1939 was 0.083 cho or 0.27 acre.

The fact that the total population has mounted rapidly while the farming population has remained nearly static and the area of cultivated land has increased only very slowly indicates that, in Old Japan at least, very little agricultural land remains to be reclaimed. "It will be seen that the exploitation of arable land in Japan Proper has virtually reached the limit, leaving little room for further reclamation even with highly expensive and thoughtful assistance from the government."[3]

[1] Shiroshi Nasu, *Aspects of Japanese Agriculture* (Institute of Pacific Relations, New York, 1941), 7.
[2] *Norinsho Tokeihyo,* 1939. [3] Nasu, *op. cit.,* 77.

According to an investigation made by the Japanese Industrial Research Bureau late in 1918, there were still about 1.6 million cho in Japan Proper capable of being converted into cultivated land. About one-fourth of this was potential paddy land, but the other three-fourths was suitable only for unirrigated upland fields. If the area reclaimed between 1918 and 1938 is subtracted from the above figure, there remains a balance of about a half million cho which may conceivably be converted into cultivated land. Much of this is very marginal land, however, difficult and expensive to reclaim. It is therefore not unlikely that a large part of it may never be utilized agriculturally. In any case much of it will never be very productive. In some years the amount of good land lost to agriculture through the expansion of cities, industry, and transportation exceeds the amount of marginal land reclaimed.[4]

In 1939 the cultivated land in Japan Proper represented not quite 16 per cent of the total area. Great Britain cultivates 22.5 per cent of her total area, France 39 per cent, Italy 44.6 per cent, and Germany 43.8 per cent.[5] The much smaller ratio for Japan is largely due to the hilly and mountainous character of the country.

With a cultivated area of only about 6 million cho and a farm population of nearly 5.5 million families, cultivated plots average only 1.1 cho or 2.7 acres per family, an almost unbelievably small figure. The area of cultivated land per person gainfully employed in agriculture is thirty times as large in the United States as in Japan, seven to eight times as large in England, five times as large in Germany, and nearly 5 times as large even in crowded Belgium.[6] Table 69 shows how very unfavorable is Japan's position as regards population per unit of cultivated land, the man-land ratio of nearly 3,100 persons per square mile being higher than in any other country in the world. Even if one considers the agricultural population alone, the density per square mile of cultivated land is still between 1,200 and 1,300, which is higher than in any other nation on earth. Japan is a country "of many men on little land," and the evidences of this great pressure of human beings on the meager soil resources are everywhere apparent:

[4] For a more detailed account of government policies and plans as related to land reclamation, see Nasu, *op. cit.*, 71–87. See also Guido Perris, "The Problem of Increasing the Land under Cultivation in Japan," in the *International Review of Agricultural Economics*, 1(1923):470–499.

[5] Karl Pelzer, *Population and Land Utilization* (Institute of Pacific Relations, New York, 1941), 112.

[6] Nasu, *op. cit.*, 14.

There are the roads always narrow and mostly at the wood's edge or the river's.

There is the straw piled on brushwood bridges off the loam and the trees only growing at the god's house, never in the fields.

There are the whole plains empty of roofs, squared into flats of water, no inch for walking but the dike backs, not as much as a green weed at the foot of the telegraph poles or a corner patch gone wild.

There are the fields empty of crows after harvest: thin picking for black wings after cloth ones.

There are the men under moonlight in the mountain villages breaking the winter snowdrifts on the paddies to save days of spring.

There are the forest floors swept clean and the sweepings bundled in careful, valuable piles.

There are the houses without dogs, the farms without grass-eating cattle.

There are the millet fields at the sea's edge following the sweet water to the brackish beginning of the salt, the salt sand not the thickness of a stake beyond.

There are the rivers diked and ditched and straightened to recover a napkin's breadth of land and the hill valleys terraced til the steepest slope turns flatwise to the sun.

There are the mountains eroded to the limestone where the axes and the mattocks have grubbed roots.

All these are in the landscape. And all these—the cheese rind eaten to the brittle crust above and the careful hoarding of the crumbs below—are like Japan.

Japan is the country where the stones show human fingerprints: where the pressure of men on the earth has worn through to the iron rock.

There is nothing in Japan but the volcanoes and the volcanic wastes that men have not handled. There is no getting away from men anywhere: from the sight of men in the open houses or from the shape of their work in the made fields or from the smell of their dung in the paddy water.

In other countries a farm is meadows and a wood lot and a corner that the plow leaves: room to turn about and time to turn about in. In Japan a farm is as rigid and tight a thing as a city lot—a patch here and a triangle there and a square or so somewhere else: every road corner of land diked and leveled off even though the growing surface is less than a man's shirt; every field soaked with manure and worked and reworked as carefully and as continuously as a European farmer works a seedbed....

... nothing thrown away, nothing let go wild, nothing wasted.[7]

It must be recognized, however, that to compare the population per square mile of cultivated land in different countries has only limited economic significance. For the productivity of land varies with such physical factors as temperature, rainfall, quality of soil, etc. The uncultivated land of some countries is practically worthless; in others it is valuable for graz-

[7] "Of Many Men on Little Land," in *Fortune,* September, 1936.

TABLE 67.—CULTIVATED AREA, 1905–39*

YEAR	CULTIVATED LAND IN CHO			YEAR	CULTIVATED LAND IN CHO		
	Total	Per Capita	Per Farm Family		Total	Per Capita	Per Farm Family
1905	5,320,668			1925	6,067,015	0.102	1.093
1910	5,715,405	0.113	1.039	1930	5,915,994	0.088	1.056
1915	5,859,170			1935	6,058,753	0.087	1.079
1920	6,084,276			1939	6,078,730	0.083	1.107

* *Norinsho Tokeihyo* for data for 1915 and later; Nasu, *Aspects of Japanese Agriculture*, for 1905 and 1910. The first fairly accurate census of cultivated land was made in 1929. The result of this survey shows a decrease of 188,000 cho over the report of the preceding year. This was probably not an actual decrease but a checking of the errors in the earlier years. Since 1929 there has been an annual increase of about 30,000 cho of agricultural land.

TABLE 68.—CLASSIFICATION OF LAND ACCORDING TO USE

YEAR	AREA (in thousands of cho)					PERCENTAGE OF TOTAL			
	Total	Cultivated	Pastures and *Gen-ya*	Forests	All Others	Cultivated	Pastures	Forests	All Others
1936	38,573	6,086	3,354	21,036	8,097	15.6	8.7	54.5	21
1939	38,573	6,079				15.8			

Source: *Nogyo Nenkan*, 1940–41, p. 136, as quoted by Andrew J. Grajdanzev in *Statistics of Japanese Agriculture*, 14, and *Norinsho Tokeihyo*, 1939.

TABLE 69.—POPULATION AND CULTIVATED LAND OF VARIOUS COUNTRIES

Country	CULTIVATED LAND		POPULATION	
	Area in Thousands of Sq. Km.	Percentage of Total Area	Total in Millions	Per Sq. Km. of Cultivated Land†
Germany* (1939)	221	40	74.83	339
France (1938)	227	41	41.98	185
Great Britain and Northern Ireland (1938)	52	22	47.49	913
Italy (1937)	153	49	43.51	284
U.S.S.R. (1934)	2,390	12	170.47	71
Japan Proper (1938)	61	17	72.22	1,184
British India (1931)	1,596	34	352.84	321
United States (1938)	1,414	18	130.22	92
Canada (1938)	236	2.6	11.21	47
Brazil (1936–37)	132	1.6	44.12	334
Australia (1937–38)	134	1.7	6.93	52

Source: Nasu, *op. cit.*, 2.
* Including Saar and Austria.
† Multiply by 2.6 for population per square mile.

TABLE 70.—NUMBER OF FARM HOUSEHOLDS MANAGING AGRICULTURAL AREAS OF
VARIOUS SIZES, 1939

(1 cho = 2.45 acres; 1 tan = .245 acres)

Size of Farm	FARM HOUSEHOLDS	
	Number	Per Cent
Less than 5 tan	1,853,610	34
5 tan to 1 cho	1,799,840	33
1–2 cho	1,325,805	24
2–3 cho	314,405	6–
3–5 cho	122,065	2+
Over 5 cho	76,113	1+
Total	5,491,838	100

Source: *Norinsho Tokeihyo*, 1939.

TABLE 71.—RATIO OF THE TOTAL OF THE AREAS OF ALL CROPS TO THE TOTAL AREA
OF CULTIVATED LAND, 1937

District	Paddy and Upland Fields	Paddy Fields	Upland Fields
Hokkaido	0.876	0.902	1.106
Tohoku	1.103	0.966	1.327
Kwanto	1.285	1.192	1.347
Hokuroku	1.230	1.187	1.393
Tosan	1.365	1.384	1.348
Tokai	1.433	1.352	1.547
Kinki	1.429	1.310	1.864
Chugoku	1.472	1.411	1.624
Shikoku	1.659	1.711	1.594
Kyushu	1.801	1.786	1.819
Japan as a whole	1.332	1.300	1.368

Source: Nasu, *op. cit.*, 92–93. Nasu also gives ratios for each prefecture. See Fig. 88 for the location
of districts.

TABLE 72.—AMOUNT OF FERTILIZER EMPLOYED IN JAPAN PROPER, 1934

Type of Fertilizer	Amount (in metric tons)	Price (in thousands of yen)
Manure	68,805,613	299,920
Farm yard manure	31,719,338	140,040
Green manure	6,288,600	24,320
Human excrement	16,195,538	56,020
Other	9,602,137	71,540
Fish manure	171,757	11,540
Soybean cakes, etc	1,194,497	72,540
Chemical fertilizer	1,918,909	109,027
Bone powder	53,485	3,765
Total	67,144,261	496,029

Source: Nasu, *op. cit.*, 118.

ing and as a source of forest products. Some countries are rich in mineral resources and fish, others not. Japan's abundant rainfall and prevailingly humid subtropical climate tend to make for high yields, which help to alleviate the scarcity of arable land, as does also the unusual abundance of fish in the surrounding seas. With the aid of these favorable features of environment, and by dint of the most intensive cultivation, Japan has performed the remarkable feat of making herself almost self-sufficient with respect to foodstuffs.

Farms and Fields

The Japanese farm unit averages only 2.7 acres (6,078,730 cho of cultivated land ÷ 5,491,838 farm families = 1.1 cho or 2.7 acres). Ninety-one per cent of the farms include less than 4.5 acres, 67 per cent less than 2.45 acres, and only 1.4 per cent more than 12.3 acres.

The size of farm units increases gradually from south to north, although there is considerable variation in individual prefectures, depending in part upon the relative amounts of unirrigated upland (principally diluvial terrace and ash plateau) and irrigated rice land. Upland farms yield less than the irrigated paddy lands and are consequently larger. In southwest Japan, except in prefectures where the area of dry fields is unusually large, the farm units are generally less than 2 acres in size; some of the prefectures along the Inland Sea average only 1.5± acres. In northern Honshu the average size has increased to 3.5 acres, and in Hokkaido it is 12.5 acres. The increasingly severe climate to the north, with shorter and less tropical summers and more severe and snowy winters, makes for smaller production per unit-area in the higher latitudes of Japan. Fall-sown cereals become less profitable in northern, and especially in snowy northwestern, Honshu and finally disappear almost entirely in Hokkaido. Per unit-area rice yields are conspicuously lower toward the north. Such subtropical cash crops as tea and silk are not acclimated to Japan's northland, tea being of little importance north of the 37th parallel, and mulberry, the exclusive food of silkworms, decreasing markedly north of 39° or 40°. This whole northern region is looked upon by the Japanese as less desirable country, well removed from the economic and cultural heart of Nippon, and having a rigorous climate which forces certain hardships upon them.

Unlike the American farm, which is usually a fence-enclosed, compact, and contiguous plot of land, the tiny Japanese farm is composed of several little unfenced parcels, scattered in many directions at varying distances from the village in which the agriculturist lives (Fig. 84). It

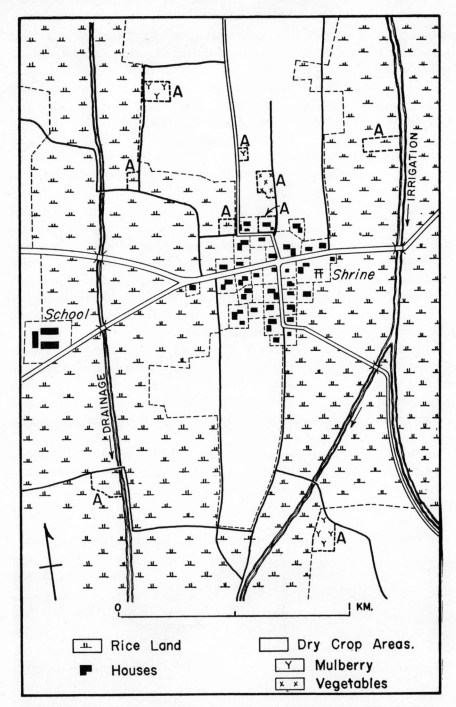

Within the map: School, DRAINAGE, IRRIGATION, Shrine

Legend:
- Rice Land
- Houses
- Dry Crop Areas.
- Mulberry (Y)
- Vegetables (x x)

Fig. 84. Layout of a representative farm. Farmer *A* lives in a small rural village. He has eight scattered parcels of land, four of them planted to rice, the four others in dry crops. The most distant fields are 1.4 km. from his dwelling. After Nasu.

199

may take him as long as an hour to walk from one of his scattered fields to another. This "open-field" system of unfenced, dispersed plots, which exists also in China and in parts of Europe, is the result of several factors. Chief of these are centuries of renting, buying, bartering, and inheriting; the farmer's desire for a diversity of crops; and the antiquated methods of irrigation. Each of the parcels of land is further subdivided into little fields of various sizes and shapes. In Old Japan (excluding Hokkaido) the rice fields average only about one-tenth to one-eighth of an acre. The more rectangular unirrigated upland fields are somewhat larger, but three-quarters of them include less than a quarter acre. Thus a representative Japanese farmer living in a village cultivates about two and one-half acres of land, part of it rented, which is subdivided into several (usually fewer than six) noncontiguous plots; these are further subdivided into fields so that the entire farm may be composed of ten to twenty individual fields of varying sizes and shapes. The Japanese farmer is fortunate if, in addition to rice land on the wet lowlands, he has other fields satisfactory for dry crops on adjacent elevated sites—beach ridges, levees, diluvial terraces, or mountain foothills.

Partly offsetting the very obvious disadvantage of the open-field system is at least one advantage: it permits of a somewhat more equitable distribution of the good and inferior lands and of those suited to only a single kind of crop. Thus a farmer prefers to cultivate upland plots where he can grow dry crops, fuel, grass, etc., as well as low alluvial land for rice culture.

Considerable areas of paddy land (from a fifth to a fourth of the total area) and tracts of upland differ from the landscape previously described in that the fields are larger, of more uniform size, and more rectangular. Where this more regular geometric field pattern prevails it usually

Fig. 85. The ordinary Japanese farm implements. Photograph by John Embree.

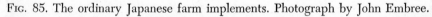

FIG. 86. Terraced paddy fields. Photograph by Natori, Black Star.

indicates that farm lands have been "adjusted" under government supervision. That is, a farmer is given one or two contiguous plots equivalent in area to his previously more numerous and scattered patches. Paths, roads, and irrigation and drainage ditches are all rearranged. By this process of adjustment a number of improvements are made: 1. The increased size of the fields to at least a quarter acre, and their greater rectangularity, expedite farm work and the use of animals and tools. 2. As a result of the straightening of the field boundaries and the destroying of many useless ones, the productive power of a given area is increased 3–5 per cent on the average. 3. The reconstruction of the canal system allows for greater perfection in both irrigation and drainage, thus increasing the land's productivity for rice by providing greater insurance against an excess or deficiency of water. Moreover, lands which prior to adjustment were too wet for winter crops, can thereafter often be sufficiently well drained for fall planting. It has been officially calculated that adjustment increases the yield by about 15 per cent.

Agricultural Practices

Japanese agriculture is extremely intensive but comparatively unscientific. Scattered plots of land tend to waste the farmer's time going to and from his village home. The tiny fields permit of no labor-saving machinery. The obsession with irrigated rice as a food crop prevents proper rotation of crops. Yet as a result of unusual amounts of hand labor, the per-unit yield of land in Nippon is extraordinarily high. Throughout Japan Proper the number of agricultural workers per cho (2.45 acres) averages 2.34 or just slightly more than one worker per acre.[8] There is no doubt, however, that the application of labor to land in Japan has reached the point of diminishing returns, that there is little hope of increasing its productivity by further intensifying the labor. In some instances it has been found possible to reduce the labor through cooperative management without any substantial decrease in production. It is the scarcity of agricultural land and the unusually high yields that are obtained from it that boosts land prices so high. Thus medium-grade paddy land is priced at 500–700 yen per tan or approximately 2,000–2,800 yen per acre.[9]

Terracing.—Striking to a foreigner's eye are the artificially terraced hillsides, where the tiny fields rise one above the other for hundreds of

[8] Nasu, *op cit.*, 115.

[9] *Ibid.*, 1. The par value of the yen is about 50 cents; but even before the war it was considerably below par.

Fig. 87. Terraced vegetable plots. Smooth boulders form the retaining walls of the fields. The upper slopes have a protective mantle of trees.

feet in the form of great stairs. Only by the most arduous labor has this terracing been accomplished, for it involves not only the carving of flattish areas out of mountain flanks and the building of retaining walls along the down-slope side of the fields, but frequently also the carrying of soil from the plains below to provide the new plot with a veneer of productive soil. The Japanese recognize two types of terraced fields: those for irrigated rice and those for dry crops, especially of the tree and bush variety. Terraced rice paddies are said to be a relic of the long period of feudalism in Japan, when the labor of farmers counted for almost nothing and the unbearable taxes levied upon the peasants forced them to expand their paddy fields up the slopes (Fig. 86). Terracing for rice is a particularly difficult undertaking, for each tiny field must be approximately flat to permit of its inundation. Intricate and difficult irrigation systems are likewise required to irrigate the slope paddies. With the abolition of feudalism and the increased appreciation of the value of labor, this type of terracing became less common and at present the number of slope paddies is decreasing.[10] On the other hand, terracing for unirrigated crops is increasing; such fields can be made with much less labor, since their surfaces can be far from flat, and difficult irrigation systems are unnecessary (Fig. 87). The terraced orchards of peaches, oranges, and other fruits along the shores of the Inland Sea and of

[10] T. Noh and K. Yosizaki, "Terrace Cultivation in Japan" (in Japanese with English summary), in the *Geographical Review of Japan*, 12(1936):352–368, 828–835; 14(1938):230–238.

DISTRICTS
OF
HONSHU
AND
SHIKOKU

Fig. 88. The boundaries of the districts are very indefinite.

oranges in Shizuoka Prefecture are examples of this more recent and still expanding type of slope cultivation.

Multiple Cropping. — In the United States it is customary to harvest only a single crop from a particular piece of land and to allow the land to lie idle thereafter until the next season's planting time. In Japan, on the other hand, numerous fields must support more than a single harvest during the year cycle. One measure of the intensity of cultivation is the ratio of total area of all crops grown during a given year to the total area of cultivated land. In 1939 the total area under cultivation in Japan was only 6.08 million cho, whereas the total area planted to crops was a third larger, 8.11 million cho. Table 71 shows the annual frequency of cultivated land utilization in Japan in 1937. The ratio is lowest in Hokkaido, only 87.6 per cent, indicating that in this northland region of relatively cold winters and short growing season some land is allowed to lie fallow throughout the entire year. This is uncommon in Old Japan. Only in one prefecture in Old Japan—Akita in far northwestern Honshu—is the ratio of crop area (sum total of areas of all crops) to cultivated area less than one. Toward the south the ratios become increasingly larger, reaching 1.66 in Shikoku and 1.80 in Kyushu. In Kumamoto in western Kyushu the ratio attains a maximum of 1.975, which means that practically all the cultivated land bears two harvests.[11]

In paddy areas, where there is practically no year-round fallowing, the ratio is the proportion between one-crop and two-crop paddy fields. The second crop in the irrigated rice fields is usually wheat, barley, rape, beans, or green manures, such as legumes. In northern Japan replanting of the paddy fields in winter is prevented largely by the short growing season, the low temperatures in fall and spring, and the heavy snow cover, especially on the Japan Sea side (Fig. 89). In subtropical Japan it is the difficulty of draining the inundated fields that offers the greatest obstacle to a winter crop. In 1939 of the 3.48 million cho in paddy fields about 2 million cho, or 57 per cent, bore only a single crop. Of the paddy

[11] Nasu, *op. cit.*, 92–93.

lands which were not cropped twice annually, 700,000 cho (1924) remained fallow in winter because the fields could not be properly drained. The remainder was not adaptable to a two-crop regime chiefly because of climatic handicaps.[12] In close proximity to urban areas some farmers can find more profitable employment than raising a second crop in the paddy fields.

Upland or unirrigated fields vary much more widely with respect to intensity of land use, which ranges from complete year-round fallow to more than two crops a year. In part these variations are due to climatic differences. Thus in Hokkaido and Tohoku most of the upland fields are planted only once a year, but farther south multiple cropping is more common, though even here the annual frequency of cultivation varies a good deal with the kind of crops grown (Fig. 90). For example, where mulberry, orchards, and tea are important, since only one crop a year is ordinarily raised, the ratio may be small even though the region has a high productivity. It

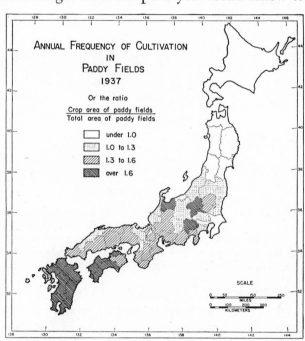

ANNUAL FREQUENCY OF CULTIVATION
IN
PADDY FIELDS
1937

Or the ratio

Crop area of paddy fields
Total area of paddy fields

under 1.0
1.0 to 1.3
1.3 to 1.6
over 1.6

SCALE

MILES

KILOMETERS

FIG. 89. In Hokkaido and in Tohoku north of about latitude 38° the rice fields lie fallow in winter. South of latitude 38° a progressively larger proportion of the rice fields is replanted to winter crops.

is common practice to follow the summer crops of vegetables with crops of wheat, barley, sesamun, and green manure planted in the fall. In the suburban districts of great cities the multiple cropping system is used for the growing of vegetables. For example, in the prefectures of Osaka and Hyogo, in which the cities of Osaka and Kobe are located, the index of double cropping for upland fields is 2.4 and 2.7.

Interculture.—Several crops of summer vegetables from the same field are made possible by interculture practices, a kind of simultaneous rota-

[12] *Ibid.,* 94.

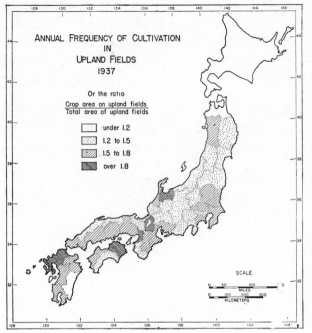

FIG. 90. In Hokkaido a great majority of the unirrigated fields are planted only once each year, in the spring, and are allowed to remain fallow in winter. Toward the south, as the growing season lengthens, there is an increasing amount of double-cropping.

tion in which alternate rows of different crops sown at different times are grown together in the same field. Thus in a field bearing a crop of winter wheat or of barley planted in rows, beans of various kinds or some other vegetable may be sown early in spring between the rows of grain. After the winter grain has been harvested other vegetables may be planted in the vacant rows between the rows of earlier vegetables. By such a close dovetailing of several crops in time and space the land is forced to yield several harvests each year.

Fertilizer.—Such practices as have just been described, by which the land is forced to grow several crops a year, can be maintained only by frequent and abundant applications of fertilizer. This is especially true of the poor upland soils which have been subjected to the strong solvent action that is inevitable in a rainy subtropical climate. To maintain crop yields, therefore, such kinds and quantities of fertilizer must be added as will compensate for the loss of fertility resulting from intensive multiple cropping and climatic solution.

Table 72 shows the kinds and amounts of fertilizer used in Japan Proper. In bulk, manures of various kinds exceed all others. Especially noteworthy is the extent to which human excrement or "night soil" is used, amounting to over half as much as animal manures. To an American one of the incongruous sights in a great metropolitan center like Tokyo is the large number of ox-drawn wagons bearing kegs of odorous night soil through the streets. Manures of various kinds are commonly dumped by the farmer into a shallow cement storage cistern, where, with water added.

the mass is allowed to decompose (Fig. 91). When used it is ladled out of the cistern and carried to the fields in large wooden buckets. It is not so much the soil that is fertilized as the growing plants that are fed, for the Japanese farmer does not broadcast the manure but pours it directly over the plants so that only the soil supporting the crop is fertilized (Fig. 92). This com-

Fig. 91. Fertilizer cisterns, in which the night soil is allowed to decompose before being placed on the soil.

mon Japanese practice of pouring liquid manure, including night soil, over growing plants is one reason why foreigners refrain from eating uncooked vegetables in Japan. Chemical fertilizers are the second most important type of fertilizer used in Japan, whose unit-area consumption of them is comparable to that of the western European countries. Soybean cake, which ranks third in value among the fertilizers used, is imported in large quantities from the adjacent continent, particularly Manchuria.

In 1933, when the total cost of producing a tan of paddy rice was 43.5 yen, expenditures for fertilizer amounted to 8.62 yen or about 20 per cent of the total cost of production.[13] In recent years about 35 per

Fig. 92. Liquefied night soil being ladled from wooden buckets and poured on growing plants. Photograph by John Embree.

cent of the total cash expenditures of the farming population has been for fertilizers.[14] At the current prices of fertilizer Japanese farmers have just about reached a ceiling with regard to the amount they can afford to apply per unit-area. There is evidence that the law of diminishing returns has begun to operate; while additional applications of fertilizer will augment production, the rate of increase steadily declines, and additional amounts of fertilizer might prove uneconomical.

In summary it bears restating that, measured by any one of three standards—human labor applied per unit-area, number of crops planted per year, fertilizer consumed per unit-area—Japanese agriculture is unusually intensive. Thus the per unit-area production of rice is two to four times as great in Japan as in French Indo-China, British India, or the Philippines. On the other hand, it is lower than in Italy and Spain, the reason being, according to Nasu, that Japan's national average is brought down by the fact that rice is grown in the northerly latitudes and in high altitudes where natural conditions are unfavorable for this subtropical plant. Per-unit production of wheat and barley in Japan is two to three times what it is in the United States and equals that of the countries of western Europe.

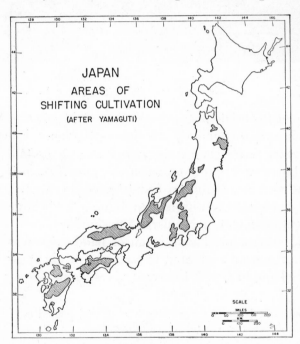

JAPAN

AREAS OF
SHIFTING CULTIVATION

(AFTER YAMAGUTI)

Fig. 93. The areas of shifting cultivation are limited to the highlands.

Shifting Agriculture.—One feature of mountain agriculture in some parts of Japan is the practice of shifting cultivation, sometimes described as *brandwirtschaft,* or "burning-field cultivation."[15] The practices involved

[13] Nasu, *op. cit.,* 122, 129.   [14] *Foreign Agriculture,* 2:53 (January, 1938).
[15] S. Yamaguti, "Distribution of the Shifting Cultivation (*Brandwirtschaft*)" (in Japanese), in the *Geographical Review of Japan,* 14:1–23 (January, 1938). Included is a folded map in color showing the distribution of shifting cultivation.

in this rather primitive type of agriculture vary from one section of the country to another, but they all include the cutting or burning off of the tree cover and the planting of unirrigated crops among the stumps or charred trunks for a few years before abandoning the fields again to trees. From seven to ten years may elapse before the abandoned fields are again brought under cultivation. There are in Japan some 152,000 farm families or close to 900,000 persons engaged in shifting agriculture. This represents close to 2.8 per cent of the country's total farm families. The practice is common throughout the hill and mountain districts from southern Kyushu to northern Honshu, the areas of highest concentration being in mountainous central Kyushu, central Shikoku, and eastern Chugoku, and in portions of mountainous central Honshu (Fig. 93).

Agrarian Conditions in Japan

Agriculture employs 40–45 per cent of the Japanese population, represents nearly half the nation's invested capital, is an extremely important factor in foreign trade, and provides more than 80 per cent of the nation's staple food. There is no doubt that agriculture is vital in the Japanese economy, and if it were as prosperous as it is vital, it would be in a flourishing state indeed. Quite the opposite is the case, however, for rural Japan presents a picture of frugality, impoverishment, economic distress, and social unrest. The fundamental factors in this situation are the scarcity of agricultural land, which cannot easily be remedied; absentee landownership and its converse, land tenancy; the heavy tax load; a huge indebtedness accompanied by exorbitant interest rates; and an agricultural income largely dependent upon two products, rice and cocoons, the prices of which fluctuate widely.[16]

Aside from the scarcity of land, the matter of farm tenancy is probably the most acute problem. In 1939 about 53 per cent of the agricultural land was tilled by proprietors and close to 47 per cent by tenants.[17] About 7.5 per cent of the landowners owned 50 per cent of the land, while an infinitely larger group—50 per cent of the landowners—own only 9 per cent of the land. Thus a few thousand wealthy parasitic landowners hold a considerable slice of the best farm land, while at the opposite end of the scale are 5.5 million poverty-stricken tenants and small holders. Of the 5.5 million farm households in 1939, only 31 per cent were independent farm owners, 27 per cent owned no land at all,

[16] W. Ladejinsky, "Agrarian Unrest in Japan," in *Foreign Affairs*, 17:426–433 (January, 1939).

[17] Nasu, *op. cit.*, 157,

and 42 per cent were part tenants and part owners.[18] Fully 69 per cent of Japan's farmers are wholly or part tenants. But the prevalence of absentee landownership does not mean that great holdings are common. A man owning 75 acres is counted among the great landowners, and the owner of 25 acres belongs to the middle group.[19] In 1938 only 3,547 land-owners, or 0.07 per cent of the total, possessed over 50 cho (122.5 acres), the average size of these holdings being 300 acres; 44,000 or .9 per cent owned properties of 10–50 cho (24.5–122.5 acres), the average being 57 acres.[20] The relatively small acreage in these figures is deceptive, however, unless one bears in mind that the size of the average farm is only 2.5 acres.

The plight of the Japanese farm tenant is due to the terrific shortage of agricultural land in the face of a rapidly growing population, and the general lack of alternative occupations. These circumstances operate to bind the tenant to the land and to force him to submit to extortionate rentals. He has no bargaining power, for he is compelled to compete for leases in a market where the demand is larger than the supply. If dissatisfied, he cannot abandon his lease, since there is no choice of other land and the opportunities for employment in other occupations are small. This is the situation that largely determines the landlord-tenant relationship. Competition for the right to work the limited amount of agricultural land has resulted in pushing rents to exorbitant heights. Rice land rents are almost universally paid in kind; for other types of land they are usually paid in cash. The normal rent for a one-crop field is about 55 per cent of the crop and for a two-crop field 60 per cent. It is common for the tenant farmer to receive only 30 per cent of the crop as his net share.[21] In the landlord-tenant contract the only responsibility the proprietor assumes is to supply the land and pay the land tax. The tenant must furnish the house and other farm buildings, the implements and seed, and whatever else he requires for growing his crops. The rental is a fixed charge per unit of land instead of a share of the crop, and is based upon yields in good years. In poor years, therefore, the tenant may be forced to urge a reduction of his rent. Out of this situation grow many of the disputes between tenants and landlords.

The tenant farmer's low standard of economic well-being arises out of this landlord-tenant relationship. From Table 73, showing the average

[18] *Norinsho Tokeihyo,* 1939, p. 8.

[19] W. Ladejinsky, "Farm Tenancy and Japanese Agriculture," in *Foreign Agriculture,* 1:433 (September, 1937).

[20] Nasu, *op. cit.,* 10–11.

[21] Ladejinsky, "Farm Tenancy and Japanese Agriculture," *op. cit ,* 435.

budget of thirty-five tenant farmers, it is clear that the income from agriculture does not cover the necessary small expenses attendant on running a farm and raising a family. The annual deficit of 44 yen or $22 would have been still greater but for the fact that the tenants spent nothing for educating children or for social activities. Moreover, no allowance was made for interest on debts, and rare is the tenant who is not burdened by debt. Another investigation conducted by the Japanese

TABLE 73.—AVERAGE HOUSEHOLD INCOME AND EXPENDITURES OF 35 TENANT FARMS
(average number of members in family, six)

Item	Japanese Currency (yen)	United States Currency (dollars)
Income		
Rice crop	1,004	502
Barley crop	64	32
All other sources	248	124
Total.	1,316	658
Farm and living expenses		
Rent	504	252
Fertilizer and farm implements	208	104
Taxation	30	15
Food	345	172
Clothing	52	26
Shelter, light, and fuel	44	22
Childrens' education	—	—
Social activities	—	—
Sake (wine made of rice)	—	—
Wages for farm labor	43	22
Miscellaneous	134	67
Total.	1,360	680
Deficit	44	22

Source: W. Ladejinsky, "Farm Tenancy and Japanese Agriculture," in *Foreign Agriculture*, 1 (1937): 436.

Department of Agriculture relative to the budgets of 208 tenant farmers revealed that the average incomes of these tenants from *all possible sources* was not sufficient to cover their poverty-level living expenses. The results of these studies are typical of Japanese tenant farmers as a class. They have always been on the border of destitution, and conditions became worse during the depression years after 1929.

The ingrained feudal deference of farmers to landlords and their deep-rooted conservatism resulted for decades in the general resignation of tenants to their unfortunate lot. It was not until after World War I that disputes between landlords and tenants became frequent. Although they numbered only 17 in 1917, they had increased to 6,824 in 1935, and continued to exceed 6,000 annually until 1938, when, with the beginning of the Sino-Japanese War, there was a remarkable falling off.[22] Excessive rents and the efforts of landlords, especially in recent years, to evict a tenant by terminating his lease have been the cause of increasing friction between landlords and tenants. The conflict has centered increasingly upon the question of the tenant's right to cultivate the land, a right established by tradition and custom rather than by law. In general, the geographical distribution of disputes reflects the acuteness of agricultural distress in the several districts of the country. Thus there has been a general shift of the dispute centers from predominantly rice areas to specialized silk districts, which were particularly hard-hit by the decline of the silk market.

Tending to further depress agriculture in Japan is the disproportionate share of the tax load borne by the farming class; Japanese taxes weigh much more heavily upon land than upon the capital invested in industry and trade. In 1934 on an annual income of 300 yen a farmer paid 35 per cent of it in taxes, whereas a merchant paid only 12.5 per cent and a manufacturer 1.1 per cent.[23] Moreover, the farmer has borne an undue share of the government's subsidization of trade and industrial expansion.

To cap these difficulties, the Japanese farmer struggles under the burden of a huge indebtedness, which in 1936 amounted to an average of 1,000 yen per farm household.[24] Part of this debt is for land purchased at inflated prices during the period of World War I. Another large portion is debt contracted to meet current household expenses. Interest rates on farm loans are often usurious; more than two-fifths of the loans carry an annual interest charge of 7–10 per cent, over half a rate of 10–15 per cent, and 6 per cent a rate of over 15 per cent.[25] The average rate on all farm loans in 1932, according to official sources, was nominally 12 per cent and the actual interest rate was much higher, probably between 20 and 30 per cent.[26] Even if the lower figure of 12 per cent is accepted, interest on debts consumes on the average about 38 per cent of the farmer's income.

Agricultural distress is also produced by the fact that so much of the farm income in Japan is derived from two products—rice and cocoons. Although the first of these, rice, is all consumed domestically, the wide fluctuations in yield resulting from variable seasonal weather causes considerable price fluctuations. Normally 85–90 per cent of Japan's silk has found a market in the United States, and thus the prosperity of large

[22] Nasu, *op. cit.*, 20. The numbers given include only those disputes involving four or more landlords and 20 or more tenants.

[23] Ladejinsky, "Agrarian Unrest in Japan," *op. cit.*, 429. [24] *Ibid.*, 429–430. [25] *Ibid.*, 430.

[26] *The Times*, London, July 5, 1932, quoted by Ladejinsky in "Farm Tenancy and Japanese Agriculture," *op. cit.* 429.

numbers of Japanese farmers has been tied up with the economic well-being of the United States. For example, during the depression years after 1929, when purchases of silk by the United States greatly declined, Japan's silk farmers suffered serious reductions in incomes. In 1937 the government adopted the Raw Silk Price Stabilization Law, which seeks, as its title indicates, to prevent serious fluctuations in the price of raw silk.

The Agricultural Scene

Japan is one small unit of the earth's greatest rice-growing region, the Monsoon Lands of southeastern Asia, where over 95 per cent of the world's rice crop is produced. In Japan rice dominates the agricultural economy of that part of the country south of Hokkaido, and it is only in the extreme northern and eastern parts of Hokkaido that it disappears entirely from the landscape. Like the Monsoon Lands of Asia in general, Japan's agriculture is a subsistence type based upon the raising of cereals for home consumption. About 73 per cent of the crop area (sum total of the areas of all crops) is planted to cereals, and because large parts of the area in fruit trees and mulberry are not suited to any other crop, the percentage of the land under rotation is actually higher than 73 per cent. Close to 70 per cent of the total value of all crops is represented by cereals. This constant cropping to cereals is unwise from the standpoint of soil conservation, for the soil is thereby exhausted. Because animal industries and pastures play an insignificant role in the Japanese agricultural economy, their benefits in a rotation system are almost completely lacking.

THE IRRIGATED LOWLANDS OF PADDY RICE SPECIALIZATION

Few countries specialize in one crop to as great an extent as Japan does in rice. In 1937 it occupied 52–53 per cent of the total cultivated area and 39–40 per cent of the total crop area, and represented nearly 57 per cent of the total value of farm products (59 per cent was the 1930–34 average) (Fig. 94). For two decades and more the total area in paddy rice has remained almost unchanged. This high degree of specialization has a historical basis and cannot be explained primarily in terms of adjustment to climatic or other physical phenomena. To be sure, the physical characteristics of central and southern Japan—subtropical climate, abundant summer rainfall, and easily irrigated alluvial lowlands—are suitable and even attractive. Moreover, the unit-area yield of rice is the highest of all the small grains and it has excellent keeping qualities under conditions of a warm humid climate. All these advantages recommend it as the standard food crop of Nippon.

Table 74.—Ratio of Area and Value of Individual Crops to Total Area and Value of Crops

Crop	1931 Area	1931 Value	1936 Area	1936 Value	1939 Area	1939 Value
Rice	41.0	56.7	39.6	62.2	39.4	57.3
Barley	4.8	2.6	4.2	2.0	4.4	2.4
Naked barley	6.0	3.2	5.4	2.8	5.0	3.0
Wheat	6.3	3.3	8.5	5.8	9.2	6.3
Beans.	6.0	2.0	5.3	2.0	5.2	2.3
Oats, millet buckwheat, maize . .	5.1	1.6	5.0	1.4	4.6	1.4
Sweet potatoes.	3.4	3.6	3.5	2.9	3.4	2.8
Irish potatoes	1.3	1.2	1.9	1.4	2.1	1.8
Vegetables	7.0	10.4	7.5	7.7	7.2	7.8
Industrial crops	3.0	4.8	3.7	3.9	3.8	4.8
Green manure crops	5.7	1.4	6.2	0.7	5.8	0.5
Mulberry	8.6	6.8	7.0	5.2	6.6	7.0
Other crops	1.8	2.4	2.2	2.0	3.3	2.6
Total.	100.0	100.0	100.0	100.0	100.0	100.0

Source: Grajdanzev, *Statistics of Japanese Agriculture, op. cit.*, 3–4. The year 1931 was the bottom of the depression; 1936 the last pre-war year.

Table 75.—Area under Various Crops, 1939

Crop	Thousands of Cho	Crop	Thousands of Cho
Rice	3,192.7	Awa (Foxtail)	63.0
Irrigated. 3,040.9		Mie (Barnyard).	32.7
Upland dry rice. 151.8		Kibi (Proso)	18.3
Barley.	353.9	Maize	53.2
In paddy fields 111.8		Buckwheat.	81.6
In upland fields. . . . 242.1		Sweet potatoes	277.8
Naked barley.	409.7	Irish potatoes.	165.9
In paddy fields 253.9		Vegetables	587.9
In upland fields. . . . 155.8		Industrial crops (rape, hemp, ramie,	
Wheat.	745.6	flax, jute, seeds and rushes, py-	
In paddy fields 364.0		rethrum, cotton, peppermint, sugar	
In upland fields. . . . 381.6		cane, tobacco, paper fibers). . . .	307.7
Oats.	123.9	Green manure crops	470.6
In paddy fields 2.0		In paddy fields 382.6	
In upland fields. . . . 121.9		In upland fields. . . . 88.0	
Soybeans.	324.4	Tea	40.4
Small beans	97.4	Mulberry	533.4
Millets.	114.0	Total crop area, including others	8,111.0

Source: *Norinsho Tokeihyo*, 1939. The area of orchards is not given in this statistical volume. According to Nasu it was about 146,000 cho in 1937.

TABLE 76.—AREAS IN FOUR MAJOR FORMS OF LAND USE, 1939

Form of Land Use		Thousands of Cho
Total cultivated area		6078.7
Paddy fields	3209.2	
Upland fields	2869.5	
Total area of dry crops		4917.0
Total crop area		8110.0

Source: *Norinsho Tokeihyo*, 1939.

TABLE 77.—USES OF FLOUR IN JAPAN, 1933–34

Product	Percentage of Total
Noodles, vermicelli, macaroni, etc.	50
Bread and rolls	14
Cakes, dumplings, and sweet goods	26
Miscellaneous	10

Source: C. L. Alsberg, "Japanese Self-Sufficiency in Wheat," in *Wheat Studies*, 12: 79 (November, 1935).

TABLE 78.—AREA PLANTED TO BARLEY, NAKED BARLEY, AND WHEAT, 1925–39

CROP	AREA IN CHO		
	1925	1932	1939
Barley	447,545	380,072	353,891
Naked barley	544,292	479,689	409,660
Wheat	467,456	508,724	745,601

Source: *Norinsho Tokeihyo*.

TABLE 79.—AREA AND VALUE OF VEGETABLE PRODUCTION, 1939

Vegetable Crop	Area (in thousands of cho)	Value (in hundreds of yen)	Vegetable Crop	Area (in thousands of cho)	Value (in hundreds of yen)
Peas	35.8	10,117	Burdock	17.7	18,677
Broad beans	29.3	7,675	Taro	51.3	40,961
Kidney beans	96.3	32,782	Lotus roots	3.8	6,660
Cucumbers	20.3	17,004	Welsh onions	20.0	19,548
White muskmelon	5.8	4,784	Onions	12.2	16,131
Squash	23.7	15,485	Cabbage	12.3	11,148
Watermelons	25.3	27,311	Lettuce	47.4	31,760
Muskmelons	5.0	3,810	Peanuts	8.3	4,996
Egg plant	29.8	24,815	Sweet potatoes	277.8	142,000
Tomatoes	10.0	10,079	White potatoes	165.9	87,560
Lily roots	1.2	2,116	Soybeans	324.4	87,606
Radishes (daikon)	109.4	69,081	Azuki or small beans	97.4	29,771
Turnips	10.3	5,786			
Carrots	12.8	10,872	Total	587.9	391,594

Source: *Norinsho Tokeihyo*, 1939.

There are three significant boundaries associated with rice culture in Japan. The first, in extreme northern and eastern Hokkaido, marks the northern limits of its cultivation (Fig. 95). Very little of Japan Proper lies beyond this boundary. At about latitude 37° in northern Honshu, slightly south of Sendai, a second line may be drawn, separating one-crop paddies to the north from the numerous two-crop paddies to the south (Fig. 95). Of the seven prefectures of northern Honshu north of this

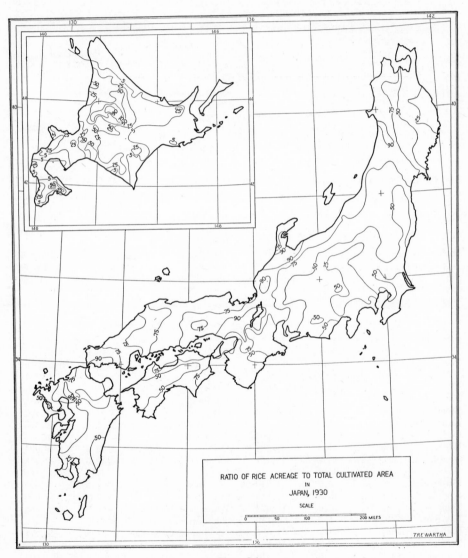

RATIO OF RICE ACREAGE TO TOTAL CULTIVATED AREA
IN
JAPAN, 1930
SCALE

TREWARTHA

Fig. 94

boundary, five have coefficients of double cropping (crop area ÷ cultivated area) of less than one; in the two southernmost, Niigata and Fukushima, they are 1.024 and 1.042, indicating only a slight amount of winter cropping of the rice fields (Fig. 89). In northern Honshu and most of Hokkaido the general absence of winter crops in the paddies is indicated by the low per-tan value of paddy field products as compared with Japan as a whole. Thus whereas the average per-tan value for the country as a

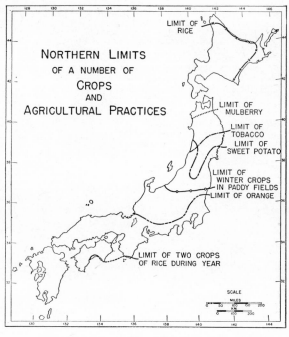

NORTHERN LIMITS
OF A NUMBER OF
CROPS
AND
AGRICULTURAL PRACTICES

LIMIT OF RICE

LIMIT OF MULBERRY

LIMIT OF TOBACCO

LIMIT OF SWEET POTATO

LIMIT OF WINTER CROPS IN PADDY FIELDS

LIMIT OF ORANGE

LIMIT OF TWO CROPS OF RICE DURING YEAR

SCALE
MILES
0   50   100   150   200
KM.
0   100   200

FIG. 95

whole is 47.02 yen, the comparable figures for the northern prefectures are as follows: Hokkaido 19.91 yen, Aomori 20.34, Iwate 22.28, Miyagi 28.87, Akita 34.00, Yamagata 29.18, and Fukushima 30.09.[27] Not only are winter crops in paddies generally lacking, but even the summer rice crop is less bountiful than in regions farther south. The average yield per tan (.245 acres) of rice for Japan Proper is about 1.843 koku; the comparable figure for Hokkaido is 0.871 and for Aomori Prefecture 1.237.[28] In the six prefectures of Tohoku district in northern Honshu, only 13,200 cho of a total of 621,000 cho in paddy fields was replanted to wheat and barley in 1939, and only 12,800 cho to green manure crops.[29] In the larger part of Japan south of about the 37° parallel not nearly all the rice fields have winter crops, for reasons before mentioned, but at least the planting of another irrigated or a dry crop in the paddy fields after rice harvest is a common practice.

The third boundary is located in the region of the Kochi Plain in southern Shikoku and in a small portion of southernmost Kii Peninsula. These are the only regions in Japan where two crops of rice are grown during the

[27] Nasu, *op. cit.*, 101.   [28] *Ibid.*, 108a.   [29] *Ibid.*, 94.

FIG. 96. A small mountain-girt alluvial plain covered with irregular paddy fields. The rural *buraku* has almost the appearance of an island.

FIG. 97. Beds of rice seedlings ready for transplanting.

annual cycle. Nearly all of Japan is too cool in winter to permit the growing of a second rice crop.

There is a fairly high degree of coincidence between irrigated rice and the low, gently sloping alluvial plains.[30] Some rice is grown on the smooth but sloping depositional surfaces of diluvial uplands and on the terraced lower slopes of hardrock hills, but these upland sites are less suitable to a crop requiring not only irrigation but months of inundation, and consequently they have more often been devoted to dry crops or left in wild grasses and shrubs. A large part (65.4 per cent) of the irrigation water for Japan's paddies is obtained from rivers; about 21 per cent is supplied by reservoirs, often only small ponds.[31] Since the plains of Nippon are very restricted in area, irrigation canals are likewise small and hence comparatively inconspicuous. They are almost never used for transport purposes as they are in China.

On the flattish delta-fans multitudes of diminutive fields, usually irregular in outline, and each enclosed by tiny dikes a foot or more wide and of equal elevation, form a landscape which is a faceted mosaic in pattern, but rather uniform in coloration (Fig. 96). At certain locations on some of the plains one can gaze for a mile or more over continuous expanses of paddy fields whose monotony is virtually unbroken, but this is the exception rather than the rule. More frequently the expanse is interrupted by villages, sometimes tree- or hedge-enclosed, rising like islands above the inundated paddies, and by the elevated footpaths and roads which traverse the plains, usually in straight-line courses. Here and there intersecting irrigation and drainage canals and ponds add a note of variation, and in some places scattered dry fields, artificially elevated two feet or more above the paddies, stand out conspicuously above the lower story of rice fields. On the sandy and elevated beach ridges which commonly border the sea margins of the delta-plains, as well as on the river dikes, paddies usually give way to dry fields. Not infrequently there are riverine belts, where laterally migrating streams have somewhat roughened the surface and deposited coarser materials. In such locations also, unirrigated fields often predominate.

The march of the seasons produces a striking succession of contrasting landscapes on these delta-plains. Spring witnesses the preparation and

[30] Only 4 per cent of the total area in rice is planted to the unirrigated upland variety.

[31] P. J. S. Cramer, "Notes on Agriculture in Japan Gathered during a Voyage in 1924," in *Communications of the General Experiment Station in Agriculture,* No. 22 (Department of Agriculture, Industry, and Commerce in the Netherlands East Indies, 1926), 31.

FIG. 98. A representative peasant
farmer of Nippon.

sowing of the rice seedbeds, which by May or June have become conspicuous green patches on what, in some parts of Japan, may be prevailingly fallow plains (Fig. 97). This practice of starting the rice in seedbeds and about two months later transplanting the seedlings to the larger paddy fields reflects the necessity for conserving the scarce factor of production—arable land. In the spring much paddy land still has on it a winter crop of wheat, barley, rape, or green-manure legumes which may not be harvested until late May or June. April, May, and June, moreover, are especially busy months for farmers, and the schedule of agricultural operations is a very tight one. The work schedule would be badly disarranged if rice were not first sown in seedbeds in April and then transplanted in June after the winter grains are harvested.

In early summer, with the transplanting of the young rice seedlings to the paddies, the flooded alluvial lowland becomes a much subdivided water surface pricked by the inconspicuous rice plants (Figs. 99–101). By midsummer the scene has changed; lush green is the prevailing color over large expanses of the plain, although the boundaries of the individual fields are still obvious, being set off from one another by the interruptions at the dikes (Fig. 102). As green changes to yellow in autumn and the ripened grain is harvested, the fields swarm with human beings engaged in cutting and threshing the precious crop (Fig. 103). Autumn is a season of great anxiety, for September and October are the typhoon months, and the heavy rain and wind that accompany the storms may do great damage to the ripening rice heavy with seed. Most of the rice is harvested in late October and November.

About 62.5 per cent of the paddy area of Japan remains fallow and unused during the winter season, much of it covered with water (Fig. 105). In other words, only 1.2 million of the 3.2 million cho in rice are planted to subsidiary second crops.[32] However, some 800,000 of the

[32] Nasu, *op. cit.*, 94, 100.

FIG. 99. Pulling up rice seedlings from seedbed preparatory
to transplanting them.

FIG. 100. Transplanting the rice seedlings to the paddy field
early in summer.

Fig. 101. Pushing the weeds under in a paddy field. Photograph by John Embree.
Fig. 102. Paddy fields in midsummer, when the rice is higher than the field dikes.

remaining 2 million cho not replanted to a second crop are in Hokkaido and the six northern prefectures of Honshu, where for climatic reasons second crops are impossible or at least unprofitable. In those subtropical parts of Japan south of about latitude 37°, where winter planting is possible, some 40 per cent of the rice fields are not planted a second time, largely because they cannot be properly drained and thus made fit for unirrigated crops. Barley and wheat occupy about 21 per cent of the total paddy area in winter, the proportions being highest in Kyushu and Shikoku and decreasing northward. Green manure crops, which occupy

Total area of paddy fields .... ±3,200,000 cho
  One-crop paddy fields .... ±2,000,000 cho (62.5 per cent)
    For climatic reasons .... 800,000 cho
    For drainage and other causes .... 1,200,000 cho

  Two-crop paddy fields .... ±1,200,000 cho (37.5 per cent)
    Wheat and barley .... 21 per cent
    Green manure crops ..... 14 per cent
    Rape, rushes, vegetables .. 2.5 per cent

FIG. 103. Harvesting rice. Cutting is being done with a hand sickle.

FIG. 104. Rice straw stacked in paddy fields from which the grain has been harvested.

FIG. 105. Poorly drained fallow rice fields in winter.

14 per cent of the rice fields in winter, reach their maximum development in central Honshu and decline in the more southern provinces. In other words, wheat and barley are areally complementary to *genge* (a pink-blossomed legume) and other green manure crops in the winter rice fields. Rape, rush of a kind used for making mats, and some vegetables are also planted as subsidiary crops in paddy lands, but their total area is small.

If the fields are to be fall-planted their surfaces are spaded up into a series of narrow parallel ridges and troughs, the former twelve to eighteen inches wide and perhaps six to twelve inches high, and on the ridges grain is sown very thickly in single or double rows (Figs. 106, 107). The practice of "ridging" for winter crops is quite essential, for the cool-season precipitation tends to make many of the planted paddies fairly wet. It is not uncommon to see water standing several inches deep in the troughs between the rows of grain or rape. The planted sections of the delta-plains are never more colorful than in late spring, when the dark green patches of winter grain in rows are intermingled with plots of brilliant yellow rape and bright-pink *genge*. Other advantages of ridging the paddy fields before planting them in winter crops in rows are that (1) the fields may be weeded by hoeing; (2) the furrows or troughs are kept clear so that other crops can be intercultured between the ridges in the spring; (3) the cultivator can walk between the rows of winter grain and apply liquid fertilizer at the base of the plant; and (4) sidewise tillering and spreading of the grain is prevented. Usually the winter grain is sown in clumps along the top of the ridge rather than spaced evenly and continuously. The Japanese believe that this helps to prevent lodging and that the grain is less likely to be beaten down by heavy wind and rain.[33]

Near cities the paddy lands are likely to get little or no rest between the major summer crop of rice and the winter crop of cereals. For example, immediately after the rice harvest a field may be ridged and a quick-maturing crop, such as the giant radish (daikon) planted on the ridges and eggplant along the bottoms of the furrows. To give them a head start these vegetables may have been sown earlier in seedbeds and the young plants subsequently transplanted to the paddy fields. Usually the daikon is mature before the eggplant interferes. After the daikon is harvested winter grain is planted on the ridge tops. The eggplant is pulled when it begins to interfere with the growing grain. In the spring

[33] Carl L. Alsberg, "Japanese Self-Sufficiency in Wheat," in *Wheat Studies*, 12:62 (November, 1935).

a quick-maturing crop, such as dwarf taro, cucumbers, or seedling melons may be planted in the troughs between the rows of young grain. The vegetables are somewhat shaded by the grain, to be sure, but they struggle up-

ward for light and finally, after the grain harvest, have the field to themselves until the time comes to relevel the field and transplant rice seedlings on it. *Genge*, rape, and millet compete to some extent with wheat and barley for the available rice land in winter.

Rice is something of a problem child in Japan. It is the almost universal food and is

FIG. 106. A field ridged for winter planting.

FIG. 107. Ridged paddy fields with rows of winter cereals and rape.

eaten three times a day by all Japanese except those who cannot afford it. Those who eat any other cereal, barley for example, do so only under compulsion. Yet the violent and unusual fluctuations in rice yield which result from variations in weather has obliged the government to intervene and attempt to stabilize rice prices by storing a portion of the crop in bountiful years and releasing stored rice in lean years. If the government had not taken this precaution, social and political hardships would have been much greater, and it would have been necessary to spend large sums to relieve acute distress.

Another indictment of domestic rice is that it is a high-cost product which can be imported more economically from Korea, Formosa, and especially southeastern Asia, where natural and labor conditions permit of cheaper production. For this reason some have advocated that the rice area in Japan Proper be reduced and more rice imported, and that greater emphasis be placed on such high-grade products as stock and poultry, tree crops of fruits and nuts, flowers, vegetables, and seeds. One objection to such an expansion of these unirrigated crops at the expense of rice is that not all of the land which is unprofitable for rice can be used for a variety of other crops. Domestic rice could no doubt be produced more economically if cooperative farming became more widespread, but this would be followed by large-scale unemployment in the rural villages and towns. To meet this anticipated complication some have advocated a great increase in village industries. But reduction of rice acreage in Japan Proper is chiefly obstructed by the work of powerful pressure groups such as the Army, the agricultural interests as represented by the Imperial Agricultural Society, and self-styled "patriotic" organizations which insist that an approximation of self-sufficiency in respect to rice is a necessary defense measure. This again is evidence of the irreconcilable conflict between economic and political objectives in Japan, "between the measures necessary to produce an adequate supply of goods and services to meet the essential needs of the people and the measures necessary to make the nation as powerful in war as other leading nations are. These two objectives cannot both be attained."[34]

UPLAND FIELDS AND UNIRRIGATED CROPS

The Japanese recognize two major subdivisions of farm land: paddy land, which is irrigated, and upland fields, which depend upon the natural rainfall for their water supply. In 1939 the area in upland farms or dry fields was about 2.87 million cho, as compared with 3.20 million

[34] Schumpeter et al., 149.

cho in paddy fields, the ratio being 43.5 to 56.5.[35] But the area in upland fields is by no means identical with the sum of the net areas in various unirrigated crops. The discrepancy is due to (1) the replanting of 35–40 per cent of the paddy land in unirrigated winter crops and (2) the multiple cropping of upland fields, part of this by interculture methods. From Table 75 the total area in dry crops can be computed at approximately 4.92 million cho.[36] Since 2.87 million cho are in upland fields, and 3.20 million cho in paddy rice, it is clear that the area in dry crops greatly exceeds that in irrigated rice, although the total area of paddy land is greater than that of upland fields.

The Small Grains.—Wheat, barley, naked barley, and oats, the combined acreage of which in 1939 was 51 per cent of that in irrigated rice, are grown under three contrasting conditions involving locational and planting differences: (1) in Hokkaido almost exclusively as spring-sown crops on upland fields; in Old Japan as fall-sown crops, (2) either as a second crop in paddy fields following the autumn rice harvest or (3) following legumes, vegetables, and other summer crops on upland fields. In the extreme northern part of Honshu the small grains are both spring- and fall-sown. Oats is almost exclusively confined to Hokkaido, where it is a spring-sown crop (Fig. 108). It is used primarily as a feed for livestock. Barley, naked barley,[37] and wheat are primarily food crops for human beings, only 10–20 per cent being fed to animals. The two barleys are consumed largely in the form of whole grain, cracked grain, and coarse meal in a mixture with rice. More than 70 per cent of the wheat crop is manufactured into flour, and nearly 21 per cent is used in the manufacture of soy sauce.[38] Japanese wheat is a soft red winter wheat characteristically starchy rather than glutenous. Two other cereals, millet and upland rice, both much less important than either wheat or the barleys, are used in a minor way for human food. Millet is a winter crop in both paddy fields and on the uplands of subtropical Japan, whereas in the north it is spring-sown on upland fields.

The two barleys are regionally complementary, naked barley being concentrated in southern Japan and little grown north of Nagoya, whereas common barley is more important in central and northern Japan and is

[35] *Norinsho Tokeihyo,* 1939.

[36] This takes no account of the small acreage of irrigated crops other than irrigated rice, such as rushes, water chestnut, etc.

[37] Naked barley is a true barley. If differs from ordinary barley chiefly in that the chaffy scales that enclose the kernel are not fused to the seed, so that the latter is readily freed from the scales. In ordinary barley a special hulling operation is necessary to free the seed.

[38] Alsberg, *op. cit.,* 78.

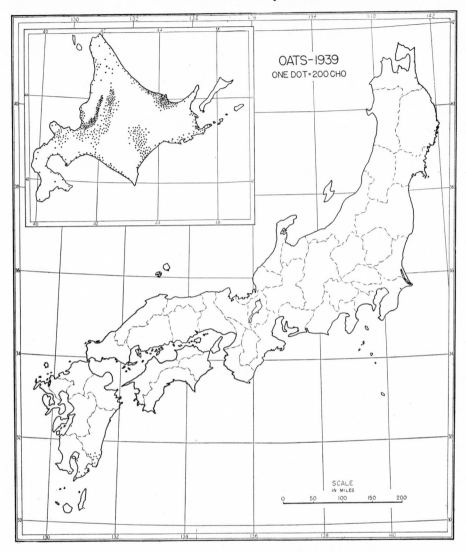

OATS-1939
ONE DOT=200 CHO

SCALE
IN MILES
0   50   100   150   200

FIG. 108. Oats reaches its maximum importance in Hokkaido.

little grown south of Nagoya (Figs. 109, 110). Strangely enough, however, considering this latitudinal distribution in Old Japan, naked barley exceeds common barley in Hokkaido. Another difference is that although both are grown in paddy fields as well as on upland fields, 70 per cent of the common barley is raised on upland farms and over 60 per cent of the naked barley is grown on paddy lands.

Wheat is more widely distributed than either of the barleys and hence

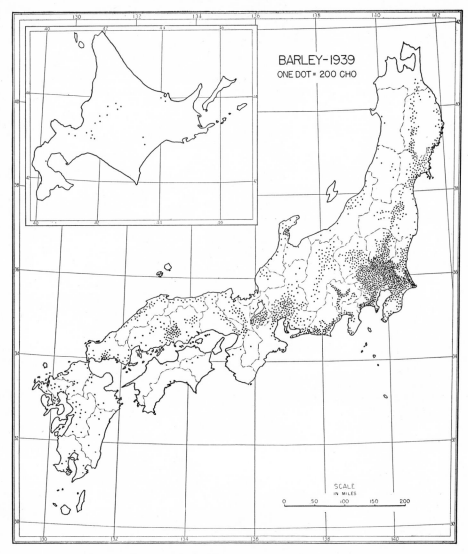

FIG. 109. Barley is more important in central and northern Japan.

competes for land with naked barley in the south and with common barley in the north (Fig. 111). The wheat crop is nearly equally divided between upland fields and paddies. Barley, because of its shorter maturing period, has some advantages over wheat in Japan's northern sections. Wheat, taking longer to mature, makes the land late for rice in summer, leaves less time in spring for the growth of quick-maturing vegetables between the harvesting of the winter crop and the time of rice planting.

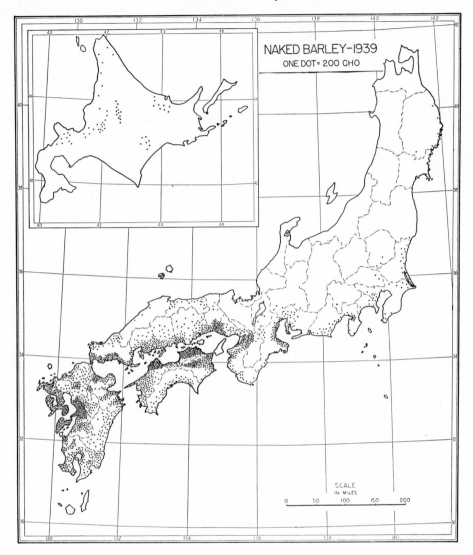

Fig. 110. Naked barley is principally concentrated in southwestern Japan.

and is more likely to be injured by the humidity of the *bai-u* season.[39] In addition its ranker growth causes it to shade the intercultured crops more completely. None of the unirrigated small grains is important in northwestern Honshu, where the heavy and long-continued snow cover makes winter cropping very difficult.

[39] W. Y. Swen and Carl L. Alsberg, "Japan as a Producer and Importer of Wheat," in *Wheat Studies,* 6:351–369 (July, 1930).

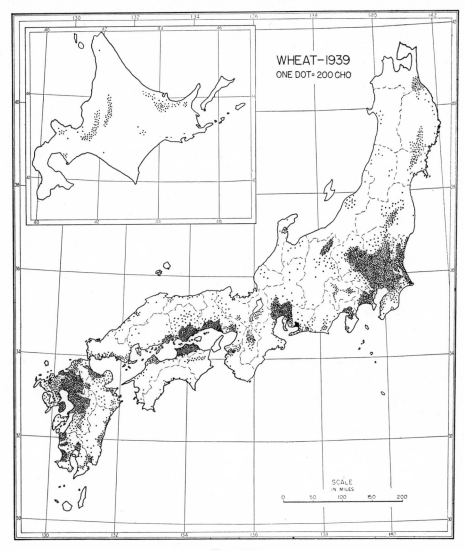

WHEAT—1939
ONE DOT= 200 CHO

SCALE
IN MILES

FIG. 111

At the present time the acreage of wheat is approximately equal to the combined acreage of the two barleys. As Table 78 shows, the barleys have been declining in importance, whereas wheat acreage has been rapidly increasing. This was the normal trend even before 1932, but thereafter it was greatly accelerated as the government instituted its five-year program for making Japan self-sufficient in respect to this cereal. This was undertaken as a war-preparation measure and its success was almost phenomenal, for with the greatly increased production of 1934 the country became almost self-sufficient. Since the area in wheat has increased nearly 100,000 cho since then, it is probable that by the close of the thirties Japan had become a wheat exporter. The increase in wheat acreage was partly accomplished by taking over land abandoned by barley, partly by winter-cropping more paddies. No doubt, also, some of the 130,000 cho reduction in mulberry acreage since 1930 has become wheat land.

Vegetables.—Next to rice, vegetables (including beans and potatoes) are the most important class of foodstuffs for the Japanese people. Nevertheless their diet is seriously lacking in vegetables, fruit, and animal foodstuffs and greatly overweighted with cereals. From the standpoint of human nutrition, cereals are deficient in mineral salts, certain proteins, and many of the vitamins. Thus the diets of most Japanese people are seriously deficient in many respects. The hopeful feature is that as a crop group vegetables have been greatly expanded in area since World War I. In the seventeen years between 1922 and 1939 the total area planted to vegetables increased from 500,000 cho to nearly 587,000 cho, or about 17 per cent. The increase has been very uneven, to be sure; some, like taro, carrots, and turnips, have barely kept pace with population growth, whereas others, like watermelons, onions, cabbages, cucumbers, and tomatoes have expanded remarkably. Except for potatoes and other tuber and root crops, the production and consumption of fresh vegetables has expanded much more rapidly than the population in the last two decades.

As might be expected, vegetable growing is widespread throughout Japan. The greatest concentrations of commercial gardening are in those prefectures which contain, or are close to, the great cities. Since the increase in population during the past few decades has taken place almost exclusively in the cities, it is to be expected that the rapid

Fig. 112. Terraced vegetable fields on the floor and flanks of a valley cut in diluvium.

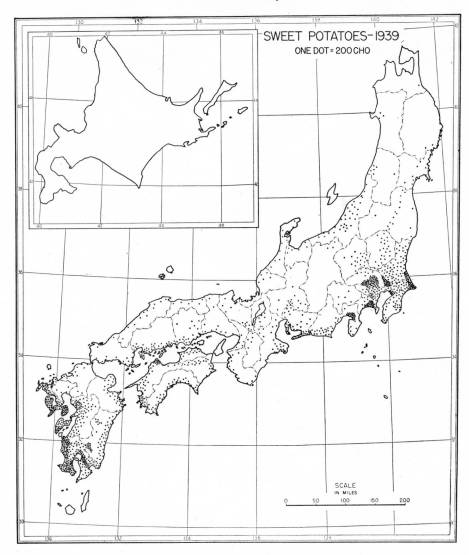

SWEET POTATOES—1939
ONE DOT = 200 CHO

SCALE
IN MILES
0   50   100   150   200

FIG. 113

expansion of vegetable gardening has likewise taken place in urban environs. On the whole, however, vegetable growing is mainly for local markets, the two chief exceptions being the Tokyo-Yokohama and Osaka-Kobe central markets, which draw from distant as well as local areas. The lack of a cold-storage system is the most serious handicap to the shipment of perishable vegetables and hence to the development of outstanding market-gardening centers.

By far the most important of the individual vegetables, in terms of value, is the sweet potato, which is widely distributed (Fig. 113). It is very unimportant in northern Honshu, however, and in Hokkaido the crop is lacking. White potatoes, on the other hand, reach their maximum development in Hokkaido and northern Honshu, the former having over half the country's acreage planted to this vegetable. The crop is much less important in subtropical Japan. Beans of various kinds, which, taken together, comprise the most important vegetable group of Japan, are also concentrated in Hokkaido. Peas have the same distribution. (See Table 79 on page 215 for the relative importance of other vegetables.)

Most of the vegetables are raised on upland fields. On these fields it is common practice to raise several crops of summer vegetables by inter-culture methods and to follow these with fall-sown cereals. The agricultural practices are much the same as those which have been described for the paddy lands, except that unirrigated crops, chiefly vegetables, take the place of the summer rice.

Fruits.—Japanese reports do not give the areas planted to fruits only the number of trees and the quantity and value of the crop. These data clearly reveal, however, that the increase in production of fruits has been only slightly less than that of vegetables. Most of them are grown on upland fields, the Japanese pear being the only important fruit commonly located on the wet lowlands.

Most important of all the fruits is the orange, the crop value of which

TABLE 80.—ORCHARDS AND FRUIT PRODUCTION, 1939

Fruit	Trees (in thousands)	Quantity (in thousands of kwan*)	Value (in thousands of yen)
Plum	5,960	421.7	8,302.3
Peach	4,991	12,381.6	6,741.2
Cherry.	428	1,306.2	1,352.2
Loquat	2,279	5,214.6	3,746.3
Pear (Japanese).	8,059	44,202.8	19,849.4
Pear (Western)	335	1,236.5	775.2
Apple	4,553	55,944.6	32,246.7
Persimmon.	18,302	70,905.9	20,231.8
Grapes.	5,651	15,860.4	9,243.0
Mandarin orange	28,506	123,571.8	44,106.5
Navel orange	1,708	5,212.2	2,684.4
Bitter orange	3,926	19,072.5	5,185.4
Other oranges.	2,414	6,222.8	1,994.8
Total			156,459.2

Source: *Norinsho Tokeihyo*, 1939.
* One kwan=8.27 pounds.

is 46 per cent of the total for all fruits. The northern limit of citrus fruits in Japan is about the 37° parallel, and much the larger part of the crop is raised south of Tokyo (Figs. 95, 114). The greatest concentration is on the Pacific coast of Japan in Shizuoka Prefecture and along the borders of the Inland Sea. The characteristic sites are the steep hillside slopes. The chief variety is the Mandarin or Satsuma orange. Of much less im-

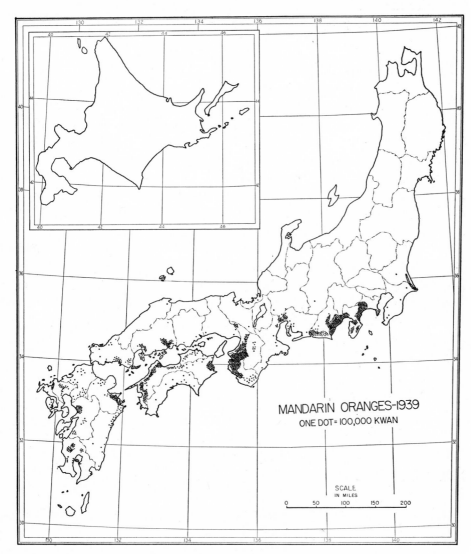

MANDARIN ORANGES—1939
ONE DOT = 100,000 KWAN

SCALE
IN MILES
0   50   100   150   200

FIG. 114. The orange crop is produced chiefly on the Pacific side of subtropical southwestern Japan, south of latitude 36°.

portance are navel oranges and the *natsu mikan* or bitter orange, which resembles grapefruit in tartness and flavor. Next to the citrus fruit in value is the apple crop, which is markedly concentrated in northern Japan, especially in Aomori Prefecture in the vicinity of Hirosaki, where nearly 64 per cent of the apple orchards are located, and in Hokkaido. Persimmons, Japanese pears, grapes, plums, and peaches follow apples in the order named.

In concluding this discussion of Japan's principal food crops it may be well to point out that despite the rapid increase in population the per capita available food supply from domestic and colonial sources has increased in quantity and quality. By increasing imports of rice the per capita consumption of this staple article of the Japanese diet has been maintained at a fairly uniform level for twenty-five years. The same is true for other cereals. The rate of consumption of fruits and vegetables has far surpassed the growth in population. There is no reason, therefore, to believe that the greatly augmented number of people has dangerously reduced the food supply. This is not to say that the Japanese people are properly nourished, for there are serious defects in the diets of the great mass of the population.

Industrial Crops.—The list of these is a long one, but they do not make a very impressive showing, as regards either area occupied or total value. Their total acreage is less than that of either common barley or soybeans, and their value is about the same as that of the barley crop. What this means is that Japan's farmers are primarily engaged in producing food and that agricultural raw materials required by industry are chiefly imported from abroad.

Most important by far of all the industrial crops, so far as value is concerned, is tobacco. It is not entirely lacking in any part of the country except Hokkaido, although 40–50 per cent of the crop is raised in four prefectures. The major concentration is in northern Kwanto and the adjacent Abukuma Lowland, and the second in far southern Kyushu in Kagoshima Prefecture. Rape, the oil of which is used both for cooking and for industrial purposes, hemp, flax, reeds and rushes, from which *tatami* or floor mats are woven, pyrethrum, peppermint, sugar cane, and fiber crops for the manufacture of native paper are among the other more important industrial crops. Rape growing is widespread; hemp is chiefly concentrated in northern Kwanto; flax is almost exclusively a Hokkaido crop, as are pyrethrum and peppermint; reeds and rushes are grown largely in Okayama and Hiroshima prefectures along the shores of the Inland Sea; and sugar cane is a special crop in far southern Kyushu.

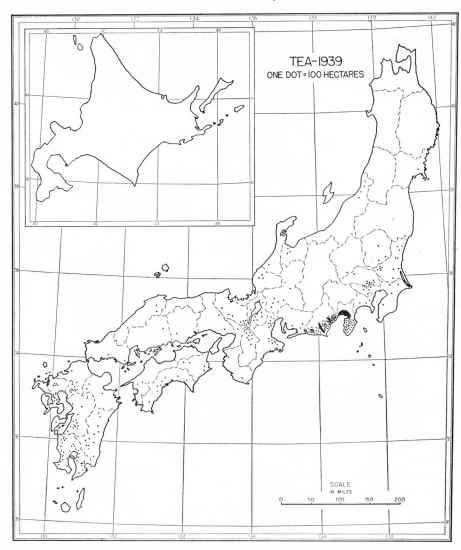

FIG. 115. Although tea is grown widely over much of central and southwestern Japan, the area of greatest concentration is in Shizuoka Prefecture at about latitude 35°.

Tea.—From 1920 to 1939 the area in tea gardens in Japan declined from a little over 48,000 cho to 40,400 cho, though in the same period the quantity of tea produced increased from 9.64 million kwan[40] to 15.33 million kwan, an increase of nearly 59 per cent. Because tea is so universal a drink among the Japanese its importance in the country's agriculture is generally overrated. Actually the area in tea gardens is less than

[40] 1 kwan = 8.267 pounds.

one per cent of the total net area in dry crops; it is less than that of so minor a crop as buckwheat, and only one-thirteenth of the mulberry area. Like China, Japan grows its tea on small patches or gardens, usually a quarter of an acre to an acre in size, rather than on large estates as in tropical South Asia. Unlike much of China's crop, however, Japan's tea gardens are well cared for and scientifically managed, with the result that the bulk of the crop is of moderate quality. About one-third of Japan's crop, which is largely green tea, is exported, chiefly to the United States

Fig. 116. Tea gardens on steep hill slopes in Shizuoka Prefecture. The rows of tea are planted at right angles to the slope.

and Canada. Most of the export is from Shizuoka Prefecture on the Pacific side of the country midway between Kwanto and Kinki.

Tea is a subtropical crop and is not grown in such regions as Hokkaido and northern Ou. In fact, very little is raised north of latitude 37°. About 40 per cent of the nation's crop is grown in Shizuoka Prefecture. Other large concentrations are to be found on the Tokyo Plain, in the general regions of Kyoto and Nagoya, and in southern Kyushu (Fig. 115). However, it is grown widely throughout most parts of southwestern Japan. Nearly all the important producing areas are on the Pacific side of the country. But even in subtropical Japan the tea bush is dormant for a considerable part of the year, so three or four pickings are the most that can be expected. This is in contrast to the much more numerous pickings

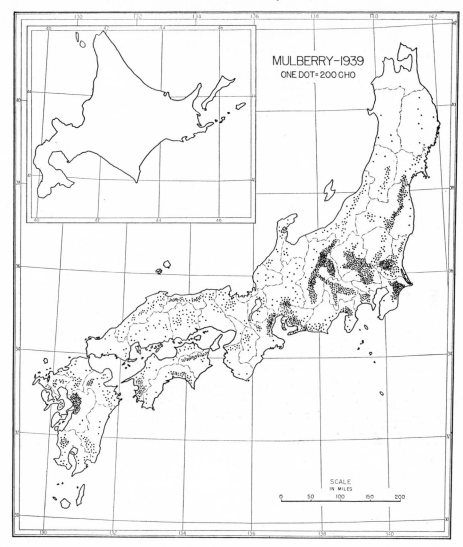

Fig. 117. Mulberry is unimportant north of about latitude 39°. It is a highly specialized crop in the basins of the Fossa Magna in central Japan, on the Kwanto Plain, and in the region around Ise Bay.

in Java, Ceylon, and other parts of tropical southern Asia, where there is no long dormant period.

About three-fourths of Japan's tea crop is raised on upland fields. The rest is grown in and around the villages in the vicinity of the farmstead for family consumption. For the most part tea does not compete with rice for the low, easily inundated land. Characteristically it occupies

FIG. 118. The silkworms are kept on bamboo trays, where they
are fed on mulberry leaves.

mountain foothills and diluvial upland sites, where there is adequate
drainage despite the heavy summer rainfall. Tea is sometimes planted,
with only very crude terracing, on slopes of 20°–30° inclination, for on
such sites the closely planted tea hedges oriented at right angles to the
slope minimize the dangers of soil erosion (Fig. 116).[41]

Mulberry, the exclusive food of silkworms, is by all odds the most
important non-food crop of Japan, occupying nearly 9 per cent of the
total cultivated area of the country. Only two other crops, rice and wheat,
exceed it in total acreage, and it ranks next to rice in value. This importance of mulberry reflects the unusual position of raw silk in the
agricultural economy of Japan. As late as 1931 over 2.21 million, or 40
per cent, of the 5.63 million Japanese farm families raised silkworms,
although by 1939 the ratio had been reduced to 30 per cent.

Mulberry is grown in all parts of the country except Hokkaido and
Aomori Prefecture in northernmost Honshu, where the more severe
climate and the sparser population make the silk industry unprofitable.
The 39° parallel is approximately the northern limit of important mulberry growing (Fig. 95). In subtropical Japan there is a marked concen-

[41] For more detailed accounts of tea in Japan see Glenn T. Trewartha, "The Tea
Crop," in the *Journal of Geography*, 18:19–24 (January, 1929), and "A Geographic
Study of Shizuoka Prefecture, Japan," in *Annals of the Association of American
Geographers*, 18:202–209 (September, 1928).

tration of mulberry growing and all other phases of the silk industry in central Honshu. This general region includes three highly specialized subregions: (1) the mountain basins along the Fossa Magna in Nagano and Yamanashi prefectures; (2) the western part of the Kwanto or Tokyo Plain; and (3) the lowlands and slopes bordering Ise Bay in Aichi Prefecture (Fig. 117). In some parts of these subdistricts the raising of silkworms is no longer an adjunct to general farming but is itself the chief agricultural interest.

Since mulberry does not require irrigation and is soil-tolerant, it is primarily a crop of the uplands. The most extensive and contiguous areas of mulberry are to be found on (1) the lower mountain foothills and (2) the diluvial terraces, ash plateaus, and steeply sloping, coarse-textured alluvial and diluvial fans. Other common, though less extensive, dry sites for mulberry are (1) the elevated sandy beach ridges along the sea margins of delta-plains and (2) the river levees and embankments. On some plains it is grown on artificially elevated patches among the rice fields.

The Japanese mulberry is predominantly of the bush type, although at the higher altitudes and in northern Honshu the hardier tree variety is grown to some extent. The bush mulberry is planted at about two-foot intervals in rows spaced three to four and one-half feet apart. It is cut off level with the ground each year, and the next year six to twelve shoots spring up, which reach heights of four to six feet.

Except for two brief periods the farmers of Japan are continuously engaged in rearing silkworms from about the middle of April until the end of October. They buy their silkworm eggs from registered dealers, whose product is carefully supervised by the government. The worms

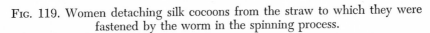

FIG. 119. Women detaching silk cocoons from the straw to which they were fastened by the worm in the spinning process.

are reared in farm homes, all possible space being given over to the work. Most of the farmers cut off whole branches of the mulberry bush with the leaves attached and put them in the trays with the silkworms. Some strip off the leaves before feeding. After the worms have formed their cocoons the farmer carts his product to the cocoon market, where he receives cash for his crop. There are three main crops of silkworms and cocoons—spring, summer, and autumn—although worms are fed almost continuously from mid-April to late October.[42]

The Japanese silk industry is extremely vulnerable, first, because over half the product is marketed abroad, and second, because the export is largely concentrated in one market, the United States. During the depression of the 1930's, several million Japanese farm families engaged in raising silkworms and depending upon the sale of cocoons for their chief source of cash income were severely affected by the great decline in silk prices. The financial, social, and political repercussions were of national scope.

In the latter part of the thirties the competition of other fibers, such as rayon and staple fiber, decreased silk exports and further aggravated the silk farmers' difficulties. Mulberry fields which in 1930 occupied 515,820 cho, had declined by 1939 to 383,998 cho. With President Roosevelt's executive order of July 25, 1941, freezing Japanese assets in the United States, trade relations between this country and Japan were completely halted. One can only surmise what the effect of this has been upon 30 to 40 per cent of the farm families of Nippon. Moreover, the strides that have been made in synthetic silk-substitute fibers, such as nylon, will no doubt greatly reduce the foreign market for raw silk in the post-war period. It is difficult to see at the present time what can take the place of raw silk as a source of cash income for the Japanese farmers.[43]

Animal Industries

Despite the abundance of rough land whose slopes are too steep for normal cultivation, Japan is conspicuously underdeveloped with respect to animal industries. The absence of herds and flocks strikes one as anoma-

---

[42] For a more detailed account of the silk industry, especially as it has been developed in the specialized subregion of the Fossa Magna basins of central Honshu, see Glenn T. Trewartha, "The Suwa Basin: A Specialized Sericulture District in the Japanese Alps," in the *Geographical Review*, 20:224–244 (April, 1930).

[43] W. I. Ladejinsky, "Japanese Silk Industry Faces a New Crisis," in *Foreign Agriculture*, 5:515–534 (December, 1941).

lous, for grazing is a specialty in many middle-latitude regions of the world that have a rugged terrain. Animal husbandry is unpopular in Japan, and what little has been developed is carried out on a very small scale, typically not more than one animal per household. The raising of livestock on a large scale by individual farmers may be impracticable over most of Japan, where the situation lends itself better to a communal type of development with a cow or two to a family.

The Japanese explain their neglect of the animal industries on grounds of both environmental and economic handicaps. Some of the slopes are too steep for the grazing of cattle. Of much greater importance, and probably the greatest of all physical factors, is the lack of good natural pasture land, for the native wild grasses of the hill lands are harsh, coarse, unnutritious, and extremely difficult to eradicate. Moreover, the sub-tropical climate of most of Japan is a handicap in the cultivation of a majority of the well known tame grasses. There seems to be considerable

TABLE 81.—NUMBER OF FARMING FAMILIES KEEPING DOMESTIC ANIMALS

Animal	1 Head	2 Head	3–4 Head	5+ Head	Total
Cattle (1939)	1,279,373	188,097	50,529	13,321	1,531,320
Hogs (1939)	377,867	130,628	45,273	22,470	576,238
Horses (1935).	937,305	123,792	40,312	10,745	1,112,154

Sources: *Norinsho Tokeihyo*, 1939, for data on cattle and hogs; Nasu, *op. cit.*, 45, for data on horses.

TABLE 82.—CATTLE AND MILK PRODUCTION

Year	Total	Milk Cows	Cattle Slaughtered	Milk Produced (in hectoliters*)
1929	1,488,240	72,281	329,004	902,177
1939	1,967,214	122,911	407,589	1,922,312

Source: *Norinsho Tokeihyo*, 1939.   * 1 hectoliter=21.417 gal.

TABLE 83.—DATA ON THE LIVESTOCK INDUSTRY IN JAPAN
(all data in thousands)

Number of	1929	1939	Number of	1929	1939
Families owning cattle	1,208	1,531	Head of sheep	20.7	149
Head of cattle	1,488	1,967	Head of goats	215.4	286.7
Families keeping pigs	393	576	Head of rabbits	———	6,604
Head of pigs	706	1,070	Head of horses	1,490	1,432†

Source: *Norinsho Tokeihyo*, 1936 and 1939, as quoted in Grajdanzev, *Statistics of Japanese Agriculture*, 26.
† For 1932.

difference of opinion respecting the possibilities of improving the hill pastures of Japan. Before an impartial verdict can be given, the nutritive value of the native wild grasses and their replacement by more valuable tame varieties need to be considered. Sheep raising in most of Japan is also handicapped by the long, hot, humid summers, as is dairying.

Besides these physical handicaps there are others of an economic nature. Much of the mountain country is owned by absentee capitalists who are loath to permit its utilization except for a fee that discourages animal raising. Furthermore, the outlay of capital and labor needed to buy animals and open up forest land for grazing is a deterrent to most Japanese farmers, for as a group they are poor and without a capital surplus. These are handicaps that can in a measure be remedied through government intervention. Dairying, however, is retarded by another factor, the extremely limited domestic market for milk and milk products. The Japanese have never acquired a taste for dairy products, and few farmers own cows, either to supply their own needs or those of a commercial market. The abundant supply of fish, and the fact that the Buddhist faith discourages the killing of animals militates against rapid increase of meat in the Japanese diet.

Cattle, like horses, are raised chiefly as draft animals. Only about 2.6 million of the 5.5 million farm households in Japan have one or more cattle or horses, which of course means that nearly half of the Japanese farmers have no animal power on their farms. Over 80 per cent of the farm families who do own cattle have only a single head. Between 70 and 80 per cent of the cattle on Japanese farms are used as draft animals or are housed at the farmstead for the manure that can be collected. In 1939 the total number of cattle in Japan was slightly less than 2 million, of which only 123,000 were classed as milk cows and 408,000 were slaughtered.[44] Thirty-six per cent of the milk cows are in Hokkaido, which is the only part of Japan except the environs of large cities that can be said to have a dairy industry.

Though the number of cattle in Japan is slowly increasing, and milk cattle more rapidly than other types, the consumption of milk and meat in Japan is extraordinarily small, which creates a serious nutritional problem for large parts of the population, especially the children. For every quart of milk consumed in Japan, we in America consume 900; for every pound of meat eaten there, we eat 360. On the other hand, they eat five times as much fish as we do. By far the largest number of cattle are located in southwestern Japan, particularly to the west and southwest of

[44] *Norinsho Tokeihyo,* 1939.

Nagoya. The principal region of concentration is the borderlands of the Inland Sea and northern Kyushu.

For military reasons statistics on the number of horses in Japan have not been published since 1936, at which time there were only 1.43 million, or 0.26 horse per farm family. Horses and cattle are largely complementary in their regional distribution, for whereas cattle are more numerous in southwestern Japan, horses are the principal work animal of central and northern Japan. It is chiefly in Kyushu that horses and cattle occupy the same general regions. Except in Hokkaido Japanese horses are usually of small size. Some 45,000 horses are slaughtered annually to augment the nation's small meat supply.

Hogs are fewer than horses and only half as numerous as cattle, the average per farm family being only 0.17. This is in contrast to China, where hogs are relatively numerous. In view of their scavenger nature and the fact that they can be cheaply raised at the farmstead, this scarcity of swine in Japan is hard to understand. Sheep and goats are both very scarce. Poultry raising as an adjunct to general farming is modestly developed, there being on the average nine or ten fowl per farm family. The value of the eggs produced in 1938 was almost as great as the total value of all meat. Rabbits, a newcomer in the statistical reports, now number over 6 million and are increasing rapidly.

Fishing

It is difficult for an American to appreciate the extraordinary importance of fishing in the economy of the Japanese nation. In most countries fishing is looked upon as the poor relation of other much more important industries and is overshadowed by them. In Japan, on the other hand, it is a leading enterprise and is genuinely big business. The total value of the fish catch of Japan Proper (not the Empire) in 1939 was 402.8 million yen, and the value of fish manufactures 462.7 million yen, a total of 865.5 million yen. More than 20 per cent of the population is engaged in, or is directly or indirectly supported by fishing, a larger percentage than in any other nation.

Nippon is the world's greatest fishing nation, the annual catch in Japan Proper amounting to 20–25 per cent of the world's total; for the Japanese Empire the comparable figure is 30–40 per cent. Fish and fish products constitute the main animal food of the Japanese, being second only to rice in the nation's diet. The annual per capita consumption of fish in Japan is probably about 65 pounds, as compared with 22–26 pounds in Germany and about 44 pounds in Great Britain. On the other hand,

Germans consume an average of nearly 100 pounds of meat per capita, Englishmen about 130, and the Japanese only 4–5.[45] To Japan its fisheries are more than equivalent in importance to all the livestock industries of this country. In normal years marine products rank third in the Japanese export list, being exceeded only by raw silk and cotton yarns and piece goods. Of the 1.41 million persons engaged in fishing in 1939, 46 per cent were farmers and other persons who catch fish as a side occupation.

This unusual emphasis upon fishing in Japan is attributable to a number of conditions: (1) the dense population in conjunction with the meager natural resources of the country, which has no doubt turned the people toward the sea more than in better endowed countries; (2) the insular character of the country and its extraordinary length of coastline; (3) the peripheral concentration of the population on small plains fronting upon tidewater; (4) the fact that the Japanese, like all the Malayan or Indonesian people, are very fond of fish and in general prefer it to beef; and (5) most important, the existence of excellent fishing grounds in the waters off eastern Asia, where the converging warm and cold waters have attracted a great variety of marine life.

Along the eastern coast of Asia from the Bering Sea on the north almost to Australia on the south is one of the earth's richest fishing regions. Through 65 degrees of latitude in the northwestern Pacific, and east as far as the 180° meridian, the Japanese carry on their fishing operations, although they are most intensively developed in the vicinity of the home islands. Other peoples bordering these western Pacific waters fish their local grounds, but none have spread their operations so far afield as the Japanese. Except for the Japan Sea, which is relatively deep, most of the waters bordering eastern Asia from Taiwan to Kamchatka are shallow, and therefore favorable to the development of marine life. Even the coastal waters off the eastern side of Japan, where there is a sudden increase of depth, and a belt of continental shelf is either lacking altogether or is but poorly developed, are one of her richest fishing grounds. It is of greatest significance also that the waters around Nippon are regions where ocean currents from tropical and from polar latitudes converge (Fig. 21), for this too creates a favorable environment for fish. The areas of marked convergence, and therefore of the mixing of unlike waters, have the most abundant plankton and marine life. The greatest zone of such convergence and mixture of waters in the western Pacific extends from about latitude 37° off the east coast of Japan northeastward toward the

[45] Fritz Bartz, "Japans Seefischereien," in *Petermanns Geographische Mitteilungen* 86:145–146 (May, 1940).

Kurile Islands. These are the most important fishing grounds of eastern Japan.

In view of the great variety of marine habitats in the vicinity of Japan, it is not surprising that the Japanese catch has such astonishing variety. More than four hundred different kinds of fish are used as food or are otherwise commercially important. Certain varieties are most abundant in cold northerly waters, others in warm subtropical waters. In the mixed waters between, both cold-water and warm-water varieties are caught. In the cool waters off Hokkaido and northward, herring, salmon, sea trout, cod, halibut, sardines, and crab are the principal commercial varieties. From the subtropical fishing grounds come bonito, tuna, albacore, frigate mackerel, swordfish, marlin, and sailfish.

Japan's fishing industry today is a curious combination of old, time-honored indigenous methods and some of the most modern methods and equipment in use anywhere. Expensive engined trawlers, motorships, and floating canneries from bases in Japan Proper operate in the more distant fishing grounds. Many of the complex fishing organizations are capitalized at figures up to a hundred million yen. At the same time much of the coastal fishing is done by families, or cooperatively by the male members of several families, with only the crudest kind of equipment. Small fishing boats dot the coastal waters for several miles offshore, and forests of masts seem to fill the numerous little harbors. Of the 354,729 fishing boats in Japan in 1939, more than 80 per cent were without engines, and of these all but about 6,500 were under five tons.[46] It is significant, however, that while the larger engined boats have been rapidly increasing, the smaller boats without engines have been declining. The number of small boats scrapped each year exceeds the number of new ones built. This trend suggests the increasingly big-business character of Japanese fishing.

The two principal subdivisions of Japanese fisheries are coastal fishing and deep-sea fishing. In 1938 coastwise fishing accounted for 61 per cent of the value of fisheries in Japan Proper; deep-sea fishing 25 per cent; fish culture 8 per cent; and trawling, near-sea whaling, and fishing in colonial waters the remaining 6 per cent.

COASTAL FISHERIES

Coastal fishing in the surrounding seas out to four or five miles from shore is the principal type of fishing in Japan. But while this form of fishing employs about 90 per cent of the fishermen, it provides only 61 per cent of the value of the catch. Obviously it is chiefly the coastal fisher-

[46] *Norinsho Tokeihyo,* 1939.

FIG. 120. Residences in a coastal fishing village. The fisher folk are usually poor and their homes show evidences of this poverty.

ies in which small-scale enterprise is still paramount. Here the fishermen are often farmers who take to the sea only in certain slack seasons. Or it may be that near-shore fishing is the principal occupation of the father of the farm family, while the wife and children till the soil. The coasts of Japan are thickly strewn with little combination agricultural-fishing villages, in two-fifths of which the total earnings from fishing are more than 50 per cent of the earnings from agriculture (Fig. 120).[47] These are the true fishing settlements of Japan. As a rule the fishermen in such settlements carry on only small-scale enterprises, commonly involving a single family. The modernization of the fishing industry in recent years under government supervision has had the effect of placing these poor fishermen-farmers in competition with large-scale, technically efficient fishing organizations. The result has been a further impoverishment of the already poor fishing settlements.

It is common for the fishing villages and towns to be located on elongated, elevated dry sites, such as beach ridges and dunes. For this reason they are often linear in dimensions—that is, of the *strassendorf* type. Generally their poverty is reflected in their dilapidated appearance, and their trade is proclaimed by the numerous boats, nets, trays of drying fish, boiling kettles, and seaweed on racks that clutter up the beach.

Coastal fishing is carried on by a large number of different techniques, and more than a hundred different methods of making the catch are recog-

[47] Bartz, *op. cit.*, 149.

TABLE 84.—NUMBER OF FISHING CRAFT

Year	WITHOUT ENGINE			WITH ENGINE		
	Newly Built	Scrapped	Total	Newly Built	Scrapped	Total
1927	17,662	18,463	333,757	3,364	922	20,797
1939	8,524	12,144	283,090	4,200	3,023	71,639

Sources: *Norinsho Tokeihyo*, 1939; *Japan-Manchukuo Yearbook*, 1940.

TABLE 85.—VALUE OF FISHERIES IN JAPAN PROPER, 1938
(in thousands of yen)

Product	Coastwise	Deep-Sea	Fish Culture	Trawling	Local Whaling	Colonial Waters
Fish	180	72.0	13.0	7.7		
Shellfish	11		5.5			
Seaweed	14		9.4			
Others	44	38.5	2.2			
Total	249	110.5	30.1	7.7	4.0	1.1

Source: *Far East Year Book*, 1941, 311.

TABLE 86.—COASTAL FISHERIES, 1938

Marine Product	Quantity (in thousands of kwan*)	Value (in thousands of yen)
Fish (total, including others)	*465,246*	*262,026*
Sardines	231,589	62,978
Herring	32,682	7,955
Mackerel	34,456	16,388
Trout	27,753	12,876
Cod	25,180	9,417
Dog salmon	13,390	13,431
Tunny	9,220	14,668
Horse mackerel	8,362	9,368
Yellowtail	5,982	11,667
Flatfish	6,248	8,731
Bonito	3,802	4,072
Shark	3,689	1,663
Red sea bream	2,918	15,248
Grey mullet	2,594	4,355
Shellfish	30,177	16,148
Special fish (total, including others)	*60,873*	*72,953*
Cuttlefish	33,826	39,928
Octopus	6,314	7,953
Prawn and shrimp	4,570	12,096
Crab	7,261	3,164
Seaweeds	*103,660*	*27,304*
Aquaculture products (eel, carp, goldfish, trout)		*43,026*
Grand total		378,431

Source: *Norinsho Tokeihyo*, 1939.   * One kwan = 8.27 pounds.

nized. The great variety of fish in Japanese waters is one reason for this multiplicity of fishing methods. For the most part they can be reduced to two primary techniques, the hook-and-line and the net. The first is most common, partly because it requires virtually no capital outlay. The variety of nets used is bewildering. Coastal fishing goes on throughout the year. A large part of the catch is consumed by the fisherman's family or is sold in the local fish markets. Any excess is preserved by drying or salting, or is converted into fertilizer or oil. For the most part it is the smaller varieties which are caught with nets, such as sardines and herring, that are dried.

In 1939 the total value of all forms of coastal fisheries in Japan was 378 million yen. Of this amount 262 million yen represented the value of true fishes, and the remainder the value of shellfish, cuttlefish, octopus, shrimp, crab, seaweed, and the products of aquaculture (chiefly eel, carp, and goldfish).[48] In Table 86 are shown the amount and value of each of the principal types of fish taken.

The sardine catch is by far the most important, measured either in quantity of catch or total value. In quantity sardines are also the most important catch of the deep-sea fisheries in home waters. Together the coastal and deep-sea catches total over 1.2 million tons or 62 per cent of the total weight of fish caught in home waters (exclusive of shellfish and special fish). Sardines are caught along the entire coast of Japan from southern Kyushu to northwestern Hokkaido (Fig. 121). Only in eastern Hokkaido is the catch unimportant. Their chief spawning grounds are in the Kyushu waters, were they spend a large part of the winter. They spawn during the early months of the year and then begin to move northward along the Pacific coast and in the Japan Sea to their northern feeding grounds.[49] The period of the year in which the sardine catch is made varies with the latitude. Most of the catch is taken from waters within ten miles of the shore. The particular method of fishing and the kind of net used varies from place to place and with the season. Most of the sardine catch is turned into oil, fertilizer, and meal; only about a third is sold as food, either in the fresh or the dried form.

Next to the sardine the most important fish of Japan's northern coastal waters is the herring. Like sardines, herring are converted chiefly into oil and fertilizer and are less used for food. Almost the whole catch is taken in the coastal waters of Hokkaido and Sakhalin (Fig. 121). Herring fishing has suffered a serious decline in Hokkaido during the past decade, the catch in 1933 being eight to nine times what it was in 1939. Besides sar-

[48] *Norinsho Tokeihyo*, 1940.   [49] Bartz, *op. cit.*, 151.

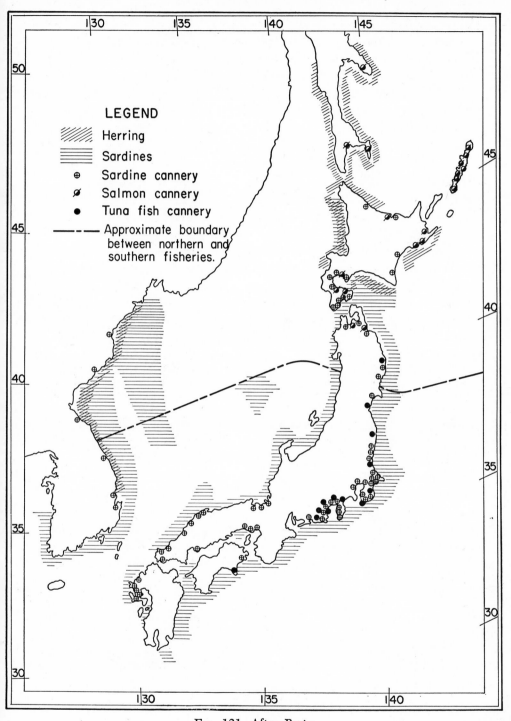

Fɪɢ. 121. After Bartz.

dines and herring large quantities of mackerel, tunny, cod, shark, flatfish, salmon, and trout are caught in the coastal waters of Hokkaido.

The coastal fisheries of middle and southern Japan yield quantities of a variety of species. Tai are taken in largest quantities in the waters off eastern Kyushu, yellowtail along the eastern coast of Honshu as far south as Nagoya, and mackerel off northeastern Honshu.

Other marine products taken by the coastal fisheries, such as shellfish, shrimp, crab, cuttlefish, and seaweed, yield over a hundred million yen each year. Cuttlefish, octopus, and crab are largely northern products, while lobster and shrimp are taken farther south. Over half the kelp collected is obtained from Hokkaido waters. One sees large quantities of seaweed drying on racks along the coast, most of which will be used as food (Fig. 122).

Coastal fishing is of greatest relative importance in Hokkaido waters. This largest northern prefecture accounts for 40 per cent of the total value of the catch (Fig. 123a), its pre-eminence being due partly to its position in the vicinity of the great oceanic convergence, partly to the fact that it is more than fourteen times as large as the average prefecture of Old Japan, and has a proportionately longer coastline. Other regions of high concentrations are the coastal waters of the Pacific side of Japan from about latitude 37° southward, and along western Kyushu.

DEEP-SEA FISHERIES

Deep-sea fishing is of two types, fishing with bases in the homeland and fishing without a home base. Representative of the latter class are the floating factories engaged in catching and processing crabs, salmon, whales, etc. The former category includes steamship trawl fishing, steamship whaling, and motorboat seine fishing. It differs from coastal fishing in several respects. Boats engaged in deep-sea fishing go out much farther from their home bases. The fishing may be in relatively deep waters or in shallow waters off the coasts of Korea and Formosa and in the leased fishing grounds of Russian territorial waters. The boats are larger and the equipment far more expensive than in coastal

Fig. 122. Seaweed drying on racks along the coast. Much seaweed is eaten by the Japanese, but some is used for the manufacture of iodine.

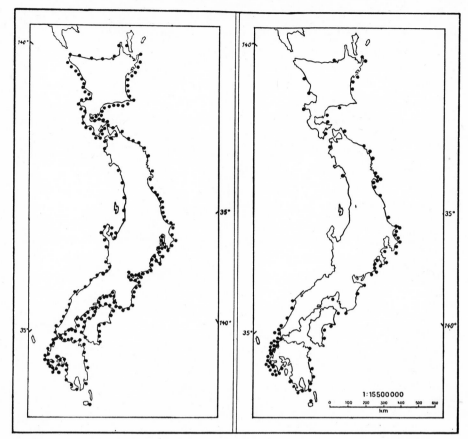

FIG. 123. Each dot equals a million yen in catch. *Left,* Coastal fishing.
Right, Deep-sea fishing. After Bartz.

fishing. Whereas the boats used in near-shore fishing are under fifty tons
and the majority are not engine-powered, the trawlers and whalers of the
deep-sea enterprises are usually between two hundred and three hundred
tons, and most of the so-called mother ships several thousand tons, some
of them as large as twenty thousand.[50] Many of the boats are equipped
with modern diesel engines and wireless apparatus.

Partly because of the expensive equipment required in deep-sea fishing,
it is of rather recent development and is for the most part large-scale
enterprise in the hands of corporations capitalized at 20–100 million yen.
Equipment and methods of fishing are much more standardized than in
the coastal fisheries. The catch is landed at far fewer ports, for the larger

[50] "Nippon Occupies First Rank in Marine Products Enterprise," in *Nippon Today
and Tomorrow* (Osaka, 1941), 115.

boats employed in this enterprise are unable to dock at all of the coastal villages. Yet the deep-sea fishing ports are sufficiently numerous to prevent any of them from standing out like the great modern fishing ports of Great Britain and the United States. Most of them are on the Pacific side of Japan.

Deep-sea fishing in home waters is a very important and profitable branch of Japan's total fishing industry, the value of the catch in 1939 amounting to 142.5 million yen (Fig. 123b). One aspect of this enterprise is fishing with hook and line, chiefly in Pacific waters, for such varieties as mackerel, bonito, cod, and tunny. In the winter months tunny and bonito are in southern tropical waters. Early in the year they move northward, and in May and June they appear in Pacific waters in about the latitude of Tokyo, and in July and August in those of northern Honshu. By the beginning of September they turn southward again. Methods of

TABLE 87.—VALUE OF CATCHES OF DEEP-SEA FISHING IN JAPAN, 1938
(in thousands of yen)

Type of Fishing	Value	Type of Fishing	Value
Trawl fishing	7,670	Fishing off coasts of:	
Steamship fishing	3,873	Chosen	89,920
Crab fishing by factory system	13,886	Formosa	14,513
Salmon fishing by factory system	14,250	Karafuto	9,660
Whaling by factory system	21,786	South Sea Islands	6,863
Fishing in Russian waters	44,007	Kwantung	7,461
Fishing off North Chishima	30,663		
Others	3,068	Total	128,417
		Grand Total	267,620
Total	139,203		

Source: *Nippon Today and Tomorrow* (1941), 115.

TABLE 88.—PELAGIC OR DEEP-SEA FISHING IN HOME WATERS, 1939

Fish	Quantity (1,000 kwan)	Value (1,000 yen)
Sardine	59,368	12,324
Bonito	23,004	23,407
Mackerel	6,506	4,701
Tunny	13,691	21,888
Cod	22,009	8,408
Shark	13,669	6,565
Sea bream	1,716	5,043
Flatfish	11,646	11,271
Skipper	3,012	2,646
Total	209,204	142,557

Source: *Norinsho Tokeihyo*, 1939.

fishing vary with the different varieties. Simple diesel-driven wooden vessels of less than two hundred tons are most commonly used. Four weeks or more may be consumed in a single trip, during which one to two thousand miles may be covered.

Trawling is of two kinds; one involves the use of relatively large vessels operating the so-called ottertrawl; the other uses smaller boats equipped only with simple trawling nets. One of the principal trawling grounds is the eastern China Sea and Yellow Sea, and the smaller trawlers fish also in the coastal waters around the main islands. The ports of Tobata, Shimonoseki, and Nagasaki are especially important as trawler bases.

High-seas fishing is also carried on in Soviet waters, along the coasts of the Maritime Provinces of Siberia, in Bering Sea, and around the Kurile Islands, Kamchatka, and Sakhalin. The catches in Russian waters are a very profitable branch of Japanese high-seas fishing, the take in 1939 being valued at over 44 million yen. Salmon, trout, and crab are the principal items in the catch, much of which has in the past been canned and sent to Great Britain and the United States. The northern fisheries are conducted from bases on Japanese soil, from land bases and fishing grounds leased from the Soviet Government, and from floating factories operated outside the three-mile limit of Russian and Alaskan waters.

Processing of Marine Products.—It was during World War I, when Japan was called upon to supply canned fish to the belligerent nations, that the processing of marine products had its most rapid development. The most important item is the canned fish, chiefly salmon, trout, crab, and sardines. Fish fertilizer and oil rank next in importance. Not only non-edible parts of fish and shellfish are used in manufacturing fertilizer and oil but also large quantities of whole herring and sardines, fish that are caught in such large quantities that they cannot readily be eaten or preserved. A large export trade in canned fish, dried fish, isinglass, and fish oil has been built up during the past two decades, the total value of which amounted to 210 million yen in 1939. Large amounts of Japanese canned salmon and sardines, isinglass, and fish oil have been imported by the United States. In 1939 only raw silk exceeded marine products in total value of exports.

Pearl Culture.—One of Japan's most unique and best known phases of the aquatic industry is the artificial stimulation of pearl development in oysters. K. Mikimoto, who originated the process, obtained the idea from the Chinese, who had for centuries produced pearl-plated Buddhas by inserting little statues of this deity within the valves of living shellfish. Millions of three-year-old oysters are gathered annually by several hundred diving girls employed by the Mikimoto firm. Bits of fresh-water mussel are then inserted into the bodies of the oysters, the resulting wounds are cauterized, and the oysters subsequently returned to the ocean where they are contained in iron baskets. During the several years following, the inserted foreign substance is incapsulated by the pearl-forming secretion. After a period of four to seven years the oysters are ready to be opened. Only about three-tenths of one per cent of the treated oysters produce pearls of marketable quality. The cultured pearls are of exactly the same substance and color as natural pearls and consequently should have the same value. The result has been a worldwide depression in the pearl market. In 1938 the Mikimoto company produced jewels valued at more than 1.5 million yen. The pearl-culture oyster beds are located near Toba village in Mie Prefecture along the western side of the entrance to Ise Bay, where they cover more than 50,000 square meters.

SELECTED REFERENCES

AGRICULTURE

ALSBERG, CARL L. "Japanese Self-Sufficiency in Wheat." *Wheat Studies*, 12:57–100 (November, 1935).

CHAMBERLAIN, W. H. "Japan's Farm Crisis." *Asia*, 36:369–374 (June, 1936).

DAWSON, O. L., and W. LADEJINSKY. "Recent Japanese Agricultural Policies." *Foreign Agriculture*, 3:263–674 (June, 1939).

FARLEY, MIRIAM. "Japanese Agriculture under War Pressure." *Far Eastern Survey*, 9:135–139 (June 5, 1940).

——. "Japan's Unsolved Tenancy Problem." *Far Eastern Survey*, July 7, 1937.

GRAJDANZEV, ANDREW J. *Statistics of Japanese Agriculture*. Institute of Pacific Relations, New York, November, 1941.

HALL, ROBERT B. "Agricultural Regions of Asia: Part VII, The Japanese Empire." *Economic Geography*, 10(1934):323–347; 11(1935):33–52, 130–147.

KAWADA, S. "Tenant Systems in Japan and Korea." *Kyoto University Economic Review*, 1:38–73 (July, 1926).

LADEJINSKY, W. "Agrarian Unrest in Japan." *Foreign Affairs*, 17:426–433 (January, 1939).

——. "Aspects of Japanese Agriculture." *Farm Economics*, 21:614–631 (August, 1938).

——. "Farm Tenancy and Japanese Agriculture." *Foreign Agriculture*, 1:425–446 (September, 1937).

——. "Japan's Food Self-Sufficiency." *Foreign Agriculture*, 4:355–476 (June, 1940).

NASU, SHIROSHI. *Aspects of Japanese Agriculture*. Institute of Pacific Relations, New York, November, 1941.

——. *Land Utilization of Japan*. Institute of Pacific Relations, Tokyo, 1929.

RUELLAN, FRANCIS. *La production du riz au Japan*. Institute for the Study of Japanese at the University of Paris, 1938.

SCHUMPETER, E. B., *et al*. *The Industrialization of Japan and Manchukuo, 1930–1940*, 116–187. The Macmillan Co., New York, 1940.

SWEN, W. Y., and CARL L. ALSBERG. "Japan as a Producer and Importer of Wheat." *Wheat Studies*, 6:351–369 (July, 1930).

"The Farmer Does Without." *Fortune*, September, 1936, pp. 87 ff.

FISHING

BARTZ, FRITZ. "Japans Seefischereien." *Petermanns Geographische Mitteilungen*, 86 (1940):145–160, with numerous maps in color.

FARAGO, LADISLAS. "Fish and Japan's War." *Asia*, 41:80–83 (February, 1941).

HERRE, ALBERT W. C. T. "Japanese Fisheries and Fish Supplies." *Far Eastern Survey*, 12:99–101 (May 17, 1943).

Nippon Today and Tomorrow, 1941. The Osaka Mainichi, Osaka, 1941.

SHOZUI, SENICHI. "Our Fishing Industry." *Contemporary Japan*, 9:698–705 (June, 1940).

YASUO, NAGAHARA. "The North Ocean Fishery in Japan's Economic Life." *Far Eastern Survey*, 8:106–108 (April 26, 1939).

CHAPTER VIII

Manufacturing

JAPAN was a latecomer into the field of capitalistic industry, but once she had been forced to open her doors to the Western world, she developed industrially at a rate that has been little short of phenomenal. Having been drawn into the maelstrom of world economic competition, she was primarily concerned with protecting herself against the humiliating fate that China had suffered at the hands of the Western nations. She was bent on making herself a military power capable of repelling economic encroachment from the outside and insurrection at home. Hence she directed her plans and her energies toward modernizing the country along Western lines at the greatest possible speed. The task that confronted the Meiji Government when it assumed control in 1868 was a formidable one—that of bridging the wide gap between the feudalism of Japan and the technologically advanced economy of the Western powers. No ordinary procedures would suffice.

The most notable features of industrial development in early Meiji Japan were, first, the government's participation in the development of modern industry and, secondly, the unusual concentration of capital, and hence of economic power, in the hands of a small group of wealthy men who financed the State. For more than a decade after the Restoration, plans for the wholesale application of Western industrial methods were implemented by the establishment of government-managed enterprises which served both as models and as schools of experience. Government protection and subsidy were also granted to new private enterprises, with the result that early Japanese capitalism was of a distinctly hothouse variety. Ultimately many of the government enterprises were turned over to private firms, but the policy of strong protection and subsidy has continued to the present day.

At the time the Meiji Government undertook to telescope centuries of Western evolution into a few decades, only a few rich merchants and money lenders had accumulated enough capital to finance large-scale industry. These few, naturally enough, were wary of investing their wealth in such untried ventures. Thus the State itself had to develop those industries that were considered essential weapons against the penetration of foreign power, political and economic. Not only the industries that were strategic for military purposes were fostered, but also those in which Japan could hope to compete with foreign products.[1] Arsenals, foundries, shipyards, and mines were brought under State control, and such other essential industries as cotton mills, chemical works, and glass and cement factories were established. Industries producing distinctly Japanese-style goods, such as silk, lacquer, and porcelain, were not Westernized but remained essentially handicraft enterprises.

The early dependence of the Meiji Government upon a small financial oligarchy for the funds needed to develop new industries forced it to take a number of wealthy families into virtual partnership. At first they served merely as bankers for the government, but later they took over the enterprises established by the State and eventually became the owners and operators of much of Japan's industry, commerce, and banking resources. The result has been a much closer association of government and big business than in most Western countries.

Still another feature of early Japanese industrialization was its great dependence upon foreign markets, since the bulk of the Japanese population—the agriculturalists—remained too poor to buy the products of the new industries. The Meiji Government's resources were devoted so exclusively to the development of manufacturing, banking, and communications that agriculture was largely neglected, despite the fact that the agricultural population comprised nearly eighty per cent of Japan's total. As a result agriculture lagged far behind the other industries in technical progress. Moreover, it was the tax on agriculture that furnished the funds for the wholesale subsidization of the government's adventures into Western capitalism. Thus Japan, lacking many of the raw materials needed by industry and having only a restricted home market, was forced to develop a foreign trade to acquire the needed raw materials and to dispose of her manufactured goods. Cheap labor was supplied by the rural districts, but few of the benefits of the new capitalism filtered down to the mass of the people.

World War I ushered in for Japan an era of unprecedented industrial and commercial expansion and prosperity, which lasted well into the post-

[1] On this topic see Kate L. Mitchell, *Japan's Industrial Strength* (Alfred A. Knopf, 1942), 3–7; also Takao Tsuchiya, "War and Japanese Capitalism," in *Kaizo*, vol. 20, no. 1 (January, 1938, Tokyo), as translated in *Industrial Japan* (Institute of Pacific Relations, New York, 1941), 1–14.

war period. The factors that contributed to this prosperity were the cessa-
tion of imports from the Western powers, the increase of Japanese exports.
including munitions, to the Allied Powers, and the expansion of Japanese
shipping and shipbuilding. After the middle of the twenties, however, the
recovery of the Western powers and the increasing trend toward economic nationalism or monopoly capitalism tended to restrict Japan's
markets and curtail her industrial expansion.

Status of Manufacturing in 1930

Judged by Western standards, Japan, although she possessed some
highly developed modern industry, was not yet in 1930 a highly industrialized nation. Agriculture supported half her population, whereas
manufacturing supported less than a fifth and commerce about 17 per cent.

Light industries greatly predominated, particularly textiles and clothing, which in 1930 employed nearly one-third of the wage earners in
Japanese industry (Fig. 124). The heavy metal and machine industries
were much less developed, employing only 13 per cent of the gainfully
employed. This predominance of textiles is shown even more strikingly
in the *Factory Statistics* issued by the Japanese Ministry of Commerce
and Industry, which includes only establishments employing five or more
workers. According to this report, more than 50 per cent of the workers
in industry were in the textile trades, which represented 40 per cent of the
total factory employment.[2] Silk and cotton industries greatly predominated
in 1929, silk reeling alone providing about two-fifths of the total factory
employment in textiles, and cotton spinning and weaving about one-third.
Taken together, all branches of the silk and cotton textile industries (including silk spinning and the bleaching, dyeing, and finishing trades),
represented nine-tenths of the textile employment.[3] In 1928–29, some 37
per cent of Japan's exports consisted of raw silk and 20 per cent of cotton
yarn and piece goods; taken together, all forms of raw and processed silk
and of cotton goods represented two-thirds of the total value of exports.[4]

Control over Japan's modern industries, trade, and banking has been
highly concentrated in the hands of a few huge business families known
as the *Zaibatsu* ("financial clique"), the greatest of which operate simul-
taneously in finance, commerce, insurance, and mining.[5] In 1937 their
trust companies held some 70 per cent of all trust deposits, and their

---

[2] G. C. Allen, *Japanese Industry: Its Recent Development and Present Condition*
(Institute of Pacific Relations, New York, 1940), 5.
[3] *Ibid.*   [4] *Ibid.*, 5–6.
[5] For a detailed description of the *Zaibatsu* and its operation see G. C. Allen,

TABLE 89.—PERCENTAGE DISTRIBUTION OF WAGE EARNERS IN THE CHIEF ECONOMIC
ACTIVITIES IN JAPAN PROPER, 1930

Agriculture.	47.7	Commerce	16.6
Fishing	1.9	Transportation and communication.	3.2
Mining	1.0	Others	9.8
Manufacturing	19.8		
		Total	100.0

Source: *Résumé Statistique de l'Empire du Japon* (1936), p. 9, as quoted by Schumpeter *et al.* in *The Industrialization of Japan and Manchukuo, 1930–1940* (New York, 1940), 76.

TABLE 90.—PERCENTAGE DISTRIBUTION OF WAGE EARNERS IN MINING
AND MANUFACTURING, 1930

Mining and quarrying	5.2	Clothing	7.8
Kiln products.	2.8	Paper and printing	4.5
Metal	6.3	Wood, bamboo, and grass	10.6
Machinery and tool	3.9	Food and drink	8.1
Shipbuilding and vehicle	3.1	Civil engineering and building	15.7
Watches, scientific instruments	0.9	Public utilities.	2.1
Chemical.	2.7	Others	2.1
Textile.	24.2		
		Total mining and engineering	100.0

Source: Kate L. Mitchell, *Japan's Industrial Strength* (New York, 1942), 17.

trading companies conducted a third of Japan's foreign trade. Three of the *Zaibatsu* alone controlled half of the coal output and owned nearly half of the merchant ship tonnage registered in Japan. Factory-scale manufacturing is largely controlled by them. A large part of the chemical industry was controlled by four great concerns, as was the heavy-machine industry. Their interests in shipbuilding, warehousing, colonial enterprises, engineering, sugar refining, flour milling, and textile manufacturing have been extensive. Two of the *Zaibatsu,* Mitsu and Mitsubishi, which controlled two of the major political parties, were able, by exerting political and financial pressure, to influence government policies, secure subsidies, and obtain government contracts. Their ownership of banks and trust companies enabled them to exercise indirect control over many enterprises not owned by them directly.

To a much larger extent than in other industrial countries, Japanese manufacturing in 1930 was still carried on in a multitude of pygmy factories. This was true not only of Japanese-style goods, but of many export commodities as well. Today the Japanese industrial structure is a combination of large modern factories and multitudes of small factories and workshops. In 1930 about half the workers in industry (excluding the

"The Concentration of Economic Control," in Schumpeter *et al., The Industrialization of Japan and Manchukuo, 1930–1940,* 625–646.

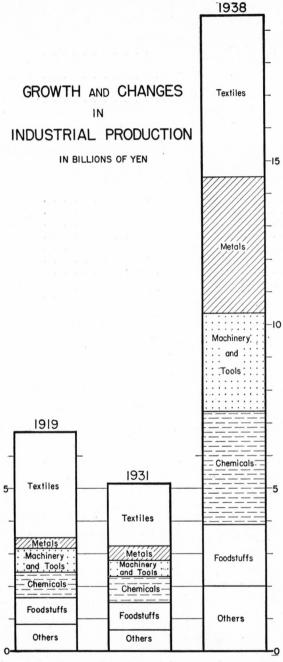

GROWTH AND CHANGES
IN
INDUSTRIAL PRODUCTION

IN BILLIONS OF YEN

FIG. 124. The 1930's saw not only a rapid expansion of industry, but marked changes in type of product.

[6] Allen, *Japanese Industry*, 26–27.

building industry) were in establishments employing fewer than five workers, and about 70 percent in factories employing fewer than fifty.[6] Opinion differs as to the efficiency of such small units. It must not be forgotten, however, that from an administrative and financial point of view the many small units are often parts of a larger, highly integrated organization which coordinates their activities.

In 1930 Japan's industrial structure was very dependent upon foreign raw materials as well as upon foreign markets. As has been said, the bulk of the country's population was too poverty-stricken to provide a large home market, although it was a reservoir of cheap labor, one of Japan's chief advantages in competition with other countries. Not only is the low-income market of Japan a small one, but many of the goods it consumes are very different from those it exports. Thus Nippon's industry differentiates between Japan-style and foreign-style goods.

Japan's Manufactural Development, 1931–37

In the interval between the outbreak of the Manchurian Incident in 1931, which marks the beginning of a quickened imperialistic policy, and the opening of the Sino-Japanese War in 1937 Nippon's industrial structure underwent some remarkable changes. Without these changes, which involved both a major expansion of industry and fundamental changes in its structure, the present war in the Far East would have been impossible (Fig. 124). Between 1931 and 1937 the number of factories employing five or more workers increased 66 per cent, the number of workers in industry nearly doubled, and the value of manufactural output more than tripled. This rapid expansion was the result of a complex of interrelated causes, the relative weight of which experts have not agreed upon.[7] The increasing power of the military in the government resulted in a speed-up of war preparations during the decade of the thirties; large expenditures were made for armaments and increased subsidies to such strategic industries as chemicals, oil refining, shipbuilding, and munitions. In a measure, then, the boom was State-financed. Abandonment of the gold standard and the depreciation of the yen created an export boom for Japanese goods. At the same time the collapse of the American silk market dealt a hard blow to the rural population. The resulting agricultural depression caused a shift of population from the impoverished farming areas to the cities, making available an abundance of low-cost labor. The competitive superiority of Japan is also manifest in her "homogeneous, highly integrated, and beautifully adapted social organization permitting a unification of national effort not possible in any other country."[8] The nation is conceived as a large clan whose chief is the Emperor and whose complete unification rests upon the strength of family tradition. The family is the prototype of the nation.

This national unity has permitted the absorption of foreign cultural influences without serious disturbances. Whereas European countries achieved the industrial revolution only at the cost of a disintegration of their closely knit feudal organization, Japan was able to fit the revolution into her regimented feudalism with no serious disruption of its structure. In the United States and much of Europe production costs are high. Modern Japan achieves low-cost production without capitalistic exploitation of the worker. For low wages, national habits of frugality, and the

[7] Schumpeter *et al., op. cit.,* 647–649.
[8] See *Fortune,* September, 1936, p. 116; also Yasuma Takata, "Kulturelle und geistige Voraussetzungen für Japans Aufsteig," in *Weltwirtschaftliches Archiv,* 46:1–13 (July, 1937).

TABLE 91.—VOLUME AND VALUE INDEXES OF INDUSTRIAL PRODUCTION IN JAPAN, 1926–37

Year	Volume Index (1929 = 100)	Value Index (1926 = 100)	Year	Volume Index (1929 = 100)	Value Index (1926 = 100)
1926	—	100	1932	97.8	86
1927	—	94	1933	113.2	113
1928	—	104	1934	128.7	135
1929	100	111	1935	141.8	156
1930	94.8	86	1936	151.1	176
1931	91.6	75	1937	170.8	236

Source: Volume index from the *Statistical Bulletin of the League of Nations*, quoted in *Japan-Manchukuo Year Book*, 1940, p. 361. Value index from the Japanese Ministry of Commerce and Industry, quoted *ibid.*, 362.

TABLE 92.—GROWTH OF INDUSTRIAL PRODUCTION AND CHANGE IN COMPOSITION OF INDUSTRY IN JAPAN

Group of Industries	PERCENTAGE OF TOTAL VALUE OF FACTORY PRODUCTION		
	1919	1931	1938
Textiles	48.9	37.3	20.3
Metals.	5.0	8.4	23.8
Machinery and tools.	10.8	9.6	19.4
Ceramics.	2.6	2.8	2.1
Chemicals	11.7	15.8	17.6
Lumber and wood.	2.3	2.8	2.3
Printing and book binding	1.0	3.4	1.4
Foodstuffs	10.9	16.2	9.1
Others.	6.8	3.6	4.0
Total value of industrial output. .	6,737,632,000 yen	5,163,400,000 yen	19,487,320,000 yen

Source: Data for 1919 and 1931 from *Japan Advertiser Annual Review*, 1939–40, p. 6; 1938 statistics from *Kojo Tokeihyo*, 1938 (*Factory Statistics*, published by the Ministry of Commerce and Industry), 15.

TABLE 93.—JAPANESE MANUFACTURING, 1936–39

Item of Data	1936	1937	1938	1939
Number of enterprises	90,602.0	106,005.0	112,332.0	137,422.0
Number of workers employed (in thousands) .	2,592.7	2,936.5	3,217.7	3,766.7
Gross value of production (in millions of yen) .	12,258.0	16,356.0	19,667.0	24,360.0
Hours worked by employees (in millions) . .	7,693.0	8,750.0	9,706.0	11,317.0
Wages and salaries (in millions of yen) . . .	971.8	1,152.3	1,442.0	1,927.3

Source: *Tokei Geppo* (*Statistical Monthly*), quoted by A. Grajdanzev in "Japan's Industrial Output Slackens," in the *Far Eastern Survey*, April 7, 1941, p. 69.

capacity to sacrifice all but the minimum essentials are as characteristic of the people today as they were in the feudal era. From the great reservoir of the agricultural population, which is inured to an existence of extreme frugality, has come a never-ending supply of eager workers willing to accept subsistence-plus wages.

A second feature of industrial development in the period 1931–37 was the changing composition of Japanese industry, with emphasis upon greater diversification of manufactures (Fig. 124). The earlier overwhelming importance of the lighter industries, particularly textiles and other consumers' goods, was reduced as a result of the expansion of the heavy industries, although this was of course a relative, not an absolute decline. Thus while metal manufactures accounted for only 5 per cent of industrial production in 1919 and 8.4 per cent in 1931, by 1938 it had skyrocketed to 23.8 per cent. In the same period the value of machinery and tools rose from 9.6 to 19.4 per cent, and chemicals from 11.7 to 17.6 per cent. At the same time the value of textiles declined from 48.9 per cent of the total value of manufactures in 1919 to 37.3 per cent in 1931, and to 20.3 per cent in 1938. This relative decline also took place in the face of an absolute increase. The volume of textile production was much higher in 1937 than in 1931, cotton cloth production being 31 per cent greater in that year than six years before. Foodstuffs declined from 16.2 per cent to 9.1 per cent.

Employment figures tell the same story. Thus in 1931 textiles employed 50.4 per cent of the people in industry as against 37.8 per cent in 1936. In the metal industries workers increased from 6.0 to 9.7 per cent of all industrial workers, in machinery and tools from 13.2 to 18.3 per cent, and in chemicals from 6.6 to 11.1 per cent.[9] These figures are an indication of the extensive changes that Japan's industrial structure underwent within the span of a few short years during the early thirties.

A third respect in which the Japanese industrial structure changed in the period 1931–37 was in the technical efficiency of factory industries.[10] Factory managers learned to make more efficient use of labor, power, and materials, and improved equipment and manufacturing processes were introduced. The results were increased output and lower production costs. In the lighter industries this increase in technological efficiency was effected most rapidly during the depression years 1927–31, but in rayon, chemicals, metals, and machine manufacturing the speed-up came largely after 1931. Again it must be said that this progress was all relative. Since

[9] Schumpeter et al., op. cit., 484.
[10] See ibid., 647–679, and Allen, Japanese Industry, 25–44.

Japan's level of industrial technique and organization, judged by Western standards, was very low in 1920, the advance she made thereafter is being measured from a low base. Despite the rapid strides she has made, her productive efficiency does not equal that of the industrial countries of the Occident. In most modern industries she still lags behind western Europe and the United States, although the gap has been appreciably narrowed.

A fourth and significant feature of Japan's industrial change between 1931 and 1937 was the increasing intervention and control of the State over industry.[11] This was not a complete innovation, for ever since the early Meiji period the State had played an important role in industrial and commercial development. But beginning in 1930 and 1931, when severe depression occasioned great suffering, this policy of State control was greatly quickened and expanded. During the early thirties political power shifted, at least in part, from the great financiers and industrialists to the military factions. With the adoption of an expansionist foreign policy in Asia, these factions insisted that all economic activities connected with national preparedness for war and with the execution of the expansion program in Asia be strictly regulated and controlled. The *Zaibatsu*, while not opposed to the policy of expansion, were inclined toward less dangerous means of attaining the goal; they favored a threat of force only if and when necessary. Despite their reservations, however, the trend during the early thirties was toward a quasi-wartime economy. Such strategic industries as iron and steel, petroleum refining, and shipbuilding were brought under strict control of the government, with the result that by 1937 the way was open for the State to take over when war broke out.

Developments in Manufacturing Since 1937[12]

With the outbreak of the Sino-Japanese War many of the industrial trends conspicuous in the earlier part of the decade were intensified. In addition there were certain distinct changes in the composition of industry, chief of which was the absolute decline in textiles and most other consumers' goods destined both for home consumption and the export market. In the preceding years these lighter industries, although they had not kept pace with the rapidly expanding heavy industries, had continued to increase also; after 1937 they suffered an absolute decline, as capital and labor were diverted to the essential war industries. The un-

[11] See Schumpeter *et al., op. cit.,* 741–786; Allen, *Japanese Industry,* 59–80.
[12] See Kate Mitchell, *op. cit.,* 34–60, and Allen, *Japanese Industry,* 59–80.

paralleled acceleration of production in the heavy metals, machinery, chemicals, and engineering to meet the demands of the armed forces necessitated greatly enlarged purchases abroad of raw materials for metal and munitions manufacture, petroleum products, high-grade machine tools, motor vehicles, etc., and inevitably resulted in a tightening of State control over peacetime industries. Japan's goal was so to expand the strategically important heavy industries that the country would be less dependent on imported raw materials. In 1938 this ambition was crystallized in the concept of the "New Order in East Asia" or "the Yen-Bloc," which was based on a Japanese organization of Japan, Manchuria, and China into an economic defense bloc. By mid-1940 this earlier organization had become only the nucleus of a greatly expanded "Greater East Asia Co-Prosperity Sphere," which was to be an independent and self-sufficient economic bloc comprising large but unspecified areas of eastern and southeastern Asia. Within this sphere Japan was to be dominant; from its resources she planned to draw the raw materials she needed, and to its market sell the products of her industry.

Between 1936 and 1939 the number of manufactural enterprises increased 52 per cent, the number of workers in industry 45 per cent, the gross value of industrial production 99 per cent, the number of hours worked by industrial employees 40 per cent, and expenditures for wages and salaries 98 per cent. The increase of almost 100 per cent in gross value of production is partly accounted for by the rapid rise in prices by 1939. In terms of 1936 prices the increase was in the neighborhood of 31 per cent. Individually and collectively these several criteria denote a very substantial growth in Japan's industrial machine after the outbreak of the war with China.

The industrial spurt that occurred in the late thirties resulted in an increase of 13.5 per cent in the total volume of manufactural production between 1937 and 1939, and 32 per cent between 1936 and 1939. The increase after 1937 comprised a 41.8 per cent *increase* in the volume of producers' goods and a 15.1 per cent *decrease* in the volume of consumers' goods. The contrast in changing volume of production since 1937 between heavy war industries and lighter peacetime industries is shown in Table 94, in which the base is August, 1937. It is significant that, despite the increasing demands of the war, both metals and machinery and chemicals declined in the year ending August, 1940. This is attributable in part to shortages of raw materials, coal, and electric power; in part it is due to other circumstances, notably the failure of some of the large financial interests to cooperate in the militarists' totalitarian pro-

TABLE 94.—VOLUME INDEX OF INDUSTRIAL PRODUCTION

(monthly average, 1931–33 = 100)

Year	General Index	Consumers' Goods	Producers' Goods
1932.	96.9	97.6	96.2
1933.	111.9	107.3	116.6
1934.	126.2	116.1	136.4
1935.	139.3	125.0	153.1
1936.	148.8	125.3	171.5
1937.	167.3	136.5	197.9
1938.	173.0	125.1	220.4
1939.	180.8	121.4	239.7
1940 (Aug.)	178.5	102.7	253.5

Source: *Oriental Economist* (Tokyo), as quoted by Mitchell, *op. cit.*, 46–47.

TABLE 95.—INDEX OF PHYSICAL VOLUME OF PRODUCTION IN VARIOUS INDUSTRIAL GROUPS

Industrial Group	August, 1937	August, 1938	August, 1939	August, 1940
Metals and machinery	100	118	145	138
Chemicals	100	99	105	97
Textiles	100	86	88	75
Ceramics.	100	82	73	74
Food	100	117	122	74
Paper	100	90	94	87

Source: *Oriental Economist* (Tokyo), as quoted by Mitchell, *op. cit.*, 48.

gram, and the declining efficiency in labor with a declining standard of living.

Distribution of Manufacturing[13]

Manufacturing in Nippon is concentrated largely in a thin belt nearly 600 miles long which extends from the Kwanto region on the northeast, along the Pacific coast to the Nagoya area and thence through the Kinki area and along the shores of the Inland Sea, to Nagasaki in northwestern Kyushu (Figs. 125, 126). By any measure of manufactural importance—value of product, number of factory workers, variety of industries, etc.—this region outranks all others. It is also the most populous and urbanized belt of Japan, 53 per cent of the country's cities of over 25,000 population being located here. In this belt are employed 75–80 per cent of the Japanese factory workers, and its industrial plants produce nearly 85 per cent of the total value of Japanese manufactured goods. About three-

[13] For a detailed discussion of Japan's industrial regions, see John E. Orchard, *Japan's Economic Position* (McGraw-Hill Book Co., Inc.), 1930.

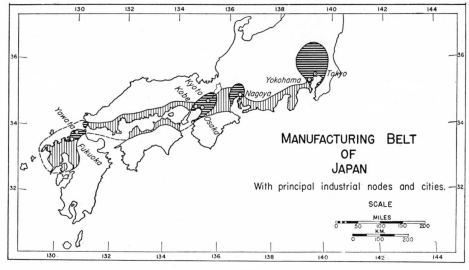

MANUFACTURING BELT
OF
JAPAN

With principal industrial nodes and cities.

FIG. 125

quarters of the pig iron of Japan Proper and probably 90 per cent of its steel originate here.

The specific advantages of this belt as a location for industry are not too striking. Certainly no single factor explains its growth. Perhaps its most important advantage, one which is common to all parts of it, is ready accessibility. No other part of Japan is equally accessible, either to foreign countries or to other parts of Japan. The whole belt is coastal in location, and the numerous bays and the Inland Sea offer excellent protection for shipping. Here are located the five ports that together handle 90 per cent of Japan's foreign trade. Numerous smaller ports, most of them engaged chiefly in domestic trade, supplement the services of the larger ones.

Even during Japan's feudal period of isolation this Tokyo-to-Nagasaki strip was very much at the center of activities. It included the old capital of Kyoto, the residence of the Emperors, and Yedo (now Tokyo), capital of the Shogunate. Osaka and Nagasaki, two other important cities of feudal Japan, were also in this belt. Of the famous highways in Tokugawa Japan, the Tokaido, connecting Yedo with Imperial Kyoto, was the greatest The Sanyodo Highway followed the northern shore of the Inland Sea from Kyoto to northern Kyushu, and another important feudal road paralleled the coast of northern Shikoku. It is not strange, therefore, in view of these historical antecedents, that when Japan was opened to Western influence, industry and trade should have been concentrated in this coastal strip, where cities were already present and which was so easily accessible. The old cities of the region grew rapidly, and new ones like Kobe, Yokohama, and those of North Kyushu came into existence. The accessibility of the Tokyo-to-Nagasaki littoral strip made it the logical region both for the importation of raw materials and for the disposal of finished products. Some of the earliest railway lines in Japan were built in this region because of the concentration there of population and cities.

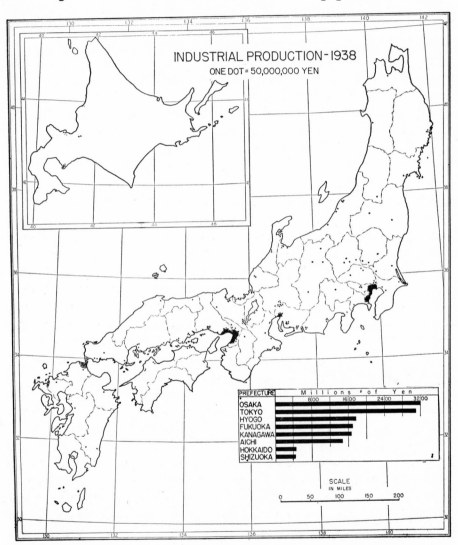

INDUSTRIAL PRODUCTION - 1938
ONE DOT = 50,000,000 YEN

PREFECTURE	Millions of Yen
	800 1600 2400 3200
OSAKA	
TOKYO	
HYOGO	
FUKUOKA	
KANAGAWA	
AICHI	
HOKKAIDO	
SHIZUOKA	

SCALE
IN MILES
0   50   100   150   200

FIG. 126. Japan's manufacturing is concentrated in four centers: Tokyo-Yokohama on the Kwanto Plain; Nagoya at the head of Ise Bay; Osaka-Kobe in Kinki; and extreme northern Kyushu.

From Tokyo to Kobe ran the Tokaido line, which was continued to Shimonoseki as the Sanyo line. At present this Tokaido-Sanyo route is the only long double-track railroad in Japan, and it has the best service and the fastest trains. The region also has the best modern motor highways.

The power resources of the region are not extraordinary. At its extreme southern end are Japan's most important coal fields, which supply coal to a large part of the belt. The lignite fields near Nagoya and the Joban coal field north of Tokyo are much less significant sources of power. The northern and central part of the industrial belt are also within reach of Japan's greatest potential and best developed hydroelectric concentration in central Honshu.

The industrial belt comprises four areas of concentration or nodes (Figs. 125, 126), which have advantages superior to those of the belt as a whole. The three northernmost of them have extensive plains whose level areas permit development of great cities and the construction of large factories. Two of the nodes, Kwanto and Kinki, have modern deepwater ports, and the other two, though somewhat inferior in this respect, are at least better equipped with port facilities than other parts of the belt. The northern and southern nodes have easy access to local coal resources. All of Japan's six great metropolises lie within three of the four centers of this industrial concentration.

The Kwanto Node.[14]—Northernmost of the four manufacturing concentrations is the Kwanto Node, whose principal urban centers are Tokyo and Yokohama. In 1940 the former had a population of nearly 6.8 million and the latter close to a million. Within the node are approximately twenty-five lesser cities, one of which has a population of over 300,000 and another over 200,000. Twelve cities have a population between 50,000 and 100,000. Nearly 30 per cent of the nation's output of industrial products is from the Kwanto or *Kei-hin* industrial district. Here hydroelectric power, derived from the mountains of central Chubu, is relatively abundant, and adjacent Joban supplies a considerable part of the coal needed. Some coal arrives also by small steamer from North Kyushu and Hokkaido. Yokohama, Japan's first or second port, depending on what year is being considered, is located on the west side of the extensive pouch-shaped Tokyo Bay, the principal gateway for the area. The extensive Kwanto Plain, the largest in Japan, is in general an ideal site for cities and factories, though Yokohama is bordered on its land side by fairly

---

[14] Each of the nodes is described in greater detail in Part III, dealing with the regions of Japan.

high diluvial terrace. Excellent rail connection and the most abundant local labor supply in Japan are other favorable factors.

The region is characterized by a great variety of manufacturing industries. Before the great expansion in heavy industries during the thirties these were chiefly industries that could be housed in small or medium-sized establishments; large factories were the exception. The war boom modified this situation considerably; by the late thirties the Kwanto center had greatly increased in importance, particularly in the heavy industries requiring large factories. Today it ranks high in blast furnaces, steel mills, machines and tools, chemicals, oil refineries, shipbuilding, airplane factories, electrical machinery and textiles. It is estimated that 10–15 per cent of the nation's pig iron and 11–12 per cent of its steel originate in this center. The principal groups of industries in Tokyo and Kanagawa prefectures, the two most industrialized prefectures within the Kwanto node, rank as follows:[15]

	First	Second	Third	Fourth	Fifth
Tokyo Prefecture	Machines and tools	Metals	Chemicals	Food	Textiles
Kanagawa Prefecture	Metals	Machines and tools	Chemicals	Food	Textiles

The Nagoya Node.—To the south of Kwanto, lying between it and the great Kinki Node, is the industrial center located on the Mino-Owari Plain at the head of Ise Bay. Nagoya, a city of 1.3 millions, which is its metropolis and chief manufactural focus, lies 140 miles by rail from Osaka and 235 miles from Tokyo. Eight or ten lesser cities are included within the node, two of them in the 100,000–200,000 group, and two others in the 50,000–100,000 group. This Ise Bay center accounts for about 10 per cent of the country's factory production. Located as it is on one of Japan's larger plains, there is ample room for urban and factory development. Good industrial coal is not available locally, although the adjacent lignite beds are utilized by the ceramics industry and some others. Coal is brought by boat chiefly from the North Kyushu fields. It is relatively close to the principal hydroelectric developments of central Honshu, and the large population cluster of the Mino-Owari Plain provides an adequate supply of local labor. Being on the main Tokaido railway line, its rail service is good, though both rail and water transportation facilities are inferior to those of the Kinki and Kwanto nodes. The improved harbor of Nagoya is not first-class. Although ships of 10,000

[15] *Kojo Tokeihyo,* 1938, pp. 25-26.

tons can enter, the port is far outdistanced by Kobe, Osaka, and Yokohama. Much of the trade of this industrial node passes through the Kinki or Kwanto ports and consequently involves a rail haul. Because of this handicap in shipping facilities the growth of the Nagoya industrial center was slow until the last decade or two, and it is still far from the equal of the Kwanto and Kinki nodes.

Essentially the Nagoya center is one of light manufactures and small-scale industry, and consequently it has not participated as much as some of the others in the wartime industrial expansion. Nagoya, its primate city and seat of the greater part of the new war industry, has grown most rapidly. Textiles, including silk reeling, cotton spinning, cotton weaving, and wool weaving, lead all other industries. In 1938 it was the only one of the four industrial nodes in which textile production held first rank. In each of the others, machines and tools or metals were in first position. In Aichi Prefecture, which includes the city of Nagoya and a large part of the Ise Bay industrial node, the principal groups of industries ranked as follows in 1938: (1) textiles; (2) machines and tools; (3) metals; (4) foods; and (5) chemicals.[16] The pottery industry of the Ise Bay node is the largest in Japan, though scarcely a major industry. Blast furnaces and steel mills are lacking, although there is a relatively important machine and tool industry. The smaller importance of heavy industry in the Nagoya area no doubt reflects its inferior facilities for water transportation, which is of great importance in the handling of bulky raw materials.

The Kinki Node.—The Kinki industrial center, at the eastern end of the Inland Sea at the head of Osaka Bay, and the Kwanto center are the two greatest industrial concentrations in Japan. In terms of total industrial output the two nodes are about on a par, each accounting for approximately 30 per cent of the nation's manufactures in 1938. In the Kinki Node are three of the country's six great cities—Osaka, Kobe, and Kyoto, the first two of which are also among the three great deepwater ports. In addition there are ten or eleven smaller cities, four of which have populations between 100,000 and 200,000 and three between 50,000 and 100,000. Excellent shipping facilities, both water and rail, are available. Extensive plains around Osaka and Kyoto provide good sites for factories and general urban development. Kobe, on the other hand, is handicapped for space, since the hills in its vicinity come down so close to tidewater that level land is scarce. Power resources are less readily available here than in some of the other nodes; coal must be brought by boat from the North Kyushu and Ube fields 250–300 miles distant. Moreover, the region

[16] *Ibid.*

is farther removed from the principal hydroelectric center of Japan than is either Nagoya or Tokyo. The power at Osaka-Kobe, based upon a dependable six months' flow, is only one-third that of Nagoya and one-fifth that of Tokyo-Yokohama.[17]

TABLE 96.—COAL BROUGHT INTO THE TOKYO DISTRICT (ABOUT 1927)	
Coal Field	Tons
Joban	1,860,000
Hokkaido	1,170,000
Kyushu	1,090,000
Motoyama (Ube)	160,000
Formosa, Korea, and imports .	620,000

TABLE 97.—COAL BROUGHT INTO THE OSAKA DISTRICT (ABOUT 1927)	
Coal Field	Tons
Kyushu	3,570,000
Motoyama (Ube)	520,000
Hokkaido	200,000
Formosa, Korea, and imported .	700,000

Source: Kaneo Nanyo, "Transportation and Distribution of Coal in Japan," in *Transactions of Sectional Meeting, World Power Conference*, Tokyo, 1929, 1: 381.

The manufacturing structure of the Kinki Node is one of great diversity. Until recently at least, textiles led all other industries, though the recent expansion in metals and machinery has created serious rivals. In 1938 the four principal groups of industries ranked as follows in both Osaka and Hyogo prefectures, the two which are most industrialized: (1) metals; (2) machines and tools; (3) textiles; (4) chemicals. In Hyogo Prefecture food ranked fifth, in Osaka Prefecture a group of "miscellaneous" industries.[18] Cotton, silk, and rayon processing are all represented in the area. In the past decade the Kinki or *Han-shin* Node has developed as one of the nation's principal iron and steel centers. If Himeji, on the shores of the Inland Sea about fifty kilometers west of Kobe, is included, the area about the eastern end of the Inland Sea is estimated to produce 25–30 per cent of the country's pig iron, about an equal share of its steel, and approximately 45 per cent of its rolling mill output. Other leading industries of the Kinki Node are iron foundries, machine industries, shipbuilding, chemicals, oil refineries, and aircraft factories. Most of these are types of industry that must be housed in large factories. The Osaka-Kobe region is as smoky, noisy, and unattractive in appearance as are most regions of heavy industry. Kyoto, the old capital and the only one of the six great cities of Japan not on tidewater, is unlike the other Kinki cities in that it has been principally a center of craft industries and therefore has been free, until recent years at least, from the grime and noise of a typical factory town.

[17] S. Mayehara and H. More. "The Electric Power Enterprise in Japan," in *Transactions of Sectional Meeting, World Power Conference*, Tokyo, 1929, 2:32–33.
[18] *Kojo Tokeihyo*, 1938, p. 26.

The North Kyushu Industrial Node.—This node is located close to the southwestern limit of the general manufacturing belt. It ranks fourth among the manufacturing concentrations, being credited with nearly 9 per cent of the nation's industrial output in 1938. In total value of manufactures it is about on a part with the Ise Bay Node. It differs from the other nodes in several ways. In the first place, being advantageously situated in close proximity to the nation's most productive coal field, it uses coal power far more than hydroelectric power. Secondly, it is the only one of the four nodes that has no great metropolis, the largest city having a population of less than 350,000. Moreover, it has no important foreign trade port, being served through such secondary ports as Moji, Nagasaki, and Wakamatsu. It also has fewer cities than any of the other nodes, only eight in all. Six of these are strategically located along the Straits of Shimonoseki, where they form an almost continuous urban belt, five on the Kyushu side and one in Honshu. West of this group and separated from it is the largest city, Fukuoka (323,000), and the small city of Ashiya. Other than Fukuoka there is only one city with a population in excess of 200,000, three others over 100,000 and two over 50,000. Two small cities with less than 50,000 population in the Chikuho coal field are perhaps also a part of this southernmost industrial node, although they are not included in the count above.

North Kyushu is the one node in which textiles are not an important element of the industrial structure. Of first importance are the heavy industries, especially iron and steel manufacturing. About a third of the pig iron and 40–50 per cent of the steel manufactured in Japan Proper is probably produced in North Kyushu. It is the chief steel supply center for other industrial regions of Japan. Cement factories, shipyards, flour mills, glass factories, and chemical factories are among the other types of industrial plants well represented in North Kyushu. Large factories are characteristic. The industries are large consumers of fuel and power and so profit by the proximity of coal, to which in large measure they owe their location. The several groups of principal industries in Fukuoka Prefecture, which contains this entire industrial node, rank as follows: (1) metals, (2) chemicals, (3) food, (4) machines and tools, and (5) china or porcelain.[19] Unlike the three other nodes the North Kyushu is not associated with an extensive local plain. The area of greatest industrial concentration is along a narrow strip of level land bordering the Straits of Shimonoseki in the extreme north of Kyushu.

[19] *Kojo Tokeihyo,* 1938, p. 26.

THE IMPORTANT INDUSTRIES
Textiles

By most of the criteria employed to measure the importance of an industry, the textile group was, until the late thirties, the most important in Japan. In 1927 this group of industries employed about half of the country's two million factory workers and contributed 45 per cent of the value of its manufactured goods and 65 per cent of its exports. In 1928 six of the ten industries that ranked highest in number of workers were branches of the textile group, the first three places being occupied by silk reeling, cotton spinning, and cotton weaving. Silk weaving came sixth; dyeing, bleaching, and finishing came eighth; and wool ninth. If statistics were available for the great number of establishments employing fewer than five workers, which are not included in the factory reports, it would be seen that textiles occupy an even more important place than

TABLE 98.—RELATIVE IMPORTANCE OF PRINCIPAL GROUPS OF INDUSTRY, 1938

Group of Industries	FACTORIES		WORKERS		OUTPUT	
	Number	Per Cent	Number	Per Cent	Value (thousands of yen)	Per Cent
Textiles	28,029	25.0	976,953	30.4	3,984,830	20.3
Metals	11,135	9.9	377,398	11.7	4,687,167	23.8
Machines and tools	17,570	15.6	860,431	26.8	3,821,881	19.4
Porcelain	4,816	4.3	105,345	3.3	403,646	2.1
Chemicals	6,146	5.5	322,205	10.0	3,460,582	17.6
Lumber and wood	10,629	9.5	113,823	3.5	457,303	2.3
Printing and bookbinding	3,932	3.5	63,568	2.0	281,170	1.4
Food and drink	16,944	15.1	190,697	5.9	1,786,275	9.1
Gas and electric	699	0.6	10,517	0.3	737,175	3.8
Miscellaneous	12,399	11.0	194,484	6.1	47,191	0.2
Total	112,332	100.0	3,215,421	100.0	19,667,220	100.0

Source: *Kojo Tokeihyo*, 1938, pp. 2, 5, 15.

TABLE 99.—VOLUME INDEXES OF TEXTILE PRODUCTION

Year	Cotton Yarn	Raw Silk	Silk Yarn	Woolen Yarn	Rayon Yarn	Cotton Fabric	Silk Fabric	Rayon Fabric	Woolen Fabric
1931–33	100	100	100	100	100	100	100	100	100
1937	140	94	76	119	483	131	110	312	57
1938	107	91	92	98	297	97	93	247	75
1939	96	79	96	118	340	97	108	216	78

Source: *Far East Year Book*, 1941, p. 370.

the above ranking suggests, for much of the silk reeling and the cotton and silk weaving is still carried on in households and small workshops.

The volume and value of textile production continued to increase until about 1937, though its relative importance in Japan's industrial structure declined during the 1930's, especially after 1937, when the heavy industries were drafted into a program of rapid expansion. In 1936 textile workers comprised only 38 per cent of all factory employees and by 1939 only 30.4 per cent. The total value of the factory production of textiles dropped to 28.5 per cent in 1936 (metals and machinery and tools increased to 31.6 per cent) and in 1939 to 20 per cent (metals and machinery and tools increased to 45 per cent and chemicals to 17 per cent).

The composition of Japanese industry prior to 1931, when chief emphasis was still being placed on textiles and other forms of light manufactures, seems to be the normal and logical industrial development for a country like Japan. Since the various forms of production in the textile group—the reeling of raw silk, the weaving of silk cloth, and the spinning and weaving of cotton, rayon, staple fiber, and wool—require no large amounts of heat, great quantities of coal are not essential and principal use can be made of hydroelectric power. The total consumption of power is not large, the machinery is light and relatively inexpensive, the factories

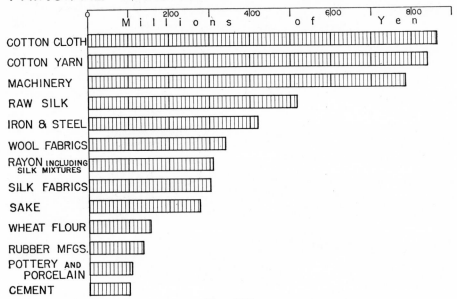

PRINCIPAL MANUFACTURING INDUSTRIES - 1936

Fig. 127

need not be large and costly, and much cheap female labor can be used. Moreover, the markets for Japanese textiles are far better than for the products of heavy industry, for the Asiatic market is a large consumer of cheap cotton cloth, and in the past at least the American market has been a large buyer of raw silk. Cotton cloth and raw silk have for decades been the two pillars of Japan's export trade. The diminishing importance of textiles in the total industrial structure and the current rise of heavy industries has represented not a normal economic adjustment, but an artificial stimulation inspired by political ambitions.

THE SILK INDUSTRY

This is one of Japan's greatest manufacturing industries, for 70 per cent of the world's silk output comes from Nippon (Fig. 127). It is the greatest of the so-called traditional trades and the most important of those traditional trades which have produced both for export and for the Japanese market. More persons are engaged in the reeling of silk and the weaving of silk cloth than in any other single branch of industry. Moreover, the industry is Japanese in almost all its aspects. The raw material is produced in Japan, silkworms being raised in millions of farm homes; and the silk cloth manufactured is largely of special types to meet the demands of the domestic market. On the other hand, the most important branch of the industry, silk reeling, produces largely an export commodity, and is thus dependent on foreign markets. Since more than three-fourths of Japan's raw silk is exported, and even 30 per cent of that processed at home is eventually sent abroad as tissue, the prosperity of the industry fluctuates with the buying power of Western nations, particularly the United States, which has in the past bought 80–90 per cent of the exported product. The world depression of the early thirties, which seriously impaired the American

FIG. 128. A large filature, or silk reeling factory, in the Suwa Basin.

market, and the increasing competition of artificial silks has had a disastrous effect upon the silk industry of Japan. Between 1905 and 1934 raw silk production in Japan increased fivefold, but recent years have seen a sharp decline. Mulberry acreage shrank from 714,000 cho in 1930 to 550,000 cho in 1939, cocoons from 334 million kilograms to 196 million, and filature basins from 418,402 to 239,013. The output of raw silk descended from an all-time high of 12 million kwan[20] in 1934 to 11 million in 1939. Volume exports of raw silk declined from 73 million pounds in 1935 to 51 million in 1939.

Silk Reeling.—The raising of silk and the production of cocoons by the peasant farmers of Japan, which is a phase of the industry that belongs to agriculture rather than to manufacturing, has been described in the preceding chapter. Manufacturing begins with silk reeling, which involves the unwinding of the silk filaments from the cocoons and the twisting of several of them into a larger filament. These are then wound into skeins for shipment. Some reeling is still done by hand in farm homes, but this type of processing is gradually declining. Over 90 per cent of the silk reeled in Japan is done in small to medium-sized factories called filatures (Fig. 128). Unless the plants are areally concentrated they are not of such size as to be very conspicuous. An average-sized filature with about 100 boiling basins employs in the neighborhood of 120 workers. Although there has been a slight trend toward larger filatures, the bulkiness of cocoons and the increasingly greater insistence upon a standardized product make it difficult for a plant with more than 300 basins to obtain the necessary supplies of standardized cocoons locally and within easy transport distance. Large factories such as characterize the cotton-spinning industry would be distinctly uneconomical for silk reeling.[21] More than half the silk reeled is from average-sized filatures with 50–300 boiling basins. Only 5 per cent of the filatures have more than 300 basins, and these represent 29 per cent of the reeling capacity.[22] Often the large cocoon warehouses, several stories high and each story's row of open windows protected by wide eaves, are more conspicuous features than the factories themselves. The small amount of power required by the filatures is usually supplied by local hydroelectric plants.

In view of the bulkiness of cocoons it is natural that the 37,442 (66,400 in 1931) silk-reeling plants should be widely distributed over the country, coinciding in general with the distribution of mulberry acreage and of cocoon production. There are very few north of latitude 40°, and the

---

[20] One kwan = 8.276 pounds.
[21] See Schumpeter *et al.*, *op. cit.*, 518–519.   [22] *Japan Year Book*, 1935-36, p. 83.

industry is almost totally lacking in Hokkaido. The principal concentrations are (1) in the basins of the Fossa Magna in Nagano and Yamanashi prefectures, (2) in western Kwanto in Gumma and Saitama prefectures, and (3) in the borderlands of Ise and Atumi bays in Aichi Prefecture (Fig. 129). The longitudinal interior basins of southern Ou or Tohoku in Fukushima and Yamagata prefectures are a lesser region of concentration.

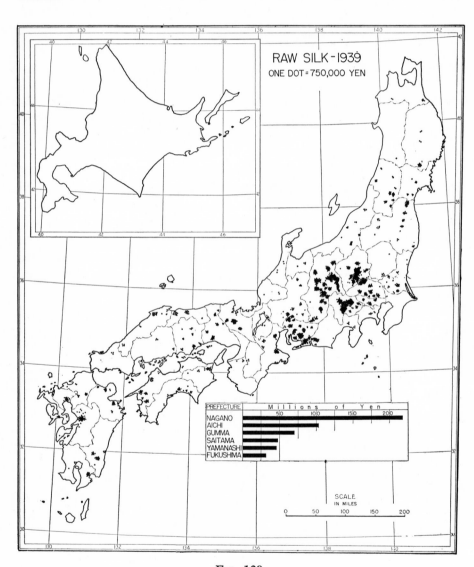

FIG. 129

Silk Weaving.—This is an industry quite separate from silk reeling. It includes the weaving of pure silk tissues and of silk and cotton mixtures. In 1937 it employed 294,000 persons, most of them women, a considerably larger number than were employed in the filatures. Several branches of the industry are recognized. Some cloth is still woven in the homes of the peasant farmers, whereas other types are products of skilled craft industries; some are luxury products, others standard silks for export

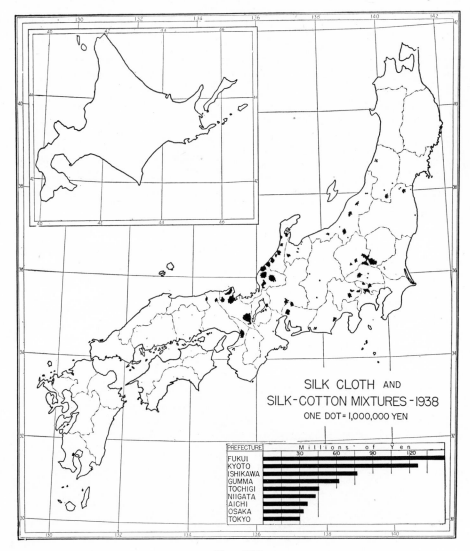

FIG. 130

FIG. 131. A large cotton-spinning mill is located at the base of the hill. The slopes in the foreground are covered with tea gardens.

FIG. 132. A representative cotton-weaving mill. Near Hamamatsu, Shizuoka Prefecture.

markets. Silk weaving is usually housed in inconspicuous plants of the domestic workshop variety, which outwardly resemble a shed. In 1934 about 85 per cent of the 73,000 silk-weaving plants were such family establishments with only one or two looms. Plants employing four persons or fewer comprised 94.5 per cent of the total number and employed two-thirds of the workers engaged in silk reeling. The larger factories produce principally for the foreign markets, chiefly the United States, British India, and Great Britain.

In such a workshop type of industry the plants need not be concentrated in large industrial centers, nor do they need to be near the centers of raw silk production. Mainly they are in towns and smaller cities, a large number of them outside the principal manufactural belt. Many of those that turn out products requiring skilled craftsmanship are in settlements that have a long tradition in silk-cloth products of a particular kind. But although the industry is geographically scattered, there are a number of centers of production. The principal one is in the prefectures of Fukui and Ishikawa (about latitude 36°) on the Japan Sea side of the country. A second is in Kyoto Prefecture, both in and around the city of Kyoto and at the Japan Sea extremity of the prefecture. Western Kwanto, in Gumma, Tochigi, and Yamanashi prefectures, is a third center (Fig. 130). Most of these silk-weaving centers are survivals of the feudal period, and much of the industry is still carried on in substantially the same fashion as a century or more ago.

THE COTTON TEXTILE INDUSTRY

The spinning and weaving of cotton is one of Japan's pillars of industrial strength (Fig. 127). Unlike the silk industry, the cotton-spinning establishments derive almost all their raw material from foreign countries, and in normal years raw cotton has been the country's most important single item of import. In contrast to silk, therefore, this branch of Japanese textiles is not based on the activities of Nippon's peasant farmers. Hence market fluctuations do not affect so large a part of the population as does a depression in the silk market. Since 1933 cotton tissues have been the leading export commodity, although in 1939, when silk prices rose abruptly, raw silk slipped back into its long-held first place. During the early and middle thirties the cotton textile industry expanded rapidly. In 1933 Japan displaced Great Britain as the world's greatest exporter of cotton cloth, and in 1937, the year that saw the beginning of the Sino-Japanese War, cotton production reached an all-time high. After 1937, as the nation applied its industrial strength to war preparations, there was a rapid falling off in the output of cotton textiles (see Table 99).

Cotton Spinning.—This is one of the Japanese industries which are controlled by large corporations and in which the operating or technical unit is the large factory (Fig. 131). Thus while there were nearly 34,000 cotton-weaving establishments in 1938, spinning mills numbered only 288 (1937). During the period of textile expansion in the thirties they increased rapidly in size, so that by the end of the decade they were comparable to those of Occidental countries.[23] Equipment in the larger and medium-sized mills is of the most modern type. Japan's world position in cotton spinning is revealed in the fact that in July, 1938, she possessed about one-third as many spindles as Great Britain, nearly half as many as the United States, and more than Germany, France, or India. With respect to raw cotton consumed Japan ranks next to the United States.[24]

The cotton-spinning industry is geographically concentrated, much the larger part of it lying within the principal industrial belt and within the three northern nodes of that belt. The major spinning concentrations are (1) the Kinki region at the eastern end of the Inland Sea, of which Osaka is the main center; (2) the borderlands of Ise Bay especially on

TABLE 100.—JAPAN'S WORLD POSITION WITH RESPECT TO NUMBER OF SPINDLES AND
CONSUMPTION OF RAW COTTON AT THE END OF JULY, 1938

Country	Number of Spindles	Raw Cotton Consumed (thousands of bales)
Japan	12,550	3,660
United Kingdom	36,879	2,500
United States.	26,376	5,750
Germany.	11,074	1,171
France.	9,794	1,149
India	9,731	3,402

Source: *Japan-Manchukuo Year Book*, 1940, p. 371.

the Mino-Owari Plain, with Nagoya as the focal point; (3) the Kwanto region; and (4) the northern shores of the Inland Sea (Fig. 133).

Cotton Weaving.—In contrast to spinning, cotton weaving is characterized by small factories, although the operating units vary greatly in size. Since 1929 there has been a substantial increase in the number of larger weaving mills and a progressive decline in the number of sheds having fewer than ten looms. As late as 1937, however, 87 per cent of the weaving establishments had ten looms or fewer, so that the characteristic operating unit is still the inconspicuous unpainted, shed-like structure which one hardly notices (Fig. 132). The number of wide power looms

[23] Allen, *Japanese Industry*, 35.
[24] *Japan-Manchukuo Year Book*, 1940, p. 371.

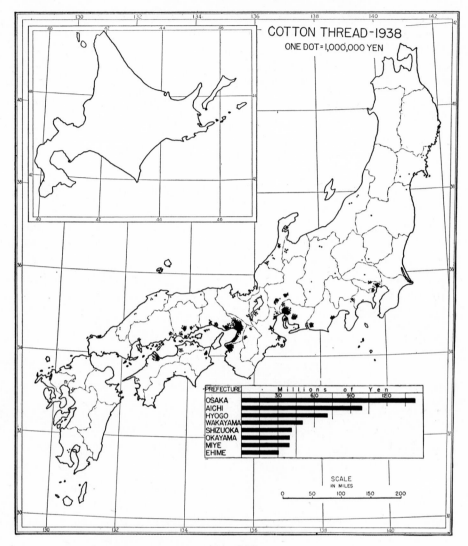

COTTON THREAD-1938
ONE DOT = 1,000,000 YEN

PREFECTURE	Millions of Yen			
	30	60	90	120
OSAKA				
AICHI				
HYOGO				
WAKAYAMA				
SHIZUOKA				
OKAYAMA				
MIYE				
EHIME				

SCALE
IN MILES

0   50   100   150   200

FIG. 133

increased rapidly during the decade of the 1930's, and the narrow power
looms and hand looms declined. The result is that in a considerable number of Japanese mills the technical equipment is very modern and efficient.
It is chiefly the small plants equipped with hand looms and narrow power
looms which produce for the domestic market,[25] and the larger plants

[25] For a detailed account of the organization of cotton spinning and weaving industries see Schumpeter *et al., op. cit.,* 568-586.

equipped with modern broad power looms that concentrate on materials for export. Cotton weaving is somewhat more widely distributed than is the spinning branch of the industry. Still there is a noteworthy concentration in the three Honshu manufacturing nodes and along the borderlands of the Inland Sea (Fig. 134). The plants are not necessarily located in the largest cities, but quite as often in the suburban areas and in the satellite towns of the metropolises and in the lesser cities.

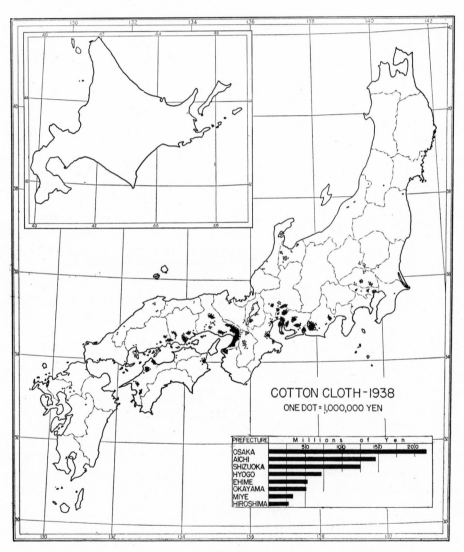

COTTON CLOTH-1938

ONE DOT = 1,000,000 YEN

PREFECTURE	Millions of Yen
	50 100 150 200
OSAKA	
AICHI	
SHIZUOKA	
HYOGO	
EHIME	
OKAYAMA	
MIYE	
HIROSHIMA	

FIG. 134

The Woolen and Worsted Industry.—This is small as compared with silk and cotton. Since World War I the processing of wool has had an important growth, mainly as a result of the increased domestic consumption of woolen clothing of foreign style. Woolen yarn production more than doubled between 1930 and 1937, yet in 1935 the spinning mills numbered only 47. The weaving industry is housed in small and medium-sized plants. Fifty-seven per cent of the mills had fewer than ten looms,

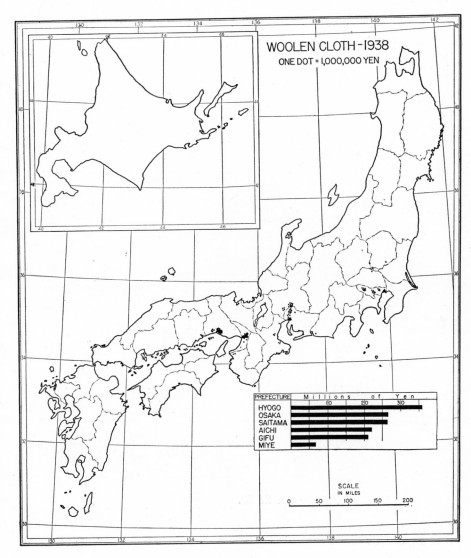

FIG. 135

37 per cent from ten to fifty looms, and only 6 per cent over fifty looms.[26] There is a high concentration of the woolen industry in the Nagoya region (Aichi and Gifu prefectures) and in Hyogo, Osaka, and Saitama prefectures (Fig. 135).

Artificial Fibers.—The development of the rayon and staple fiber[27] (rayon yarn cut into fiber lengths for spinning) industries in Japan has been phenomenal, and in 1937 she led the world in this field. Rayon yarn production rose from 5 million pounds in 1926 to 334.4 million pounds in 1937. Staple fiber increased from about a half million pounds in 1932 to 174.8 million in 1937 and 375 million in 1938.[28] The rapid growth in artificial fibers has compensated to a certain extent for the decline in raw silk. But since the raw material for this industry is domestic and imported wood pulp, its expansion has not compensated the farming population for the shrinkage in silk exports. Part of the recent rapid increase in staple fiber in Japan resulted from government regulations requiring manufacturers to mix 20–30 per cent staple fiber with wool (after November 1, 1937), and to mix 30 per cent staple fiber with cotton (after February 1, 1938) in the manufacture of cloth for the home market.[29] These regulations were designed to curtail imports of cotton and wool.

Fig. 136. A large and modern rayon factory at the southern end of Lake Biwa.

Rayon and staple fiber goods designed for the domestic market are made from relatively low-grade wood pulp obtained in Japan and Manchuria, while the export textiles use higher grade pulp imported from the Scandinavian countries, the United States, and Canada.[30] The exports of

[26] *Shokosho Tokeihyo,* 1938, pp. 29-30.

[27] See Keijiro Ishiyama, "Our Staple Fiber Industry," in *Contemporary Japan,* 5:400–406 (December, 1936).

[28] C. H. Barber, "Impact of War on the Japanese Cotton Textile Industry," in *Foreign Agriculture,* 5:300 (July, 1941).

[29] Schumpeter *et al., op. cit.,* 218.   [30] Barber, *op. cit.,* 300.

yarn and tissues made of artificial fibers rose rapidly until 1937, when their total value was 233 million yen. In 1937 the exports of rayon fabrics alone amounted to 21 per cent of the total value of cotton cloth exported. Most of this export surplus was taken by the Asiatic market.

Partly because of its very recent development the manufacture of rayon and staple-fiber yarn and thread is concentrated in large and modern factories, the average rayon factory employing between 1,000 and 2,000

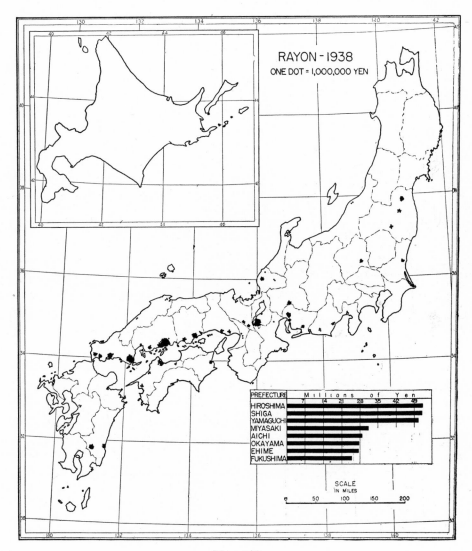

RAYON - 1938
ONE DOT = 1,000,000 YEN

PREFECTURE	Millions of Yen						
	7	14	21	28	35	42	49
HIROSHIMA							
SHIGA							
YAMAGUCHI							
MIYASAKI							
AICHI							
OKAYAMA							
EHIME							
FUKUSHIMA							

SCALE
IN MILES
0   50   100   150   200

Fig. 137

workers (Fig. 136). In 1938 there were only 51 establishments manufacturing rayon, but these had an output valued at over 400 million yen. Distribution of the plants is widespread, but the large majority of them are in the general manufacturing belt (Fig. 137). The weaving of rayon cloth, on the other hand, was taken up by the already existing silk-weaving sheds, or sometimes by cotton-weaving establishments. It was natural that the plants manufacturing silk cloth should be the first to experiment with

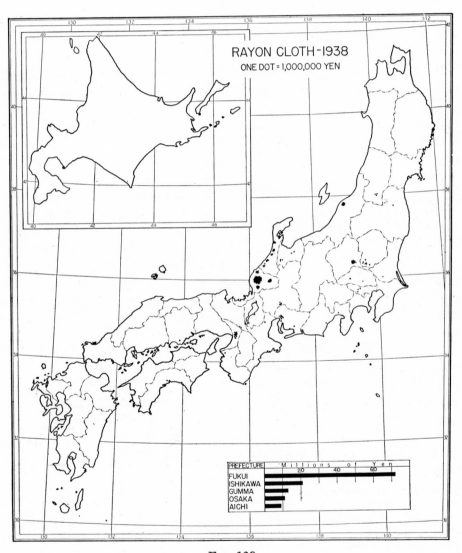

FIG. 138

the new product. Rayon weaving is restricted to fewer areas than is silk weaving, but within the general areas where the processing of rayon does exist, the distribution of the industry is much the same as silk weaving (Fig. 138). Thus about 60 per cent of the rayon piece goods are produced in Fukui and Ishikawa prefectures on the Japan Sea side of the country.[31] The product here is chiefly for export. Gumma Prefecture, in western Kwanto, and Kyoto Prefecture are lesser centers of production which produce chiefly for the home market.

The Heavy Industries

IRON AND STEEL

It was said above that in the remarkable industrial expansion of the thirties it was the heavy industries of Japan that surged ahead most rapidly. There is no doubt that this unnatural emphasis on the iron and steel and the machine and tool industries was motivated by the State's policy of making the country as self-sufficient as possible as regards the materials essential to modern warfare. This seemed imperative in view of Japan's declared expansionist policy with respect to eastern and southeastern Asia. In 1930 only 1.2 million tons of pig iron were produced in Japan Proper, and in 1931 less than a million tons. Steel ingot production was only 2.2 million tons in 1930. By 1936 the output of pig iron had nearly doubled over that of 1930, and steel production had more than doubled. No official figures for production have been issued since 1936, but estimates from various sources suggest that by 1941 or 1942 Japan Proper's pig iron output may have increased to 6 or 7 million tons and steel to about the same amount.[32] If the Japanese-owned plants in Manchuria and Korea are included, the Empire's output of pig iron may have been close to 10 million tons and of steel over 8 million tons. At about the same time the average monthly production of steel in the United States was about 7 million tons. If the estimate for 1941 is approximately correct, it indicates a threefold expansion in blast furnace output since 1936, placing Japan in sixth place among the steel-making countries of the world, the countries taking precedence being the United States, Germany, Russia, the United Kingdom, and France.

[31] Schumpeter et al., op. cit., 527.
[32] See Iron and Steel Facts, August, 1942, p. 4; "Japan No Match for United States in Essential Metal Supplies," Steel, 109:23 (December 15, 1941); "Decade's Scrap Imports Supply Japan with Iron, Steel Stockpile," Steel, 111:48 (August 24, 1942); Alvin Barber, "Steel in Japan's War Economy," Amerasia, 5:264 (August, 1941); The Japan Advertiser Annual Review, 1938–39, p. 48; 1939–40, p. 49; Japan-Manchukuo Year Book, 1940, p. 345.

Pig Iron.—Production of pig iron in Japan is based largely upon imported iron ore. In 1936 only about 15 per cent of the country's pig was manufactured from domestic ore. During the decade of the thirties remarkable changes occurred, not only in the magnitude of the blast-furnace industry but also in its geographical distribution. In 1931 there were four centers of pig iron production, of which North Kyushu was outstanding, producing 75–80 per cent of the country's total. Kamaishi in northeastern Honshu came next with a little over 13 per cent and then Muroran in Hokkaido and Yokohama, each producing from 6 to 7 per cent. In the next decade a new center, which has become one of the most important, sprang up in the Osaka-Kobe-Himeji region at the eastern end of the Inland Sea, and the other centers changed, both with respect to the magnitude of the industry and their positions of relative importance.

TABLE 101.—THE IRON AND STEEL INDUSTRY

A. OUTPUT AND IMPORTS IN JAPAN PROPER

(in thousands of metric tons)

Year	IRON ORE		PIG IRON		FERRO-ALLOYS		Scrap Imports	Output of Ingot and Cast Steel†
	Output	Imports*	Output	Imports	Output	Imports		
1926	130	892	810	504	12	4	80	1,506
1927	159	1,106	896	576	16	5	228	1,685
1928	158	1,842	1,093	709	17	4	367	1,906
1929	178	2,259	1,087	792	25	3	496	2,294
1932	227	1,634	1,011	650	26	1	559	2,398
1933	321	1,779	1,424	801	33	1	1,013	3,198
1934	432	2,312	1,728	779	44	—	1,413	3,843
1935	516	3,646	1,907	1,093	58	—	1,692	4,703
1936	620	4,023	2,008	1,095	65	—	1,497	5,223

B. OUTPUT IN JAPANESE-CONTROLLED TERRITORY

(in thousands of metric tons)

Year	IRON ORE				PIG IRON				STEEL INGOTS AND CASTINGS			
	Japan Proper	Ko-rea	Man-chukuo	Total	Japan Proper	Ko-rea	Man-chukuo	Total	Japan Proper	Ko-rea	Man-chukuo	Total
1929	178	559	781	1,518	1,087	154	295	1,536	2,294	—	—	2,294
1934	432	570	1,133	2,136	1,728	211	476	2,415	3,843	60	—	3,903
1935	516	598	1,478	2,592	1,907	211	608	2,726	4,703	97	137	4,937
1936	620	629	1,905	3,154	2,008	217	633	2,858	5,223	87	344	5,654

Source: Both sections of the table based on Mining Section of Department of Commerce and Industry, *References for Steel Works*, 1935 and 1936 (in Japanese), as quoted in Schumpeter *et al.*, *The Industrialization of Japan and Manchukuo*, 597–598.

* Including imports from colonies and Manchukuo.   † Including crucible and electric-smelted steel.

Fig. 139a. The government steel mills at Yawata in northern Kyushu.
Photograph by Natori, Black Star.

As of about 1942 it is estimated the Japanese Empire was probably
producing about 10 million tons of pig iron, of which nearly 7 million
tons or 69 per cent came from Japan Proper, 23 per cent from Manchurian
centers at Mukden and Penhsihu, and close to 8 per cent from the Kenjiho
and Seishin centers in Korea. American estimates indicate that 30–35
per cent of the pig iron produced in Japan Proper came from Yawata and
Kokura in North Kyushu; 8–10 per cent from Himeji on the shores of the
Inland Sea some 25–30 miles west of Kobe; 18–22 per cent from Kobe–
Osaka; 11–14 per cent from Tokyo–Yokohama; 7–9 per cent from Kamai·
shi, and 16–18 per cent from Muroran (Fig. 139b). Of great significance
is the much wider dispersion of blast-furnace capacity that took place
within a decade.

Relatively the North Kyushu center had suffered a serious decline as
blast furnaces expanded in other areas, although its absolute production

had multiplied threefold. This center has the advantage of close proximity to Japan's most productive coal field, and like the others it has the advantage of tidewater location, which makes a rail haul of imported iron ore unnecessary. On the other hand, it is handicapped in that it is somewhat removed from the principal markets for iron and steel products. The new Osaka-Kobe-Himeji center at the eastern end of the Inland Sea probably had by 1941 a blast-furnace capacity not far short of that of North Kyushu. These two centers combined, one old and the other new, probably produced about 60 per cent of the country's total pig iron. Removed

TABLE 102.—PRODUCTION AND IMPORT OF PIG IRON
(in thousands of metric tons)

Year	Home Production	IMPORTS FROM			Imports from Colonies	Total Supply
		Manchuria	British India	Total, including Others		
1931	917.3	242.1	150.4	399.5	95.1	1,411.9
1932	1,010.7	322.4	117.8	444.4	205.9	1,661.1
1933	1,423.8	453.9	172.0	640.8	160.4	2,225.1
1934	1,728.1	409.4	202.2	614.3	164.1	2,506.7
1935	1,906.7	382.7	338.3	961.9	130.6	2,999.3
1936	2,007.5	271.2	375.4	971.9	122.9	3,102.4

Source: *Japan-Manchukuo Year Book*, 1940, p. 340.

from both coal and iron ore fields, the Kinki center finds its chief advantage in being in and near the most important steel market. The Tokyo–Yokohama center, which in the decade since 1931 multiplied its output of pig iron twelve to thirteen times, has many of the same market advantages as the Kinki center and in addition fairly close proximity to the Joban coal field. All iron ore must be imported, and supplementary supplies of coal come by water from both Hokkaido and Kyushu. Kamaishi, in northeastern Honshu, smallest producer of all the centers, was established in that location to make use of the local iron ores produced in the Kamaishi and Sennin mines. Coal is obtained chiefly from Hokkaido. The blast furnaces at Muroran were designed to make use of local Hokkaido ore and coal. Iron ore comes from Kutchan and other lesser mines, and coal from the Ishikari field.

Since the beginning of the war in the Pacific, shortages of iron and steel have forced the Japanese to revert to some of the inefficient and expensive methods of iron production that were practised in the feudal period. Prime Minister Tojo, discussing steel production before the Diet on February 4, 1943, stated that numerous very small blast furnaces, capable of being constructed in three months' time, were utilizing iron-sand deposits widely scattered throughout the country.[33] This type of iron production is uneconomical and is entirely an emergency measure.

Steel.—In steel manufacture, too, Japan Proper relies greatly on raw materials derived from outside. In 1936 only about two-thirds of the pig consumed in Japanese steel mills was produced at home; the remaining third came from British India, Manchuria, Korea, and other sources. After 1934 imports from Manchuria declined as steel manufacturing was expanded in that Yen-Bloc area, but between 1931 and 1934 imports of pig from all sources increased 2.4 times.

Besides imported pig iron large amounts of scrap iron, both foreign and domestic, were consumed in steel making in Japan. Between 1931 and 1936 imports of scrap multiplied five or six times, and the imported product amounted to about 60 per cent of the total used in the steel mills. In 1935 some 80 per cent and in 1936 about 68 per cent of the scrap obtained from overseas came from the United States and most of the remainder from British India, Dutch East Indies, Australia, England, and China. Not all the imported scrap, by any means, was currently consumed in the steel mills, for huge stock piles were accumulated as an emergency precaution. Statistics on total scrap imports are not available for years later than 1936, but some indication of their increased volume may be obtained from the fact that exports from the United States to Japan increased from 1.06 million gross tons in 1936 to 2.03 million tons in 1939. In 1934, the year preceding the marked rise in steel production, about four-fifths of all the steel and foundry products of Japan Proper were derived from materials—ore, pig iron, and scrap—obtained from outside sources. Even if supplies from Manchuria and Korea are considered as home production, half of the materials for steel production in Japan came from foreign sources in 1934, and the proportion was still greater in 1936.[34]

In 1936 about 94 per cent of Japan's steel was produced in basic open-hearth furnaces. Bessemer output was insignificant—less than 0.1 per cent. Electric-furnace steel has increased remarkably since 1932; in 1936 it amounted to over 6 per cent of the total. The abundance and cheapness of hydroelectric power in Japan offers bright prospects for further increases in electric-furnace steel.

Prior to 1931 Japan's steel production was largely by the "hot-metal"

[33] Andrew J. Grajdanzev, "Japan's Economy Since Pearl Harbor," pt. 2, in the *Far Eastern Survey*, 12:132 (June 30, 1943).

[34] Schumpeter *et al.*, *op. cit.*, 599–600.

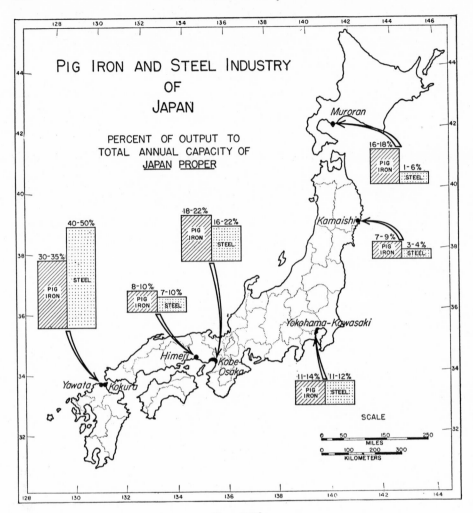

FIG. 139b

or "one-heat" process, by which iron ore is converted into steel in a single continuous operation.[35] However, with the greatly increased imports of scrap iron and pig that were required after 1931 to carry out the steel expansion program, it became necessary to revive the cold-metal process and to establish steel mills in areas where there were no blast furnaces or where the local supply of pig iron was insufficient. In 1935, it is estimated, half of Japan's steel was manufactured by this process.[36] The average ratio of scrap to pig in all Japanese foundries was 58 to 42.[37] After

[35] *Ibid.*, 447.   [36] *Ibid.*, 602.
[37] *Japan-Manchukuo Year Book*, 1940, p. 341.

the beginning of the war with China, in 1937, this trend toward an increasing use of imported scrap was reversed and the "hot-metal" process became increasingly important as the government tried to make the domestic iron and steel industry less dependent on American supplies. In 1939 the maximum percentage of scrap in steel was set at 60 per cent; at the beginning of 1940 it was reduced to 50 per cent and plans were outlined to reduce it to 20 per cent if and when an embargo was declared by the United States.[38]

An estimated 86–91 per cent of the steel produced in the Japanese Empire in recent years came from Japan Proper. Nearly all the remainder came from plants located at Anshan and Penhishu in the vicinity of Mukden in South Manchuria; a trifling amount may have been produced at the Kenjiho works in Korea. Some 6–11 per cent of the steel production in Japan Proper was probably manufactured in small, widely scattered plants; the remainder was concentrated in the centers of blast-furnace production described above. Not all the steel plants are also producers of pig iron, however, and there are some blast-furnace plants that are not integrated with steel mills. To a greater extent than pig iron, steel manufacturing is concentrated in North Kyushu. Inasmuch as 40–50 per cent of the steel produced in Japan Proper in 1942 is estimated to have come from the Yawata and Kokura mills located there, North Kyushu is the chief steel supply center for the engineering and foundry plants of the country (Fig. 139b). Next in rank is the steel center at the eastern end of the Inland Sea, where the combined output of the plants at Himeji and Osaka-Kobe represent 25–30 per cent of the country's total. Three plants in the Tokyo-Yokohama district account for about 11 per cent of the nation's production, 3–4 per cent comes from Kamaishi, and an estimated 1–6 per cent from Muroran in Hokkaido. Rolling mills are chiefly concentrated in the Kinki and North Kyushu centers.

THE ENGINEERING AND SHIPBUILDING INDUSTRIES[39]

This group of industries includes those making all kinds of machinery and tools, those manufacturing equipment for the generation of power, light, and heat, and all industries processing equipment used in transporting men or goods by land, water, or air. Such trades develop only in countries that have reached a relatively advanced stage of economic development, for they are based on diversification of industry, large accumulations of capital, and an expert knowledge of technical processes. It is

---

[38] Schumpeter et al., op. cit., 447.
[39] For additional details on these industries see Schumpeter et al., op. cit., 608–616.

only recently that Japan has been able to meet these prerequisites. The development of the engineering industries has been particularly rapid since 1932, when the government began to make a determined effort to free the country from its dependence on foreign sources for industrial equipment essential in war industries. Such marked strides toward self-sufficiency have been made in these trades that many classes of steel material are no longer imported. Even large and complicated pieces of

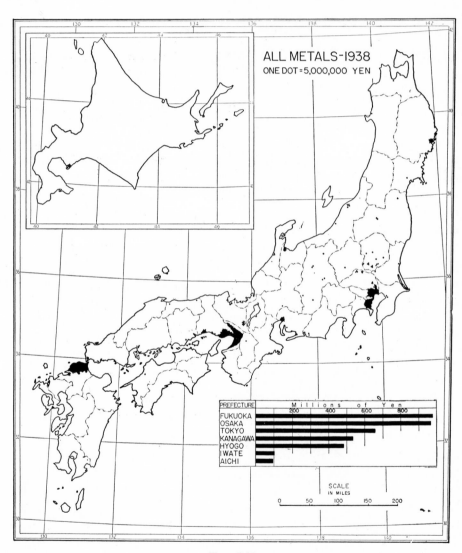

ALL METALS–1938
ONE DOT = 5,000,000 YEN

PREFECTURE	Millions of Yen
	200 400 600 800
FUKUOKA	
OSAKA	
TOKYO	
KANAGAWA	
HYOGO	
IWATE	
AICHI	

SCALE
IN MILES
0   50   100   150   200

FIG. 140

engineering equipment, such as marine engines, steam and water turbines, railway engines, airplane motors, electric dynamos, and motors, are now being manufactured at home. Indeed, some classes of machinery are actually being exported.

Domestic production in the machinery industries increased from a total value of 616 million yen in 1930 to about 2.4 billion in 1937. Machine tools, textile machinery, and electrical machinery and equipment also ex-

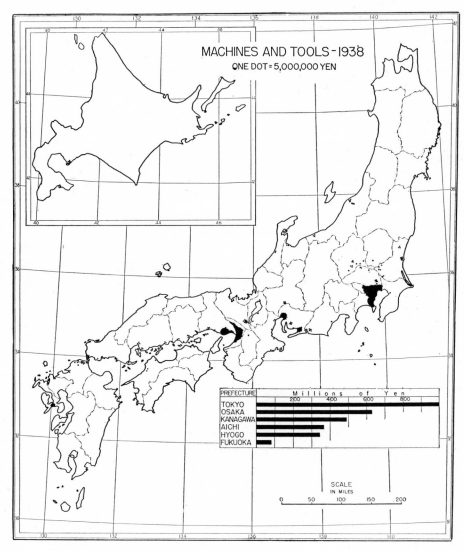

FIG. 141

panded with unusual speed. The number of laborers in machine-tool factories increased from 5,196 in 1931 to 30,957 in 1937, nearly 500 per cent, and the value of the output multiplied at about the same rate.[40] Much of this greatly increased production still comes from small and medium-sized plants. Yet despite this great domestic expansion, imports of machine tools have increased in response to the expansion of the engineering trades as a whole and the government's heavy expenditures on war industries.

A marked feature of the engineering industry is its concentration in a few firms and the large size of its plants, almost all of which manufacture a great range of products. Although individual plants are scattered throughout Japan, they tend to be concentrated in the Kinki and the Kwanto industrial nodes and, to a smaller extent, in North Kyushu and the district around Nagoya (Figs. 140, 141).[41]

Shipbuilding.—Like the other forms of heavy industry, shipbuilding expanded markedly after 1933. In 1937, for example, the tonnage of ships launched was more than six times what it had been in 1933 and nine to ten times as great as in 1932; the total exceeded that of any other country except Great Britain. Japan's yards are equipped to build every kind of

TABLE 103.—SHIPS OF OVER 1,000 TONS LAUNCHED IN JAPAN, 1932–37

Year	No. of Ships	Tons	Year	No. of Ships	Tons
1932.	10	43,760	1935.	24	111,650
1933.	10	68,685	1936.	63	270,710
1934.	20	124,180	1937.	93	419,665

Source: *Japan-Manchukuo Year Book*, 1940, p. 226.

ship, from small lowly tramps to luxury liners. The industry is concentrated in the Yokohama area, at Kobe-Osaka, Nagasaki, Shimonoseki, and Tamashima on the shores of the Inland Sea in Okayama Prefecture.

Other large-scale factory industries of importance in Japan's industrial structure are those concerned with the manufacture of industrial chemicals, fertilizer, cement, beer, glass, and paper, and with the refining of petroleum products and sugar. Most of these are of a type that is charac-

[40] Translation from the *Economist* (Toyko), April 12, 1939, in *Industrial Japan* (Institute of Pacific Relations, New York, 1941), 88–90.

[41] See the map of Japan's war plants accompanying an article by T. E. Lloyd, "Kyushu and Honshu Islands Focal Points of Japan Industry," in *Iron Age*, 149:83–91 (April 30, 1942). See also the map accompanying the unsigned article, "Design for Bombing Japan," in *Steel*, 115:75 (August 28, 1944).

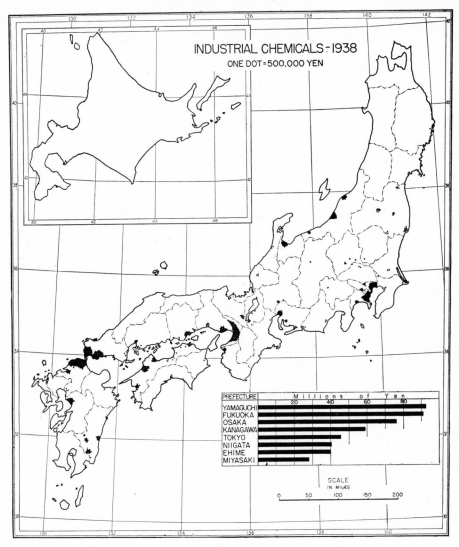

INDUSTRIAL CHEMICALS - 1938
ONE DOT = 500.000 YEN

PREFECTURE	Millions of Yen
YAMAGUCHI	
FUKUOKA	
OSAKA	
KANAGAWA	
TOKYO	
NIIGATA	
EHIME	
MIYASAKI	

SCALE
IN MILES

FIG. 142

teristically housed in large factories and employs techniques copied from
Western nations. Japan is especially advanced in the chemical industries,
in which giant strides were made between 1931 and 1937. The total
value of their 1937 output was 3.7 times that of 1931, and in 1938 their output was valued at 17.6 per cent of the country's entire industrial production, being exceeded only by textiles, metals, and the machine industries.
The chemical industries, like many other industries of a strategic nature,

TABLE 104.—THE PRINCIPAL CHEMICAL INDUSTRIES, 1938

Industry	Value of Output (yen)	Number of Factories	Numberof Workers
Industrial chemicals	604,585,414	486	37,502
Dye stuffs, paints, and pigments	142,159,752	66	11,574
Rubber	188,571,947	842	30,959
Paper	419,481,899	795	41,372
Rayon.	427,674,520	51	87,560
Fertilizer.	387,391,448	502	15,855

Source: *Kojo Tokeihyo*, 1938, p. 19.

felt the urgent necessity of national self-sufficiency, and with respect to industrial chemicals this was virtually accomplished (Fig. 142).

The Workshop Industries

Besides the large-scale factory industries which have copied Western methods of technology and organization, there are a host of home and workshop trades engaged chiefly in producing traditional Japanese goods for the domestic market. This is not to say that no Japanese-style goods are produced on a large scale in modern factories. Some are, but such wares are more commonly processed in homes or local workshops, whereas producers' goods and consumption goods for foreign markets, are more likely to originate in large factories. The small workshop industries are typical of Japan.[42]

In the cottage and workshop industries producing Japanese-style goods for the local market, part of the dwelling house often serves as the factory, the necessary labor usually being supplied by members of the family with perhaps an additional employee or two. Only simple tools are needed and power machinery is not commonly used. Typical products of such home industries are certain Japanese foods such as *tofu* (bean curd), noodles, *sushi* (rice with fish), *mochi* (rice cakes), *tatami* (floor mats), *shoji* (screens), and *geta* (wooden shoes). These cottage industries are as widely dispersed throughout the country as is the population itself. Since there is no strict segregation of commercial, industrial, and residential functions in most Japanese towns and cities, such trades are not areally concentrated in the settlements.

Besides the workshop industries catering to local needs there are those producing goods of a more elaborate character and for a national market.

[42] Teijiro Uyeda, *The Small Industries of Japan* (Institute of Pacific Relations, New York, 1938).

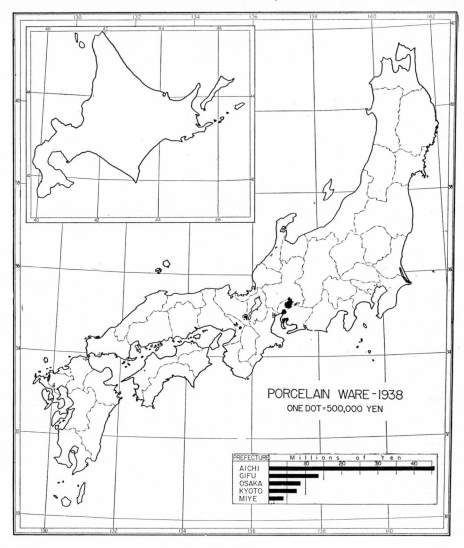

PORCELAIN WARE - 1938

ONE DOT = 500,000 YEN

PREFECTURE	Millions of Yen			
	10	20	30	40
AICHI				
GIFU				
OSAKA				
KYOTO				
MIYE				

FIG. 143

Cottage industries of this type, although composed of small operating units, may be merely a cog in a larger machine, the whole organization of which is governed and financed by a large corporation. Japanese-style pottery, lacquerware, silk textiles, *hibachi, kawara* (roof tiles), fans, and paper lanterns are representative industries of this type. Many of these trades are craft industries and regionally concentrated to take advantage of the presence of raw materials or of a trained labor supply (Fig. 143).

Power machinery is more common in these workshop industries than in those producing for local needs, and the operating unit may range in size from the family residence to sheds housing as many as thirty employees.[43] Certain of the newer trades, such as the manufacture of bicycles, electric lamps, hosiery, rubber goods, etc., as well as those which are native to Japan, are characterized by small-scale organization.

[43] See Schumpeter *et al., op. cit.,* 491–542.

SELECTED REFERENCES

ALLEN, G. C. *Japanese Industry: Its Recent Development and Present Condition.* Institute of Pacific Relations, New York, 1940.

"American's Appraisal of Japanese Chemical Industry." *Chemical and Metallurgical Engineer,* 49:116–117 (February, 1942).

BARBER, ALVIN. "Steel in Japan's War Economy." *Amerasia,* 5:256–265 (August, 1941).

BARBER, C. H. "Impact of War on the Japanese Cotton Textile Industry." *Foreign Agriculture,* 5:299–306 (July, 1941).

GRAJDANZEV, ANDREW J. "Japan's Industrial Output Slackens." *Far Eastern Survey,* April 7, 1941.

———. "Japan's Economy Since Pearl Harbor." *Far Eastern Survey,* June 14, 1943, pp. 119–123; June 30, 1943, pp. 128–133.

Industrial Japan (Aspects of Recent Economic Changes as Viewed by Japanese Writers). Institute of Pacific Relations, New York, 1941.

KAMII, YOSHIO. "Industrial Transformation in Japan." *International Labor Review,* 40:516–533 (October, 1939).

LADEJINSKY, W. "The Japanese Cotton-Textile Industry and American Cotton.' *Foreign Agriculture,* 1:589–618 (December, 1937).

———. "The Japanese Silk Industry Faces a New Crisis." *Foreign Agriculture,* 5:515–534 (December, 1941).

LLOYD, T. E. "Kyushu and Honshu Islands Focal Points of Japan Industry." *Iron Age,* 149:83–92 (April 30, 1942), with map.

MITCHELL, KATE. *Japan's Industrial Strength.* Alfred A. Knopf, 1942.

SCHUMPETER, E. B., EDITOR. *The Industrialization of Japan and Manchukuo, 1930–1940,* 477–861. The Macmillan Co., New York, 1940.

UYEDA, TEIJIRO. *The Small Industries of Japan.* Institute of Pacific Relations. New York, 1938.

CHAPTER IX

Communications and Trade

I N ITS several types of communications Japan presents remarkable contrasts. Crude and slow land and water transport characteristic of the feudal period exists alongside the most modern and rapid forms of transit. On the whole Japan's road system is antiquated, and highway motor transport only very meagerly developed. Its rail and shipping services, on the other hand, are comparatively modern and efficient, and air transportation has made rapid strides in recent years.

Certain physical conditions have operated to encourage the development of water transportation. Most important is the fact that Japan is an insular country, and not a single island but several. The elongated shape of the main island and its much indented shoreline place every part of the country close to tidewater, and the great number of protected bays and natural harbors have permitted hundreds of local ports to develop. It is not surprising, then, that a coastwise trade carried by thousands of small boats should have developed to serve the large and dense population peripherally concentrated on small littoral plains, and that the seaway should be the highway for much of Japan's domestic trade. Contributing factors are the hilly and mountainous land surface of Japan, which tends to discourage the development of efficient and fast land transport, and the limited supplies of coal, iron ore, and petroleum. The abundance and cheapness of hydroelectric power, on the other hand, has resulted in a notable development of tramlines.

Roads and the Traffic They Carry

The Taikwa or Great Reform of the mid-seventeenth century included a provision for a regular development of roads, ferries, barriers, and post-horses. This plan for an integrated post-road system was the product of a centralized government, whose chief goal was to facilitate the movement of the men in its service. During the two and a half centuries of the Tokugawa or Yedo regime (1602–1867), the post-road system was laid out and developed The shoguns in what is now Tokyo recognized that if they were to control the domains of the great feudal lords or daimyos and maintain peace throughout the country, good communications must be maintained between the capital of the realm and its outlying parts. Like the Roman roads, therefore, those of early Japan served political rather than commercial ends.

The trunk lines of the Tokugawa road system were five great roads: the *Tokaido*, Yedo to Kyoto along the coast, 310 miles; the *Nakasendo*, Yedo to Kyoto through the interior, 324 miles; the *Nikko-kaido*, Yedo to Nikko, 89 miles; the *Ushu-kaido*, Yedo to Aomori, 465 miles; and *Koshu-kaido*, Yedo to Shimosu-wa, 132 miles (Fig. 144).[1] It was these trunk highways of feudal Nippon along carefully selected natural routes that set the pattern for Japan's modern transportation system. Many of them were chosen at a later date as the routes of rail lines, some of which retained even the names of their post-road ancestors. Many of the motor roads of a still more recent period also coincide in general with the routes of the ancient Tokugawa post-roads.

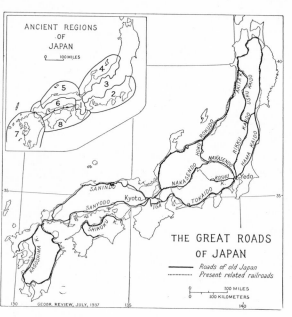

FIG. 144. Map by Hall. From the *Geographical Review*, published by the American Geographical Society, New York.

Japan's road system is still a very primitive one, quite inadequate for the requirements of a modern nation. Not only are most of the roads archaic, but they are heterogeneous in character, uncoordinated into an effective system. Except in the vicinity of great cities and certain famous tourist centers good roads are few. Strangely enough, the remarkable progress Japan has made in other lines of development since 1930 is quite unmatched in the field of public highways. It is an anomaly that a coordinated national system of roads should have been so neglected in a nation

[1] Robert B. Hall, "The Road in Old Japan," in *Studies in the History of Culture* (Menasha, Wisconsin, 1942), 122–155.

where the central government has played such a prominent role in the promotion of industry and other forms of transportation. Although the railway system is State-built and operated and the merchant marine has been heavily subsidized by the government, there were in March, 1939, only 8,610 kilometers of national roads, about the same mileage as had already existed for several decades. In part, no doubt, this lag in highway development reflects the small use that is made of the motorcar in Japan. The few passenger cars that do exist are chiefly taxicabs operating in the larger cities. Recently a few well-graded and drained express highways (minimum width 39.4 ft.) have been built. One of these follows the Tokaido route, and others the Nakasendo and Ushu-kaido. Two others lead from Tokyo north to Sendai and west to Kofu.

In Japan four classes of roads are recognized—national, prefectural, municipal, and town and village. By law national roads have a normal width of more than 24 feet, and the ruling grade on them is 1 in 30. Some of these are of military significance, including roads from Tokyo to headquarters of army divisions and to naval stations; others connect Tokyo with the Great Shrine at Ise and with prefectural capitals. For the prefectural and important municipal roads a minimum width of 18 feet is stipulated, and their grades may be steeper than those of national highways. Town and village roads must be more than 12 feet wide. Regulations governing bridges on national and prefectural roads stipulate that

TABLE 105.—ROAD STATISTICS FOR JAPAN
(in kilometers)

Year	National	Prefectural	Municipal	Town and Village	Total, including Others
1932	8,146	99,257	37,063	806,123	956,962
1935	8,463	109,584	45,108	807,377	971,442
1939	8,617	114,466	56,863	735,376	915,322

Source: *Far East Year Book*, 1941, p. 200.

TABLE 106.—MOTOR VEHICLE REGISTRATIONS IN JAPAN

Type of Motor Vehicle	Average 1930–33	1940
Passenger cars	56,173	106,000
Trucks.	30,976	50,000
Busses.	9,802	29,800
Motorcycles	35,419	62,900
Total	132,370	248,700

Sources: *Foreign Commerce Year Book;* Motive Products Division, U.S. Dept. of Commerce for 1940 figures.

they be able to carry a uniform load of a hundred pounds per square foot, a 12-ton steam roller, or an 8-ton wagon.[2]

The great majority of the roads in Japan are narrow and winding, and their grades are steep. On the alluvial plains the roads are distinctly elevated, standing several feet higher than the wet paddy fields (Fig. 146). Their narrowness and elevation make them dangerous for any but slow-moving traffic. Two cars may even find it difficult to pass. On the other hand, most of the roads have a well compacted gravel foundation, which is a great asset in a rainy region like Japan. Good materials for surfacing are at hand, and many decades, or even centuries, of traffic have added to the compacting of the roads. So although their surfaces are by no means smooth, there is little danger of getting mired in deep mud. Even the local roads have all-weather surfaces. On most highways bridges are narrow and appear none too substantial.

The traffic on Japanese highways is predominantly local and slow-moving, bicycles and man- and animal-drawn carts and wagons prevailing (Figs. 145–147). Motor traffic, except in the vicinity of cities, has been a feature of only the past two or three decades and is still relatively unimportant. Much of the bus service is of the local interurban type, but even this has revealed the need for improved highways. In 1937 there were 23,630 motorbuses in operation by privately owned transport companies,[3] but only 624 trucks, an astonishingly small number. In addition, the Department of Railways operates a motorcar service. The latter carried nearly 9 million passengers in 1937 and 73,724 metric tons of freight, and private lines in 1936–37 carried 334,234 metric tons of freight and nearly 9 million passengers.[4] At the end of 1935 about 87 per cent of the 74,000 passenger cars in Japan were taxicabs, the rest private cars.[5] Motor traffic in Japan is complicated by the numerous villages which line the roads, their narrow and congested streets thronged with pedestrians and slow-moving conveyances—man- and animal-drawn carts and bicycles. One's patience and nerves are worn thin when traveling by bus over the narrow, rough, crowded highways of Japan.

Railroads

By contrast with her highway system, Japan's rail system and service impress one as excellent. About 73 per cent of the trackage of the operating lines is State-owned and operated. These are the main lines. The local

[2] *Far East Year Book*, 1941, p. 200.
[3] *Japan Year Book*, 1940, p. 581.　　[4] *Ibid.*, 370, 581.　　[5] *Ibid.*, 581.

Fɪɢ. 145. The country roads of Japan are narrow, winding, and often rough, although most of them have well compacted gravel surfaces which make them serviceable even after long-continued rains. They are used principally by slow-moving traffic, which makes motor transport difficult and even dangerous. Photograph by Bailey from Three Lions.

Fig. 146. On the low alluvial plains, in order to provide drainage, the roads are elevated. This feature, in conjunction with their narrowness, increases the hazards of motoring. Photograph from the National Geographic Society, Washington, D.C.

Fig. 147. *Above:* A Japanese serving as a beast of burden. *Below:* Ox-drawn wagons loaded with kegs of night soil passing through the streets of Tokyo.

railroads are minor lines, privately owned, which serve chiefly as feeders to the government lines (Fig. 149b).

Japanese railroads are narrow-gauge, 3'6" having been adopted as standard. This gauge was originally adopted for economy of construction, an important consideration in a mountainous country where tunnels and bridges are numerous, but a change-over to standard gauge is seriously contemplated. Because of the narrow gauge, Japanese trains are much inferior to those of the United States and most European countries, both in speed and in carrying capacity. For example, a passenger express train takes about thirteen hours to make the trip from Aomori to Tokyo, a distance of 456 miles, and nearly eleven and a half hours for the trip from Tokyo south to Okayama on the shore of the Inland Sea, a distance of

310

454 miles.[6] The narrow-gauge tracks determine the rolling stock, which is small in size and light in weight (Fig. 148). Because of the steep grades and numerous curves necessitated by the hilliness of the country, individual trains comprise few cars and the proportion of engines to cars is very large. The character of the terrain likewise makes numerous tunnels inevitable, their total length on government lines being about 700 kilometers in 1937. On certain lines they actually spoil one's enjoyment of the trip, so incessantly do they cut off the geographical scene from observation.

Rail travel, being very cheap, is popular in Japan, and the third-class coaches are usually filled to overflowing. It is used for short trips much more than in this country. For example, the average length of rail journey per passenger in 1937 was only 24.8 kilometers.[7] Freight cars are less numerous than passenger cars, for a good deal of the domestic freight movement is handled by small coastwise ships. Fare receipts are higher than freight receipts in the ratio of about 5 to 4 on the State railways and 3 to 1 on the local lines, which is the reverse of the situation in the United States. Over a billion passengers were carried by State railways in 1937, while the local railways carried 576,000 passengers, the average trip per passenger on the latter being only 8.7 kilometers.

Of the freight hauled by the State railways coal is by far the most important, amounting to over 44 per cent of the total in 1938. Other freight items in the order of their importance are timber, ores, fertilizers and rice.

The Rail Net.—For so mountainous a country the rail net of Japan seems very dense. With its 7.1 kilometers of rail per 100 square kilometers of area, Japan has more trackage per unit-area than the United States, although much less than England, Germany, or France (Fig. 149b). It much resembles Italy in the areal density of its rail net. On the other hand, the amount of track per capita is only one-eighth that of the United States and one-third to one-half that of Germany. Thus Japan's rail net, measured in terms of either area or population, is not the equal of western Europe's. But it is far superior to that of other Oriental countries.

Fig. 148. Rolling stock on the narrow-gauge railroads is light-weight.

[6] *Far East Year Book*, 1941, p. 195.
[7] *Japan-Manchukuo Year Book*, 1940, p. 196.

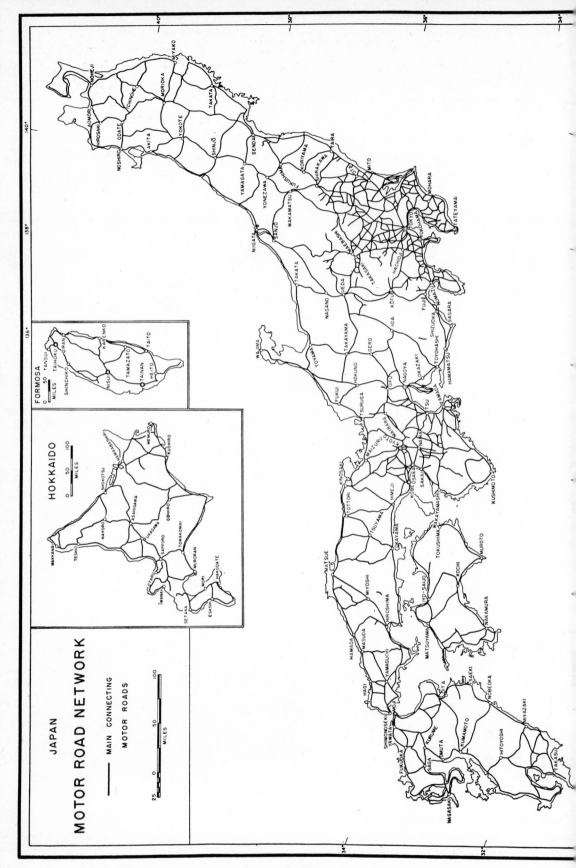

JAPAN

MOTOR ROAD NETWORK

—— MAIN CONNECTING
     MOTOR ROADS

MILES

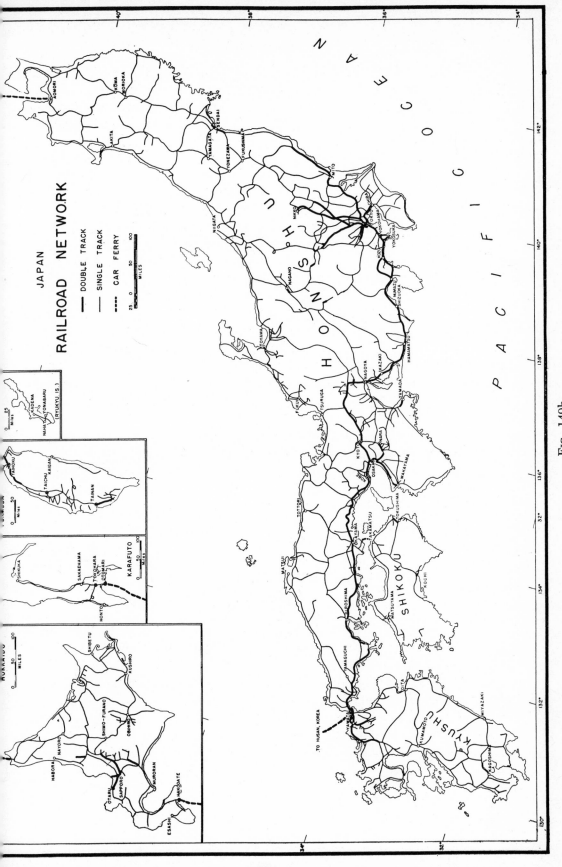

JAPAN

RAILROAD NETWORK

DOUBLE TRACK
SINGLE TRACK
CAR FERRY

25 0   50   100
MILES

Fig. 149b

The trunk rail lines in general follow the coasts, thus avoiding mountain grades as much as possible and at the same time serving the numerous and populous coastal lowlands. In Honshu and Kyushu the pattern of the rail net may be described as a crude trellis pattern (Fig. 149b). Major rail traffic follows the long axis of the main island, and traffic on the transverse lines connecting the Japan Sea and Pacific coast is much lighter. In northern Honshu the peripheral concentration of rail lines is less marked. There, because of the meager development of plains on the Pacific side, the main rail line north from Tokyo follows the longitudinal Abukuma-Kitakami interior valley east of the central range. The main trunk line of the Japanese rail system, including the Tokaido and Sanyo divisions, extends along the Pacific side of Honshu from Tokyo to the Straits of Shimonoseki, where it makes connection with the Kyushu lines by means of the submarine Kwammon tube and by ferry. Practically the whole of this stretch is double-tracked. It connects all the six great cities of Japan and the most populous and industrially important parts of the country. Other than this Tokyo-to-Shimonoseki line only short stretches are double-tracked, about 1,950 kilometers in all. Most of these are on the Kwanto Plain, the longest one connecting Tokyo with the Joban coal field. Shorter double-tracked lines are to be found in northern Kyushu, in the vicinity of Osaka, and in the Ishikari region of western Hokkaido. Only a little over 2 per cent of the total government lines are electrified, and most of these are in the Tokyo and Osaka districts. In 1937 the State railways operated about 2,000 kilometers of motorcar service, hauling both passengers and freight. Five rail ferries have also been operated—between Aomori and Hakodate; Shimonoseki to Fusan (Korea); Hokkaido to Karafuto; Uno to Takamatsu; and Shimonoseki to Moji. The later may have been greatly reduced in importance, perhaps actually discontinued, if the opening of the Kwammon submarine tunnel was completed in 1942, as planned.

Air Lines

Commercial aviation in Japan has lagged behind that of the other great powers, partly, perhaps, because the distances between important centers are short and the advantages of time-saving air transport proportionately less. The mountainous terrain of the country may have been another deterrent. Not until after 1935 was expansion of commercial aviation distinctly accelerated, but by 1938 the distance flown by regular Japanese air service companies was three times what it had been in 1935. Even so, it was only a third of the mileage flown by British and German

TABLE 107.—STATISTICS ON JAPANESE RAIL LINES FOR YEAR ENDING MARCH 31, 1939

Item of Data	State Railways	Local Railways	Tramways
Operating lines (km.).	18,179	6,664	2,346
Passenger train mileage (km.)	117,800,036	775,510	406,111,629
Passenger earnings (yen)	402,581,232	84,638,887	120,183,527
Freight train mileage (km.)	85,092,200	8,989,103	6,636,053
Freight earnings (yen)	328,724,929	25,887,295	1,251,623
Freight-passenger train mileage (km.).	17,996,827	6,423,807	—

Source: *Far East Year Book*, 1941, p. 190.

TABLE 108.—IMPORTANT GOODS HAULED BY STATE RAILWAYS, 1938
(in thousands of metric tons)

Commodity	Amount	Commodity	Amount
Rice.	3,169	Ores	4,541
Wheat, barley, etc.	1,156	Iron and iron ore.	1,785
Timber	9,695	Fertilizers.	3,895
Charcoal.	1,257	Cotton yarn and cotton fabrics . .	518
Coal.	38,525	Cement.	1,402

Source: *Far East Year Book*, 1941, p. 193.

TABLE 109.—JAPAN'S COMPARATIVE POSITION WITH RESPECT TO RAILROADS ABOUT 1939

Country	Mileage		
	Total in km.	Per 100 sq. km.	Per 10,000 population
Japan Proper	24,843*	6.5	3.6
United States	405,279	5.2	31.2
Germany	54,556	11.6	8.0
England	32,317	14.1	7.0
China.	13,086	0.1	0.3

Source: *Far East Year Book*, 1941, p. 190.
* Tramlines subtracted.

TABLE 110.—JAPANESE AIR SERVICE BY ROUTES, 1938

Route	Distance (km.)	Cumulative Freight Distance (thousands of km.)	Passengers Carried (number)	Goods Carried (kg.)	Mail Carried (kg.)
Tokyo-Sapporo	940	408	3,404	3,167	24,298
Fukuoka-Taihoku (Formosa) . .	1,610	1,041	8,737	37,089	112,223
Tokyo-Dairen (Manchuria) . . .	2,132	1,721	20,698	81,218	353,528
Tokyo-Hsinking (Manchuria) . .	2,320	1,355	14,574	102,547	217,833
Tokyo-Peking (China)	2,505	359	3,020	13,063	22,807
Fukuoka-Nanking (China) . . .	1,220	359	7,119	29,990	23,529
Total, including others	16,212	6,503	73,684	302,505	829,051

Source: *Japan-Manchukuo Year Book*, 1940, p. 212.

companies, and less than half of that covered by American lines. In 1939 all civil aviation was brought under State control, and since that time the government has managed all air traffic.

The civil air lines operated by Japanese companies in 1938 had a total length of 16,212 miles. Within Japan Proper the principal services connect Tokyo and Osaka with Sapporo in Hokkaido and with Fukuoka in North Kyushu. Shorter lines reach out to the Japan Sea side of the country and to Shikoku. Rapid expansion of air service to the colonies and to Japanese-dominated areas began in 1937–38, about the time of the outbreak of the war with China. In 1936 service to Formosa and to Mukden in Manchuria was begun, and the latter was soon extended to Hsinking. In 1937 service to Tientsin was inaugurated, and within a couple of years to Peking, Nanking, Canton, and Palau in the Mandated Islands. The new air mail route from Tokyo to Bangkok in Thailand was established in 1940.

Water Transportation and Trade

River transportation in Japan is negligible, largely because the streams are so short, swift, and shallow. On a few rivers there is some floating of logs downstream from the interior mountain lands, and on a number of them shallow, poled boats carry charcoal and other forest products to markets on the plains. There is also an important small-boat traffic on the river distributaries and canals in the vicinity of such great cities as Tokyo, Osaka, and, to a smaller extent, Nagoya (Figs. 151, 152). The short stretches of the rivers and canals leading from the harbors into the industrial and business sections of these Venice-like cities are crowded with small freight-carrying craft serving the numerous industrial and business enterprises fronting on the waterways.

THE MERCHANT MARINE

In the summer of 1939 Japan ranked third among the countries of the world in tonnage of merchant ships, but she was a relatively poor third, for her fleet was only half the size of that of the United States and slightly less than a quarter that of Britain. It is noteworthy, however, that during the thirties Japan's merchant fleet expanded at a more rapid rate than that of any other nation—31.7 per cent as compared with 19.0 per cent for Germany and 6.1 per cent for Norway. In the single year ending June 30, 1939, the gross tonnage of Japan's merchant marine increased 12 per cent. As a result of this recent acceleration in ship construction, her merchant fleet has an unusually large proportion of fast and modern ships; on June 30, 1939, almost 28 per cent of its tonnage was less than five years old and over 38 per cent less than ten years old. Some of Japan's newer line ships in the North American trade are among the finest operating in the Pacific Ocean. The number of vessels with a speed of over fifteen knots increased from 762,000 to over 1.3 million registered tons in the period 1929–36. At the same time, however, as a result of her policy of purchasing old vessels from foreign countries during the 1920's, nearly 39 per cent of Japan's shipping is over twenty years old.[8] Table 113 shows also that a large proportion of the registered merchant ships are of small tonnage. Nearly half the vessels are less than 100 tons. The unregistered steamers are small, all between five and twenty tons. By far the largest part of the steamship tonnage (86 per cent until 1939) is of the tramp variety.

Japan's merchant fleet operates a great variety of services. In August, 1938, fifty-seven vessels were engaged in the overseas subsidized service: six to the North American west coast; eight to South America, five to the east coast and three to the west; ten to western Europe; three to Australia; three to Dakar in West Africa; five to South Africa; eight to Java; ten to the Near East and the Persian Gulf; and four to Central America.[9] Government subsidies are granted companies maintaining regular service to Europe, North and South America, Australia, and Africa. Only vessels of over 4,000 tons with a speed of 12.5 knots or more, built and registered in Japan, and less than twenty-five years old are qualified for this overseas service. Subsidies are also granted to companies conducting regular shipping services to China, Siberian ports, Korea, and the South Seas. In August, 1938, fifty-seven vessels were operating in these so-called near-sea and South Seas services. Tramp service, which is not government-subsidized, was allocated as shown in Table 114. A striking feature is the large proportion of tramp tonnage engaged in coastwise trade.

During the depression years of the early thirties about three-quarters of the value of Japan's overseas trade was carried in her own vessels. In 1936, the last year for which statistics are available, the proportion had fallen to about two-thirds. Apparently the expansion of her foreign trade during the first half of the thirties was more rapid than the increase in the tonnage of her merchant marine.[10]

[8] *Far East Year Book*, 1941, p. 211.
[9] *Japan-Manchukuo Year Book*, 1940, p. 219.
[10] *Financial and Economic Annual of Japan*, as quoted in Katherine R. C. Greene and Joseph D. Phillips, *Economic Survey of the Pacific Area, Part II: Transportation and Foreign Trade* (New York, 1942), 26.

TRADE: COASTWISE AND FOREIGN

Coastwise Trade.—As indicated in an earlier connection, the coastal seaway is a most important highway in Japan. Regular shipping service is maintained between the principal coastal cities, and several thousand tramp steamers and sailing vessels supplement this line service. As of June, 1939, about 1.9 million tons of tramp steamers, or 40 per cent of the country's total, were engaged in the coasting trade. In addition there were 54,000 sailing vessels (1937), engaged mostly in fishing and coastwise trading. In Japan Proper some 760 ports are served by sea-borne traffic, although statistics are available for only about 180 of these. A foreigner in Japan is impressed by the scores of small craft of various kinds that crowd the harbors of local ports. Although the tonnage of Japan's merchant marine increased rapidly during the decade of the thirties, the percentage of the tramp tonnage employed in domestic trade declined only slightly between 1928 and 1938—from 45 per cent to 40 per cent— indicating an expansion of coastwise commerce paralleling that of foreign trade. Statistics on the value of domestic water-borne trade are not easily obtained. In 1926, according to Mecking, it was more than double that of the country's foreign commerce. As of that year, the value of foreign trade exceeded the coastwise trade in only four ports—Kobe, Yokohama, Shimizu, and Yokkaichi.[11]

Foreign Trade.—Japan's phenomenal industrial expansion of the 1930's was paralleled by a similar boom in foreign trade. In fact, this has been one of the most significant developments in world trade during the past decade, carrying in its wake serious economic and political repercussions for extensive areas of the earth. Yet even as late as 1937 Japan's share of the world's total export trade was not impressive—3.7 per cent as compared with 11.8 for the United States and 13.5 for the United Kingdom. Similarly, Nippon's per capita value of exports was only one-sixth that of Britain and 40 per cent that of Germany. It is clear that even with the remarkable advance made by Japan in overseas commerce, she still lagged well behind the more important nations of the West.

The low-water mark in Japan's foreign trade was reached in 1931. After that, however, the trend was increasingly upward. By 1934 the value of overseas trade exceeded the average for the boom years 1925–29, and by 1937, which saw the beginning of the Sino-Japanese War, it had reached 170 per cent of the 1928 figure and 292 per cent of the depression figure of 1931. There was a sharp drop in 1938, but the rapid re-

[11] Ludwig Mecking, *Japans Häfen* (Hamburg, 1931), 139.

. 150. The rolling stock on very narrow-gauge, pri-ely owned railways of the country of Japan is neces-ly small and light-weight. cause of the many steep des an individual train can nprise only a few cars at st. The rolling stock on the te-owned railways is larger, t still small by American ndards. Rail transportation Japan is much better de-oped than is highway mo-transport.

FIG. 151. The numerous swift-flowing rivers of Japan are used to some extent as routes of transportation. The prod-ucts of the forest, including logs, firewood, and charcoal, are carried down from the highlands of the interior to the densely populated plains. Scene on the Tenryu River in Shizuoka Prefecture.

. 152. Here one of the er irrigation canals is be-used to transport vege-les from the neighboring itory to the local markets the vicinity. Ordinarily, vever, the irrigation canals little used for purposes of isportation. Scene in the a Basin.

TABLE 111.—JAPAN'S PLACE IN WORLD SHIPPING, JUNE 30, 1939*
(in thousands of gross tons)

Country	Tonnage	Country	Tonnage
British Empire	21,002	Germany	4,483
United States.	11,362	Italy	3,425
Japan	5,630	The Netherlands.	2,970
Norway	4,834	France	2,934

Source: Lloyd's *Register of Shipping*, as quoted in the *Far East Year Book*, 1941, p. 211.
* Exclusive of steamers under 100 tons and sailing vessels.

TABLE 112.—NUMBER AND TONNAGE OF SHIPS IN JAPAN PROPER, SEPTEMBER 30, 1938

Type of Ship	Registered Ships	Unregistered Ships
Steamers		
Number.	3,969	3,688
Tonnage	5,073,695	42,775
Sailers		
Number	16,442	39,649
Tonnage	966,433	527,242
Total including "other" sailers		
Number.	20,862	43,337
Tonnage	6,115,990	569,997

Source: *Far East Year Book*, 1941, p. 212.

TABLE 113.—NUMBER AND TONNAGE OF STEAMERS OF VARIOUS SIZES IN JAPAN, 1938
(in thousands of capacity tons)

Size	Number	Gross Tonnage	Size	Number	Gross Tonnage
20–100.	1,924	87	3000–6000	431	1,932
100–500	735	178	6000–10,000 . . .	213	1,591
500–1000.	227	169	Over 10,000 . . .	28	359
1000–3000	411	781			

Source: *Far East Year Book*, 1941, p. 213.

TABLE 114.—ALLOCATION OF JAPAN'S TRAMP STEAMERS OF 2,000 TONS AND OVER
(in thousands of tons)

Region	December 1, 1936	June 1, 1939
Europe and Africa.	303.1	35.8
North America (Pacific coast).	213.3	449.9
North America (Atlantic coast)	499.1	179.5
Australia and India	261.2	249.6
South Sea Islands and Straits Settlements	373.9	685.2
Coastwise	1,606.0	1,880.2
In docks	74.4	249.9
Others.	14.6	1,013.4
Total, including others.	3,380.0	4,841.1

Source: *Japan-Manchukuo Year Book*, 1940, p. 221.

covery in 1939 continued, with the result that an all-time high was
reached in 1940 (Fig. 153).

Since Japan has had to import large quantities of raw materials for
her export industries and for home consumption, the value of imports
has usually equalled or slightly exceeded exports. Recently the apparent

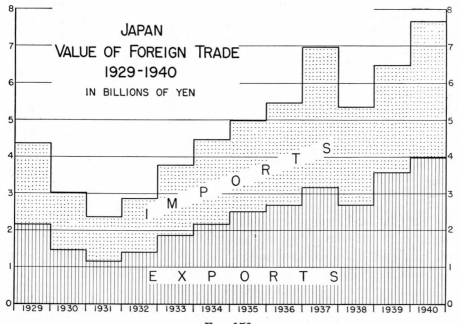

JAPAN

VALUE OF FOREIGN TRADE
1929-1940
IN BILLIONS OF YEN

FIG. 153

excess of exports was due to capital exports to Manchuria and North
China. It is well to keep in mind that a portion of the unusual increase
in the value of Japan's foreign trade is the result of a rise in prices, especially after 1936. A comparison of the value indexes and volume indexes
given in Table 115 will make this clear. Thus although the value of foreign
trade in 1937 was 292 per cent of what it had been in 1931, the volume
was only 165 per cent. Moreover, the volume increase in exports was
far greater than that of imports.

Japan's expansion in foreign trade, especially in exports, after 1931 is
striking not only by reason of the extent and rapidity of its recovery, but
even more the fact that it occurred in the midst of a world depression
when world markets were shrinking and the trade of most nations was
markedly declining. Grave concern was felt by many countries lest their
industries and trade be inundated by a flood of cheap Japanese products.
One of the first jolts to Occidental countries came in 1933, when the ex-

TABLE 115.—FOREIGN TRADE IN MERCHANDISE OF JAPAN AND KARAFUTO.

Year	Value in Millions of Yen			Value Index (1928 = 100)	Volume index (1928 = 100)		
	Exports	Imports	Total		Total	Exports	Imports
1911–14*	531	584					
1916–20*	1,748	1,594					
1925–29*	2,093	2,308					
1929	2,149	2,216	4,365	104.7	107.8	111.2	104.8
1930	1,470	1,546	3,016	72.4	97.0	102.6	92.1
1931	1,147	1,236	2,383	57.2	103.9	105.8	102.2
1932	1,410	1,431	2,842	68.2	112.3	125.0	100.9
1933	1,861	1,917	3,778	90.6	120.5	138.1	104.6
1934	2,172	2,283	4,455	106.9	136.1	163.4	111.6
1935	2,499	2,472	4,971	119.3	149.2	185.3	116.9
1936	2,693	2,764	5,457	130.9	163.5	202.5	128.5
1937	3,175	3,783	6,959	166.9	171.6	210.7	136.5
1938	2,690	2,663	5,353	128.6	135.2	174.3	101.1
1939	3,576	2,918	6,494	156.1			
1940	3,972	3,709	7,681	184.5			

Source: *Far East Year Book*, 1941, p. 451.   * Average.

port of Japanese textiles passed the declining British total. Japan had become the chief foreign supply center for cheap cotton cloth. In Malaya, within a three-year period during which British sales of cotton cloth were halved, Japan's sales doubled. In Ceylon, India, the British African colonies, Egypt, and Jamaica the general picture was much the same. Japanese exports to Java exceeded those of the Netherlands in 1933. Germany and the United States felt keenly the effects of Japanese competition in Latin America.

As a result of the serious inroads made by Japan in old established markets, many of them parts of colonial empires, restrictive measures were taken against the new competitor by almost every Japanese export market.[12] Toward the end of 1936 thirty-three foreign markets were reported as enforcing discriminatory tariffs against Japanese goods, and forty-three had placed them on a quota basis.[13] Such action was irritating to the native peoples in the Asiatic and African colonies which had benefited from Japan's bargain goods, and it is doubtful whether they would have been willing to accept indefinitely the situation imposed upon them by their mother countries. The obstructionist tactics of the mother countries against the importation of Japanese products by their colonial

[12] See Greene and Phillips, *Economic Survey of the Pacific Area, Part II: Transportation and Foreign Trade*, 119–130.

[13] V. P. Copping, *Expansion of Japan's Foreign Trade and Industry* (U. S. Department of Commerce, *Trade Information Bulletin*, No. 836, Washington, D.C., 1937), 55.

markets had serious repercussions in Nippon. It served to bring home forcibly to the Japanese the vulnerability of their position in a world of colonial autarchy and increasing economic nationalism.

Japan can support her population only by industrial and commercial expansion, for her homeland is poorly endowed with natural resources and she lacks a large colonial empire which could serve as a source of needed raw materials and as a market for manufactured goods. Trade barriers made it difficult for her to sell her manufactures and thereby obtain the credits necessary for purchasing raw materials. After the Manchurian Incident Japan was unable to borrow abroad, and even the usual short-term commercial credits were restricted. The generally negative policy toward Japan on the part of the Western Powers, which discriminated against her in their commercial and immigration policies at the same time that they insisted upon the maintenance of the territorial *status quo* in the Far East, was discouraging to the moderate elements in Nippon. The extreme groups in the nation, which preferred the way of the sword in international affairs, found in this same negative attitude of the powers potent propaganda material for a policy of forcible territorial expansion.[14]

Factors Influencing Japan's Trade Boom.[15]—The fact that resource-poor Japan was able to buy foreign raw materials, process them, and sell her finished goods abroad at a considerably lower price than countries much better endowed with raw materials has been something of a mystery to the West. This achievement, which has enabled Japan to build her modern industrial structure to an unusual extent upon foreign rather than domestic markets, is attributable to certain competitive advantages which she has had. These include several relatively permanent advantages springing from her unique social and economic structure. As was suggested in the preceding chapter, among the factors which in combination have resulted in unusually low-cost production are Japan's great reservoir of cheap surplus labor inured to the most frugal kind of living; the homogeneous, unified character of the industrial workers, in whom old feudal loyalties are still so strong that they are willing to subjugate self-interest to the welfare of the State; and, finally, the abundance of cheap hydroelectric power.

In addition, certain more transitory advantages contributed to the

[14] On this general theme see Elizabeth Boody Schumpeter, "What America Wants from Japan," in the *Oriental Economist*, 7:25–30 (January, 1940).

[15] On this topic see V. P. Copping, *op. cit.*, 6–16, and "The Proof of the Pudding," in *Fortune*, vol. 14, no. 3 (September, 1936), 77 ff.

unusual export boom of the thirties. Among these was the depreciation of the yen in terms of foreign currencies. Other countries, to be sure, were also depreciating their currencies, but the relatively greater fall of the yen, to about one-third of its former gold value, gave Japanese goods a genuine advantage in foreign markets. The almost simultaneous drop in the world prices of those commodities which Japan had to purchase abroad eased the financial strain of a depreciated yen at home. Boycotts instituted in 1933 by certain markets against German-manufactured goods also worked in Japan's favor. Orders for toys, novelties, and miscellaneous small articles which once had gone to Germany were transferred to Japan. Large-scale government spending for defense purposes and the opening of Manchuria as a new investment field after 1931 contributed further to the trade boom. Finally, the predominance of small factories in Japan is a source of strength during a depression period such as that of the early 1930's. Low overhead costs permit these workshop factories to carry on much more economically in lean years than is possible for large concerns.

THE NATURE OF JAPAN'S FOREIGN TRADE

A fundamental feature of Japan's overseas trade is that raw materials and semi-manufactures bulk large in the import trade, whereas manufactured goods comprise the greater share of the exports. These are the marks of an industrial nation. In 1936 almost 64 per cent of the total exports were finished goods and over 29 per cent semi-processed materials. Together these two groups accounted for nearly 93 per cent of Japan's sales in foreign markets. Raw materials, on the other hand, constituted only 5.1 per cent of the total.

In the import groups the emphasis was quite different. In 1936 about 63 per cent of Japan's purchases abroad were raw materials for industry, and raw materials and semi-processed goods comprised 80.4 per cent of the imports. Contrary to what one might expect in view of the dense and rapidly increasing population, foodstuffs comprise only a small proportion of the nation's purchases (8.3 per cent in 1936). Moreover, during the decade 1926–36, when the annual increment in population was largest, the ratio of imported foodstuffs to total imports fell from 14.7 per cent to 8.3. In 1935 Japan actually became a net exporter of food products. In this respect she is unlike the great industrial countries of Europe, whose food imports are large.

Exports.—Textiles, especially cotton cloth and raw silk, are by far the most important of Japan's exports, but it is also noteworthy that their

TABLE 116.—PROPORTION OF JAPAN'S EXPORTS PRODUCED IN FACTORIES EMPLOYING FEWER THAN 15 WORKERS

Commodity	Per Cent	Commodity	Per Cent
Cotton piece goods	29.5	Woodwork products	77.9
Woolen piece goods	33.5	Metal toys	77.5
Silk piece goods	66.7	Hats	54.1
Rayon piece goods	32.6	Canned foods	31.4
Hosiery	80.4	Buttons	50.2
Marine products	57.8	Chinaware	70.6
Pencils	79.8	Braids	77.9
Imitation pearls	56.8	Brushes	48.5
Bicycles	74.6	Umbrellas	52.4

Source: V. P. Copping, *Expansion of Japan's Foreign Trade and Industry* (United States Department of Commerce, *Trade Information Bulletin*, No. 836, Washington, D.C., 1935), 12.

TABLE 117.—JAPAN AND KARAFUTO: EXPORTS AND IMPORTS BY COMMODITY GROUPS
(in thousands of yen)

Commodity	1929		1936		1939	
	Value	Per Cent	Value	Per Cent	Value	Per Cent
EXPORTS						
Food products	160.1	7.6	203.7	8.3	432.0	12.1
Raw materials	88.7	4.3	126.6	5.1	183.4	5.1
Semi-processed goods	883.8	42.1	716.4	29.1	948.9	26.6
Finished goods	937.3	44.5	1563.4	63.5	1939.3	54.4
Total, including others	2103.7	100.0	2641.5	100.0	3564.3	100.0
IMPORTS						
Food products	271.2	12.2	231.2	8.3	230.7	7.9
Raw materials	1223.9	55.2	1737.7	63.1	1414.1	48.7
Semi-processed goods	355.4	16.5	476.6	17.3	860.0	29.6
Finished goods	345.9	15.6	294.3	10.6	390.6	13.4
Total, including others	2213.4	100.0	2753.3	100.0	2905.3	100.0

Source: *Far East Year Book*, 1941, p. 452.

TABLE 118.—EXPORTS OF RAW SILK, 1922–39

Year	Quantity	Value	Year	Quantity	Value
1922	305.2	527.0	1936	487.3	378.1
1927	507.5	776.0	1937	525.0	429.8
1932	550.9	336.5	1938	467.1	371.6
1935	526.0	302.4	1939	436.1	379.9

Source: *Far East Year Book*, 1941, p. 304.

combined relative importance was less in 1936 or 1939 than in the 1920's (Fig. 154). These two items, which together accounted for 54.5 per cent of the value of all exports in 1922, were down to 25.5 per cent in 1939. In other words a greater variety of goods were now being exported. For example, raw silk, which accounted for 40.9 per cent of the exports in 1922 and 38.3 per cent in 1928, declined to 14.5 per cent in

TABLE 119.—PRINCIPAL JAPANESE EXPORTS AND IMPORTS
(value in millions of yen and as percentages of totals)

Commodity	1936		1937		1938		1939	
	Value	Per Cent	Value	Per Cent	Value	Per Cent	Value	Per Cent
EXPORTS								
Cotton tissues	483.6	17.9	573.1	18.1	404.2	15.0	403.9	11.3
Raw silk	392.8	14.5	407.1	12.8	364.1	13.5	506.8	14.2
Clothing (including knitted goods)	181.2	6.7	229.9	7.2	145.0	5.4	168.5	4.7
Machines and machinery	174.5	6.5	227.7	7.2	267.2	10.0	370.3	10.3
Metal manufactures	76.5	2.8	98.8	3.1	100.1	3.7	147.8	4.1
Minerals (including coal)	24.3	0.9	23.9	0.8	24.6	0.9	33.5	0.9
Grains, flour, starches, seeds	29.9	1.1	46.0	1.4	74.7	2.8	79.0	2.2
Foodstuffs, tinned and bottled	71.7	2.6	86.9	2.7	92.8	3.5	132.0	3.7
Silk tissues	68.0	2.5	72.3	2.3	49.4	1.8	47.4	1.3
Artificial silk	149.2	5.5	154.9	4.9	115.8	4.3	137.5	3.8
Ores and metals	103.1	3.8	125.4	3.9	121.0	4.5	139.0	3.9
Cotton yarn	38.3	1.4	54.9	1.7	39.4	1.5	71.1	2.0
Drugs, dyes, chemicals	81.5	3.0	90.7	2.9	73.7	2.7	107.5	3.0
Oils, fats and their manufactures	74.8	2.8	75.4	2.4	52.3	1.9	88.3	2.5
Pottery	43.5	1.6	54.0	1.7	40.5	1.5	48.6	1.4
Glass and its manufactures	25.6	1.0	33.6	1.1	25.9	1.0	27.1	0.8
Tea	13.1	0.5	23.2	0.7	12.1	0.4	23.5	0.7
Fishery and sea products	22.2	0.8	21.9	0.7	21.9	0.8	61.9	1.7
Sugar	21.0	0.8	18.6	0.6	23.7	0.9	28.7	0.8
IMPORTS								
Raw cotton	849.6	30.7	849.6	22.4	436.8	16.4	462.0	15.8
Ores and metals	374.9	13.5	901.1	23.8	661.9	24.9	848.5	29.1
Machines and machinery	153.1	5.5	242.2	6.5	313.4	11.8	288.2	9.5
Wool	200.9	7.5	298.4	7.9	94.4	3.5	72.6	2.5
Oils and fats (including petroleum products)	197.5	7.1	297.9	7.9	326.9	12.3	262.5	9.0
Beans and peas	82.6	3.0	92.5	2.4	102.2	3.8	123.6	4.2
Rice and paddy	5.1	0.2	4.0	0.1	2.8	0.1	6.3	0.2
Wheat	33.7	1.2	29.6	0.8	9.6	0.4	4.1	0.1
Timber	55.5	2.0	64.8	1.7	28.2	1.1	32.3	1.1
Oil cakes	35.8	1.3	45.3	1.2	60.1	2.3	104.6	3.6
Pulp for rayon and paper	67.1	2.4	116.7	3.1	42.2	1.6	56.5	1.9
Crude rubber	73.0	2.6	99.2	2.6	51.4	1.9	57.5	2.0

Sources: *Annual Return of the Foreign Trade of Japan*, Tokyo; *Japan-Manchukuo Year Book*, 1940; *Fortieth Financial and Economic Annual of Japan*, pt. 3; *Far East Year Book*, 1941.

1936 and to 12.8 per cent in 1937. From Table 118 it is clear that the decline in value of silk exports was more the result of lower prices than of greatly reduced volume. It was not until after 1937 that the volume decline became marked. Cotton textiles maintained their percentage rank at about 18 or 19 per cent until 1937. In 1934 and the four years thereafter they outranked raw silk as the principal export commodity. After 1937, as foreign markets for cotton tissues became increasingly re-

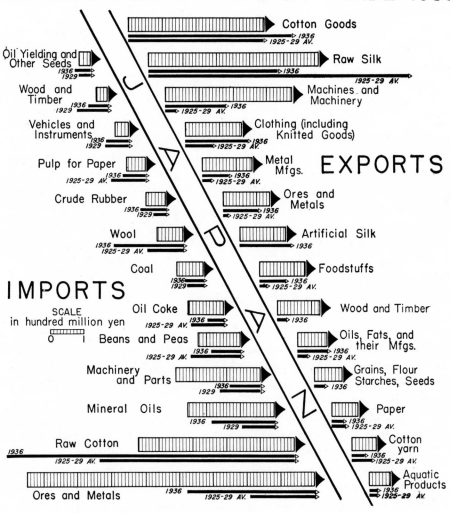

FIG. 154

stricted, and at home more emphasis was placed on the heavy strategic industries, the importance of this export item began to decline, and in 1939 its ratio to total exports was only 11.3 per cent. Despite a sharp decline in quantity of raw silk exported, the rise in silk prices put this commodity back in first place in 1939.

It becomes evident that during the decade of the thirties basic changes were occurring in Japan's export trade. As raw silk and cotton textiles, the two leaders, declined in relative importance (silk beginning earlier in 1931 and cotton textiles not until 1938), machinery, iron manufactures, wood, rayon tissues, wool tissues, paper, and canned foods showed healthy gains. Metal manufactures rose from 0.6 per cent of all exports in 1909–13 to 4.1 per cent in 1939. Exports of machines and machinery increased from 0.7 per cent of the total in the period 1909–13 to 7.2 per cent in 1937 and 10.3 per cent in 1939.

Imports.—For several decades raw cotton and ores and metals have been the chief imports of Japan (Fig. 154). Together they accounted for 40.7 per cent of the total imports in the period 1909–13, 37.8 per cent in 1925–29, 44.2 per cent in 1936, and 44.9 per cent in 1939. The relative importance of the two leading items, however, has shifted. For more than two decades prior to 1936 the ratio of raw cotton to total imports fluctuated around 30 per cent. After 1926, as the war industries waxed in importance and textiles waned, raw cotton began to decline, and by 1939 the ratio was only 15.8 per cent. In 1939 the volume of imported raw cotton was only about two-thirds as large as in 1936. Ores and metals, on the other hand, which had made up 8–10 per cent of the imports during the fifteen years prior to 1925, rose to 13.5 per cent in 1936 and 29.1 in 1939. In the period, therefore, in which the raw cotton ratio was being nearly halved, the ores and metals ratio more than doubled. These were signs that Japan was preparing for war and for one of greater magnitude than the conflict in China. In the first half of the thirties there were also noteworthy increases in other raw materials—mineral oils, pulp for rayon, crude rubber, wool, drugs, and chemicals. After 1936, however, many of these suffered a sharp decline, which was coincident with a still sharper rise in such semi-manufactured items as machines and machinery and petroleum products. This change reflected the urgency of the needs in the strategic industries.

Thus it becomes evident that the decade of the thirties includes two important phases of Japan's trade development, the year 1937 serving to mark the transition. The year 1932 marks the beginning of a trade boom gauged in part to offset its loss in raw silk exports to the United States.

With this expansion came certain basic changes in Japan's trade, with respect both to the relative importance of particular commodities and the areas of import and export trade. But to a large extent it was a normal type of change based largely upon the interplay of economic and geographic forces. Since 1937 Japan's industry and trade have been straight-jacketed for war, with the result that even more serious dislocations have occurred with respect to the commodities and regions of her foreign trade.

PRINCIPAL TRADING REGIONS AND COUNTRIES

In 1929 Nippon's trade moved in two primary streams of almost equal importance, one connecting with eastern and southern Asia (41 per cent) and the other with the United States (36 per cent). In the same year Europe accounted for only 13 per cent. By 1936, however, Asia had increased its share to 44.5 per cent, and that of the United States had declined to 26 per cent (Fig. 155). In the abnormal trading years of the late thirties a still larger percentage of Japan's commerce was with Asiatic countries. Moreover, these percentages become still more significant in the light of the fact that the exports to Asia were almost entirely staple manufactured goods whose processing gave employment to a large number of industrial workers. Exports to the United States, on the other hand, were largely raw silk, a luxury product, whose sale benefited chiefly the farming classes.

It is especially in Japan's export trade that the Asiatic countries have become increasingly important. Whereas Asia and North America took almost equal shares of Japan's exports in 1928—42.3 and 43.5 per cent respectively—by 1936 the ratios were 50.9 and 22.6, and by 1939, 64.9 and 18.4. It is to the Yen-Bloc countries of Asia, which have recently been brought under Japanese domination, that the increased exports have largely gone.

Among individual countries, the United States and China have, under normal conditions, been Japan's best trading areas, and next British India and the Netherlands Indies. After the Manchurian Incident of 1931, China's trade with Japan was badly disrupted as a result of boycotts and later war, but in 1928 China took 15.4 per cent of Japan's exports and provided her with nearly 8 per cent of her imports. Important items in the sales to China are textiles, machinery, paper, wheat flour, and sugar, in return for which Japan buys from China raw cotton, coal, hides and skins, and oil-yielding materials. After July 1, 1932, Manchuria's trade was included with Kwantung's instead of China's. In 1933 Manchuria

TABLE 120.—DISTRIBUTION OF JAPANESE EXPORTS AND IMPORTS BY CONTINENTS

Continent	Percentage of Total Value							
	1919	1925	1928	1931	1936	1937	1938	1939
Asia								
Imports.	49.4	47.2	41.1	40.0	38.3	34.3	38.5	40.6
Exports.	45.5	43.3	42.3	44.0	50.9	51.8	61.9	64.9
North America								
Imports.	35.6	27.4	31.6	30.6	33.4	36.4	37.9	38.8
Exports.	40.9	44.8	43.5	38.3	22.6	20.8	16.4	18.4
Europe								
Imports.	7.5	17.4	18.4	16.1	11.9	13.3	14.2	10.6
Exports.	9.3	6.6	8.1	9.1	11.4	11.2	9.7	6.7
Africa								
Imports.	2.5	1.6	1.5	1.5	3.9	5.5	2.3	3.2
Exports.	1.2	1.9	2.2	5.1	7.3	7.6	5.1	4.3
South America								
Imports.	0.8	0.3	0.6	0.6	4.1	4.3	3.4	4.0
Exports.	1.0	0.8	1.1	0.9	2.6	3.4	2.2	1.9
Oceania								
Imports.	3.1	6.0	6.2	9.5	7.6	5.9	3.7	3.0
Exports.	2.2	2.6	2.7	2.3	3.6	3.4	3.6	2.7

Source: Schumpeter *et al., Industrialization of Japan and Manchukuo*, 832–833. The percentages here given are not identical with those in the *Financial and Economic Annual of Japan*.

TABLE 121.—JAPAN'S TRADE WITH YEN-BLOC COUNTRIES AND WITH
FOREIGN CURRENCY COUNTRIES

(value in millions of yen and as percentages of total)

Regions	1936		1937		1938		1939	
	Value	Per Cent	Value	Per Cent	Value	Per Cent	Value	Per Cent
Yen-Bloc Countries								
Exports	658	24.4	791	25.3	1,157	43.0	1,747	48.9
Imports	394	14.3	438	11.6	564	21.2	683	23.5
Foreign Countries								
Exports	2,035	75.6	2,384	74.7	1,524	57.0	1,829	51.0
Imports	2,370	85.7	3,345	88.4	2,099	78.8	2,235	76.5

Source: *Japan Year Book*, 1940–41

took 16 per cent of Japan's exports and by 1939 the percentage had risen to 36.2 per cent; in the same period imports from the region increased from 8.8 per cent to 16 per cent (Fig. 155).

By 1939 the Yen-Bloc area of China-Manchuria-Kwantung had displaced the United States from first place among the countries with which Japan trades. To Manchuria go such items as machinery, iron manufactures, textiles, wheat flour, and paper, and from it Japan receives oil

TABLE 122.—JAPAN'S TRADE WITH PRINCIPAL COUNTRIES
(value in millions of yen and as percentages of totals)

Country	1936		1937		1938		1939	
	Value	Per Cent	Value	Per Cent	Value	Per Cent	Value	Per Cent
United States								
Imports.	847.5	30.7	1269.5	33.6	915 3	34.4	1002.4	34.4
Exports.	594.3	22.1	639.4	20.1	425.1	15.8	641.5	17.9
Manchuria and Kwantung								
Imports.	239.4	8.7	294.3	7.8	399.5	15.0	467.3	16.0
Exports.	498.0	18.5	612.0	19.3	852.6	31.7	1291.6	36.1
British India								
Imports.	374.6	13.6	453.6	12.0	172.2	6.5	182.3	6.3
Exports.	272.9	10.1	318.0	10.0	188.0	7.0	211.0	5.9
China								
Imports.	154.8	5.6	143.6	3.8	164.6	6.2	215.7	7.4
Exports.	159.7	5.9	179.3	5.6	312.9	11.6	455.5	12.7
Netherlands Indies								
Imports.	113.5	4.1	153.5	4.1	88.2	3.3	71.6	2.5
Exports.	129.5	4.8	200.1	6.3	104.1	3.9	137.8	3.9
Great Britain								
Imports.	73.0	2.7	105.8	2.8	63.2	2.4	24.4	0.8
Exports.	147.3	5.5	1168.0	5.3	135.0	5.0	132.1	3.7
Australia								
Imports.	181.9	6.6	165.3	4.4	82.9	3.1	71.0	2.4
Exports.	68.8	2.6	72.1	2.3	69.4	2.6	72.1	2.0
Germany								
Imports. . ; : . .	115.5	4.2	176.4	4.7	171.2	6.4	141.0	4.8
Exports.	35.1	1.3	43.3	1.4	33.0	1.2	25.0	0.7
Malaya								
Imports.	80.3	2.9	115.6	3.1	101.0	3.8	115.8	4.0
Exports.	61.2	2.3	71.3	2.2	22.9	0.9	22.4	0.7
Canada								
Imports.	73.2	2.7	104.7	2.8	91.3	3.4	126.0	4.3
Exports.	14.6	0.5	20.0	0.6	15.2	0.6	17.2	0.5
Total, including others								
Imports.	2763.7	100.0	3783.2	100.0	2663.4	100.0	2917.7	100.0
Exports.	2693.1	100.0	3175.4	100.0	2689.7	100.0	3576.4	100.0

Source: *Fortieth Financial and Economic Annual of Japan*, 1940, pp. 134–135.

cake, coal, beans, peas, and oil-yielding materials. Trade with southern Asiatic countries consists chiefly of textile materials, cotton and rayon cloth ranking highest. From British India Japan purchases chiefly raw cotton; from the Netherlands Indies, petroleum, crude rubber, and sugar.

Japan's trade with the United States has been basic to her development as a great power.[16] It has given her access to the natural resources of the world's richest nation and has been the means of introducing the

[16] William W. Lockwood, "American-Japanese Trade: Its Structure and Significance," in *Annals of the American Academy of Political and Social Science*, 215:86–92 (May, 1941).

TRADE WITH PRINCIPAL COUNTRIES-1939

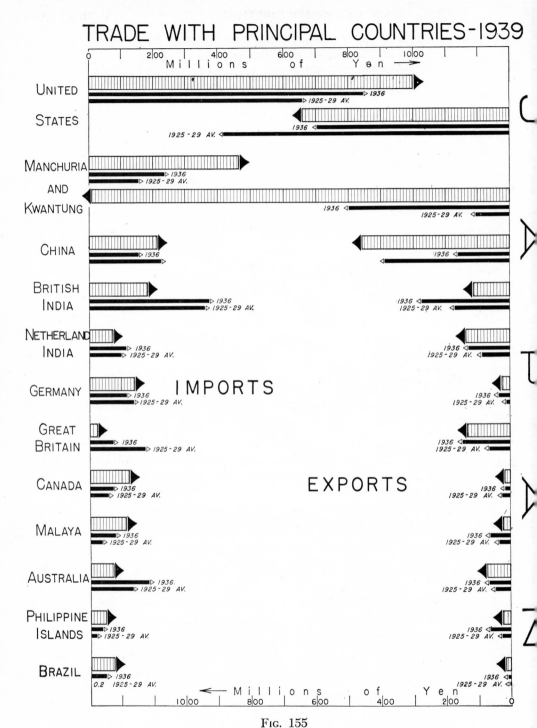

Fig. 155

tools and technology of the Occident for the creation of a new center of industrial power in the Orient. As for the United States, trade with Japan has been her principal stake in the Far East; in 1936 Nippon ranked next to Canada and the United Kingdom in our foreign trade. Over the decade of the thirties, however, very significant changes occurred in this Japanese-American trade. One of these changes has been the decline in America's proportion of Japan's trade, even while its absolute value continued to increase, at least until 1937. More important were the changes in the character and content of the trade. Prior to 1931 Japan's trade with the United States was based upon the sale of raw silk, a luxury product. Our share of Japan's exports throughout the latter half of the 1920's was more than 40 per cent, four-fifths of which was accounted for by raw silk. The sale of raw silk sustained the whole economic structure of Japan. But in the two years ending in June, 1931, the price of this commodity fell 60 per cent in Japan. By 1934 the value of exported raw silk was only a third of what it had been in 1925. In other words, the commodity which had comprised 38 per cent of the value of Japan's export trade in 1925 was down to 13 per cent in 1934. This was no temporary slump but the outcome of a losing battle in competition with rayon and staple fiber. Japan was in a dilemma. Some export substitute for raw silk was urgently needed.

An export boom, based chiefly upon cotton textiles and miscellaneous consumers' goods, was launched and it continued until 1937. The falling off in silk prices caused a marked decline in the value of total exports to the United States. Our share of Japan's total sales abroad declined from 42.4 per cent in the period 1925–29 to 15.8 in 1938. At the same time, since Japan's industrial expansion required increasing amounts of American materials, imports from the United States increased, with the result that the trade balance turned heavily against Nippon. She became the largest buyer of American cotton, taking one-fourth of our total exports in the period 1931–36. Her imports of wood pulp, iron and steel, machinery, and automobiles also increased.

In the period 1932–37 American industries, especially cotton textiles, began to feel the intensified competition of Japan. There was some increase in cheap consumers' goods imported from Japan, such as cotton cloth, pottery, canned fish, toys, and light bulbs, but these scarcely made up for the decline in raw silk. To a large degree the economies of Nippon and the United States were complementary rather than competitive. With the beginning of the trade boom more competitive elements were introduced, but these were much less serious for the United States than for some other nations. This country had much to sell Japan and so profited from her trade expansion.

After 1937 military aims began to outweigh economic considerations in Japan's trade policies. She sought to free herself from dependence upon the United States and Great Britain in order to be better equipped to pursue her imperialistic ambitions. After 1936 the volume of most Japanese export items to this country declined, but raw silk still amounted to about two-thirds of the total. Imports from the United States changed not so much in amount as in composition. Raw cotton, tobacco, pulp, lumber, automobiles, and tin plate declined markedly after 1936, whereas such war essentials as petroleum, machine tools, iron and steel products, copper, lead, and aluminum, increased sharply. By 1940 petroleum, metals, and metal-working equipment comprised more than two-thirds of American sales to Japan, whereas in 1936 they had been less than one-third. Raw cotton imports from the United States dropped 62 per cent in this period; in 1940 they were only 13 per cent of the value of total sales to Japan.

THE GATEWAYS OF TRADE: JAPAN'S PORTS

In 1939 over forty Japanese ports were officially open to foreign trade.[17] Of these only a few are of real significance (Fig. 156). The three leading open ports, Yokohama, Osaka, and Kobe, handled 82 per cent of the country's foreign trade in 1938 and only slightly less the next year, 79.4 per cent. It is these large ports which serve the most populous regions of the country as well as the nation's two principal industrial nodes. It should not be assumed, however, that these are primarily ports for local areas, important as these local areas are; rather they are great national ports serving the entire country. Next in rank, but much less important than the three big ports, are Moji, Nagoya, and Wakamatsu. Nagoya serves the industrial center associated with the Mino-Owari Plain, and the other two the heavy-industry node of North Kyushu.

Among the three great ports there is at present fair equality in the amount of foreign trade handled, although there have been considerable variations in recent years. After the great earthquake and fire of 1923, Yokohama lost a portion of its silk trade to Kobe, which then became

---

[17] The *Far East Year Book*, 1941 (p. 477) states that there are 44 open ports in Japan Proper and Karafuto. But in 1940 the ports of Shimonoseki and Moji were combined into one port known as Kammon, and in 1941 the ports of Yokohama and Tokyo were combined to form the port of Keihin. See *Geographical Journal*, 98 (1941): 165. The *Annual Return of the Foreign Trade of Japan* for 1938 lists 44 ports in Japan Proper as participating in the country's foreign trade in that year.

TABLE 123.—VALUE OF EXPORTS AND IMPORTS BY PRINCIPAL PORTS, 1932–39
(in millions of yen)

Port	Exports	Imports	Port	Exports	Imports
Kobe			**Hakodate**		
1932.	499.3	535.6	1932.	10.4	14.7
1935.	910.9	821.6	1935.	24.0	2.0
1936.	970.8	958.2	1936.	35.1	2.3
1937.	1,107.6	1,119.5	1937.	33.5	2.7
1938.	774.0	706.3	1938.	36.8	4.7
1939.	959.9	686.5	1939.	54.7	3.2
Yokohama			**Wakamatsu**		
1932.	400.7	355.4	1932.	7.8	23.5
1935.	626.0	616.6	1935.	26.1	72.4
1936.	678.3	687.0	1936.	22.4	74.2
1937. . ;	800.0	1,047.6	1937.	18.0	118.1
1938.	681.1	878.0	1938.	28.5	85.8
1939.	951.0	929.1	1939.	41.5	159.9
Osaka			**Nagasaki**		
1932.	334.2	268.0	1932.	5.7	10.0
1935.	620.1	546.8	1935.	4.5	15.2
1936.	672.2	593.3	1936.	7.7	16.8
1937.	853.1	835.2	1937.	10.7	24.3
1938.	800.3	518.1	1938.	13.0	19.4
1939.	1,034.0	611.1	1939.	15.5	20.4
Nagoya			**Yokkaichi**		
1932.	64.5	69.6	1932.	3.4	15.6
1935.	129.5	95.5	1935.	6.5	70.7
1936.	131.5	108.8	1936.	7.4	67.3
1937.	147.9	148.3	1937.	13.8	94.7
1938.	115.1	74.1	1938.	12.3	31.0
1939.	144.9	76.7	1939.	10.4	47.8
Moji			**Niigata**		
1932.	41.0	44.4	1932.	0	7.3
1935.	62.8	89.4	1935.	1.3	7.7
1936.	64.7	98.0	1936.	1.1	10.5
1937.	66.4	175.1	1937.	2.3	14.1
1938.	89.4	188.3	1938.	4.2	16.1
1939.	127.2	205.8	1939.	15.0	18.4
Shimizu			**Total including others**		
1932.	11.6	11.8	1932.	1,410.0	1,431.5
1935.	17.3	19.0	1935.	2,499.1	2,472.2
1936.	22.2	25.7	1936.	2,693.0	2,763.7
1937.	38.3	26.9	1937.	3,175.4	3,783.2
1938.	28.5	25.5	1938.	4,689.7	2,663.3
1939.	46.2	30.4	1939.	3,576.4	2,917.7

Sources: Data for 1932 to 1938 compiled from *Annual Return of the Foreign Trade of Japan,* 1938; data for 1939 from *Far East Year Book,* 1941, p. 478.

the first port of Japan. In 1929, for example, Kobe handled 36 per cent of the nation's foreign trade, Yokohama 31 per cent, and Osaka, a poor third, only about 17 per cent. In 1936, the last fairly normal trading year, Kobe still retained its 1929 position fairly well, handling over 35 per cent of the total foreign trade; Yokohama's share had dropped to 25 per cent, and Osaka's had risen to 23 per cent. Since Kobe and Osaka are a single great conurbation whose ports serve the same industrial

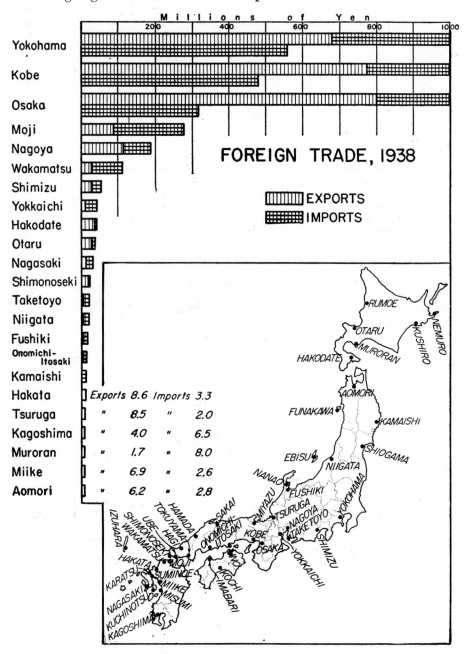

FIG. 156

region, these figures indicate that the two Kinki ports were handling nearly 60 per cent of the nation's total foreign trade in 1936, as against one-quarter for the Kwanto port of Yokohama. After 1936, when the structure of industry and foreign trade began to change rapidly as a result of the war with China and preparations for an even more serious conflict, there were significant changes in the proportions of trade flowing through the three great ports, respectively. As a result of the unusual concentration of strategic industry in the Kwanto district, Yokohama increased its trade faster than the others and by 1939 was again the nation's first port, a position she had lost in 1923. It was particularly in imports that Yokohama outstripped its rivals. Osaka increased more rapidly than Kobe and by 1939 almost equal amounts of foreign trade were passing through the two ports. In that year Yokohama held 29 per cent of the total foreign trade, and Kobe and Osaka each about 25 per cent. Together the Kinki ports still handled slightly more than 50 per cent of the nation's total foreign trade. The rise of Osaka to equality with Kobe and Yokohama as a gateway of foreign commerce was one of the principal port developments of the thirties.[18]

[18] A detailed analysis of these ports and their trade is contained in Part III below.

SELECTED REFERENCES

COPPING, V. P. *Expansion of Japan's Foreign Trade and Industry. Trade Information Bulletin*, No. 836, United States Department of Commerce. Washington, D.C., 1937.

GREENE, KATHERINE R. C., and PHILLIPS, JOSEPH D. *Economic Survey of the Pacific Area, Part II: Transportation and Foreign Trade* (New York, 1942), 25–31, 119–131, 159–161, 187–189.

LOCKWOOD, WILLIAM W. "American-Japanese Trade: Its Structure and Significance." *Annals of the American Academy of Political and Social Science*, 215:86–92 (May, 1941).

NISHIMOTO, S. "Mode of Transport in Japan." *Comptes Rendus du Congrès International de Géographie*, Amsterdam, 1938, Vol. 2, Sec. IIIB, pp. 113–114.

PART THREE
The Regional Subdivisions of Japan

CHAPTER X

Hokkaido

IN PARTS I and II attention was focused upon Japan as a whole rather than upon regional differences in detail. In the following chapters areal differentiation is the dominant theme. The land of Nippon is a mosaic of areas of varying sizes, differing from one another in one or more of the principal physical or cultural elements. Each subdivision has a degree of unity with respect to at least one of the important geographic elements. In some areas the dominant and unifying feature is terrain; in others climate; in still others it may be location or a type of land use.

Three principal subdivisions are recognized: (1) Hokkaido, (2) Tohoku or Ou, the northern part of Honshu, and (3) central and southwestern Japan. These in turn are broken down into a number of lesser provinces of various ranks.

The scheme of subdivisions here presented is only one of several equally satisfactory ones which might be employed in describing Nippon.[1] It is not based on a rigid methodology but is simply a convenient device for organizing regional description. The boundaries of the subdivisions are not to be regarded as precise and rigid, for the emphasis is upon the interrelated and interdependent features that together comprise the geographic character of the areas rather than on their exact boundaries. Since the country is so fragmented geomorphically, the character of the terrain is frequently the most convenient criterion for delimiting a subdivision.

❁   ❁   ❁   ❁   ❁

Surface Characteristics—With respect to at least one geographic feature—the general predominance of rugged hill land and mountain—Hokkaido much resembles the rest of the country. Probably no more than 15–20 per cent of the island is of sufficiently low relief to be satisfactory for agricultural use.

[1] See K. Tanaka, "Geographical Units of Japan" (in Japanese), in the *Geographical Review of Japan,* 3:1–21 (January, 1927).

Next to Honshu, Hokkaido is the largest of the Japanese islands, its area being about 31,200 square miles. Its maximum north-south length is 260 miles, and its greatest east-west dimension 280 miles. The main mass of the island is roughly rhombic in outline. Appended to it on the southwest is a fish-tail peninsula that marks its closest approach to Old Japan, from which it is separated by the Strait of Tsugaru. Prominent marine erosion terraces are conspicuous features of most of the island's circumference. It will be recalled that Hokkaido is one of the nodes in the Japanese Archipelago where two mountain arcs join to form an irregular bunch of highlands with associated volcanoes. Peninsular Hokkaido is a northward continuation of the volcanic chains of western North Honshu. Numerous volcanoes, some of them active, rise both to the north and to the south of large crescentic Volcano Bay.

Separating the hilly southwestern peninsula from the main part of the island is the Ishikari-Yufutsu Lowland, the most extensive plain of Hokkaido and one of the largest in all Japan (see front end paper). This is very much the population and economic centrum. The main, or central and eastern, part of the island has a backbone of old rocks which extends in a northwest-southeast direction from the angle formed by Cape Soya on the north to that formed by Cape Erimo on the south. Volcanic cones, a number of them reaching altitudes of over 6,000 feet, stud the crest of this mountainous backbone. The east-west Chishima Volcanic Chain forms the eastern angle of the island and intersects the north-south line of highlands in mid-Hokkaido to form the Central Massif containing the island's highest elevations. Lowlands of new alluvium are scarce in this main part of Hokkaido. Elevated wave-cut terraces of variable width provide small amounts of nearly level land in the immediate vicinity of the coasts, and the area of littoral plain is often expanded somewhat in the vicinity of stream mouths, but these coastal alluvial patches are likely to be poorly drained. A north-south chain of small intermontane basins within the highland backbone also offers some low land, but the most extensive plains of all central and eastern Hokkaido are in the Nemuro-Kushiro-Tokachi region in the southeastern quadrant, where there are unusually broad marine terraces, as well as smaller amounts of diluvium and wet alluvium.

Climate, Vegetation, and Soils.—The significant general features of Hokkaido's relatively severe continental climates have been described in Chapter II. Further details on the climatic characteristics of different parts of Hokkaido are presented later. It may be useful at this point to recall that the nearest climatic counterparts of Hokkaido on this continent are probably northern New England and the Maritime Provinces of Canada (Fig. 32).

The climatic differences between east and west are emphasized by associated contrasts in native vegetation and soils (Figs. 34, 40). In the southwestern part a broadleaf deciduous forest predominates, which consists chiefly of beech, oak, ash, and elm interspersed with maple, linden, alder, and willow. Conifers are by no means lacking, and some authors describe the forest as a mixed one. A thick undergrowth of bamboo grass hinders the natural propagation of this forest. In central, northern, and eastern Hokkaido the broadleaf trees decline in importance, and needle trees, principally fir and spruce, increase. The upper limit of forest growth is at 3,000–4,000 feet elevation. It is estimated that 72 per cent of the North Island has a forest cover. Large areas of moor and swampy vegetation are characteristic of the alluvial lowlands, the most extensive of which are in the plains of the Ishikari and Teshio rivers. The drier moor areas have a cover of grasses and sedges, and the wetter ones are sphagnum in character.

Mikhailovskaia uses this boundary between the broadleaf-mixed forest and the boreal needle forest as the soil boundary separating the brown soils (burozems) of southwestern Hokkaido from the podsolic soils of the north and east.[2] Some Japanese soil experts question the existence of such a soil boundary in Hokkaido, and Dr. Seki's soil maps do not show it. According to the latter, Hokkaido soils fall into three principal classes: (1) true podsols, which are found only in the extreme northern part; (2) weakly podsolized soils, widely distributed over the greater part of the island except where (3) young volcanic detritus prevails, as it does over extensive areas in the southern and eastern portions of the island (Fig. 40).[3] These infertile volcanic soils of the Tokachi and Nemuro districts in southeastern Hokkaido have been important elements tending to retard settlement. Alluvial soils, which are the most fertile, are of limited extent (estimated at 6 per cent), and their quality is frequently impaired by poor drainage. The largest areas of moderately fertile alluvium are in two locations: (1) the Ishikari Plain in the southwest and (2) the Tokachi Lowland in the southeast.

Colonization[4] *and Population.*—The Ainu were the original inhabitants of Hokkaido, as they were in the rest of Japan, but they scarcely penetrated

[2] Mrs. O. N. Mikhailovskaia, "On the Soils of Japan," in *Contributions to the Knowledge of the Soils of Asia,* vol. 1 (Academy of Science of the U.S.S.R., 1930).

[3] *Ibid.,* Figs. 2 and 3. See also Seki's 1930 soils map of Japan, a simplified version of which appears as Fig. 40 in Chapter III above.

[4] In dealing with the history of colonization I have drawn freely from Alfons

the interior of the island, which was still largely in a virginal state when the first Japanese settlers arrived. The hostility of the Ainu toward the settlers was one factor retarding colonization. Although Japanese traders and fishermen visited the North Island before the seventh century, and permanent settlements may be traced as far back as the twelfth century, it is estimated that as late as 1800 there were no more than 30,000 Japanese in the whole area. Most of these were concentrated along the coasts of the southwestern peninsula, where they exploited the fish resources, making extensive use of Ainu labor. Estimates of the early population of Hokkaido are as follows:

Year	Ainu	Japanese
1600	50,000	12,000
1700	30,000	20,000
1800	20,000	30,000

Since the slow increase in the Japanese element was paralleled by a decrease in the number of Ainu, the total population for two centuries after 1600 was static or even declining.

In the first decade of the nineteenth century, when Russia's expansionist policy in the Far East threatened Japanese security, the Tokugawa Government took over the administration of Hokkaido. Thenceforth the colonial policy was based on the political considerations involved in safeguarding the North Island as Japanese territory. To prevent Russian inroads, attempts were made to settle more Japanese upon the agricultural lands of the interior. But despite government subsidies to agricultural colonists the area of cultivated land increased little, and fishing remained the predominant economy. Population increased very slowly, from 30,000 in 1800 to 60,000 in 1870, and most of it continued to be concentrated along the coast, largely in the southwestern peninsula. Even as late as 1860 less than seventeen hundred acres of land were under cultivation.

After the Meiji Restoration in 1868 Hokkaido was declared a part of Japan Proper; an office called the *Kaitakushi* (Colonial Office) was established to promote settlement; and the name of the island, *Yezo* (wild), was officially changed to *Hokkaido*, meaning "North-Sea Road." Despite the lack of a well-defined policy of land colonization, population grew from 58,000 in 1869 to 244,000 in 1882. No attempt was made to locate the newcomers, with the result that a majority of them chose to reside

Scheinpflug, "Die japanische Kolonisation in Hokkaido," *Mitteilungen der Gesellschaft für Erdkunde zu Leipzig*, 53 (1935), 33-88.

in the coastal areas and the interior continued to be nearly uninhabited (Fig. 157). At first a bonus was paid for clearing the land, but later this policy was abandoned, although the land remained tax-free for nearly a decade. The colonists' early attempts to grow rice were not very successful, and this experience tended to retard agricultural colonization, for the Japanese peasant farmer dislikes living where rice cannot be grown. Foreign crops and agricultural practices were introduced, but they made headway only very slowly. Railroads and roads were built, postal and telegraph communications established, mineral areas surveyed, and industrial plants founded. But in spite of these government improvements fishing remained the dominant economy of the population.

Beginning in 1875, a number of military settlements, patterned after

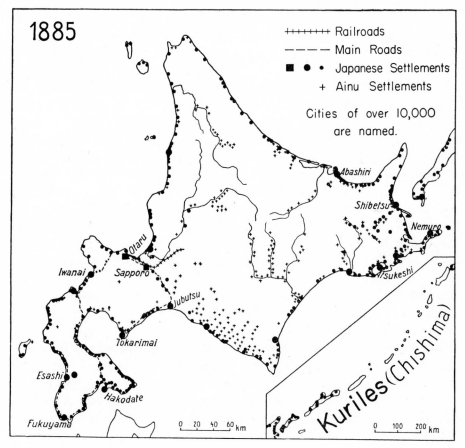

FIG. 157. Distribution of settlement in Hokkaido in 1885. At that time there were 287,000 Japanese and 18,000 Ainu in Hokkaido. After Scheinpflug.

Cossack settlements in Siberia, were established. The colonists received land and house, implements and seeds, and transportation to their destinations, in return for which they agreed to serve eight years in active service and twelve years in the reserve. The Ishikari region became the center of this colonization scheme, and gradually the settlers penetrated from the coastlands into the interior. Both village and dispersed settlements were tried, the latter being more popular. In the quarter century ending in 1900, when military colonization was abandoned, 39,911 soldier-colonists and 556,634 civilian immigrants entered Hokkaido. The importance of the numerically less important military colonies lies in the fact that they were the frontier nuclei which attracted the civilian settlers. The farmer-soldiers and their families were the vanguard of the much larger stream of colonists that were to follow.

After 1885, when Hokkaido was granted a central government, direct aid to prospective settlers was discontinued, and colonization benefits took the form of measures designed to improve and develop the island's economic conditions. A land survey was made to determine what areas were best fitted for cultivation. The surveyed land was divided into a rectangular grid patterned after the American system of land surveying. A grid of straight roads about a mile (5,400 feet) apart was constructed which divided the land into squares of 675 acres (5,400 feet square). Each 675-acre plat was divided into nine equal units of 75 acres (1,800 feet square), and these in turn into six equal parts 12.5 acres in area and 900 by 600 feet in dimensions. This smaller unit was estimated to be the area required to support a family, and it therefore tended to become the common farm unit, corresponding somewhat to the quarter section in the Upper Mississippi Valley in this country.[5] Theoretically the area allotted to each settler was limited to 83 acres, but many exceptions were made. Later the limits were increased to 1,250 acres for farming, 2,083 acres for livestock pasturing, and 1,666 acres for forest property. The result has been a development of leaseholdings which endanger the small independent farmer.

Until the turn of the century, however, fishing remained the chief economy of Hokkaido. As late as 1891 over 70 per cent of the North Island's total population was still engaged in some phase of that extractive economy, and was therefore concentrated along the coast (Fig. 157). Railroad building began in 1880, when a line was started at Otaru to connect with Sapporo on the Ishikari Plain and the coal fields in the hill

[5] See *American Influence upon the Agriculture of Hokkaido* (College of Agriculture, Tohoku Imperial University, Sapporo, 1915).

lands along its eastern margins. By 1890 this line had been extended to serve other portions of the Ishikari region, and in another decade rail construction had reached the Asahigawa Basin. A comprehensive railroad net was slowly created, which was focused on the three ports of Otaru, Hakodate, and Muroran. By 1910 eastern Hokkaido had been drawn into the rail system, and by 1930 new construction rendered accessible virtually all the potential agricultural land of Hokkaido.

The forest industries were the first to benefit from the extension of railroads. Indeed, the cutting of timber progressed so rapidly that it became necessary to pass a stringent forest law in 1907 (amended in 1927), which put forest exploitation under government control. Railroad building also resulted in a greatly increased mining of coal, much of which was shipped to Old Japan, since the local demand was small.

The extension of the rail net was at least partly responsible for the fact

TABLE 124.—POPULATION OF HOKKAIDO, 1870–1939

Year	Number of Inhabitants	Numerical Increase	Year	Number of Inhabitants	Numerical Increase
1870.	66,618		1905.	1,192,394	207,090
1875.	183,630	117,012	1910.	1,610,545	418,151
1880.	223,290	39,660	1915.	1,911,166	300,621
1885.	286,941	63,651	1920.	2,359,183	448,019
1890.	427,128	140,187	1925.	2,498,679	139,486
1895.	678,215	251,087	1930.	2,812,342	313,663
1900.	985,304	307,089	1939.	3,273,000	539,000

Sources: Scheinpflug, "Die japanische Kolonisation in Hokkaido," op. cit., 69; Norinsho Tokeihyo, 1939.

TABLE 125.—STATISTICS OF IMMIGRATION AND EMIGRATION FOR HOKKAIDO, 1918–30

Year	New Arrivals	Emigrants	Net Gain
1918.	83,925	17,433	66,492
1919.	91,465	21,455	70,010
1920.	80,536	23,543	56,993
1921.	69,974	24,379	43,595
1922.	60,412	26,560	38,852
1923.	58,203	27,869	30,334
1924.	58,315	43,846	14,469
1925.	60,104	33,457	26,647
1926.	56,312	28,489	27,823
1927.	57,890	28,745	29,145
1928.	53,931	28,054	25,877
1929.	58,471	27,219	31,252
1930.	60,126	26,235	33,891

Source: Scheinpflug, "Die japanische Kolonisation in Hokkaido," op. cit., 72.

that population trebled between 1900 and 1930. This increase is notable, considering that the period was one of free settling, since military colonization had been discontinued in 1900. The growth of the cities was more rapid than that of the island as a whole; between 1887 and 1930 Sapporo increased from 13,000 to 168,000 and Otaru from 10,000 to 144,000. Yet it is surprising, in view of the pressure of population in Old Japan, that the trek into Hokkaido was not more rapid. Reliable statistics are difficult to obtain, but it seems to be fairly certain that the annual influx of new settlers from the motherland, most of whom emigrated from northern Honshu, reached 100,000 in only a few favorable years. In most years they numbered 50,000–80,000. Moreover, from 10,000 to 20,000 of them came for seasonal work only, chiefly in the fishing industry, and returned to Old Japan with the arrival of the cold season. Finally, the annual increment of new settlers was partly offset by a relatively large stream of discontented and discouraged emigrants returning to their earlier homes in Old Japan. During the period 1920–25 there was a decided slowing up of the population growth of Hokkaido, an increase of only 139,486 being recorded for the five-year period. This period of retarded growth was coincident with the post-war economic depression, when not only was the flow of immigrants reduced but the stream of emigrants considerably enlarged. During the period 1923–27 the number of people leaving Hokkaido annually for the homeland averaged about 56 per cent of the total number of new settlers entering the North Island. Portions of western and northwestern Hokkaido actually declined in population during the period 1920–25. This trend was largely halted in the latter years of the thirties, however, and in the next decade the rate of increase was again normal.

The fact remains, however, that in the sixty years 1869–1929 less than a million and a half new Japanese settlers arrived in Hokkaido, by no means a large number in view of the overcrowded conditions in Nippon. It is evident that the Japanese are not eager to pour into the North Island, despite the government's inducements in the form of reduced railway and steamer fares, loans at a low rate of interest to those who want to purchase land, and subsidies for drainage and irrigation projects. The explanation resides largely in the fact that the physical character of the North Island, particularly its severe climate, is unattractive to a people whose culture traits are those of a tropical or subtropical people. Some would add that it reflects also the lack of a pioneering and colonizing spirit in the Japanese, who seem to prefer the close community life of the long-established village.

During the period 1930–39 the area under cultivation in Hokkaido increased by nearly 147,000 cho, a remarkable growth considering the fact that the cultivated area had declined after 1920 and by 1930 had recovered only to the point of approximating the 1920 acreage. It has been estimated that the total area of land fit for cultivation is about 1.6 million cho,[6] including peat beds and swamps covering 250,000 cho. Including the wet land, there were in 1939 slightly over 600,000 cho which under the most favorable conditions might be brought under cultivation. Much of this, however, is inferior land which is of dubious value and will be slow to attract settlers, however liberal the government's subsidies may be. The region with the largest areas of potentially arable land, which are of course the regions with the greatest influx of agricultural settlers, is eastern and southeastern Hokkaido in Nemuro, Kawanishi, and Urakawa provinces. But even if all the potentially arable land were eventually brought under cultivation, which is extremely unlikely, it would provide farms for only 100,000–120,000 additional farm families. The Hokkaido government's estimate of a future population of 6 million seems optimistic.

Because of the relative recency of its settlement—for most of Hokkaido was still an unoccupied wilderness at the time of the Imperial Restoration seventy-five years ago—many of the North Island's occupance features are distinctly un-Japanese. In 1939, when the population had reached almost 3.3 million, the average density was only about 48 per square kilometer or 108 per square mile, less than one-fifth of that for the country as a whole; even the prefectures of northernmost Honshu have two to three times as great a density. On the other hand, since only about 11 per cent of Hokkaido is cultivated, the density per square mile of tilled land is 950–1,000; even this, however, is only about 30 per cent of the average for the country as a whole. Between 1925 and 1939 the number of farm families in the North Island increased only 20,304 and the area in farms from 786,337 cho to 978,470.[7] During the same period the total population increased by 783,000, which seems to indicate that a majority of the settlers coming to Hokkaido do not become farmers. During the first two decades of the century approximately half the immigrants to the North Island were farmers, but in 1927 the proportion was down to 24 per cent. Five per cent were technicians, 5 per cent tradesmen, and 1 per cent fishermen.

A large share of Hokkaido's three and a quarter million people are concentrated in the western and southwestern part of the island, by far

[6] Shiroshi Nasu, *Aspects of Japanese Agriculture* (New York, 1941), 77–78.
[7] *Norinsho Tokeihyo*, 1925, 1931.

the greatest concentrations being in or close to the Ishikari Plain, Hokkaido's largest, most accessible, and most fertile lowland, and in the southwestern peninsula (Fig. 158). Thus while most of the northern, eastern, and southeastern parts have a population density of only 10–25 per square kilometer (26–66 per square mile), the Ishikari region and the southwestern peninsula have a concentration four or five times as great. The attraction of the Ishikari Lowland is not difficult to under-

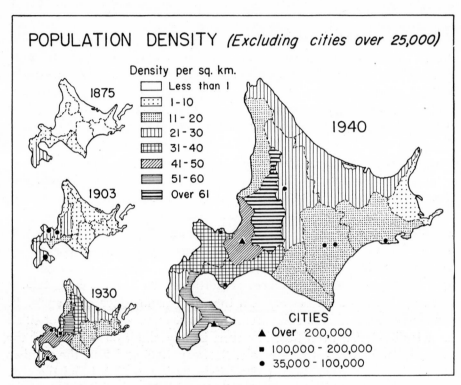

FIG. 158. Maps for 1875, 1903, and 1930 after Scheinpflug. Data for the 1940 map is taken from *Horei Zensho*, April, 1941.

stand, but that of the hilly and mountainous peninsula is less obvious. Proximity to the homeland, the abundance of fish in the coastal waters, and a climate which closely resembles that of North Honshu and is not too unfavorable for rice growing—all these help to offset the unfavorable terrain. As in other parts of Japan, there is a high degree of coincidence between settlement and lowlands. A patchy population pattern is therefore prevalent. Besides the Ishikari concentration there are other smaller ones, which coincide with the longitudinal chain of fault basins in the central mountain range, with the Tokachi Lowland in the southeast, which contains the cities of Obihiro and Ikeda, and with the Nokkeushi Basin in the northeast. In the southern provinces of Hokkaido the last remnants of the Ainu, the aboriginal inhabitants of the Japanese islands, occupy a number of dilapidated villages (Fig. 159). This primitive group, numbering some 16,000, is virtually stationary, perhaps even decreasing. Since they intermarry freely with the Japanese, they will eventually disappear as a distinct element of the population, as they already have in the rest of Japan.

Houses and Settlements.—Since the first colonists to arrive in Hokkaido engaged in fishing, the oldest settlements are on the coast. The character of the fishing settlements varies with the nature of the coast and its hinterland. Compact villages with well defined street patterns are most common in those coastal areas that have flattish hinterlands. Where the area of level land is restricted by the sea in front and a wave-cut cliff behind (Fig. 160), the crudely built huts more often stand isolated or are only loosely grouped into an approximation of the *strassendorf* settlement. In general the fishing setttlements have a sorry appearance. Cluttering the shore is an array of small boats, fishing nets, trays of drying fish, boiling kettles, racks of kelp, and storage sheds.

The inland non-urban settlements are chiefly those of farmers and, to a smaller extent, of loggers. These have developed more recently and deviate far more from Japanese standards than do the coastal fishing

Fig. 159. An Ainu settlement near Noboribetsu on the south coast of Hokkaido.

Fig. 160. Asari, a one-street, shoestring fishing village along the west coast of Hokkaido. Here the terrace is very narrow and the hills come so close to the coast that there is little room for settlements. Note the drying nets and the rutted street. Photograph by D. H. Davis.

FIG. 161. A house of thatch construction, resembling those of sub-tropical Japan, in the Asahigawa Basin. Note the fallow rice fields and the irrigation canal. Photograph by D. H. Davis.

FIG. 162. A frontier farmyard in northern Hokkaido near Nokkeushi. House at back, stable and shed at right. Photograph by D. H. Davis.

FIG. 163. Farmstead on a dairy farm on the Ishikari Plain near Sapporo. The gambrel-roofed stock and hay barn, silo, and substantial small house look Occidental. Maize in the foreground.

settlements. Not quite a third of the households in Hokkaido are those of farmers or part-time farmers, as compared with about 40 per cent in the country as a whole. The oldest farming settlements are of the village type, which provided the greatest security to the newcomers. It was easier for the group-colonists, who usually came from the same village, to face the hazards of frontier life together than to do so separately. Since many of them came from North Honshu, it is not surprising that the Echigo type of farm village, elongated in form and strung out along a highway, should be common. The houses, with their narrower gable ends facing the highway, frequently have their shingle roofs weighted down with boulders. This shoestring Echigo type of settlement is most characteristic of dry-field areas, where farms are larger. A somewhat more compact type of farm village, resembling the Yamato type of Old Japan, is common in paddy areas, where the irrigation systems require the close cooperation of the cultivators. Most striking, however, of the types of rural settlement in Hokkaido, because it is most un-Japanese in appearance and is widely distributed, is the isolated farmstead. Dispersion of farm dwellings is especially typical of those lands which are divided into a grid pattern in accordance with the American system of land surveying (Figs. 175, 182).

As a consequence of the larger landholdings, requiring as they do more animal labor, the Hokkaido farmstead differs in appearance from the village farmstead in Old Japan. It more nearly resembles an American farm in that it occupies a greater area than its counterpart in subtropical Japan, and its barns and sheds are more numerous. In this region animals must be protected against severe winter weather, and space must be provided both for housing them and for storing bulky animal feed over several months. There is commonly a well defined barnyard, sometimes fence-enclosed, which contains a barn of very modest proportions, sheds, wagons, and manure piles (Figs. 161–163). Reflecting the deep and long-continued snow cover are the sleds one commonly sees in Hokkaido barnyards (Fig. 162).

Farmhouses in Hokkaido are of various types, embodying different influences which have impinged upon settlement in this semi-frontier land. When the Japanese government turned its attention seriously to the peopling of this northland region, American agricultural experts were called in to advise on such matters as housing, land division, crops, and animals. Their influence is apparent in the log and clapboard cabins, glass windows, sheet-iron stoves, and occasional split-rail fences. Russian, German, and Danish influences are also observable. Moreover, the settlers in

Hokkaido, who came from all parts of Old Japan, have done what most colonists do—tried to duplicate their old homes so far as possible. In general house construction is sturdier and offers better protection against cold weather than elsewhere in Nippon, but an American finds it surprising that no greater modifications of the subtropical house have been made, considering the severity of Hokkaido's winter weather. He is amazed to see with what tenacity the Japanese have clung to their traditional mode of living in this colder land. Many elements of the flimsy construction common to Old Japan are still in use here. Tile and thatch as roofing materials, although not absent, are much less common than shingles and galvanized iron (Figs. 161, 162). Solid immovable walls made of wood siding and containing glass windows frequently replace the mud and wattle walls and the sliding *shoji* so common in subtropical Japan, and heating by stoves is characteristic. Externally the Hokkaido farmhouse and farmstead bear more resemblance to some American farmsteads than to those of subtropical Japan, although one must admit that they suggest the least desirable features, not the best, in American farmsteads. The houses and other farm buildings are small, unpainted, and none too substantial.

It is striking that even in the North Island the urban population outnumbers the rural. Between a quarter and a third of Hokkaido's population resides in the eight cities whose population exceeds 25,000. Two of these, Sapporo and Hakodate, have over 200,000 inhabitants, and Otaru and Muroran have more than 100,000. All eight cities are located either on the coast or on the larger of the interior plains. Four of them—Hakodate, Otaru, Muroran, and Kushiro—have tidewater locations and are primarily port cities of local importance. Sapporo, the capital of the prefecture, is likewise the

Fig. 164. The main street of Sapporo. Note its unusual width. Typical two-wheeled Hokkaido cart. The horse is being driven with reins rather than led as is the custom in Old Japan. Photograph by D. H. Davis.

metropolis and a center of local industry. Of the three remaining inland cities only Asahigawa has the multiple functions that are characteristic of cities, while Obihiro and Ikeda in the Tokachi Lowland function chiefly as market towns. Most of the larger settlements give evidence of Western influence in their rectangular street patterns and wide streets. The smaller towns of Hokkaido are largely market centers for the local farm and fishing areas. Most of them have no factory industries.

Agriculture.—In 1939 only 11 per cent of Hokkaido's total area was under cultivation, as against nearly 16 per cent in Japan as a whole. Even if the estimated potentially cultivable 1.6 million cho were eventually brought under cultivation, the percentage would still be only 18 per cent. It is evident that much the larger part of this northern island, because of its relief, climate, soil, and drainage, is unfitted for the cultivation of crops.

The agricultural landscape of Hokkaido is in many ways a contrast to that of Old Japan. Conspicuous is the grid pattern of roads and fields and the isolated farmsteads described earlier. In these and other respects American and European influence has been strong. During the ten years following 1870 Governor Kuroda of Hokkaido brought seventy-five foreign experts to the North Island, of whom forty-five were Americans.[8] The average Hokkaido farm (cultivated area) is 12–13 acres in area, or about five times as large as in Old Japan; more than one-third of the farms exceed 12 acres, and 55–60 per cent of the farm families cultivate more than 7 acres. In paddy areas landholdings are somewhat smaller than in sections where dry crops prevail, although the rectangular pattern still persists, and the individual rice fields are only a fraction of an acre in size. The larger farm of Hokkaido reflects in part the lower productivity of the land; in other words, a greater area is required to support a family. In part also it reflects the government's offer of larger farms as an inducement to settlers. Ordinarily the landholding is in one contiguous plot as contrasted with the scatter-field system typical of Old Japan. Individual fields in dry crops are not infrequently from one to several acres in area, which gives the landscape a degree of coarseness unlike that of Old Japan. In some places one is reminded more of the mosaic of agricultural fields in Europe or America. In paddy areas the fields are considerably smaller but still rectangular in outline. As in Old Japan, field fences are rare, for the pasturing of livestock is not common.

The larger farms in turn require certain modifications of farm practices

[8] See *American Influence upon the Agriculture of Hokkaido* (College of Agriculture, Tohoku Imperial University, Sapporo, 1915).

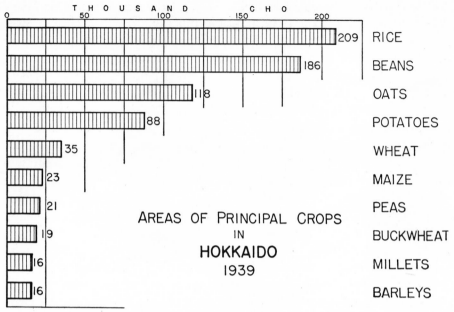

FIG. 165a

common to Old Japan. Animal power and farm machinery are used more generally, for it is quite impossible to cultivate a farm of 12 acres entirely by hand. Horses replace the slow-moving oxen as draft animals, the ratio of horses to farmhouses being more than 7 times what it is in Old Japan. Moreover, the horses of Hokkaido are sturdier than those to the south and they are driven with reins instead of being led, as is the practice in Old Japan. Some very modern machinery is employed on the Government Experimental Farms and similar equipment is gradually getting into the hands of the individual farmers. Most of this machinery is American in type, though it is made in Japan. The intensive methods of hand cultivation so universal in Old Japan are impossible on the larger farms of Hokkaido. Night soil is less abundant, hence fish and animal manures are more widely used. The consequence of these various practices is to reduce the unit-area production in Hokkaido considerably below the average for the country. In 1934 the value of farm production per tan was only 12.55 yen, as against 40.01 for the country; for paddy fields the comparable figures were 19.91 and 47.02.[9]

In at least three respects Hokkaido's agriculture differs from that in Old Japan: (1) the reduced emphasis upon paddy rice, (2) the general

[9] Nasu, *op. cit.*, 99, 101.

absence of winter cropping, or even of multiple cropping of the same field in summer, and (3) the greater importance of animals in the farm economy. In 1939 rice occupied only 19 per cent of the total cultivated area in Hokkaido as compared with 52 or 53 per cent for the country as a whole. The remarkable thing, however, in view of the latitude and climate of Hokkaido, is that it should be as important as it is. Rice is still the most important single crop, although its relative importance has been declining, the acreage having increased at a much slower rate in the thirties than in the twenties. It would appear that the easily available paddy land had already been reclaimed and that further expansion must be slow. Oats is the most important dry-crop cereal, and white potatoes also rank high. Wheat, buckwheat, millets, and maize are locally important. Although statistical volumes seem to make no mention of hay crops, one sees many fields of clover, alfalfa, and timothy, testifying that the climate is satisfactory for these Occidental forage crops and that animals have a significant place in the farm economy of Hokkaido (Fig. 165b). Crops are spring-sown, the fields remaining fallow in winter.

Many of the subtropical crops so important in subtropical Japan are not grown in Hokkaido. Tea and sweet potatoes are lacking altogether and mulberry nearly so. White potatoes and beans replace tea and mulberry as commercial crops. Dairying is somewhat less neglected here than elsewhere in Nippon. Nearly 36 per cent of all the milk cows of Japan are in Hokkaido, and 34 per cent of the country's milk is produced there. By far the largest proportion of the dairy cattle are in the possession of farmers who own only a cow or two. In the vicinity of a few cities there are farms with small herds of cattle, chiefly Holsteins, which sell milk to urban processing plants. Over half of the condensed milk, three-fourths of the butter, and four-fifths of the cheese of the country are manufactured in Hokkaido. To be sure, these figures are all relative, and the total output of all these products is small. For example, only about a fifth of the farm families have a milk cow. Actually the ratio of cattle to people is higher in Old Japan than it is in Hokkaido, but there most of the cattle are draft animals, whereas those of Hokkaido are for milk and meat. Horses are four times as numerous as cattle in Hokkaido. The ratio of hogs to people

Fig. 165b. A relatively large hayfield on the Ishikari Plain. No hayfield of these dimensions would ever be seen in Old Japan.

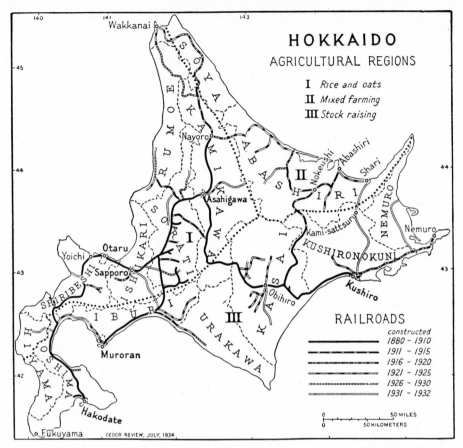

FIG. 166. On the above map, by D. H. Davis, three principal agricultural subdivisions are recognized. The boundaries and names of the administrative subdivisions, *shichos*, are shown. From the *Geographical Review,* published by the American Geographical Society, New York.

is about the same as it is for most other regions of Japan and for the country as a whole.

Regional Agriculture.—It is in the west, on the Ishikari Plain and in the Asahigawa Basin, that agriculture is best established. Paddy fields occupy the low wet areas of peat and peaty soils, and unirrigated crops the uplands. Rice is the most important crop, occupying as much as 60 per cent of the cropped area on some alluvial tracts. Where the alluvium is not too wet there is likely to be a considerable acreage of dry crops intermingled with the paddies. In the northern and eastern parts of the island, where agricultural land is still being reclaimed from the forest, the countryside has a frontier aspect. In many cultivated fields the tree stumps have not yet been removed. The summers being cooler, rice declines in importance, and oats, beans, potatoes, rye, and wheat become relatively more important. In the extreme east and southeast, where cool and foggy summers prevail, all crops become less important, rice being lacking altogether, and the breeding of horses becomes an agricultural specialization.

Davis[10] classifies the three principal agricultural regions in the North Island as (1) the western or "Rice and Oats Regions"; (2) the northern or "Mixed Farming Region"; and (3) the southern or "Stock Raising Region" (Fig. 166). In the first region, which includes the Ishikari Plain and the chain of longitudinal basins in the central highlands, rice is the most important crop, occupying 20–60 per cent of the cropped area.

Oats is of almost equal importance, and beans and potatoes are important secondary crops. In the northern Mixed Farming Region both rice and oats are much less important, though each crop occupies 25 per cent or less of the cropped land. Wheat, rye, peas, beans, potatoes, and buckwheat are also of considerable importance and occupy about equal acreages. In the southern Stock Raising Region crop production is less important, and

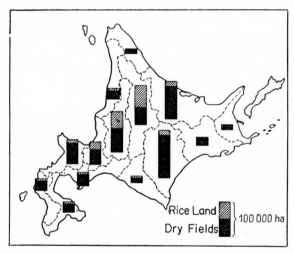

FIG. 167. Distribution of rice land and dry fields. The unit of measurement is the hectare. After Scheinpflug.

chief emphasis is placed on the breeding and pasturing of horses, large numbers of which are sold to the army. The principal crops raised are oats, beans, potatoes, buckwheat, and peas, rice being significant only on the alluvium in the Tokachi Lowland (Fig. 167).

Individual Crops.—The fact that a subtropical plant like rice should be the most important single crop in a region of severe continental climate

[10] Darrell H. Davis, "Present Status of Settlement in Hokkaido," in the *Geographical Review*, 24(1934):386–399.

TABLE 126.—AREA IN RICE LAND AND DRY FIELDS IN HOKKAIDO, 1870–1939
(in hectares; 1 hectare = 2.43 acres)

Year	Paddy Fields	Dry Fields	Total Cultivated Area
1870.	347	738	1,085
1880.	1,035	9,695	10,730
1890.	2,240	42,895	45,135
1900.	9,984	231,326	241,310
1910.	35,085	502,949	548,034
1920.	83,846	755,224	839,070
1927.	158,914	630,515	789,429
1929.	192,540	633,000	825,540
1939.	204,100	766,520	970,620

Source: For 1927 and earlier data, Scheinpflug, "Die japanische Kolonisation in Hokkaido," *op. cit.*
82; later statistics from *Norinsho Tokeihyo*. The statistics here given are for land according to its
classification as irrigated fields or dry fields. Since they refer to the planted area in a particular year
the figures differ slightly from those in Table 127.

TABLE 127.—AREA PLANTED TO VARIOUS CROPS IN HOKKAIDO
(in cho; 1 cho = 2.45 acres)

Crop	1917	1925	1930	1939
Rice.	63,900	128,586	186,869	183,997
Beans (soy, azuki, and kidney)	171,700	183,272	234,000	209,056
Oats.	63,200(1914)	106,859	114,222	117,964
Potatoes	76,100	45,443	45,163	88,168
Millets.	20,900(1918)	17,174	16,500	16,228
Naked barley and barley.	31,300(1918)	24,934	20,287	15,761
Wheat.	10,700(1918)	9,189	13,616	35,012
Buckwheat.	18,400	22,994	21,275	19,250
Maize	20,600	20,501	16,312	23,003
Flax.	19,700	21,275	8,589	28,966
Peppermint.		9,221	13,803	20,933
Total cultivated area	746,500	786,337	831,879	978,470

Source: Data for 1917 from Wellington D. Jones, "Hokkaido," in the *Geographical Review*, 11 (1921):
16–30; data for 1925, 1930, and 1939 from *Norinsho Tokeihyo*.

(Dbf) reveals how compelling is this requirement in the basic Japanese
diet. Careful breeding of strains which mature in 100 days or less has
carried the rice crop progressively farther northward and eastward until
at present it is grown in lowland sections of the entire island except in
the extreme north and east (Figs. 95, 167). According to Kawaguti[11] the
critical factor in rice growing is the temperature during the growing
season, especially in the month of August.

The present limit of rice cultivation is the temperature belt of 19°–

[11] Takeo Kawaguti, "Rice Culture in Hokkaido, Its Northern Boundary in Japan"
(in Japanese with English summary), in the *Geographical Review of Japan*, 11(1935):
1–23, 155–196.

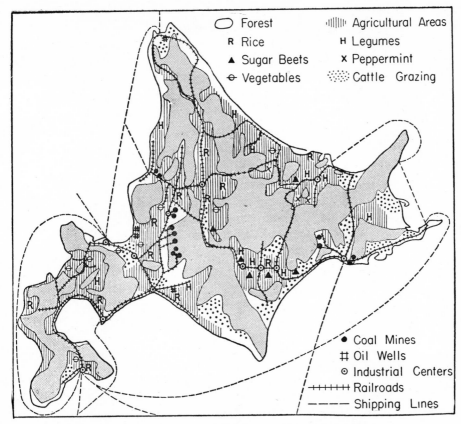

◯ Forest	⊪⊪⊪ Agricultural Areas	
R Rice	H Legumes	
▲ Sugar Beets	× Peppermint	
⊖ Vegetables	⣿ Cattle Grazing	

• Coal Mines
♯ Oil Wells
◉ Industrial Centers
++++++ Railroads
------ Shipping Lines

Fig. 168. Agriculture and industry. After Scheinpflug.

19.5° C. (66.2–67.1° F.), where the growing season is 110–130 days.[12] But this forcing of the rice crop into a climatic environment to which it is unsuited has resulted in lower yields, the average yield per unit-area being only 42 per cent as large in Hokkaido as in the country as a whole.[13] On the wet, peaty soils of the alluvial plains rice is, however, the most productive crop, and in such areas it is not likely to be displaced by others. Probably 50 per cent or more of Hokkaido's rice crop is sown directly in the paddy fields instead of being transplanted from seedbeds as in Old Japan. The raising of rice seedlings in seedbeds for later transplanting is chiefly characteristic of the warmer southwestern districts, whereas direct seeding in paddy fields is typical of the north and east.[14]

[12] Ibid., p. 196, Fig. 4; p. 16, Fig. 5; p. 17.   [13] Nasu, op. cit., 191.
[14] Kawaguti, op. cit., p. 175, Fig. 12. See also J. W. Robertson Scott, The Foundations of Japan (London, 1922), 337.

Of the other cereals, by far the most important is oats, which is used both as animal feed and as a human food in the form of oatmeal. It is grown chiefly on the uplands, although it is found also on the drier parts of alluvial plains. In some sections, especially in the north and east, it exceeds rice in acreage. Wheat, barley, buckwheat, rye, millet, and maize vary in importance from one locality to another, their combined acreages being less than that of oats and only 60 per cent of the rice acreage. Much the larger part of the barley crop is of the "naked barley" variety. Peas and several varieties of beans, used both as animal and as human food, are also important crops. Fifty-three per cent of the country's white potato acreage is in Hokkaido, the crop being widely dispersed. It is a staple article of diet and is also used as stock feed and as the basis of a fairly important starch-manufacturing industry. Minor commercial crops are sugar beets, hemp, and peppermint (Fig. 168).

Other Economies.—Hokkaido's earliest settlers were fishermen, and as late as 1885 almost the whole population was peripherally located. Even today fishing is one of the principal economies. About 14 per cent of the country's entire fishing population is concentrated here, and scores of shabby-looking fishing settlements dot the coasts (Fig. 160). In 1939 the number of *persons* engaged in fishing slightly exceeded the number of *farm families.* Since the fishermen are preponderantly adults, and over 70 per cent of them males, most of whom are presumably heads of families, it seems fair to assume that fishing supports from half to three-quarters as many persons as farming. In volume and value of the catch, coastal fishing far outranks deep-sea fishing, the value ratio being roughly five or six to one. Virtually the whole of the herring catch is taken in Hokkaido's coastal waters, where sardine fishing, too, is very important. Most of the Hokkaido catch is sent to Hakodate and Otaru for shipment to Old Japan. At least fifteen sardine-fabricating plants and half as many salmon canneries are located in tidewater settlements of the North Island.

From Hokkaido's forests comes about one-sixth of the timber cut of Japan, and over a fourth of the pulp. With the canning and preservation of fish and the fabrication of metals, the production of lumber, pulp, and paper are Hokkaido's chief manufactures. The important blast furnace and steel center at Muroran on the south coast, which uses local and imported iron ore and Ishikari coal, has the largest pig iron capacity north of the Kobe-Osaka center. There is no marked regional concentration of industrial plants in Hokkaido, although the most important ones are in the port cities along the south coast or adjacent to the Ishikari Plain at Otaru and Sapporo (Fig. 168). Most of Hokkaido's manufacturing industries are rooted in the soil and are based on the raw materials of the region. The chief exception is the iron and steel plant at Muroran, which requires large amounts of imported ore.

GEOGRAPHICAL SUBDIVISIONS

Peninsular Southwestern Hokkaido

Separated from the main body of Hokkaido by the Ishikari-Yufutsu depression and lowland, the oddly shaped fish-tail peninsula which forms its southwestern appendage (Region A on Fig. 169, p. 364) is morphologically a northward continuation of the central and western highlands of northern Honshu. Its peninsular character accounts for the prevalence here of the most marine climate in Hokkaido. Hakodate at the southern extremity is fairly representative of the lowlands throughout the peninsula.

CLIMATIC DATA FOR HAKODATE

Temperature				Precipitation in Inches		
Mean January	Mean August	Mean Minimum January	Mean Maximum August	Mean Annual	January Average	July Average
27.1	70.5	32.7	78.1	45.2	2.4	5.1

This southwestern peninsula, which is the part of Hokkaido closest to Old Japan, is the funnel through which the immigrants from the south have moved into the northern island. Hence it was the first part of Hokkaido to be settled, and as late as 1875 was almost the only section of the island that was moderately well populated. It is still the main bridge between Honshu and Hokkaido proper; and the ferry terminal port of Hakodate, which is also the southern terminal of Hokkaido's rail lines, is the second largest city of the northern island. Like its physical counterpart in northern Honshu, peninsular Hokkaido is divided into two dissimilar segments separated by fault valleys, (1) a western hill land composed chiefly of weak Tertiary rocks and (2) two eastern areas of volcanic mountains.

The Oshima Hill Country (Subregion 1, Fig. 169).—This section of prevailingly weak Tertiary rocks is a thoroughly dissected hill country of moderate relief. In only a few places does the relief exceed 1,500 feet and for the most part it is considerably less. Rivers have opened up relatively wide valleys, the floors of which are partially under cultivation.

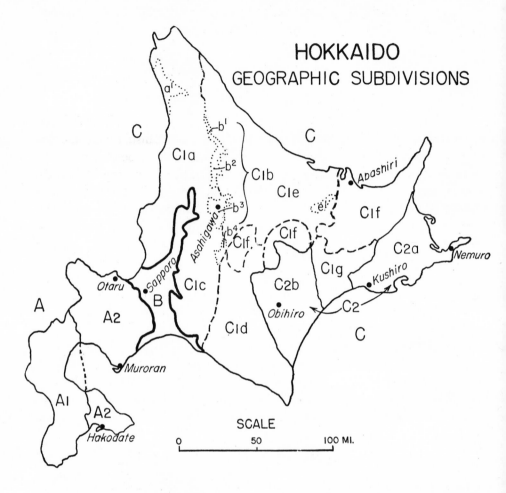

FIG. 169. HOKKAIDO: GEOGRAPHIC SUBDIVISIONS

A. PENINSULAR HOKKAIDO
   A1. Oshima Hill Country
   A2. Volcanic Lands

B. ISHIKARI-YUFUTSU LOWLAND

C. CENTRAL AND EASTERN HOKKAIDO
   C1. Hill and Mountain Lands and Associated Depressions
      C1a. Teshio Hills
         a^1. Teshio Delta
      C1b. Central Fault Depressions
         b^1. Tombetsu Lowland
         b^2. Nayoro Basin

         b^3. Kamikawa or Asahigawa Basin
         b^4. Furano Basin
      C1c. Yubari Hill and Mountain Land
      C1d. Hidaka Mountains
      C1e. Kitami Mountain Land
         e^1. Nokkeushi Basin
      C1f. Volcanic Chain
      C1g. Shiranuka Hill Land
   C2. Southeastern Lowlands
      C2a. Nemuro-Kushiro Terrace
      C2b. Tokachi Lowland

364

Where more resistant andesites and granites prevail the elevations are higher (3,000–3,500 feet), the relief greater, and the whole terrain more rugged. In such districts population is very sparse. A deciduous woodland mantles much of the hill land, which furnishes more fuel than lumber. Because of the general prevalence of slopeland, unirrigated crops are much more important than rice. The principal sites of agricultural development are on the coastal terraces and on floodplains of the main rivers.

Much of the coast is steep and rocky. Hills come down almost to the water's edge, and conspicuous marine erosion terraces, some of them over 200 meters in elevation, border much of the coast, although they are much less extensive here than along the coasts of Hokkaido proper. Along Volcano Bay the railroad follows the very narrow coastal strip between the ocean and the steep terrace fronts. Crops are raised both on the narrow, sandy strip of lowland at the foot of the terrace and on the surface of the terrace itself. Combination fishing-agricultural villages are numerous, for this is one of the North Island's most important areas of coastal fishing. The west coast is still more abrupt and forbidding; cliffed headlands are numerous, rail service lacking, and population sparse.

The Volcanic Lands (Subregion 2, Fig. 169).—This division is composed of two fragments separated by the caldron-like depression occupied by Volcano Bay. Its confused terrain is dominated by ash-and-lava cones, some active, in various stages of dissection, by caldera lakes, and by dissected andesite plateaus. The apparent confusion and lack of order in the terrain features is due to the existence of several volcanic systems, which have originated at separate points of eruption. In the more southern of the two subdivisions, at the entrance to Volcano Bay, is Komagatake (1,140 meters), which became active in 1929. Yotei-san (1,893 meters), in the larger volcanic mass on the northern side of Volcano Bay, has also been very active in recent years. Because of its unusually perfect conical form this volcano is called the "Hokkaido Fuji." Lakes Chikotsu and Toya occupy volcanic caldera, and the caldron-shaped depression of Volcano Bay, festooned by numerous cones, is likewise of volcanic origin. The coasts are characteristically steep and are lacking in sizeable plains.

In general the hilly and mountainous nature of the region has discouraged settlement, although agriculture is practiced in some of the valleys and on the low, gently sloping ash aprons, and fishing villages dot the entire coastline. At Tomakomai on the south coast is a huge pulp and paper mill employing over 1,500 hands, which uses timber from the mountainous hinterland. In the same region are some of the largest Ainu settlements in Hokkaido—agglomerations of frame-and-thatch huts.

Associated with the igneous activity are the numerous small deposits of copper, gold, silver, tin, wolfram, and sulphur, which support mining communities of different sizes. At least four sulphur deposits of the solfatara type are being worked. The Kutchan Mine is one of the two most important iron mines in Japan Proper, employing 94 men and producing in 1935 some 147,000 tons of 45–50 per cent limonite, all of which is used in the iron and steel plant at Muroran on the shores of Volcano Bay. The reserve is very small, being estimated at less than 6 million tons. In addition about 41,000 tons of iron ore of the bog iron type were being mined in 1935 from pits along the northern margin of Volcano Bay.

On the seaward margins of these volcanic lands are located three of Hokkaido's largest cities, all of them ports of some consequence. *Muroran*, a city of nearly 108,000 people, is located at the southernmost extremity of the northern volcanic segment, on the northern side of the entrance to Volcano Bay. The site is the concave side of a curved spit and its land-tied island, the whole being shaped like a fishhook and enclosing a well protected harbor (Fig. 170). Two moles at the relatively narrow western entrance of the harbor prevent entrance of the strong waves generated by the boisterous west winds of winter. The harbor has an area of about four square miles. Depths of ten meters exist in mid-harbor, and boats of 8,000 tons can be accommodated at one of the buoys.[15] In normal times the port's domestic trade is many times as large as its

TABLE 128.—FOREIGN TRADE OF MURORAN, 1938

Exports in Yen		Imports in Yen	
Coal	1,066,249	Ores and metals	6,256,900
Sulphur.	621,521	Coal	778,713
		Paper-making machinery . . .	394,766
Total, including others . . .	1,737,665		
		Total, including others . . .	8,030,116

Source: *Annual Return of the Foreign Trade of Japan*, pt. 3 (Department of Finance, Tokyo, 1938)

foreign trade, and exports, chiefly bulky products, exceed imports. The chief items of domestic export are coal; wood, pulp, and paper; and marine products. The relatively small foreign trade of the port is weighted

[15] Ludwig Mecking, *Japans Häfen* (Hamburg, 1931), 573.

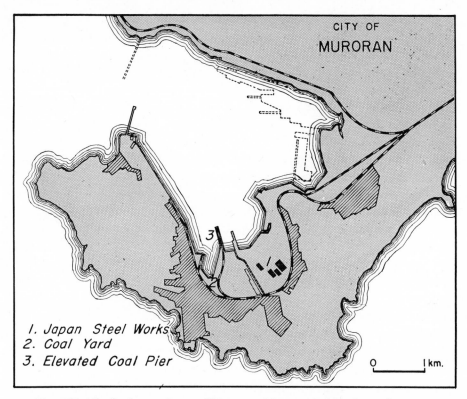

FIG. 170. The harbor and city of Muroran. Muroran is Japan's northernmost
center of primary iron and steel manufacturing.

heavily on the import side, ores and metals for the local iron and steel
plant being by far the most important, followed by coal and paper-
making machinery. The small amount of foreign exports consists largely
of coal and sulphur. An up-to-date, well equipped coaling pier extends
nearly 1,200 feet into the harbor. Some coal-carrying boats anchor at
buoys and are loaded by lighters. Large coal-storage yards occupy waterfront locations. East of the coal pier is another equipped with cranes,
which serves principally the smelting industries of the city.

As an industrial city Muroran is most noted for its pig iron and steel
production. Some 17 or 18 per cent of the pig iron and 1–5 per cent of
the steel manufactured in Japan Proper originate in plants of the Wainishi
Iron and Steel Works and the Nippon Seikojo in Muroran (Fig. 170).
Iron ore for the blast furnaces is obtained both from the Kutchan, Abuta,
Horomoe, and Nakadoya mines not far distant and from foreign sources.
It is unfortunate that the ironworks are not situated on the waterfront,
where they could make the most economical use of the imported ore.
Local coal arrives by rail from the Ishikari Field about 250 kilometers
distant, and some special coals, such as coking coal, are imported from

foreign sources. Several batteries of ovens produce an inferior brittle coke from a mixture of local and imported coal, and a modern by-products plant is close at hand.

Hakodate (204,000), at the extreme southern end of the peninsula, is the second city of Hokkaido and one of its two greatest ports. Its harbor and site resemble those of Muroran, being on a fishhook peninsula composed of a strongly fortified island (over 300 meters high) and a narrow spit which ties it to the mainland. Unlike Muroran, however, Hakodate in un-Japanese fashion spreads up the adjacent hill slopes for 40 meters or more in a picturesque manner. It is one of the three oldest ports of Japan open to foreign trade and was for a time a summer base for the British Oriental Squadron. The Occidental influence born of these contacts is conspicuous, especially in the considerable number of ancient buildings of semi-foreign style. Hakodate is important chiefly as a fishing and ferry port, although it is a fortified site, the most important business focus of the island, and a local manufacturing center of some importance, producing cement, fish products, hemp cloth, and fishnets. As one of the nation's greatest fishing centers, it serves as the collecting and distributing center not only for Hokkaido's aquatic products but for those from Sakhalin, Kurile, and Siberian waters. Its harbor is usually crowded with fishing craft, and marine products are its most important trade commodity, usually comprising half or more of the exports. Fish manure is especially noteworthy.

Though Hakodate is located at the southern extremity of a hilly peninsula, and though it lacks an important local hinterland and is removed from the more important agricultural, forest, and mineral regions, it is nevertheless favorably situated, for it profits by its proximity to Honshu and its position as the southern terminus of the Hokkaido railway system. These advantages have made it an outstanding port of domestic trade. Its foreign trade, consisting chiefly of marine products shipped to Asiatic countries and the United States, is of much less importance.

Otaru (164,000), on the north coast of the volcanic province, has for its hinterland the Ishikari Plain, one of the earliest settled and the most productive part of Hokkaido, and the Ishikari Coal Field. Since the sea margins of Ishikari are smooth and harborless with coastal dunes, Otaru, occupying a rocky indentation in the adjacent andesite hills just to the south, has developed as its port. The bay opens to the northeast, so a protective mole and breakwaters have been necessary. Harbor depths inside the breakwaters are 7–8 meters. Transfer of cargo is almost exclusively by lighters, although boats of 4,000 tons can come alongside the

TABLE 129.—FOREIGN TRADE OF HAKODATE, 1938

Exports in Yen		Imports in Yen	
Canned salmon	19,477,903	Salt beef	2,023,568
Canned trout	6,088,787	Vehicles and vessels	1,065,189
Canned sardines	1,232,233	Oils and fats	463,522
Salted trout	1,959,633	Phosphate	372,998
		Ores and metals	313,141
Total, including others	36,773,674	Wheat bran	103,283
		Total, including others	4,707,720

Source: *Annual Return of the Foreign Trade of Japan*, pt. 3 (Department of Finance, Tokyo, 1938).

TABLE 130.—FOREIGN TRADE OF OTARU, 1938

Exports in Yen		Imports in Yen	
Peas	2,638,340	Sulphate of potash	2,190,000
Kidney beans	3,579,112	Ores and metals	2,936,159
Potato starches	1,799,872	Bean cake	1,699,145
Fresh onions	403,080	Sulphate of ammonium	630,000
Condensed milk	1,483,615	Salt	583,254
Canned salmon	1,423,200		
Dried plants for insecticides	1,117,925	Total, including others	10,035,113
Coal	1,270,126		
Wood, logs, and wood veneer	6,704,151		
Total, including others	29,078,178		

Source: *Annual Return of the Foreign Trade of Japan*, pt. 3 (Department of Finance, Tokyo, 1938).

300-meter-long coal pier.[16] Coal and lumber storage yards occupy considerable portions of the waterfront. Marine and agricultural products and coal are the most important exports. Coal is largely a domestic export, going principally to the ports of northwestern Honshu; it is also consumed as bunker fuel by the numerous fishing and coasting steamers operating in Hokkaido waters. European as well as Japanese lumber-shipping firms have offices in Otaru, since some of the product goes directly to European, chiefly British, markets. Fishing has been fostered not only by the excellent fishing grounds adjacent but by the abundance of cheap bunker coal. Herring is the chief species of the region. A portion of the catch is turned into fertilizer and oil, as is attested by the great iron boiling kettles and ovens along sections of the waterfront. The port's domestic trade is valued at several times its foreign commerce, which consists predominantly of exports (Table 130).

[16] Mecking, *op. cit.*, 580.

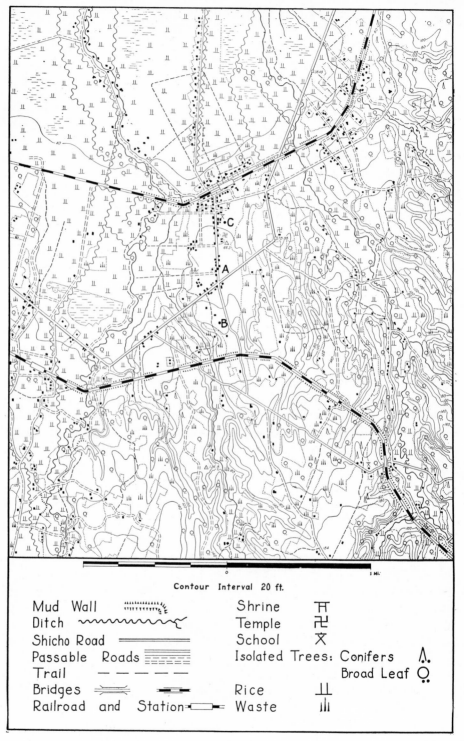

Contour Interval 20 ft.

Mud Wall	Shrine
Ditch	Temple
Shicho Road	School
Passable Roads	Isolated Trees: Conifers
Trail	Broad Leaf
Bridges	Rice
Railroad and Station	Waste

The Ishikari-Yufutsu Lowland

This asymmetrical Y-shaped depression (Region *B*, Fig. 169), which separates Hokkaido into two very unequal eastern and western parts, is the northern counterpart of the Kitakami-Abukuma tectonic lowland which in northern Honshu marks the boundary between the Inner and the Outer Zone. In a very real sense it is the heart of Hokkaido, for it is by far the most extensive lowland in the island and as such has become the focus of agriculture and its attendant industries and settlements. On it is located Sapporo, the provincial capital and the island's metropolis.

This extensive detritus-filled depression, whose floor is the product of rapid aggradation by adjacent volcanoes and by the river Ishikari and its tributaries, is monotonously flat, and part of it is poorly drained. The rivers wander sluggishly over its flat surface in very shallow channels, describing broad meander belts bearing numerous scars of old crescentic channels, not a few of which contain oxbow lakes. Large areas of wet peat bog are still unreclaimed for agriculture and support only tall wild grasses and reeds, although some of the none too fertile peat soils are now growing a crop of rice. Unquestionably the drainage handicaps of the Ishikari Lowland present the most serious obstacle to its more complete occupance. In spring when the heavy snow cover is melting the plain is a quagmire. Where it fronts upon the ocean the coasts are bordered by barrier beaches with dunes, their smooth contour providing no natural sites for ports. Extensive fragments of diluvial terrace flank the inner margins of the lowland, most of which have considerable areas of smooth to rolling upland surface (Fig. 171). Volcanic ash is a large constituent of the terraces and their surface soils.

Its accessibility to Old Japan and its comparatively large areas of new alluvium are important reasons why Ishikari was one of the first parts outside the peninsula to be settled, and why at present it contains the largest population cluster in Hokkaido. After the first railroad was built from Otaru to Sapporo, early in the 1880's, and soon thereafter extended to other parts of the Ishikari Plain, there was a large influx of population from Old Japan into Hokkaido, which tended to concentrate on the Ishikari Plain.

FIG. 171. A section of the Ishikari Plain. Alluvium with rice in the northwestern part; diluvial upland in woodland, moors, and unirrigated crops to southeast. Cropped areas on the diluvium are bounded by dotted lines, but non-rice areas have no crop symbols as do the rice fields. Rural settlement is prevailingly dispersed. Map by D. H. Davis, from a Japanese topographic map.

All the Ishikari Plain is now occupied except certain swampy alluvial areas and portions of the bordering diluvial uplands whose poor volcanic-ash soils have discouraged reclamation. A rectangular road and land-subdivision system and dispersed isolated farmsteads are characteristic of most of the plain. These isolated farmsteads tend to congregate along the highways but there are many exceptions. Farm villages and market towns are frequently located at the intersections of main roads. Surrounding the homesteads and paralleling the highways, rows of trees, often poplars, break the force of the strong winter winds as they sweep across the flat terrain, piling up the snow. The highways, broader than in Old Japan, are elevated and are paralleled by drainage ditches. Large horses in single harness drawing heavy two-wheeled carts equipped with wide, high wheels are conspicuous on the highways. Teams of horses are less common. The Ishikari Plain is the center of Japan's dairy industry, so one sees Holstein cattle in some of the farmyards, as well as conspicuous hay barns and silos (Fig. 163). Some maize is grown for silage. It is in the vicinity of Sapporo that these features are most common, but one sees large numbers of milk cans at the railway stations and on the trains, indicating that milk is also being brought from some little distance.

Apparently the cattle are always fed at the farmstead and are never pastured, although occasionally one sees horses and cows tethered along the roadside. Fences are rare.

Over the plain as a whole dry crops probably occupy a larger area

FIG. 172, *above*. Relatively large fields of unirrigated crops, and isolated farmsteads with windbreaks on the Ishikari Plain.

FIG. 173. Large, rectangular rice fields and a farmstead on the Ishikari Plain. The barn and outbuildings are joined to the house, as they are in snowy New England.

than rice, which is, however, expanding rapidly in acreage (Fig. 173). Oats is the most important dry crop, but fields of soybeans, potatoes, buckwheat, peas, and wheat are also numerous. The Ishikari Lowland is one of the most important rice-growing regions of Hokkaido. In some parts of the plain the crop occupies 50–75 per cent of the total cultivated area, though this is the exception. No doubt it is the combination of a large amount of wet land unfit for dry-crop cultivation with relatively warm summers which has produced this paddy specialization. Gradually the peat bogs are being reclaimed and converted into paddy fields, so this amphibious crop tends to be concentrated in the wetter parts of the plain. The monotonous rectangular pattern of small, right-angled paddy fields in the areas devoted exclusively to rice constitutes a quite different and a far less varied landscape than that of the dry-crop regions (Fig. 172).

On the peripheral diluvial terraces, which have elevations of 30–40 meters above the alluvial floor, the land is put to different use. Their rolling surfaces, poorer ash soils, and incised streams generally preclude rice cultivation. Large areas are woodland, some of which contains good timber, though more of it does not. Near Sapporo the terraces are quite generally used for dry-crop agriculture, which gives them somewhat the same apperance as the dry-crop areas on the alluvium except that the surface is rolling and is occasionally deeply cut by ravines and gullies. In some places apple orchards are conspicuous. By and large, however, woodland seems to predominate.[17]

In summary it may be stated that the Ishikari-Yufutsu Plain presents four general types of rural landscape: (1) the unreclaimed peat bogs, (2) the areas on the lower alluvial lands devoted more exclusively to paddy rice, (3) the dry-crop areas with some rice on the slightly higher alluvium, and (4) the partially cultivated diluvial terraces.

Sapporo (223,000), provincial capital and metropolis, is located close enough to the hardrock hills so that there is sufficient slope of the alluvium to provide drainage. It is a planned city on a flat plain, unhampered by topographic configuration. Avenues 160 feet wide intersect at right angles with streets 100–120 feet wide, making an almost perfect grid pattern (Fig. 164). These were laid out before a single house was built. The commercial core has a number of substantial foreign-style buildings, including at least one large department store. It is the center of much of Hokkaido's industry and is on the rail line which crosses Ishikari from the Yubari Coal Field through Sapporo to the port of Otaru. The city

[17] Darrell Haug Davis, "Type Occupance Patterns in Hokkaido," in the *Annals of the Association of American Geographers*, 24:206–209 (December, 1934).

has large breweries, a mill for spinning and weaving flax, and a mill for spinning hemp yarn. At Ebitsu on the railroad east of the city is one of the largest paper mills in Japan.

Central and Eastern Hokkaido

The roughly rhombic shape of central and eastern Hokkaido (Region C, Fig. 169) is occasioned by the arrangement of its mountains, the north-south axis being a series of ranges corresponding to the Pacific or Outer Zone of North Honshu. This region has no extensive plains of new alluvium, and even its small ones are so wet as to be largely unfit for cultivation without preliminary drainage. The two largest areas having flattish surfaces are the Tokachi and the Kushiro-Nemuro lowlands in the southeastern quadrant, but these are largely diluvium and ash-covered terraces. Its more severe continental climate, its greater isolation from Old Japan, the deficiency of well drained alluvial plains, and the prevalence of poor ash soils on the uplands have combined to keep eastern Hokkaido very much a frontierland. Throughout the region the extractive industries—lumbering, fishing, grazing, and mining—give employment to a large proportion of the population.

The Hill and Mountain Lands with Their Associated Depressions (Subregion 1, Fig. 169): *The Teshio Hills* (Area *a*).—The landward margins of this subdivision are marked by fault-scarps overlooking the Central Fault Depression and the northern arm of the Ishikari Plain. Structurally it is an upwarped block composed chiefly of Tertiary rocks, whose surface configuration is relatively subdued, only the highest peaks exceeding 800 meters. Toward the southern end a huge dissected shield volcano presents a much more mountainous relief. Along the coasts, marine erosion platforms are conspicuous. In the coastal sections dilapidated huts of fishermen and farmers are strung out along the highway that parallels the seashore. Occasionally there is a tiny compact settlement at the mouth of a valley where a secondary road meets the coastal highway. On the land side of the highway the abrupt wave-cut front of the marine terrace rises to an elevation of 30–60 meters. Both on the narrow plain at the foot of the terrace and on the latter's upland surface some land is cultivated, dry crops predominating. Isolated residences are common. Behind the terrace rise the higher hills, covered with deciduous and mixed woods or moorlike areas. In those valleys which are wide enough to contain flattish floodplain and river-terrace land, a frontier type of agricultural settlement prevails. Summers are so cool and short that few cereals can be raised, and hence vegetable crops predominate.

Most of the area lies close to or beyond the limits of rice cultivation. At the little port of Wakkanai, which is the northern terminus of the Hokkaido rail system, connection is made by ferry boat with Karafuto.

The Teshio River, after draining a portion of the Central Fault Depression, crosses the Teshio Hills in an antecedent gorge. A wide, barren barrier beach with dunes characterizes the coastline at its mouth, and back of the beach is an extensive swampy lagoon lowland, which is being gradually filled with estuarine deposits. Only small parts of the *Teshio Delta* (Subarea a^1) are cultivated, this being on the northern frontier of rice.

Oil has been found in a number of anticlines and domes scattered throughout the Teshio Hills. Very small amounts of petroleum are being produced in the Koitoi Field near Soya at the extreme northern end of these Tertiary hills. Considerably more, but also a very small amount, is derived from the Ishikari Field at the extreme southern end of the Teshio Hills. In 1935, the last year for which data are available, Ishikari's production amounted to only 4,827 cubic meters, valued at 154,467 yen. In the same year natural gas from the Ishikari Field was valued at 11,578 yen.[18] Since development in this field began as early as 1887, it is one of the older producing areas of Japan. In recent years, despite the urgency of increasing domestic oil production, the output of Ishikari has fallen off sharply, from 9,000 cubic meters in 1931 to a little more than half that amount in 1935.[19]

The Central Fault Depression (Area *b*).—This elongated meridional depression, bounded on the east and west by the scarps of the Kitami and Teshio highlands, is composed of four detritus-filled basins (from north to south: Tombetsu, Nayoro, Kamikawa, and Furano). These are separated by much more constricted segments of valley in which there is almost no level land. A railroad follows the depression throughout its entire length. Throughout the basin areas extensive remnants of diluvial terrace, whose surfaces are moderately rolling, are conspicuous. Its interior location and basin configuration combine to give this subregion one of the most severe continental climates anywhere in Japan Proper (Fig. 174). At Asahigawa the average January temperature is 14.2°, and as low a temperature as 42° below zero has been recorded. At the same station the mean minimum temperature is 3.0°. In all Hokkaido only Obihiro, located east of the principal meridional mountain range, seems

[18] *The Mining Industry of Japan, 1935* (Japan Bureau of Mines, Tokyo), 51–55.
[19] *Ibid.* For 1931 figures see "Die japanische Mineralölwirtschaft," *Wirtschaft und Statistik*, 21:139 (April, 1941).

to have a colder climate and there it is only slightly more severe. Brigh. sunshine is very meager in winter. At Asahigawa the average number of clear days in December is only 0.1 and in January 0.5, whereas the cloudy days number 23.4 and 20.7 respectively. The average date of the first frost is October 2 and of the last, May 27. Thus the growing season is only 118 days. Again, only Obihiro has a shorter growing season. Snow falls on 131 days of the year and totals over 100 inches. As early as November the snow remains on the ground, and at Asahigawa the mean maximum depth in this month is 23 centimeters. In December it increases to 47 centimeters, in January to 71, and in February to 87; in March and April it decreases again to 69 and 19 centimeters respectively. Midsummer temperatures are very pleasant, averaging 67.1° and 68.5° at Asahigawa in the months of July and August. The mean maximum temperature in August is only 80.1. But conducive as these temperatures are to physical comfort, they are not ideal for the growing of crops. In these basins, surrounded as they are by hills and mountains, there is a good deal of cumulus cloud development in summer, so genuinely clear days are rare (0.9 in July and August) and cloudy days frequent (17.8 in July and 15.8 in August). Annual precipitation amounts to only 42.3 inches, which is relatively low for Japan. The months of January through June constitute the driest period, and late summer the period of maximum precipitation, September being the wettest month of the year. The autumn is distinctly wetter than the spring.

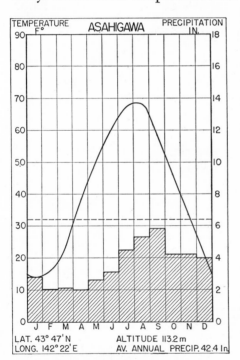

FIG. 174. Asahigawa has a continental climate (Daf).

The Tombetsu Lowland (Subarea *b*[1]), farthest north, is unlike the others in that it has no sizeable area of flattish floodplain. Instead the narrow basin appears to be nearly filled with diluvial terraces and fans. The agricultural population seems to be small, the isolated farmsteads look new, and many of the fields still contain stumps and girdled trees, evidence that this is a frontier region only recently reclaimed from the forest. The villages seem to be primarily logging and lumbering centers, for sawmills and huge piles of logs are conspicuous features of the landscape.

The Nayoro Basin (Subarea b^2), next to the south, is 40–45 miles long and has a distinct alluvium-covered floor 2–4 miles wide, in some places twice this width if the terraces are included. Much of the valley floor is so wet and poorly drained as to be unused, although in recent years new settlers have reclaimed large areas and planted them to rice. On drier portions of the basin floor and on the rolling terrace uplands adjacent to it the larger fields of dry crops prevail. The rectangular system of highways and land subdivision and the isolated farmsteads remind one of Ishikari. There are, however, two conspicuous differences; the stumps and girdled trees in many of the fields proclaim that the Nayora Basin is more recently settled than Ishikari; and the huge piles of logs and lumber in the little settlements testify to the greater importance of the forest industries. The buildings on some of the farmsteads look new and unweathered. In traveling northward from Sapporo the Nayoro Basin is the first region one comes to in which girdled trees and stumps in the fields are conspicuous.

Next to the south is the *Kamikawa* or *Asahigawa Basin* (Subarea b^3), less elongated and more octopus-shaped, where several valleys converge radially upon a central core or basin. It differs from the other basins in being more densely populated and more completely utilized. Since the railroad extending northward from Otaru and Sapporo reached this region before 1900, it was settled fairly early. Today it is one of the most densely populated and most completely utilized areas in Hokkaido. The well drained floor contains little wasteland, most of it being covered with paddy fields laid out in rectangular pattern (Fig. 175).[20] This is one of the most exclusively rice areas in Hokkaido; in some parts of it 90 per cent of the cultivated land is planted to this one crop. No stumps and girdled trees are to be seen. Rectangular roads and dispersed farm dwellings, spaced rather uniformly or, in some places, concentrated along the main highways, are characteristic features. Asahigawa is much more similar to Ishikari than to northern Hokkaido. Along the streams there is often a slightly irregular riverine zone where dry crops prevail. Similar utilization is made of parts of the adjacent terraces, which have been cleared of their woodland cover. The city of Asahigawa (87,500), the metropolis of north-central Hokkaido and a focus for railroads from all

[20] Davis, "Type Occupance Patterns in Hokkaido," *op. cit.*, 202–205.

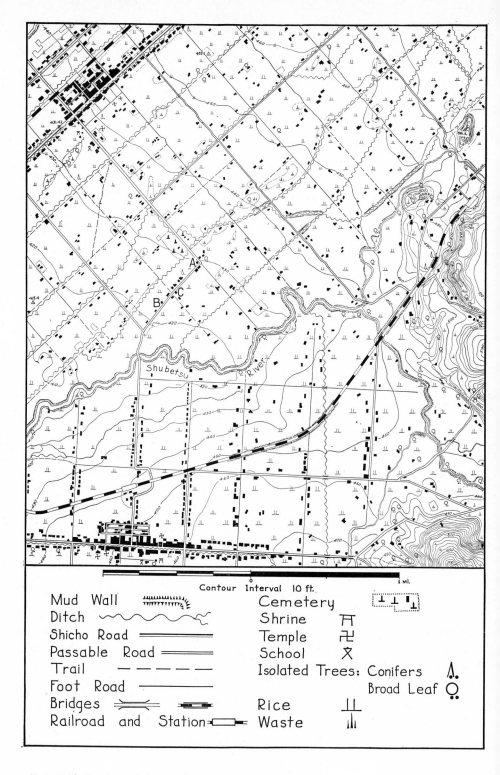

Mud Wall
Ditch
Shicho Road
Passable Road
Trail
Foot Road
Bridges
Railroad and Station

Contour Interval 10 ft.

Cemetery
Shrine
Temple
School
Isolated Trees: Conifers
Broad Leaf
Rice
Waste

Fig. 175. Section of the Asahigawa Basin where paddy rice is the prevailing crop. Dispersed rural settlement is most common. Map by D. H. Davis, from Japanese topographic map.

directions, has developed into an important collecting and distributing commercial city. As headquarters of the Seventh Army Division it has become the military center of the North Island. Its broad streets of rectangular pattern remind one of Sapporo. Despite the severe winter climate its houses betray little foreign influence; instead the flimsy construction typical of subtropical Japan, even to the thatched roofs, is very apparent.

The fourth and most southerly basin, the *Furano* (Subarea b^4), is relatively small. Its northern part is poorly drained, but where it is not a wasteland, rice predominates. The alluvial piedmont farther south has the usual rectangular pattern of roads and fields common to dry-crop areas in Hokkaido.

The Yubari Hill and Mountain Land (Area *c*).—Structurally the Yubari Highland is a tilted block or blocks, in which the more elevated and rugged eastern front has a rather continuous elevation of over 1,000 meters.[21] Several higher peaks, such as Yubari (1,668 meters) and Ashibetsu (1,727 meters), rise above the general ridge level. The northern boundary of the subdivision, separating it from the Teshio Hills, is the gorge of the Sorachi River. Its eastern boundary, in the north, is a bold fault-scarp overlooking the Furano Basin. Strong relief and steep slopes characterize much of the northern and eastern sections of Yubari. The backslope of the block to the south and west has lower elevations and a moderate relief more characteristic of hill country than of mountains. Still it is chiefly the larger streams that have sufficiently wide valleys and floodplains to permit of significant agricultural development.

However, this region is notable chiefly for its mineral wealth. The western margins of the Tertiary backslope of the Yubari Block contains what is probably the largest single coal reserve in Japan. The Ishikari (or Yubari) coal field occupies a narrow belt 80–100 kilometers north-south by 16–24 kilometers east-west (Figs. 41, 42, 168). The terrain of the area is distinctly hilly. Coal seams are numerous, totaling 150 or more if thin ones are included. They vary greatly in thickness, from less than a foot to 60 feet.[22] The geological structure of the coal field is complicated, and the coal-bearing strata have been so disturbed by foldings and faultings that the dip of the coal seams is fairly steep, usually between 15° and 50°. This complicated structure makes anything like an

[21] Robert Burnett Hall and Akira Watanabe, "Landforms of Japan," in *Papers of the Michigan Academy of Science, Arts, and Letters*, 18(1932):168–169.

[22] Kinosuke Inouye, "The Coal Resources of Japan," in *The Coal Resources of the World* (International Geological Congress, Canada, 1913), 1:305. This report contains detailed descriptions of each section of the Ishikari Field.

accurate estimate of reserves very difficult. The Ishikari coal is predominantly bituminous of only fair quality, which makes only an inferior grade of coke. In 1935 Ishikari was, next to Chikuko in northern Kyushu, the largest producing field, having about eight active large mines and many more small ones. At at least seven points along the north-south rail route paralleling the eastern margin of the Ishikari Lowland, branch lines take off from the main line and work back along the small river valleys to the coal mines in the hills. Ishikari coal serves chiefly that part of Japan that lies north of Tokyo. Most of the export passes through the ports of Muroran and Otaru.

At the extreme southwestern margin of the Yubari Hills, near the town of Atsuma, in eastern Iburi Province, is the second of the oil-producing localities of any significance in Hokkaido. In 1935 this Atsuma Field produced 8,011 cubic meters of oil valued at 240,316 yen and 1.3 million cubic meters of natural gas valued at 15,694 yen. The oil output of the Atsuma Field has declined slightly since 1931 but less than that of the Ishikari Field. In 1935 Atsuma's production was about 166 per cent of Ishikari's.[23]

The Hidaka Mountains (Area *d*) are the southern limb of the longitudinal highland axis of Hokkaido. Except for certain isolated volcanic peaks these are the highest mountains of the northern island, at least one peak attaining an elevation of 2,000 meters. The general structure is that of a block tilted sharply upward on the east, with the result that an abrupt and bold fault-scarp faces to the east and a backslope with more moderate inclination drops off to the southwest. The crest of the dissected eastward-facing fault-scarp has a general elevation exceeding 1,500 meters. Strong relief and steep slopes prevail. Still there are, near the top of the range, the characteristic flattish crests that suggest old erosion surfaces.

Settlement is of course meager and is largely confined to the narrow bottom lands of river valleys and to certain shallow upland depressions in which sediment has accumulated. Settlements on the latter sites can be observed along the rail line from Obihiro to Furano, which crosses the Hidaka Range. There are almost no minerals. Multi-cycled marine abrasion terraces with sea cliffs are conspicuous along the south coast, the southern tip at Cape Erimo having a wave-cut platform 320 meters in elevation and a maximum horizontal depth of 15 kilometers.[24] Small combination fishing-agricultural settlements, approximating the *strassendorf* pattern, parallel the highway, which runs close to the water's

[23] *The Mining Industry of Japan, 1935.*   [24] Hall and Watanabe, *op. cit.*, 168.

edge. Isolated farm residences are conspicuous in the short but wide-bottomed valleys cut in the weak Tertiary rocks adjacent to the coast.

The Kitami Mountain Land (Area *e*).—North of the Volcanic Range and east of the Central Fault Depression is a mass of subdued mountains and rugged hill country with coarse-textured slopes of gentle declivity, developed on igneous and sedimentary rocks. Over much of the region the highest elevations are 750–950 meters, although in the western part they exceed 1,000 meters. The western margin of this upwarped block is a fault-scarp descending to the Nayoro Graben. A number of distinct erosion levels or "piedmont benchlands" have been recognized in the Kitami Mountainland.[25] Occupance is relatively meager and recent; the farmsteads appear new, and stumps and girdled trees in the fields are common. Except for a little gold, mineral production is unimportant. forests providing the chief source of extractive wealth. The most conspicuous features of the little towns along the railways are the huge piles of logs, and here and there a sawmill.

Its coastal margin along the Sea of Okhotsk is bordered by a very broad marine terrace several kilometers wide, which often terminates in low abrupt sea cliffs at the water's edge. The highway and railway follow the sea margins of the terrace throughout most of their courses. Where small rivers reach the seacoast there are little bulges of wet delta material. A number of such sites contain small gray fishing-lumbering-agricultural hamlets. River-mouth location is further significant in that these valleys are the routes by which logs are brought down from the interior to the coastal towns and railroad. In the valleys and on the marine-terrace upland are the scattered stump-cluttered fields of the

CLIMATIC DATA FOR ABASHIRI

Mean Temperature			Frost-free Season	Precipitation
January	July	August		
19.4	62.1	66.4	122 days	33 inches

recent settlers, but even yet much of the level land remains in trees or wasteland. There was some immigration into this region by way of the sea as early as 1880, but because of lack of rail facilities most of this northern coast area was not utilized until after 1915–20 (Figs. 176, 177).[26]

[25] Akira Watanabe, "Piedmont Benchlands of the Kitami Mountainland, Northeastern Hokkaido," in *Comptes Rendus du Congrès International de Géographie*, Amsterdam, 1938, vol. 2, Sec. IIa, pp. 198-204.

[26] Davis, "Type Occupance Patterns in Hokkaido," *op. cit.*, 210.

The cool and foggy summers, the short growing season of only 120 days, the small amount of precipitation, and the occasional droughts discouraged the newcomers and tended to retard settlement. Sections of the coast have barrier beaches capped with dunes and back of them extensive lagoons. Rice is almost entirely lacking along this north coast, the summers being too cool, foggy, and short for its cultivation. The chief crops are oats, peas, beans, potatoes, rye, and buckwheat. Of outstanding importance as a commercial crop is peppermint, 30,000–35,000 acres being planted to this crop. Nearly 90 per cent of Japan's acreage of peppermint is grown in this northern region of Hokkaido. From the dried leaves of this plant small local distilleries extract the raw oil. Apple orchards are also conspicuous in certain localities. Fishing is less important along this north coast than in the other coastal sections of Hokkaido.

In the eastern portions of the Kitakami area, in the vicinity of Nokkeushi, Bihoro, and Abashiri and the adjacent coastal sections of the volcanic region just east of Abashiri, is one of the larger areas of recent colonization in Hokkaido. This new settlement is partly on the wet alluvium and the drier marine terraces along the coast, but extends also into the interior valley in which Bihoro is located, especially in the *Nokkeushi Basin* (Subarea e^1). Since the alluvial lands are inclined to be wet and peaty, diluvial terrace sites have been more attractive to the agricultural settlers; until about 1922 little use was made of the lowlands, most of

Fig. 176. A frontier farmstead along the northern coast of Hokkaido near the village of Nakanobetsu.

Fig. 177. A graded, surfaced highway along the northern coast of Hokkaido near the village of Nakanobetsu. Observe how the farmsteads are concentrated along the highway, as they commonly are in this country.

which required drainage before they could be brought under cultivation (Fig. 178). Because of their wet nature they were more suited for paddy rice than for dry crops, but the cool summers and short growing season made rice culture practically impossible. In the Nokkeushi Basin, however, which is some distance inland and is therefore removed from the cool ocean waters, the summer temperatures are sufficiently higher than along the coast to permit the new quick-maturing varieties of rice to be grown. The basin's floor is comprised of coarse alluvial deposits, and drainage is so poor that a good deal of wasteland remains, although a fairly large acreage has been recently reclaimed for paddy land. Stumps and girdled trees in the rice fields testify to the recency of this form of land utilization. An extensive border of diluvial terrace surrounds the low alluvial lands, and these drier uplands are more completely utilized than is the new alluvium. The rolling diluvial uplands covered with relatively large rectangular fields of dry crops in various hues and the dispersed farmsteads remind one somewhat of an American rural scene.[27]

Abashiri, the local port of this most important settlement area of northern Hokkaido, is a fishing center of some consequence, but has only very minor importance as a port. In winter it is handicapped by ice and severe storms. Regular steamboat traffic with Otaru in winter is maintained only with difficulty.

The *Volcanic Chain* (Area *f*) of eastern Hokkaido produces the eastern angle of the rhombic-shaped island. Three separate volcanic groups, composed of strato, shield, and lava-dome volcanoes in various stages of dissection, comprise this chain. These Hokkaido volcanoes continue northeastward into the Kurile Islands. The Kutsharo, the easternmost and largest of the three volcanic groups, consists of a central core of volcanoes containing caldera lakes, surrounded by extensive ash aprons with moderate slopes. Some of the volcanoes comprising the group have erupted within historic times. Kutsharo Caldera in the center has a diameter of 20–25 miles and is believed to be the largest in Japan. In general not only the higher slopes but the lower ash uplands are either forested or in moorland, and therefore are uncultivated. Some of the river valleys and their terraces contain new frontier homesteads, crops being planted among the stumps and girdled trees. In the vicinity of Abashiri the seaward margins of the ash apron are fairly well cultivated, as are the drier parts of the swampy lagoon plain. This coastal area east of Abashiri appears to be the only portion of the whole littoral of northern Hokkaido in which the cultivation of irrigated rice has been at all successful.

[27] For a description of agricultural settlement in the area, see Davis, "Type Occupance Patterns in Hokkaido," *op. cit.,* 210–213.

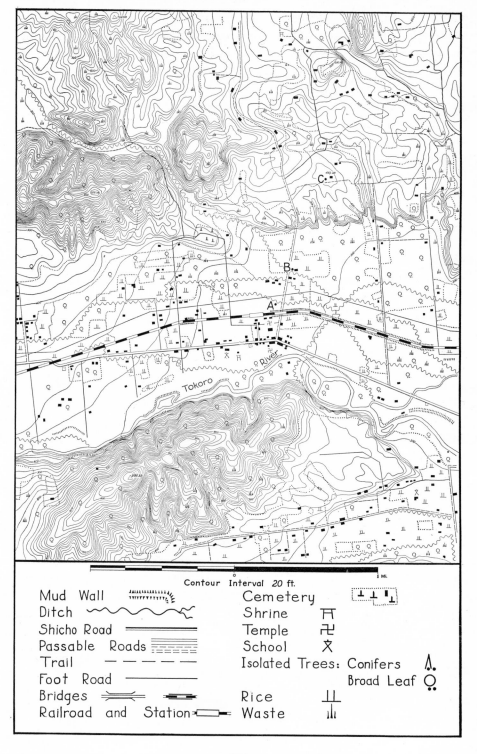

Contour Interval 20 ft.

Mud Wall	Cemetery	
Ditch	Shrine	开
Shicho Road	Temple	卐
Passable Roads	School	文
Trail	Isolated Trees: Conifers	
Foot Road	Broad Leaf	
Bridges	Rice	川
Railroad and Station	Waste	川

The central or Shikaribetsu, and the western or Tokachi volcanic groups are smaller in area than the eastern one just described, but higher and more rugged. Ash uplands of moderate slope are much less extensive. In the Tokachi group are volcanic peaks exceeding all other mountains of Hokkaido in height. Several peaks exceed 2,000 meters and Mt. Asahi, the highest, reaches an elevation of 2,290 meters. Mount Tokachi, which had been considered extinct, erupted in May, 1926, and the resulting mud flow engulfed the little village of Kami-Furano in the Furano Basin with a loss of more than 150 lives.[28] Population is very sparse, and land utilization other than logging is minor. The only significant agricultural settlement is located along the saddle between the central and eastern volcanic groups, which is followed by the railway running from Abashiri and Nokkeushi on the north to Obihiro and Ikeda in the Tokachi Lowland near the south coast.

The Shiranuka Hill Land (Area g).—Between the Tokachi and the Nemuro-Kushiro Lowlands is a region of weak Tertiary rocks which stream erosion has reduced to hill-country character. Maximum elevations do not exceed 600–700 meters, and the slopes, covered with mixed forests, are only moderately steep. Relief averages 200–300 meters. On the aggraded alluvial floors and on the terraces of the river valleys, agricultural settlement is fairly well developed, but because of the cool foggy summers little rice is grown. The lower ends of the valleys are often swamps. The abrupt coast is bordered by marine abrasion platforms. In some places the coastal railroad runs along the inner margin of the beach at the base of the sea cliff, while in others it follows the crest of the lowest terrace. Here and there frontier homesteads and little cultivated clearings on terrace platforms can be seen from the train. Close to the shore are the usual number of fishing villages, each surrounded by a restricted hinterland of cropped fields, many of them containing large piles of logs. In the coastal sections of this area the fog is sometimes so dense in summer as to permit only a very short-range view.

Several small and unimportant coal fields, notably Tokachi, Akan, and Shiranuka (Fig. 41) are located in this Tertiary hill land. The seams of

[28] *Guide-Book Excursion A-2* (Pan-Pacific Science Congress, Tokyo, 1926), 24.

Fig. 178.   A section of the Nokkeushi Basin in northeastern Hokkaido, a frontier region of recent settlement. Alluvial lowland, diluvial terrace, and mountain foothills are all represented. There is some rice on the alluvial floor of the basin but more is in dry crops (areas bounded by dotted lines but bearing no crop symbol) and in woodland. The diluvium is chiefly in dry crops. Rural settlement is largely dispersed. Map by D. H. Davis from Japanese topographic sheet.

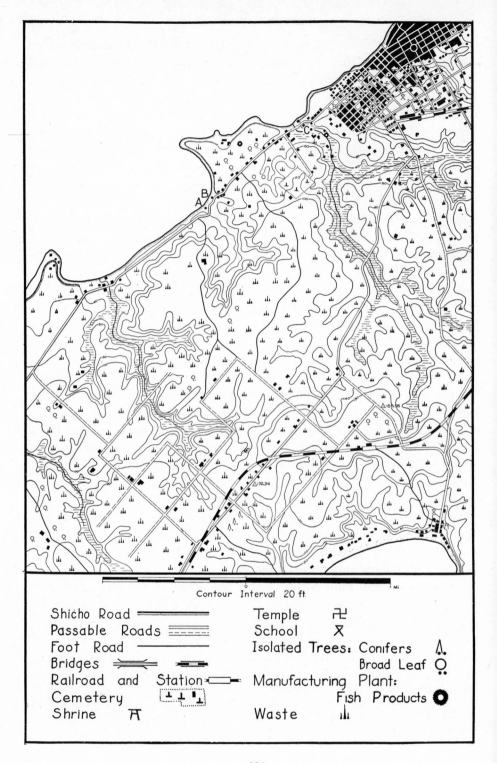

Contour Interval 20 ft.

Shicho Road
Passable Roads
Foot Road
Bridges
Railroad and Station
Cemetery
Shrine

Temple   卍
School   ✕
Isolated Trees: Conifers
      Broad Leaf
Manufacturing Plant:
    Fish Products
Waste

coal are generally thin and the product of low quality. Coal outcrops along the hillsides over a relatively wide area. The "Map of Important Mines, 1935," published by the Japanese Mining Bureau, shows only two mines in this coal district, whose combined output in 1935 was only slightly over 300,000 tons. However, there appear to be other mines of less importance whose production is not indicated. The difficulties of transportation retard greater exploitation of these coal fields. Most of the output is consumed locally, although small amounts are shipped through the port of Kushiro and some is consumed there as bunker fuel.[29]

The Southeastern Lowlands (Subregion 2): *The Nemuro-Kushiro Terrace* (Area *a*).—In the extreme southeastern part of Hokkaido is a marine abrasion surface which is so extensive that it takes on the aspects of a plain. In some places it may be traced inland as far as 50 kilometers, the wide, flat, or gently sloping interstream areas being covered superficially with ash and diluvial deposits. Much of the upland surface is less than 75 meters in elevation. The shallow, steep-sided valleys and the flattish interstream areas indicate an early stage in the erosion cycle (Fig. 179). In the western portion of the subdivision, inland from Kushiro, the terrace upland is somewhat more irregular. The valley floors are excessively swampy, as a result, perhaps, of recent slight submergence. A man-altered vegetation cover, consisting of cut-over woods and moors, mantles the area.

Adverse climatic and soil conditions have greatly retarded agricultural land use. The entire eastern and southeastern coast is washed by the cool Oyashio Current from Bering Sea, the southward surge of cold waters being most marked in summer. As a result the region has a deficiency of both sunshine and heat in summer, and dense fogs are common in June and July. In both Kushiro and Nemuro 86 days of the year are foggy, including about half of the days of June, July, and August. Inland portions suffer less. The average temperature for May at both Nemuro and Kushiro is only 43° or 44°; June 49°–51°; and July 57°–59°. Only in August does the average temperature rise above 60° (Nemuro 62.4°; Kushiro 64.0°). The mean maximum temperature for May at both stations is only 51° and

[29] Detailed descriptions of these minor fields are given in Inouye, "Coal Resources of Japan," *op. cit.*, 315–316. Data on reserves are given in Table 41, p. 92 above.

Fig. 179. A section of the Nemuro-Kushiro marine terrace in eastern Hokkaido. The city in the northeast corner is Nemuro. The river bottoms are largely swamps, while the terrace upland has a moor vegetation. This is beyond the rice zone and even unirrigated crops are meager. Fishing and grazing are paramount. Map by D. H. Davis from Japanese topographic sheet.

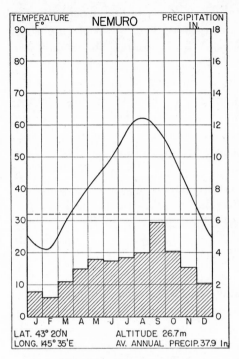

LAT. 43° 20'N
LONG. 145° 35'E
ALTITUDE 26.7m
AV. ANNUAL PRECIP. 37.9 In

FIG. 180. Note the low summer temperatures of Nemuro.

for June 57° or 58°. The period between frosts is about 130 days. Because of the low spring temperatures cereals must be sown at least a month later here than elsewhere in Hokkaido. Moreover, the cool summers retard plant growth. The soils, which are largely weathered ash, are not only very infertile in their virgin state, but stubbornly resist improvement. The sphagnum and moor peat soils of the uplands appear to be permanently nonagricultural in character,[30] and the alluvial soils of the marshy river bottoms, although they are somewhat better, are far from satisfactory for most crops.

The cool, foggy springs and summers, severe winters, infertile soils, and wet swampy valleys of this isolated peripheral Kushiro-Nemuro area have deterred the agricultural settlers in Hokkaido from developing it, and it is today one of the most completely frontier regions of the island (Fig. 181). Much the larger part still remains unoccupied, though a small stream of unwilling immigrants is being forced into the region by population pressure in Old Japan. Of 1,445 immigrant farm families who settled on government lands in Hokkaido during the four-year period 1923–26, 790 took up farms in the Nemuro-Kushiro area, where they eke out a meager livelihood.[31] In addition to the 10 cho (25 acres) of land with which the immigrant family is provided, he receives in cash 300 yen ($150 at par) to aid him in building a cabin, and to purchase tools, seeds, fertilizer, and work animals. Very light, narrow-gauge railways and a system of roads, both government-financed, are making various parts of the region accessible to agricultural settlers. The pattern of the roads is conspicuously rectangular, although they conform to the terrain rather than to the cardinal directions. In the scattered areas of cultivation, most

[30] Davis, "Type Occupance Patterns in Hokkaido," op. cit., 218.
[31] Effect of the Colonization Program Permitted by Hokkaido (Colonial Department, Hokkaido, 1929; in Japanese).

of the fields are relatively large, often several acres. Stumps and girdled trees are conspicuous in many of them (Fig. 181). Oats and soybeans are the most important crops in point of acreage, but buckwheat, potatoes, and rape are also grown. The cool springs and summers make rice cultivation impossible. Handicapped as the region is in the production of cereals by the cool, moist, foggy climate, it would seem to be better fitted for grasses and the animal industries. It has a local reputation as a horse-breeding area, and in traveling through it one sees horses in considerable numbers pasturing on the indigenous grasses.

Along the coast are the usual dismal fishing settlements. The region is one of the most important fishing littorals of Hokkaido, and the sea is the principal source of sustenance for the population. There are a number of salmon- and sardine-canning factories along the coast. Piles of logs and sawmills in the villages reflect the importance of still another extractive industry. Kushiro (63,000), the metropolis of eastern Hokkaido, is the one significant commercial port of that region. It owes its original development to the fisheries, and even today aquatic products are an important item of export. More sailing vessels, many of them fishing craft, entered Kushiro in 1929 than any other Hokkaido port. Several hundred Kushiro vessels are engaged in tunny fishing. Outgoing domestic cargo consists principally of coal, wood (including pulp and paper), marine products, and, to a less extent, farm products. Although it is an "open port," Kushiro has only a small foreign commerce, amounting to 2.2 million yen in 1938, 88 per cent of which was represented by exports. The one significant import is a fertilizer, nitrate of soda. Kushiro has only a shallow (2.3 meters) river-mouth harbor and is further handicapped by the prevalence

Fig. 181. A frontier farm in the Nemuro region recently reclaimed from the forest. Note the large stumps still remaining in the fields.

TABLE 131.—FOREIGN TRADE OF KUSHIRO, 1938

Exports in Yen		Imports in Yen	
Wood and lumber	742,735	Nitrate of soda	262,359
Fish fertilizer	302,339		
Aquatic products.	288,827		
Kidney beans	264,808		
Total, including others . . .	1,931,398	Total, including others	264,775

Source: Annual Return of the Foreign Trade of Japan, pt.3 (Department of Finance, Tokyo, 1938).

of dense summer fogs. Freight is transferred largely by lighter, although there is a coal pier at which small boats can dock.

The relatively unimportant Kushiro coal field just to the east of Kushiro city resembles those in the Shiranuka Hill Land. Thin seams and inferior quality handicap large-scale production. In 1935 only two mines in this field were producing enough coal to warrant their inclusion on "The Important Mines" map which accompanies *The Mining Industry of Japan, 1935,* published by the Japanese Bureau of Mines. One of these was listed as having had an annual production of 94,000 tons. For the other no figures are given. It seems reasonable to conclude, therefore, that the total production of the field was very small, probably less than 200,000 tons. Much of the output is used for bunker purposes and as locomotive fuel.

Nemuro, on Cape Noshappu at the eastern extremity of the island, is the principal Hokkaido port in the Kurile trade. It is primarily an export port, specializing in fish and fish products, which normally comprise 90 per cent of its trade. In 1938 its foreign trade amounted to less than 1.62 million yen, all of it exports and all aquatic products except a mere 1,200 yen. Nemuro is an old, dilapidated-looking town with narrow streets which are usually wet and muddy in summer as a result of the prevalent fog. Thick fog in summer and ice in winter so greatly handicap navigation that most boats operate in and out of Nemuro only from April to November.

The Tokachi Lowland (Area *b*).—Unlike Kushiro-Nemuro, the Tokachi Plain is not a marine abrasion terrace but consists of unconsolidated coastal plain and fluvial and ash deposits of diluvial age, resting unconformably upon an irregular surface of Tertiary rocks. Volcanic detritus undoubtedly comprises much of the surficial cover. In some places the Tertiary basement rocks are exposed along the valley sides, and over considerable areas they rise above the diluvial surface as "islands" or spurs of higher and rougher land. Along the western margin of Tokachi at the foot of the Hidaka fault-scarp is a piedmont zone composed of fan and talus deposits. Over most of the area, however, the diluvium consists of terrace benches at several levels, which probably represent successive stages of uplift. The Tokachi River and its tributaries have further complicated the relief by adding a series of alluvial river terraces. Thus the entire lowland is composed of relatively smooth flattish or sloping surfaces at a succession of levels. The margins of the terraces are occasionally precipitous, though more frequently the transition from one level to another is less abrupt. From certain vantage points one can view the even, conspicuous skylines of the higher terraces, which extend for miles unbroken. The immediate floodplains of the rivers, especially along the lower course of the main stream, include a great deal of swamp and peat bog. Along the coast, except at the mouth of the river, the front of the terrace ends abruptly almost at the water's edge.

Along the Tokachi littoral the summer months are cool and foggy, as in the Nemuro region farther east. At Obihiro in the interior of the lowland, on the other hand, the climate is of a distinctly more continental

CLIMATIC DATA FOR OBIHIRO

Temperature			Precipitation in Inches		
Mean January	Mean August	Frost-Free Season	Mean Annual	Mean February	Mean September
12.6	67.1	112 days	37.7	1.4	5.6

type, early summer temperatures being 5°–8° higher and winters 6°–10° colder. Obihiro has a January mean temperature of only 12.6° and an August mean of 67.1°—in other words, an annual range of 54.5°. The frost-free season is only 112 days. The Tokachi region vies with the basins of the Central Fault Depression as the area of most severe climate in Hokkaido. The original vegetation cover in this region was deciduous and mixed forest, Tokachi being the only part of eastern Hokkaido where this type of woodland predominated. While the ash soils are admittedly infertile, the Colonial Office in Sapporo has expressed the opinion that they are somewhat less so than those of the cool foggy Kushiro-Nemuro region farther east, which is in the boreal forest zone, where needle trees are prominent.[32]

With respect to extent of occupance and density of population Tokachi appears to be intermediate between the Ishikari region to the west and

[32] Mikhailovskaia includes the soils of Tokachi in the "brown-soil" group, and those of Kushiro-Nemuro in the "podsolized and slightly podsolized" soil region.

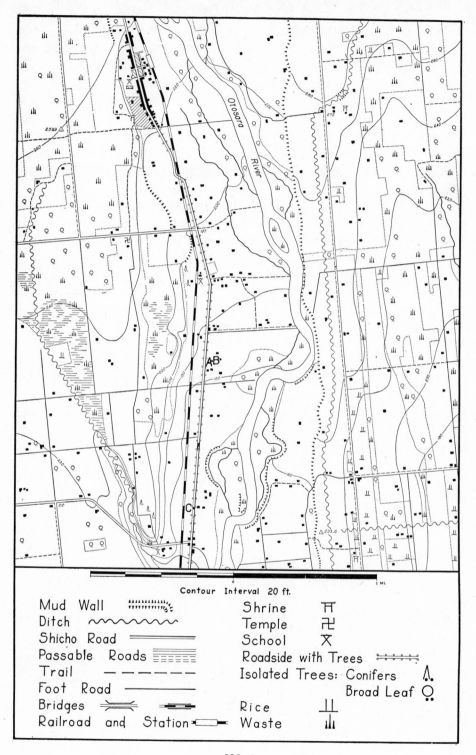

Contour Interval 20 ft.

Mud Wall   Shrine 开

Ditch   Temple 卍

Shicho Road   School X

Passable Roads   Roadside with Trees

Trail   Isolated Trees: Conifers Λ

Foot Road   Broad Leaf ♀

Bridges   Rice 山

Railroad and Station   Waste 山

Nemuro-Kushiro to the east. It was not until 1910, when the railroad from Asahigawa reached Obihiro, that active settlement of the region began. The director of the Colonization Office at Obihiro stated, in a personal interview, that there was still enough satisfactory land in the region to take care of 5,000 additional immigrant farm families, but the influx amounts to less than 200 families a year. The land still available for colonization is on the higher, less accessible, and more remote terraces and fans, now cut-over woodland. On these more elevated sand and gravel benches it is something of a problem to obtain an adequate water supply.

The present concentration of agricultural population is on the lower diluvial and the alluvial terraces, and on the newer flood plains where these are not too poorly drained. Dispersed settlement and a rectangular system of land subdivision and highway pattern prevail (Fig. 69). Lying close to the rice frontier as it does, paddy land is not conspicuous in the area, being confined to certain low alluvial lands along the rivers. Of the dry crops, beans of various kinds exceed all others in acreage (Fig. 182). These are a commercial crop, large quantities of the dried product being shipped to Old Japan. Peas, oats, and buckwheat are likewise important. Tokachi is the center of sugar beet culture in Nippon, and a refinery has been established at Obihiro for the processing of the local product. Horse breeding is a somewhat specialized branch of agriculture in the Tokachi region, and Kasai Shicko, in which the Tokachi area is located, ranks first in Hokkaido in number of horses.[33]

Since there is no port along the smooth and abrupt Tokachi coast, Kushiro serves as the outlet for agricultural produce emanating from the Tokachi Lowland. This is the least important part of the entire Hokkaido littoral, even fishing villages being few. On the lowland the two cities of Ikeda (35,000) and Obihiro (36,500), both of them on the railroad and at confluence sites, serve as local merchandising centers.

[33] Davis, "Type Occupance Patterns in Hokkaido," *op. cit.*, 214–216.

Fig. 182. A section of the Tokachi Plain near Obihiro. The land in rice is meager. Areas in dry crops are delimited by dotted lines but contain no crop symbols. Woodland and moors still occupy large areas. Map by D. H. Davis from Japanese topographic sheet.

SELECTED REFERENCES

DAVIS, DARRELL HAUG. "Agricultural Occupation of Hokkaido." *Economic Geography,* 10:348–367 (October, 1934).

————. "Present Status of Settlement in Hokkaido." *Geographical Review,* 24: 386–399 (July, 1934).

————. "Type Occupance Patterns in Hokkaido." *Annals of the Association of American Geographers,* 24:201–223 (December, 1934).

JONES, WELLINGTON D. "Hokkaido, the Northland of Japan." *The Geographical Review,* 11(1921):16–30.

KAWAGUTI, J. "The Cultivated Region in Hokkaido as Related to Density of Population" (in Japanese with English summary). *Geographical Review of Japan,* 13 (1937):649–668, 689–705.

MECKING, LUDWIG. "Japans Häfen." *Mitteilungen der Geographischen Gesellschaft in Hamburg,* 42(1931):558–592.

SCHEINPFLUG, ALFONS. "Die japanische Kolonisation in Hokkaido." *Mitteilungen der Gesellschaft für Erdkunde zu Leipzig,* 53(1935):1–132.

CHAPTER XI

The Ou or Tohoku District of Northern Honshu

T HE Ou or Tohoku District includes that portion of northern Honshu poleward from about latitude 37°. Not only in position but in climate and many features of culture it is transitional between Hokkaido on the north and older subtropical Japan to the south; and it is this transitional character that gives the region its chief claim to geographic distinctiveness. Being a part of Old Japan south of Tsugaru Strait, it resembles the south in more respects than it does Hokkaido. Nevertheless numerous similarities to Hokkaido do exist.

Terrain Features.—Like Nippon in general, Tohoku or Ou is a hilly and mountainous region, in which areas of level lowland are relatively scarce. More than in any other part of Japan the terrain features have a striking meridional trend. Three roughly parallel north-south systems of highland are separated from one another by longitudinal structural depressions, parts of which widen into conspicuous basin-like areas. Each of the three highland systems has some features of an elongated upwarped arch with margins that are flexure- or fault-scarps (Figs. 3 and 4).

The easternmost of the three longitudinal highlands is not continuous but is composed of two spindle-shaped masses separated by the Bay of Ishinomaki. North of the bay is the Kitakami Highland and to the south the Abukuma. Only in the region of Sendai, inland from Ishinomaki Bay, is the Pacific side of Tohoku bordered by lowlands of conspicuous breadth, for both the Abukuma and the Kitakami Highland descend with considerable abruptness to the sea. The more elevated Central Highlands, which extend almost without interruption throughout northern Honshu, are the backbone of Tohoku. A number of fairly low saddles, however, make communication between the lowlands on either side of the Central Range not too difficult. Several volcanic clusters rise above the general upland level to form the highest elevations. The Western Highlands vary greatly in elevation and relief, in some parts giving the appearance of low hill land, in others rising to elevations of more than 1,000 meters. Several rivers originating in the higher Central Range cross the Western Highlands, their transverse valleys providing natural routes of communication between the coast and the interior basins. A few huge youthful volcanic cones along the coastal margins of the Western Highlands stand out by contrast with the prevailingly non-volcanic terrain.

Separating the Eastern from the Central Highlands is the Kitakami-Abukuma Depression, which contains a number of interior basins. In mid-Ou, in the break between the Kitakami and the Abukuma Highland, this depressed zone widens into the Sendai Plain, which fronts upon Ishino-maki Bay. On this lowland is Sendai, the metropolis of eastern Ou. The basins of the Kitakami-Abukuma depressed zone have restricted floors of new alluvium and more extensive areas of diluvial upland. An extensive alluvial-diluvial piedmont belt, composed of a series of composite fans and cones deposited by streams from the Central Range, flanks the eastern meridional depression on its western margins. A chain of eight to ten detritus-choked basins marks the depressed zone separating the Central from the Western Highlands. Drainage from these basins is west-ward to the Japan Sea. Unlike the Pacific side of Ou, the Japan Sea margins have a series of five or six depositional plains. These western plains are flanked on their sea sides by wide belts of beach ridges and dunes, which obstruct drainage and cause the plains back of them to be unusually wet. Geographically it is of significance that in Ou a much larger proportion of the lowlands are interior plains than is true for Japan as a whole.

The climate of Tohoku is definitely transitional between the cold winter (D) climates of Hokkaido and the mild winter (C) climates of subtropical Japan. Since the freezing isotherm (32° F. or 0° C.) for January, which has been employed as the boundary between D and C climates, is in the latitude of Sendai in eastern Tohoku, and from there loops southward to include the Central Highlands, it is clear that all of northern Tohoku and much of the highland of southern Tohoku are included in that cli-matic division designated as "continental with warm summers" (Daf). The climate of the lowlands of Tohoku south of Sendai are classified as "humid subtropical" (Caf). Hot-month average temperatures, unlike those of Hokkaido, are above rather than below 70°. Average August tempera-tures range from 72° and 73° in northern Ou to 76° along its southern margins. As a consequence of the cool Oyashio Current which parallels the east coast, warm-month temperatures are a few degrees cooler on the

Pacific than on the Japan Sea side. Summer fogs are also more numerous on the Pacific side, where the cool current prevails; 20–35 days with fog, nearly all of them in summer, are characteristic of stations along the east coast. Occasional rice failures occur during abnormally cool and foggy summers. A frost-free season of 160–200 days is normal. This represents a month or two more of growing weather than most of Hokkaido has, but is on the other hand a month or two shorter than the frostless season in southwestern Japan. January temperatures range from about 27° in northern Ou to 33° in the south. In the United States the nearest counterpart to Ou's climate in respect to temperature is to be found in southern New England and the Middle Atlantic states, and from southern Wisconsin to about St. Louis in the Mississippi Valley.

The eastern and western sides of Tohoku differ more in the amount and seasonal distribution of precipitation than they do in temperature. The smaller amount of precipitation on the Pacific side is markedly concentrated in the warmer seasons, August and September in the typhoon

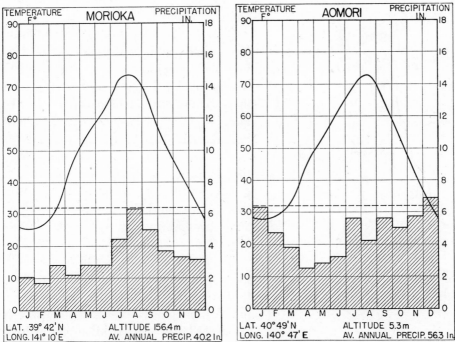

FIG. 183 (*left*). In Morioka in northeastern Tohoku the maximum precipitation occurs in summer.
FIG. 184 (*right*). Aomori in northwestern Tohoku has a continental (Daf) climate. Note the winter maximum of precipitation.

period usually being the wettest months and midwinter months the driest (Fig. 183). The somewhat heavier precipitation on the Japan Sea side has less seasonal periodicity, although in general there is a fall-and-winter maximum, much of it in the form of snow brought by the northwest monsoon (Fig. 184). Spring is the season of least precipitation. The region to the east of the Central Range has considerably less cloudy weather and snow than the Japan Sea side of Ou, but the contrast is less than elsewhere in Honshu. Thus whereas Akita on the western side of Ou has about 26 cloudy days in both December and January, Morioka to the east of the Central Range has only 14.0 and 11.8 respectively. However, the Central Range is not high enough to prevent some of the effect of the strong winter monsoon from spilling over the mountains onto the lee side. Nearly all of Ou has a winter snow cover, although it is much less deep on the Pacific side and ceases to be continuous for any length of time south of Koriyama at about latitude 37.5°.

It is in Tohoku that the temperate forest belt of Japan, characterized by broadleaf deciduous trees and mixed stands of hardwoods and conifers, is most extensively developed (Fig. 34). In fact, at low elevations the southern boundary of this broadleaf and mixed-forest zone coincides fairly well with the southern boundary of Tohoku. At greater altitudes in northern Honshu the conifers and deciduous trees which are representative of the boreal forests prevail.

Population density in Ou is also definitely intermediate between the regions to the north and south. The average population density of Ou as a whole is about 113 per square kilometer, which is approximately three times that of Hokkaido, but only one-third to one-half that of subtropical Japan south of Ou. Even in Ou itself there is an increase in

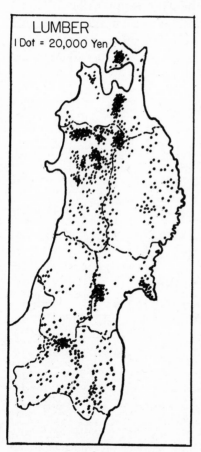

LUMBER
I Dot = 20,000 Yen

Fig. 185. Tohoku, especially the northern section, is important for the production of lumber and other forest products.

population density toward the south; whereas the average density in the three northernmost prefectures is nearly 89 per square kilometer, in the three southern ones it is about 138. It is significant geographically that, despite the lack of large-scale industry and the unflourishing state of agriculture in much of Ou, certain parts of it were among the rural areas of Japan which increased most rapidly in population between 1920 and 1935. One wonders whether this population increase is not unfortunate in view of Ou's limited resources. As elsewhere in Japan, the lowlands are in general the areas of dense settlement. Each plain of Tohoku stands out as a cluster of unusually dense population as compared with the surrounding hills and mountains. Since many of the lowlands of northern Honshu are interior basins, the population of Ou is largely concentrated on plains that have no frontage upon the sea—probably to a greater extent than in any other large subdivision of Japan. Even those plains that do face on salt water are poorly endowed with useful ports because of the harborless nature of the coast. Hence the people of Tohoku are more dependent upon rail transport than in most parts of Japan. On the whole life is cruder and harsher than it is farther south, partly because of the more severe climate, partly because the region was settled later, being farther removed from the old culture centers in southwestern Japan from which settlement moved progressively northward.

Cities and Industries.—A large proportion of the population of northern Honshu lives in rural villages or in small market towns. Cities are few, for the functions which result in urban growth are poorly developed in this subdivision. There are only nineteen urban centers with a population of 25,000 or more. Ten of these are located back from the seacoast and have no port functions. Sendai, with a population of 224,000, is the metropolis and the only city of more than 100,000. Six others have between 50,000 and 100,000 population. Of the 3.6 million workers in factories in Japan in 1938, only about 97,000 or 2.7 per cent were inhabitants of the six prefectures included in the Tohoku subdivision. Even in Hokkaido a relatively larger percentage of the total population is engaged in manufacturing. Of the five prefectures in Japan Proper having the smallest number of factory workers in 1938, four were prefectures in Ou.[1] Only Yamagata and Fukushima prefectures in southern Ou have any importance as industrial centers, and even they rank low among the prefectures —sixteenth and eighteenth from the bottom. There is in Old Japan no contiguous area of similar size in which factory industry is so meagerly developed as in the four prefectures of Aomori, Akita, Iwate, and Miyagi,

[1] *Kojo Tokeihyo,* 1939.

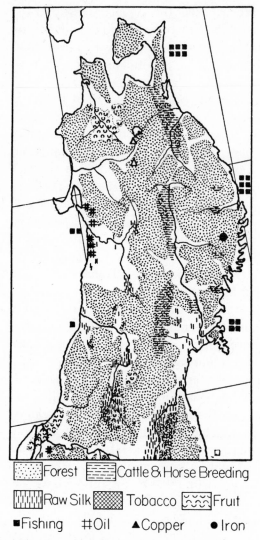

Forest [::::::] Cattle & Horse Breeding [≡≡≡]

Raw Silk [▥] Tobacco [▨] Fruit [≈≈]

■Fishing #Oil ▲Copper ●Iron

Fig. 186. Land use and industry in Tohoku. After Rosinski.

which comprise northern and eastern Tohoku. The blast furnace and steel plant at Kamaishi in Iwate Prefecture is probably the largest industrial establishment. The raw silk or filature industry, situated largely in the southern half of Ou, is the most important and the most widely distributed class of manufacturing. A modest amount of silk cloth is processed in Yamagata and Fukushima prefectures, and the latter is also of some consequence as a porcelain center. In general, however, the industries of Ou are of the household and workshop type, producing Japanese-type goods for a local market.

In all Ou there is no first-class port. Aomori, the ferry port at the extreme northern end of Honshu, is the most important of the five or six usually listed as open to foreign trade, and it is engaged chiefly in domestic shipping. The minor ports of Shiogama, serving the Sendai Plain, and Kamaishi, the gateway for the iron and steel center of the same name, are the only ones of consequence in eastern Tohoku. Sakata, Akita, and Funakawa hold a similar position in western Ou. The rail net of Tohoku has a conspicuous ladder pattern, the main north-south lines following the meridional depressions and the west coast, and shorter east-west lines making connections across the mountains. Along the east coast a rail line runs north from Tokyo only as far as Sendai.

Like Hokkaido, Ou occupies a position of some importance in the extractive industries. Within Old Japan that section of northern Honshu which is included in the three prefectures of Aomori, Iwate, and Akita is one of the nation's foremost timber-producing areas (Fig. 185). Off the eastern and northern coasts of Ou are some of the most important fishing grounds in Japan, and numerous and important fishing ports dot the coasts of Aomori, Iwate, and Miyagi prefectures. Measured in terms of the value of the catch, Miyagi prefecture ranks third in deep-sea fishing, Aomori and Iwate second and fifth in coastal fishing.[2] Mining in Ou is also of some importance. About 70 per cent of Japan's domestic supply of petroleum is derived from the Akita Field in western Ou, and in eastern Abukuma lies the Joban coal field, the most important in Honshu. From the Sennin and Kamaishi mines in eastern Iwate Prefecture comes about three-fifths of the domestic iron ore production, and four of the country's dozen most important copper mines are in Akita Prefecture.

More than in most large subdivisions of Japan, agriculture is the principal economy of the people of Tohoku despite the handicaps that climate imposes. Resembling Old Japan more than Hokkaido, rural settlement is mostly of the hamlet or village type, although isolated individual farmsteads are by no means lacking. In the extreme north, farm residences bear some resemblance to the somewhat more substantial and winterproof frame houses in Hokkaido. To a greater extent than in the south thatched roofs have been superseded by shingles and galvanized iron.

Agriculture in Ou differs from that of older subtropical Japan in a number of respects. Most of these differences are attributable to the fact that in Ou the subtropical climates of the south and central parts of Nippon give way to more severe continental ones. The climate of northern Honshu results in lower productivity, which in turn is accompanied by an increase in size of farm. Instead of the 1.5–2.5 acres characteristic of farms in subtropical Japan, they average 3.5–4 acres here. In this respect, therefore, Tohoku is intermediate between Hokkaido to the north and subtropical Japan to the south. There is no appreciable decline in the relative importance of rice over the Tohoku region as a whole. In fact, the wet plains of western Ou are so specialized in rice that they have a large surplus for shipment to other areas of the country (Fig. 94). Most of Ou lies beyond the northern limit of winter cropping of the paddy lands. The rice fields are ordinarily allowed to lie fallow in the winter season, since the winters are too severe and long and the growing season too short to permit a dry crop to mature between the fall harvest and

---

[2] *Norinsho Tokeihyo,* 1939, pp. 344, 383.

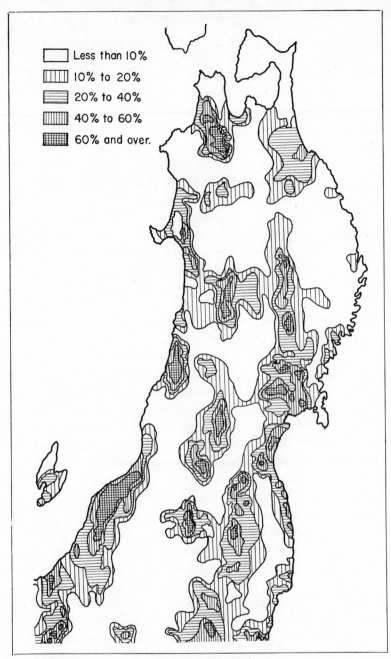

Fig. 187. Percentage of the total area of Tohoku in cultivated
crops. After Matui.

spring planting of rice. Only south of the 38th parallel in the Abukuma Lowland are an appreciable number of the paddy fields planted to winter cereals (Fig. 95). On the other hand, fall planting in upland fields is relatively common in eastern Ou, but in the snowier west even this practice is not maintained. In the extreme northeast, as in Hokkaido, some grain is sown in spring, although over the region as a whole the cereals other than rice are fall-planted.

A number of boundaries delimit areas of specific crops and agricultural practices (Fig. 95). Sweet potatoes, which are so universally grown in subtropical Japan, are a minor crop even in southern Tohoku and practically disappear in the northern half (Fig. 113). The northern boundary of important sweet potato culture is, therefore, at about the southern limits of Tohoku. The same is true of tea, another subtropical crop. Latitude 38° is the approximate northern boundary of bamboo growing and between 37° and 38° is the northern limit of fall-sown cereals in the rice fields. North of latitude 39° or 40° the production of raw silk becomes of minor significance. A north-south line approximately paralleling the Central Mountain Range separates an eastern region where winter cropping of the upland fields is common from a western region where fall cropping is rare. Virtually no citrus is grown in Ou, which lies beyond the northern limit of important commercial citrus growing at about latitude 35° or 36°. Compensating somewhat for the lack of citrus is the greater emphasis upon deciduous fruits, especially apples. Throughout Ou horses are used as draft animals instead of oxen as in southwestern Honshu and Shikoku. Northern Ou with its somewhat better grasses is an important region of horse breeding.

Although Ou is not one of the country's principal regions of "shifting cultivation," there are in the six prefectures of northern Honshu about 12,000 acres of land that are farmed in this fashion by 18,000 families (Fig. 93).[3] What is called shifting cultivation in Japan does not involve the relocation of residences as it does among many tribal groups in the tropics. Instead it involves chiefly the burning of the forest cover and the planting of crops in the burned plot for a few years before it is permitted to revert to a wild state. It is in reality a system of field-and-forest rotation. In Tohoku shifting cultivation is influenced by seasons of poor crops, damage by frost, and the like. The principal crops planted on the burned-over forest land are buckwheat, millet, barnyard grass, soybeans, and red beans.

[3] Yaichiro Yamaguchi, "Shifting Cultivation or 'Hackbau' in Northeastern Japan" (in Japanese with English abstract), in the *Journal of Geography* (of Japan), 51(1939):561–571; 52(1940):68–78.

GEOGRAPHICAL SUBDIVISIONS

The Eastern Highlands of Tohoku

Comprising the Eastern Highlands (Region A, Fig. 188, p. 410), which form the outer zone of the Honshu Arc, are the two elliptical highland masses of Kitakami and Abukuma, separated from each other by the Sendai Lowland.

Kitakami Hill and Mountain Land (Subregion 1, Fig. 188).—This more northern of the two highlands is composed of complicated old sedimentary formations, Paleozoic in age, and ancient intrusives, the whole mass having at one time been peneplaned, then elevated into a dome-like structure, and subsequently reduced to slopes by normal river erosion. External features do not conform to internal structure, nor do they have any regularity as a mountain system. A steep and dissected flexure-scarp marks the highland's descent on the west to the Kitakami and Mebechi fault depressions, which sharply separate it from the Central Range to the west. Remnants of the old peneplain surface still exist at about 1,000 meters elevation, and monadnock peaks rise several hundred meters higher, the maximum elevation being 1,914 meters. The high central portion can best be described as subdued mountains which on all sides descend to lower, but still rugged, hill country. A complicated network of valleys whose axes extend in various directions divide Kitakami into irregular masses of mountains and hills. The northern third of the coast, having suffered emergence, is smooth in contour and is characterized by high terraces of marine abrasion and deposition with abrupt wave-cut fronts. Some of the terraces have a maximum elevation of 300 meters. The southern half of the coast, on the other hand, has experienced subsidence, which has produced a deeply indented ria type of coastline with rugged wave-notched peninsulas enclosing narrow bays 4–6 kilometers long.

In Kitakami the amount of level land suitable for cultivation is very small. The relatively meager population, less than 50 per square kilometer in the northern half, is concentrated in the labyrinthine valleys and on the tiny delta-fans at the heads of the long southern bays. Both isolated farmsteads and small rural villages are common. Both because the land suited to irrigation is so meager and because the summers tend to be cool, rice is relatively less important than in most parts of Ou, occupying less than 20 per cent of the cultivated land throughout considerably more than a third of the area. Upland farming and animal husbandry are more widespread here than in other regions of Ou, and farming tends to be more extensive. Millet, beans, barley, buckwheat, and vegetables are the important dry crops of Kitakami, not only occupying the lower hill slopes but competing with rice for parts of the valley floors. In the northern part of Kitakami some of these cereals are sown in spring as well as in winter. Along the northeast coast, where smooth terrace surfaces are common, the interstream uplands are largely in woodland, though some land has been cleared and planted to dry crops, and rice largely monopolizes the valley floors. Some of the farmers of western Kitakami make a specialty of horse raising, using the hill slopes for pasture lands. Shifting cultivation is practiced in parts of Kitakami. After the cutting and burning of the forest such crops as *hi-e* ("barnyard grass" or "barnyard millet"), millet, and buckwheat are sown.[4] Since the first crop from the newly cleared forest land is usually poor, *hi-e* is commonly planted to hold the soil and keep it from washing down the denuded slopes. The crop reaches its most specialized development in Kitakami, the single prefecture of Iwate producing 45 per cent of the country's total. It is used as forage to supplement the natural pastures.[5] In the practice of shifting cultivation, slopes with an inclination as great as 45° are sometimes cultivated. Usually the fields are planted for three or four years and then permitted to rest and revert to a wild condition for eight or ten years before cropping is resumed. Along the much indented southern coast fishing is extensively developed, sardines making up three-quarters of the total catch. Most of the residents of the little bay-head delta towns are fishermen as well as farmers. The seaway is the principal coastal highway. Hence no railway parallels the Kitakami coast for its entire length from north to south, although there are certain stretches that are so served. Two transverse east-west railways cross the highland, connecting the Kitakami Valley with the coast, and a third comes close to making a complete crossing.

Other than a few relatively unimportant gold mines in Kitakami, the only mineral resource is iron ore. The Kamaishi and Sennin mines in Iwate Prefecture produce about 60 per cent of the domestic output of iron ore, but by world standards the total amount is very small. In 1926 it was estimated that the reserve of the Kamaishi-Sennin region was 35 million tons of magnetite ore, averaging 60 per cent.[6] In the next ten years mining operations reduced this reserve by 1–2 million tons. In addition there are

[4] Yaichiro Yamaguchi, *op. cit.*, 12. See also Y. Yamaguti, "Distribution of Hi-e (Barnyard Grass) in Tohoku District" (in Japanese), in the *Geographical Review of Japan*, 16(1940):38–57.

[5] Yamaguti, *op. cit.*, 38–57.

[6] Olin R. Kuhn, "World Iron-Ore Resources Now Exceed 57,000,000,000 Tons," in the *Engineering and Mining Journal*, 122:89(July 17. 1926).

estimated to be 35 million tons of low-grade ore averaging only 30 per cent and having a high silica content. Under normal conditions it is usually considered unprofitable to work such ores.[7]

At Kamaishi the ore occurs along the contact zone between granite intrusives and limestone. The mining district, located about twenty kilometers inland from the port of Kamaishi, covers an area 24 kilometers long and 16 kilometers wide. The terrain is generally steep and rugged, and in higher parts elevations average 1,000 meters. Since the ore beds outcrop along the flanks of the hills some 400 or 500 meters above the nearest drainage level, the ore must be carried by wire cables to the valley below. The Kamaishi deposit was one of the first to be worked in Japan. It was discovered about 1823, and the smelting of the ore was begun in 1849. In the Sennin mining area, located somewhat farther back from the coast, the ore bodies occur mostly in limestone and sometimes in schist at or near the contact with granite. The terrain is similar to that at Kamaishi.

Other than those in Hokkaido these iron ore bodies of Kitakami are the only ones in Japan large enough to warrant the erection of a local smelting plant. At Sudzuko, a suburb of the port city of Kamaishi, about a mile inland from the coast, is located the smelting plant of the Kamaishi Iron and Steel Works. This center is the smallest of the principal iron and steel centers of Nippon, but like most of the others has been markedly expanded during the past decade. The exact nature of the present plant equipment is not known. Its pig iron output is probably less than half that at Muroran. Its steel production is probably as great, perhaps greater. Foreign ores as well as those of local origin are used in the blast furnaces, and coal and coke are brought from Hokkaido and from China. Kamaishi, the port of this industrial area, is a city of 42,000 population. Only very recently has it been made an open port and therefore qualified to engage in foreign trade. In 1938 no exports were listed for Kamaishi, but imports to the amount of about 13.6 million yen were reported. Practically all the imports, composed of ores and metals, coal, and machinery, are used by the iron and steel industry. See Table 132 on page 414.

At Kuji, a small coastal city on the northeastern coast of Kitakami, a plant has been erected for the smelting of the iron sands that occur there in the form of ancient beach deposits located on terraces 500–1,000 feet above sea level. The ore body, largely low-grade 33–40 per cent hematite

[7] J. H. Ehlers, *Raw Materials Entering into the Japanese Iron and Steel Industry* (U. S. Bureau of Foreign and Domestic Commerce, *Trade Information Bulletin*, No. 573, 1928), 4.

and limonite containing a high percentage of titanium oxide, is estimated to have a reserve of 150 million to a billion tons, but the recoverable amounts are unknown. At the sea-level smelting plant at Kuji, which uses Hokkaido coal, the ore is reduced to finely powdered sponge iron, pressed into 4×5 inch briquettes, and shipped to open-hearth furnaces in other parts of Japan. The problem of producing sponge iron from iron sand as an essential part of the Japanese iron industry has not been completely solved. Whether the difficulties are of a metallurgical or an economic character, or both, is not clear.[8] If the problem is chiefly an economic one, then in the present emergency the Kuji deposits will probably have been brought into production on a larger scale.

Except for the iron and steel plant at Kamaishi the Kitakami region has very little in the way of industrial enterprise. Actually Iwate Prefecture, the largest part of which is included in the Kitakami Highlands, is one of the most non-industrialized prefectures in Japan. What little manufacturing is carried on is chiefly the processing of native foods and other goods for local consumption.

Abukuma Hill Land (Subregion 2).—Like Kitakami, Abukuma is an uplifted and dissected peneplain of complex structure. It differs from Kitakami in that (1) it is composed chiefly of granite rather than old sedimentaries; (2) its elevations average only half as high; (3) it is bordered on its sea side by a narrow belt of low Tertiary hills and coastal plain, from which it is separated by a fault-scarp; and (4) it contains many fault valleys. Abukuma's average elevation is about 400 meters, although the highest points reach nearly 1,000 meters. The upland surface is strongly rolling but scarcely to be described as rugged. Peneplanation having been more complete than in Kitakami, there is greater uniformity of upland levels, and larger remnants of the abrasion surface remain.

Reflecting its lower altitude and latitude, its more moderate slopes, wider valleys, and closer proximity to Kwanto, density of population in Abukuma (100–150 per sq. km.) is from two to three times that of Kitakami. Along the western margins there are several relatively open, hill-studded alluvium-floored drainage basins where there are important nodes of agricultural settlement. Isolated farmsteads are abundant. Rice and mulberry are both relatively more important in this southern hill land than farther north, and winter cropping of paddies is practiced to some extent. The low and dissected western margins of Abukuma specialize in the

[8] *Ibid.*, 8–9. See also J. H. Ehlers, *The Production of Iron and Steel in Japan* (U. S. Bureau of Foreign and Domestic Commerce, *Trade Information Bulletin*, No. 612, 1929), 18–22.

growing of mulberry, for this portion of the highland is part of the important Fukushima-Koriyama silk area.

At Hitachi in southern Abukuma, about five miles inland from Suke-gawa Station, is one of the larger copper deposits of Japan. It is of hydrothermal-replacement origin and is adjacent to a diorite intrusion. The ore averages 2–4 per cent pure copper. The hilly terrain in which the mine is located makes it most economical to transport the ore by aerial tram to the smelter at Daioin two and a half miles distant from both the mine and from Sukegawa Station. Still farther down the valley from Daioin, and connected with it and Sukegawa by an electric railway, is the refining plant and, adjacent to it, a wire-drawing and electrical-equipment mill. The smelter and refinery serve not only the Hitachi mine but others in the northeastern part of the country.[9] In 1936 the Hitachi mine produced 10,790 tons of copper, attaining fourth rank among the copper mines of the country. It also accounted for 17.9 per cent of the gold and 13.8 per cent of the silver mined.[10]

The Coastal Belt (Area a).—Where rivers pass the abrupt fault-scarp which marks the eastern margin of granitic Abukuma, and enter the lower narrow belt of weak Tertiary shales and sandstones five to six miles wide which parallels the coast, their valleys widen immediately. The inter-stream uplands, portions of which are flattish marine abrasion or deposition surfaces, are low in elevation, usually less than 150 meters. In the wide alluvium-floored valleys rice is the all-important crop, although the riverine belts are often in dry crops. The sea margins of the valleys are bordered by low, dune-capped beach ridges behind which are occasional lagoons. These elevated beach sites are also common locations for dry crops. The smooth coast being without harbors, no port has developed. Combination agricultural-fishing villages dot the coast, and there are a number of sardine- and tuna-processing plants. The interstream terrace uplands ordinarily terminate at the water's edge in low wave-cut cliffs. Where there are considerable areas of flattish diluvial upland, the woodland cover has been partially removed and dry crops planted, but the irregular surfaces of the Tertiary hills are usually in woodland. Artificial ponds are numerous, the impounded waters furnishing irrigation water for valley paddies. A major highway and railway follow this coastal lowland, connecting Tokyo and Sendai.

In the southern half of this coastal belt is the Joban coal field, the

---

[9] "The Hitachi Copper Mine," in *Guide-Book Excursion C-2* (Pan-Pacific Science Congress, Tokyo, 1926).

[10] "Kohle und Metalle im Yenblock-Gebiet," in *Vierteljahrshefte zur Statistik des Deutschen Reichs*, 50(1941), Heft 1, p. 89.

third most important producing field in Japan. It extends 80 kilometers from north to south and 4–20 kilometers from east to west. On the *Map of Important Mines, 1935*, published by the Japan Bureau of Mines, eight mines were located in Joban. Only three of these produced over 250,000 tons in 1935, and the output of all Joban mines producing over 10,000 tons was only 2.22 million tons.[11] In 1912 the reserves were estimated at 306 million tons; if the amounts mined since then are subtracted, the figure at present cannot be greatly in excess of 200 million tons. A number of seams are being actively worked, although most of them are only a few feet thick.[12] Being only 160 kilometers from the Tokyo-Yokohama industrial area, Joban coal finds its principal market in that region. Shipment is entirely by rail. A serious handicap to mining are the frequent upwellings of enormous amounts of hot water in the mines, which often do serious damage.[13]

The Eastern Lowlands of Tohoku (Region B)

The Mutsu (Sambongi) Diluvial Plain (Subregion 1, Fig. 188).—Elevated fluviatile and marine sediments here form an extensive seaward-sloping plain whose inland margins, where they merge with the ash aprons of several volcanoes of the Central Range, reach elevations of 60–70 meters. The smooth crescentic coastline is formed by beach ridges behind which are shallow lakes and partially filled lagoons. The wide alluvium-floored river valleys are likewise so wet that large areas remain swampy wasteland, although much has been reclaimed for rice. In such locations the paddy landscape is monotonously uniform. Scarcely an object breaks the broad expanses of inundated fields, for the villages seek drier sites along the margins of the valleys.

The flattish or slightly rolling upland surfaces have three contrasting cover forms: moorland, woodland, and cropped areas. In some of the cultivated areas the rectangular pattern of roads and land subdivision resembles that of Hokkaido, although the dispersed farmsteads are largely lacking. The landscape also resembles that of Hokkaido in the more substantial houses with glass windows and shingle and metal roofs, and in the amount of planted grains. When I saw the region in mid-August, shocked grain in the fields was a conspicuous feature, although I was told

[11] *Mining Industry of Japan, 1935* (Japan Bureau of Mines, Tokyo).
[12] For details of structure see Kinosuke Inouye, "The Coal Resources of Japan," in *The Coal Resources of the World* (International Geological Congress, Toronto, 1913), 1:318–320.
[13] Shigeyasu Tokunaga, "Geologic Structure of the Joban Coal-field," in the *Proceedings of the Third Pan-Pacific Science Congress*, Tokyo, 1926, 2:1557–1560.

TOHOKU (OU)
GEOGRAPHIC SUBDIVISIONS

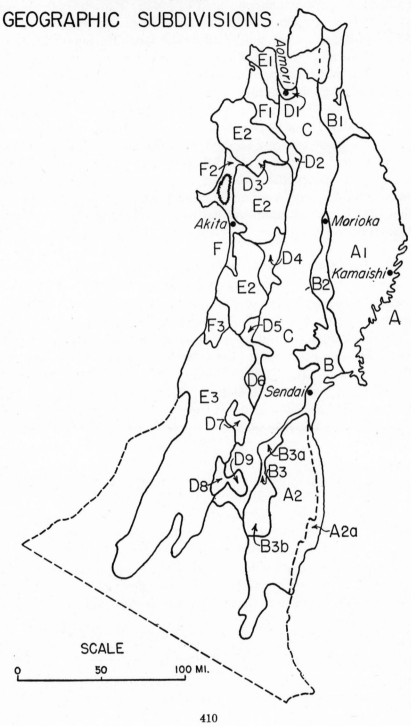

SCALE

0   50   100 MI.

that fall planting was also a common practice. Millet is a particularly important crop on these infertile uplands. On the moor-like areas considerable numbers of horses are grazed; in fact, the Sambongi Plain is famous throughout Japan as a horse-breeding center.

The Kitakami Lowland (Subregion 2).—The northern part of this meridional tectonic depression, which lies along the western flanks of the Kitakami Highland and drains northward by way of the Mabechigawa, is only a narrow valley without an extensive floor area. Throughout this section ash and lava deposits from the volcanoes to the west have so constricted the lowland as to forbid continuous settlement. At Sannoke, where the railroad turns abruptly south, mulberry, of the tree type, makes its first appearance. The trees are planted not in plots or fields, but usually promiscuously here and there, although not infrequently they are set along field boundaries. The hardier tree mulberry seems to be better adapted to these higher latitudes of Japan where spring frosts are damaging. In some places fruit trees are also conspicuous, apples predominating.

South of the low divide which separates Mabechi from Kitakami drainage, resemblances to Hokkaido landscapes seem to disappear, for cereals here are fall-sown, and less substantial thatched houses become conspicuous. From Morioka southward to about the 39th parallel the valley broadens until it takes on the proportions of a basin. Its western two-thirds is occupied by a wide piedmont zone of diluvial-fan material which the streams have carved into a series of terraces, forcing the Kitakami River to the east, where it flows through a relatively narrow flood-

---

FIG. 188 (*opposite*). GEOGRAPHIC SUBDIVISIONS OF TOHOKU OR OU

A. EASTERN HIGHLANDS

    A1. Kitakami Hill and Mountain Land

    A2. Abukuma Hill Land
        A2a. Coastal Belt

B. EASTERN LOWLANDS

    B1. Mutsu (Sambongi) Diluvial Plain
    B2. Kitakami Lowland
    B3. Abukuma Lowland
        B3a. Fukushima Basin
        B3b. Koriyama Basin

C. CENTRAL MOUNTAIN RANGE

D. WESTERN INTERMONTANE BASINS

    D1. Aomori Plain
    D2. Hanawa Basin

D3. Odate Basin
D4. Yokote Basin
D5. Shinjo Basin
D6. Yamagata Basin
D7. Yonezawa Basin
D8. Wakamatsu Basin
D9. Inawashiro Basin

E. WESTERN RANGE OF MOUNTAINS AND HILL COUNTRY

    E1. Tsugaru Horst
    E2. Dewa Hills
    E3. Echigo Mountains

F. WESTERN PLAINS

    F1. Tsugaru (Iwaki) Basin
    F2. Noshiro-Omono Plain
    F3. Shonai or Mogami Plain

plain against the flanks of the Kitakami Highland. It is significant that the conspicuous diluvial piedmont accumulations throughout the eastern longitudinal depression of Tohoku are on the western sides of the basins. This probably reflects not only the heavy rainfall along the high Central Range, but also the abundance of easily removed volcanic ash which characterizes it. Except for a riverine belt where such dry crops as vegetables, winter grain, mulberry, and fruit trees are grown, the flood-plain is largely in rice. Since the paddies are not sown to winter grains, rice is planted fairly early and when I saw the district in mid-August the crop was ripening, being far more advanced than rice in southwestern Japan, where double cropping of paddies is customary. The diluvial pied-mont, although dissected by streams, has considerable areas of flattish or moderately sloping surface, large parts of which have been cleared and are in farms. Rice as well as the usual dry crops is conspicuous, the arti-ficially terraced paddies occupying various levels and receiving their irri-gation water from numerous man-made ponds. Patches of woodland, scattered plots of fruit and mulberry trees, and numerous isolated farm-steads surrounded by hedges and windbreaks give the alluvial piedmont belt a confused and cluttered appearance, so that extensive views are rare. On the piedmont dispersed settlement appears to be the rule, while on the lower floodplain the isolated farmstead, the compact village, and intermediate forms of settlement are all represented. Morioka (40,051), the capital of Iwate Prefecture and formerly an old castle town of the Nambu Family, is at present famous for its horse fairs, Nambu ponies from Iwate being known throughout Japan.

South of parallel 39° the diluvial piedmont belt disappears and the character of the Kitakami depression changes. Here complicated faulting with subsequent vertical movement has occurred, with the result that irregular masses of low Tertiary hills, archipelagic in character, now stand out above the equally irregular alluvium-filled depressions. The hill masses are thoroughly dissected, rice occupying the labyrinthine valleys, and the slopes being largely in grass or tree-covered. Along the lower slopes of the hills a fair percentage of the land has been planted to dry crops, especially mulberry. In this milder region the more sensitive bush mulberry has largely displaced the tree variety, and the silk industry is important. The alluvial lands are low and wet, areas of swamp and lake being prominent. Great expanses of monotonous paddy landscape, much of it in perfectly rectangular fields, are characteristic. The villages of the cultivators are commonly located along the elevated and diked rivers or along the bases of the Tertiary hills. Riverine zones of dry crops, especially mulberry, are conspicuous variations from the paddy landscape. Villages of the *strassendorf* type are common.

In the gap between the Kitakami and the Abukuma Highland the Kitakami Lowland finally reaches the seacoast. This Sendai Plain, although not extensive, is the site of the single compact, and the most important, coastal settlement along the whole eastern side of Tohoku. The coastline is prevailingly smooth; beach ridges fringe the sea margins except where interrupted by the cliffed headlands of the sunken Matsushima Block, which encloses shallow, island-studded Matsushima Bay. The archipelago of irregular pine-clad islands in this bay is one of the "Three Great Sights" of Japan, famous in art and literature and as a resort of Japanese and foreigners alike. The parallel sandy beach ridges, both to the north and south of Matsushima, are the sites of dry fields, the outermost ridge bearing a wall of conifers which acts as a windbreak and a barrier to drifting sand. On the inner margins of the narrow alluvial lowland back of the beach ridges are rather extensive diluvium-mantled uplands having some flattish surfaces 20–50 meters in elevation.[14] Back of these rise the higher and more irregular Tertiary hills, in whose numerous open valleys are important settlements. The Sendai Plain lies close to the northern limit of bamboo culture and of fall-sown cereals in the rice fields. The city of Sendai (223,630), whose old daimyo castle occupies a diluvial spur overlooking the whole plain, is the metropolis of northern Honshu, capital of the prefecture, and site of an Imperial university. It is neither a port nor an industrial city, although it does serve as the commercial focus of the Sendai Bay settlements and of the population of the entire Kitakami Lowland, at whose mouth it lies. The Abukuma Lowland to the south is served more by Tokyo and Yokohama than by the cities of the Sendai Plain. Since most of the important lowlands of eastern Tohoku are interior rather than coastal, there is hardly a commercial port along that side of Honshu between Aomori and Yokohama. The latter city, through rail connections, serves as the port of the interior basins.

Shiogama, situated on a shallow indentation of Matsushima Bay and serving the one conspicuous coastal settlement cluster of eastern Ou, is the single port of consequence which handles general cargo in northeastern Japan and it is likewise an outstanding fishing center. Recent harbor improvements, including a dredged channel, now permit boats of 3,000 tons to enter and dock at the pier. Its trade is composed principally of imports of salt, coal, and oil cake destined for Sendai, the large consuming

[14] "Sendai and Matsushima," in *Guide-Book Excursion C-3* (Pan-Pacific Science Congress, Japan, 1926).

center of the district.[15] The total foreign trade of Shiogama was only 2.2 million yen in 1938, all of it imports. Petroleum and fertilizers comprised a large percentage of the incoming cargo.

TABLE 132.—FOREIGN IMPORT TRADE OF KAMAISHI, 1938

Commodity	Value in Yen
Coal.	2,362,549
Ores and metals.	8,270,921
Machines	2,388,012
Total, including others.	13,555,768

TABLE 133.—FOREIGN IMPORT TRADE OF SHIOGAMA, 1938

Commodity	Value in Yen
Salt	202,302
Oils, fats, and waxes	906,972
Phosphorite	525,799
Clay	113,256
Bean cake.	342,977
Total, including others	2,171,464

Source: *Annual Return of the Foreign Trade of Japan*, pt. 3 (Department of Finance, Tokyo, 1938). No Exports listed.

The Abukuma Lowland (Subregion 3).—Although it is the valley of a single northward-draining river, the Abukuma Lowland is not continuous, for a low divide separates the northern Fukushima Basin from the Koriyama Basin farther south. Still farther south this same tectonic depression is continued in the northern arm of Kwanto Plain.

The Fukushima Basin (Area *a*).—Diluvial sediments in the form of piedmont fans fill the northern and western part of the basin. Natural and cultural features are in most respects similar to those in the mid-portion of the Kitakami Basin, except that in this more southerly depression winters are milder and snowfall less, mulberry is of the bush type and occupies a much greater area, population is somewhat less dispersed, and paddy fields are winter-cropped. Not only on the hill lands surrounding the basin and on the diluvium, but also on the recent floodplain sediments, mulberry is an important crop; numerous filatures and cocoon warehouses in the villages testify to a specialized sericulture industry. The Fukushima-Koriyama depression is one of the country's important raw-silk areas. In some of the upland districts in the basin as much as 40–50 per cent of the cropped area is in mulberry.[16] Fukushima city (48,287), a castle town, is known chiefly for its silk-reeling industry. More characteristic of this basin than either the isolated farmstead or the compact rural village is the semi-dispersed or amorphous type of settlement. When the region was

[15] Mecking, *Japans Häfen* (Hamburg, 1931), 505–510.
[16] Hatsuo Yasuda, "The Physiognomy of Fukushima Basin, Fukushima Prefecture," in the *Journal of Geography* (Tokyo), 60(1939):381–387.

observed in August, 1932, rice seemed less advanced here than in the Kitakami region farther north, probably because of later planting consequent upon some winter-cropping of the paddies.

The Koriyama Basin (Area *b*).—In the broader lineaments of its geography there is little to distinguish Koriyama from its smaller northern neighbor. Diluvial piedmont deposits occupy much the larger part of the basin. These detritus-choked basins of the Abukuma Lowland, specialized as they are in the growing of mulberry and the production of raw silk, much resemble the Suwa, Matsumoto, Nagano, and other Fossa Magna basins of central Chubu. Until about 1873 virtually the only areas of the Koriyama Basin that were used for agriculture were the floodplains of recent alluvium. The western diluvial piedmont was still largely in its natural state. Shortly thereafter, however, groups of samurai from different parts of the country settled in the basin and began to reclaim the diluvial uplands. When water for irrigation was brought from Lake Inawashiro just to the west, more settlers were attracted and occupation of the land proceeded rapidly.[17] Like northern Kwanto just to the south, Koriyama is an important tobacco-growing region. This is approximately the southern limit of a durable snow cover on the Pacific side of Japan. Koriyama, a city of 57,000, is the metropolis and the industrial centrum of the basin.

The Central Mountain Range

Decidedly a watershed, this medial range of Tohoku (Region *C*, Fig. 188) is a climatic divide and perhaps to some extent a culture one. Structurally it is an elongated, warped dome with faulted margins, having a core of ancient granites and gneisses whose flanks are covered with recent sedimentary strata. Crowning the range are seven distinct and about equally spaced volcanic clusters, whose cones provide the maximum elevations; at least one reaches 2,000 meters. The copious precipitation of this watershed has been put to use in the form of hydroelectric power and irrigation water in the basins lying to the east and west.

The region is sparsely populated, since most of the valleys are gorges offering little cultivable land. In the weak Tertiary rocks along the flanks the elevations are lower, the valleys wider, cultivation more general, and irrigation ponds often numerous. At the extreme northern end of the range along the lower slopes of Mt. Hakkoda's ash apron is the one region where agriculture is fairly well developed, although population is far from dense. Settlement is principally on the wide valley floors and terraces

[17] Hatuo Yosuta, "Changes in Landscape in the Koriyama Basin" (in Japanese with English summary), in the *Geographical Review of Japan*, 14(1938):321–338; 428–448.

Fig. 189. Huge piles of logs at the basin end of a mountain valley in northwestern Honshu. In the foothills of the Iwaki Basin east of Kuroishi.

incised into the unconsolidated ash, but to some degree also on flattish sections of the interstream upland. As pasture sites for the grazing of cattle and horses the ash slopes are also of some consequence. Parts of the Central Range are covered with valuable timber whose exploitation supports small communities (Fig. 189). Others are maintained by the local mineral resources. Gold, silver, copper, iron, and sulphur are mined in various sections, copper in normal years topping all the others in value. In northern Akita Prefecture are two of the most important copper mines of Japan: Kosaka, which in 1936 produced 8,679 tons of copper, and Osarizawa, which produced 4,888 tons. These two mines are also important producers of gold and silver.[18]

The Western Intermontane Basins

The depressed zone (Region *D*, Fig. 188) lying between the Central and the Western Range is not continuous but is a series of eight or ten tectonic basins, some of which are isolated from the others by formidable topographic barriers. Hence they are not followed by a continuous rail line from north to south as are the eastern lowlands. Most of the basins are occupied by the headwaters of streams which cross the Western

[18] "Kohle und Metalle im Yenblock-Gebiet," *op. cit.*, 89.

Range in antecedent valleys now occupied by rail lines. Thus these inland settlement areas are chiefly tributary to, and the hinterlands of, the delta cities and ports along the Japan Sea. This is less true of the southernmost basins, which have easy access to the great Kwanto cities and whose trade is attracted to them. All the basins have larger or smaller areas of flood-plain floor, but piedmont belts of alluvial and diluvial fan deposits are also conspicuous features, as they are in the eastern lowlands. In general the major diluvial piedmont deposits have been derived from streams descending from the Central Range and so are best developed along the eastern margins of the depressions.

TABLE 134.—MAXIMUM DEPTH OF SNOW ON THE GROUND AT SELECTED STATIONS IN OU
(in centimeters)

Station	November	December	January	February	March	April
WEST COAST						
Akita	2	30	64	58	41	—
Sakata	—	24	37	29	8	—
Tsuroka	2	49	75	92	71	—
WESTERN INTERMONTANE BASINS						
Kosaka	3	47	80	81	66	3
Odate	1	49	108	114	86	1
Yokote	0	90	143	151	129	10
Yamagata	—	40	45	39	23	2
Yonegawa	5	59	99	100	92	27
Wakamatsu	—	35	49	48	28	—
EASTERN LONGITUDINAL LOWLANDS						—
Morioka	6	23	27	25	16	1
Fukushima.	—	16	18	10	8	

Source: T. Okada, *The Climate of Japan*, 265–269.

The climate of these basins cannot be described in detail because few weather stations have been established to collect data. Only for Aomori in the extreme north and Yamagata in the south are relatively complete data available. On the whole, although there are exceptions, winter weather conditions in the Western Intermontane Basins resemble those of the Japan Sea side of Ou rather than the Pacific side. At Aomori maximum precipitation occurs in winter, but at Yamagata the months of July, August, and September are wetter than the wettest winter month. A comparison of the maximum depth of snow cover, for which more complete data are available, reveals that the depth of snow is much greater in the Western Intermontane Basins than in the Kitakami-Abukuma Lowland to the east of the Central Range (Table 134). There are, however, marked differences between the several basins and even between local areas within the same basin, differences which are due in part to the exposure of a given locality with respect to the air masses of the winter monsoon.[19] No generalization can be made about the depths of snow cover on the west coast as compared with those in the western basins. On the whole the depth seems to be greater in the basins than along the west coast, but there are exceptions. Much dark, gloomy weather and numerous days with snowfall are characteristic of the winter in most of the basins.

These western basins contrast markedly with the eastern depressions in that there is little winter cropping, not only of the rice fields but of upland fields as well. The lowlands north of the 39th parallel produce practically no wheat, barley, or naked barley, which are the principal fall-sown cereals, and even in those south of 39° these crops are not very important. The deep and long-continued snow cover would compel so early a planting and so late a harvest of any fall-sown crop that the period of growth for summer crops would be unduly shortened. The 39th parallel, which is the approximate poleward limit of extensive mulberry culture and important silk spinning in the eastern valleys, may also be taken as the boundary of these forms of land use in the western basins.

In these snowy regions of western Tohoku, despite numerous snow-sheds, rail traffic is frequently suspended for days at a time. In some villages where the snow is excessively deep people are forced to inhabit the upper stories of their homes if they wish to enjoy daylight. Special forms of architecture are common, such as wide eaves and covered side-walks, called *gangi,* which when fitted with temporary outer walls in winter form corridors through which pedestrians may walk, protected from the weather (Fig. 190). Shingle roofs likewise appear to be more numerous to the west than to the east of the Central Range.

The Aomori Plain (Subregion 1), at the extreme northern end of Honshu, although it is a coastal rather than an interior lowland, is here included with the Western Intermontane Basins because it lacks certain characteristic features of the Japan Sea plains and because it is a part of that same longitudinal zone of depression along which the Western Intermontane Basins are developed. It is a narrow crescentic strip of lowland whose landward portions are a dissected diluvial bench, where woodland, rice, dry crops, and apple orchards intermingle, and whose seaward sections are paddy-covered new alluvium. Rural settlement is almost exclusively of the village type. Aomori (99,065), the one important

[19] M. Nagai, "Geographical Distribution of Snowfall in Yamagata Prefecture and Other Related Studies" (in Japanese with English abstract), in the *Geographical Review of Japan,* 10(1934):443–466.

city of the plain, has no near rival among the ports of North Honshu. Its hinterland is not only the immediate lowland but the relatively large Tsugaru or Iwaki Basin just to the west, which has no port, and the extensive ash and diluvial uplands to the south and east. In a sense much of northern Honshu is served by Aomori. However, like Hakodate, it is less a center dependent upon a local hinterland than a terminus for the ferry service between Honshu and Hokkaido and the northern terminus of the rail lines of Tohoku. Several boats of 3,500 tons each leave for and arrive from Hakodate daily, and a somewhat less frequent service is maintained with Muroran. It is primarily a port engaged in coastwise trade, most of it with Hokkaido. Imports are principally soybeans, fish, and fish products; toward Hokkaido move exports of rice, textile and metal wares, tobacco, and petroleum. Not only as a freight transfer point but as a passenger and fishing port Aomori is important. Its foreign trade, amounting to nearly 9 million yen, is only a fraction of its coastwise commerce. Canned fish and ores comprise a large proportion of its shipments abroad, and petroleum and beancake fertilizer are the chief items in the incoming cargo from foreign sources. The harbor faces north on a broad open bay and is exposed to the winter monsoon. This has made necessary the construction of extensive breakwaters to enclose an artificial harbor whose depth is approximately ten meters. Industries are chiefly those engaged in producing goods for local consumption.

The Hanawa and Odate Basins (Subregions 2 and 3), which occupy portions of the Noshirogawa drainage basin, are for the most part floored with diluvium. Some of this diluvium retains its original fan shape, but other parts have been carved into a series of flattish river terraces. The usual form of settlement is the compact village, which is situated on the lower terraces rather than on the periodically inundated floodplain. When I saw the region after a period of heavy rain in August, the floodplain paddies were deeply flooded and the rice crop had been ruined. On the lower terrace benches are paddies as well as dry fields. Numerous artificial

TABLE 135.—FOREIGN TRADE OF AOMORI, 1938

Exports	Amount in Yen	Imports	Amount in Yen
Canned trout.	1,771,789	Oil, fats, and waxes	2,175,891
Canned salmon	974,886	Bean cake	358,376
Sulphur	380,700		
Other ores	2,800,016	Total, including others.	2,837,496
Total, including others.	6,166,818		

Source: Annual Return of the Foreign Trade of Japan, pt. 3 (Department of Finance, Tokyo, 1938).

ponds provide the necessary irrigation water for the rice fields lying above the level of the rivers. The higher diluvium is largely in woods or is wasteland. Conspicuous features in the villages along the railroad are the sawmills and the huge piles of logs, which reflect the forest wealth of the surrounding mountains and hills (Fig. 185).

The Yokote Basin (Subregion 4) is next to the south and is the largest of all the western grabens. It occupies the upper drainage basin of the Omonogawa, and comparatively high volcanic masses separate it from the northern depressions. Hence only a roundabout rail connection with them is made by way of the west coast. Along the northeastern margins of the basin is a piedmont belt of diluvial fans, the gravelly upper slopes of which are largely in woods and wasteland, and the lower elevations in dry fields and dispersed farmsteads. On the new alluvium, where rice predominates, the denser population is congregated into compact as well as semi-dispersed settlements. Definite riverine belts of dry fields and wasteland parallel some of the streams. What with the very numerous small settlement units, the riverine zones, and the maze of roads and irrigation channels, many of which are lined with trees, the plain has a confused and cluttered appearance. Toward the southern end of the basin mulberry becomes increasingly prevalent, as it does everywhere in northern Honshu in the vicinity of the 39th parallel.

Occupying portions of the Mogamigawa drainage basin are the *Shinjo, Yamagata,* and *Yonezawa* depressions (Subregions 5, 6, and 7). *Shinjo* is composed of wide irregular valleys and basins separated by spurs of Tertiary hills, which contain numerous irrigation ponds. Rural settlements are of the village type. *Yamagata,* more compact and more regular in outline, specializes markedly in sericulture. Not only on the extensive diluvial

Fig. 190. Covered sidewalks, or *gangi,* are characteristic of the settlements along the snowy western side of Tohoku.

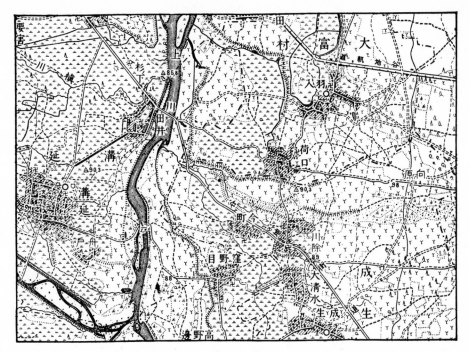

FIG. 191. A section of the Yamagata Basin west of the central range in Tohoku. Rice occupies the low alluvium except in the riverine zone, where dry crops prevail, especially mulberry. The eastern third is diluvial piedmont, where mulberry is the main crop. Section of Japanese topographic map, scale 1:50,000.

piedmont and on the riverine belts, but also on the new alluvium, where it competes with rice, mulberry is a crop of first importance (Fig. 191). Yamagata city (69,184), an old castle town and the present prefectural capital, is famous as a filature center, as are most of the large towns which dot the plain. *Yonezawa*, a less compact basin in which dispersed settlement units are more numerous and the landscape cluttered and confused, reminds one of the Yokote Basin. Here, too, mulberry fields are very numerous and specialization in raw silk is a conspicuous feature. A north-south rail line joins all three basins and extends northward to the Yokote depression. Connection is made with the Japan Sea coast by two east-west lines following the Mogamigawa and Omonogawa Valleys, and the trellis pattern is completed by two other transverse lines which cross the Central Range and reach the Kitakami and Abukuma Lowlands.

Along the upper waters of the Aganogawa are the relatively small *Wakamatsu* or *Aizu*, and the *Inawashiro depressions* (Subregions 8 and 9).

Scars of migrant stream channels and marked soil variations characterize the basin floor of the former, and hence dry fields intermingle with paddy lands, mulberry being conspicuous. Wakamatsu city (48,091), an old castle town, is at present an important filature center. Most of the Inawashiro Basin is occupied by a lake resulting from the blocking of drainage by ash and lava deposits from an adjacent volcano. Delta-fans along the lake margins support a narrow, interrupted belt of cultivated fields.

The Western Range of Mountains and Hill Country

The *Western Range* (Region E) is an elongated dome containing a crystalline core from whose crest the sedimentary cover of Tertiary rocks has in many places been removed. Four rivers cross the range, dividing it into several segments, whose antecedent valleys are important rail and highway routes. Somewhat attenuated belts of population and cultivation along these transverse valleys serve to join the larger nodes of settlement at their upper and lower ends. The result is roughly a dumbbell pattern of occupance, which is repeated for each of the four drainage basins. Several magnificent volcanic piles occupy in-sinking basins along the western flanks of the range.

The Tsugaru Horst (Subregion 1) is an unimportant hilly region which on the east drops down by abrupt scarps to a narrow alluvial-diluvial plain bordering Mutsu Bay and on the west to the Tsugaru (Iwaki) Basin.

The Dewa Hills (Subregion 2), whose highest elevations only rarely exceed 1,000 meters, are more typically hill country than mountain. The gorge of the Mogami River, which marks the southern boundary of this subdivision, separates it from the higher and more rugged Echigo Range. North of Akita and the Omono River the Dewa Hills are higher and more rugged than in the southern half, where the general elevation is only about 400 meters and there are extensive flattish surfaces.[20] Gold, silver, copper, and sulphur are mined in small amounts. Logging is very important (Fig. 185). In the low Tertiary hills bordering the Japan Sea, in a belt about 170 kilometers long and 30–50 kilometers wide extending from north of Noshiro to south of Honjo, is the Akita oil field, whose ten or more separate producing districts produced 207,000 kiloliters of petroleum in 1935. An oil refinery at Akita processes the locally produced crude petroleum as well as some of the imported product.

[20] Hall and Watanabe, "Landforms of Japan," *op. cit.*, 182. See also Ryoichi Ohashi, "Physiographical Evolution of the Dewa Region Since the Pleistocene Epoch," in the *Proceedings of the Fifth Pacific Science Congress*, Toronto, 1933, pp. 1577-1583.

The Echigo Mountains (Subregion 3).—South of the Mogamigawa, where granite is much more abundant, relief and elevation are greater. Indeed, the terrain is genuinely mountainous, maximum elevations being in excess of 2,100 meters. Abrupt fault-scarp margins are conspicuous on both the eastern and western flanks. That part of the coast between the Mogami and the Niigata Plain where the Echigo mountains reach the sea is bordered by precipitous wave-cut cliffs.

The Western Plains of Ou

Along the Japan Sea littoral is a series of four aggradational plains (Region F), of which the three northernmost occupy portions of in-sinking kettle depressions associated with volcanic activity. In two of them, Tsugaru and Shonai, the basins are partially filled with huge symmetrical ash-and-lava cones, which tower above the adjacent lowlands. Each of the four plains is at the sea end of an antecedent river whose sediment has been deposited in the shallow waters of lagoons back of wide belts of dune-capped beach ridges or bars. Drainage is generally poor, and in some of the plains large areas of swamp and shallow lake persist. Strong waves and currents generated by the boisterous winter monsoons have tended to smooth the coast, developing wave-cut cliffs where hardrock highlands reach the sea, and barrier beaches and bars along the alluvial portions. Natural harbors are few, and the two or three ports that have developed are of only minor importance.

Like all of western Ou, these plains are afflicted with dark, stormy, snowy winter weather. The snow cover is deep and continuous, though perhaps less so than in the Western Intermontane Basins or on the plains of Hokuroku farther south, where the highland barrier to the rear of the coast is higher.

Fig. 192. Along the western coast of Tohoku, where the winter winds are strong, house roofs are often weighted down with boulders.

Winter winds are strong, frequently blowing with the force of a gale. At Akita the wind velocity during three winter months is twice that at Tokyo on the Pacific side of the country. It is common practice, especially in towns near the coast, to weight down the shingle roofs with boulders (Fig. 192). The fishermen's miserable huts along the shore and on the dunes seem poorly equipped to withstand this onslaught of the winds, despite the windbreaks in the form of hedges, walls of trees, and lattices filled with brushwood or moss. Piles of fuel are tied down to prevent their dislodgement. Fishing is less important along this Japan Sea coast than on the Pacific side of Ou, partly because of the rougher seas and lack of harbors.

FIG. 193. The poorly drained plains of western Tohoku and Hokuroku are so specialized in rice that there is an excess for domestic export. Bags of rice at the Kuroishi station (Iwaki Basin) awaiting shipment to sections of Japan that are deficient in rice.

The low and poorly drained plains are almost exclusively planted to rice, which is one of the important domestic exports of the region (Fig. 193). Because climatic handicaps prevent winter cropping, the small grains (wheat, barley, and naked barley) which are so important to the east of the Central Range, are unimportant on these western plains. Unirrigated crops occupy cleared patches on the diluvial terraces, riverine strips along the principal streams, and wide belts on the series of parallel beach ridges which border the coasts. Silk culture is less important on these western plains than it is in the Eastern Lowlands or in the Western Intermontane Basins of Ou. Virtually no mulberry is raised on the two northernmost plains (north of 39°).

Tsugaru (Iwaki) Basin (Subregion 1).[21]—This northernmost of the western basins, which is also one of the largest (350 square miles), well repre-

[21] This subdivision of Ou has been described in some detail in Glenn T. Trewartha,

sents their common characteristics. In at least one respect, the fact that it is Japan's principal apple district, Tsugaru departs from the normal. It is an alluvium-floored structural depression whose sea end is blocked by a wide belt of dune-capped beach material. No port has developed along its exposed smooth, harborless coastline; Aomori, only 30 or 40 kilometers distant, serves in that capacity. Even fishing settlements are almost completely lacking. The lower northern end of the basin back of the belt of dunes is wet, and the paddy fields are interspersed with areas of shallow lake and swamp. Completely surrounding the low alluvial floor, except at the sea end, are terraces of diluvium, covered with a veneer of volcanic ash. Back of these rise the hills and low mountains which enclose the depression and force the railroads to pass the eastern and southern barriers by means of tunnels. Above the western margin of the valley towers the symmetrical ash cone of Mt. Iwaki (1,588 meters), which helps to break the force of the winter gales that fill the basin with snow during the winter months.

Population decreases toward the wetter, more exposed, lower (northern) end of the basin. Settlement is prevailingly of the agglomerated type. Except for the wide eaves and covered sidewalks or *gangi,* there is little evidence that house construction and architecture have been especially adapted to the severe winter weather. The metropolis of Hirosaki, an old castle city of about 50,000 population in the upper end of the basin, occupies a strategic position on a high prong of terrace and an adjacent lower portion of the plain where several valleys converge.

The floor of the depression is largely covered with irrigated rice fields, except in the riverine belts of variable widths along the main streams, where the terrain is somewhat uneven and is scarred with relict forms left by migrating stream channels (Figs. 194, 195). Here a variety of unirrigated crops are raised, notably apples and potatoes, which are grown as commercial crops, and rape, some of which appears to be fall-sown. The diluvial terraces with their poor ash soils are in part covered with scrubby trees or a moor-like vegetation, although large areas, particularly in the south end of the valley, are utilized much as the riverine strips are. Here apple orchards are most extensively developed. More than 75 per cent of the apple crop of Japan is grown in Aomori Prefecture and much the larger part of this is concentrated in Iwaki, giving this basin a degree of national fame. The superabundance of farm labor is reflected

---

"The Iwaki Basin: Reconnaissance Field Study of a Specialized Apple District in Northern Honshu, Japan," in the *Annals of the Association of American Geographers,* 20:196–223 (December, 1930).

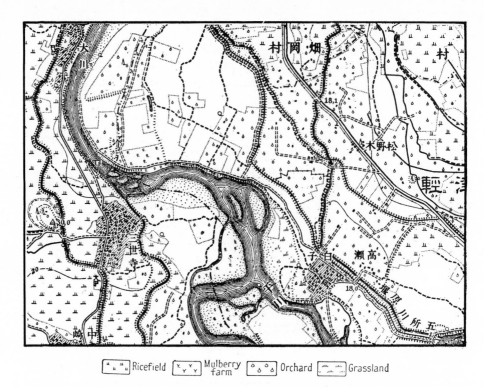

⌐ "ˌ " Ricefield　⌐ʸ ˌ ʸ Mulberry farm　⌐° ˌ ° Orchard　⌐··· ·· Grassland

FIG. 194. A part of the riverine zone in Iwaki Basin. The slightly irregular surface and greater elevation of the plain close to the river has resulted in the planting of dry crops instead of rice. Section of Japanese topographic map, scale 1:25,000.

FIG. 195. A view of the riverine zone of the Iwaki Basin near Fujisaki.

in the practice of encasing each young apple in a paper sack made of newspaper, to protect it from insect and fungus pests (Fig. 196). Not only the diluvial benches and the riverine zones, but also the lower mountain foothills, are common locations of apple orchards, although these slope orchards give smaller yields than those on the lower sites. Numerous artificial ponds in the diluvium serve as sources of irrigation water for rice fields on the lower alluvium.

Noshiro-Omono Plain (Subregion 2).—This lowland is composed of two small aggradational plains at the mouth of the Noshiro and Omono rivers and narrow strips of coastal sediments which

FIG. 196. In the specialized apple district in the Iwaki Basin the young apples are covered with paper bags to prevent injury to the fruit by insects and fungus.

enclose Hachiro Lagoon and connect hilly Oga Peninsula with the mainland. Thus it lacks compactness. The northern part, or Noshiro Plain, is composed largely of low diluvial terrace, much of it uncultivated. Its seaward margins have the usual belt of beach ridges and dunes, which are sparsely occupied and meagerly utilized. A few of its depressions have pond-irrigated rice and there is a little dry cropping, especially along the inner margins of the dune belt, which is also the site of a highway and a number of villages. Between the coastal zone of beach ridges and the landward belt of diluvial terrace is the meager alluvial area, which is devoted to rice, only the riverine zone being excepted. Noshiro city (34,054), at the mouth of the Noshiro River, is an anchorage port for coastwise steamers, which call chiefly for cargoes of logs and lumber. The city is something of a sawmill center.

The delta-plain of the Omono River is in many ways similar to that of the Noshiro. Strong northward-flowing currents cause the river to bend in the same direction, so that it flows parallel with the coast for some distance back of the belt of beach ridges before breaking through the barrier. Akita, the site of an oil refinery, is a castle town of about 96,000 population which is situated several kilometers behind the protective wall of pine-capped beach ridges. Its port, Tsuchisaki, five kilometers from Akita near the mouth of the Omono River, is so severely handicapped by river floods and its exposed north-facing harbor that traffic practically ceases during winter months. Its domestic exports are chiefly rice from the immediate plain and the tributary interior lowlands, and logs and oil from the adjacent hill and mountain country.

The sandy strips joining hilly Oga Peninsula to the mainland and enclosing Hachiro Lagoon, composed of a series of beach ridges and dunes, have a marked linearity and parallelism of their natural and cultural lineaments. Some of the inner ridges show a considerable amount of dry-crop cultivation, rice occupying the intervening swales. Villages following the ridge tops are of *strassendorf* dimensions. A branch line of railroad follows the southern belt of beach ridge from Akita to Funakawa, 30 kilometers distant on the southern side of Oga Peninsula. The latter is a supplementary port which is used chiefly in winter when the unprotected river-mouth harbor of Tsuchisaki is unfit for anchorage. Funakawa's small foreign trade consists almost exclusively of petroleum products. A small amount of kerosene (184,500 yen) is exported, and a somewhat larger quantity of crude oil (1,870,000 yen) is imported, which is destined for the Akita refinery.

The Shonai or Mogami Plain (Subregion 3).—Compact, and composed entirely of new alluvium, the Mogami Plain supports a very sizable population group. Settlement forms, except on the beach ridges, are prevalently small, tree-enclosed clusters of dwellings. A dense network of drainage channels, some having riverine belts specialized in dry crops, covers the lowland. Large areas of paddy have been "adjusted," giving the landscape a very precise geometric pattern. Considerable sections, especially the inner margins, of the coastal belt of beach ridges and dunes are under cultivation, a larger proportion than in similar locations farther north, although protective walls of conifers are very conspicuous on the outer ridges. Vegetables, mulberry, and fruits are the most important crops. Sakata (31,958), the port not only of the immediate plain but of the interior basins along the Mogamigawa, has all the disadvantages of an open roadstead harbor on a stormy coast. The water is so shallow

that only lighters and small sailing vessels can enter the river and approach the city. Rice is the one important domestic export; imports are
varied. Tsuruoka (35,986), a castle town located behind the protective
wall of beach ridges, has some local fame as a cotton and silk-weaving
center.

On the northern margin of the Shonai Plain is the lordly volcanic
cone of Chokai (2,230 meters), the lower and flatter slopes of whose
ash apron are partially under cultivation. Along its northwest margins,
dissection is so far advanced that a labyrinthine valley pattern has resulted, the floors of which are covered with paddy fields.

CHAPTER XII

Central and Southwestern Japan

SOUTH and west of Tohoku is old subtropical Japan, the Japan of legend and tradition, of ancient occupance, and mellowed living. In a very real sense Hokkaido, and to a less degree Tohoku, are the "provinces," where many of the features which foreigners, and even the Japanese themselves, consider to be typical of Nippon are either lacking or greatly modified. This subtropical Japan, the land of warmth and climatic bounty, of tiny farms, terraced fields, and intensive cropping, of tea gardens, bamboo and orange groves, cherry blossoms and fans, lies principally south of the 37th parallel.

The generalizations and descriptions for Japan as a whole which have been given in Part I apply more often or more specifically to central and southwestern Japan than to the two northern subdivisions. To avoid repetition, therefore, no overall summary is given here as was done for Hokkaido and Tohoku. Central and southwestern Japan is so much the standard for things Japanese that it is the deviations from this base level, as exemplified by Hokkaido and Tohoku, that need general summaries.

As a basis for description subtropical Japan may be divided into three general areas. These subdivisions have no such regional distinctiveness as do Tohoku and Hokkaido. Therefore only brief summaries of them are warranted. It will be recognized immediately that these subdivisions of central and southwestern Japan are based primarily upon terrain contrasts. Within each of the three subdivisions are numerous local areas, many of them of unusual importance and having striking individuality, and it is with the numerous local areas that the rest of the book deals.

CHUBU[1] OR CENTRAL JAPAN

Chubu includes that rugged, highest, and broadest part of Honshu where the mountain systems of north and south Japan coalesce to form a confused highland mass largely lacking in order and symmetry (front end papers and Fig. 4). In an earlier section this has been called the

[1] "Chubu" is a regional name used by K. Tanaka. See his article on "Geographical

Gifu Node. Through the center of this mountain knot, extending from coast to coast in a NNW–SSE direction runs a great transverse tectonic depression, the Fossa Magna, which is partially filled with recent volcanic materials and young sedimentary rocks, but also contains a series of detritus-choked fault valleys. Along the Hokuroku or Japan Sea coast, to the east of Noto Peninsula, is the alluvial piedmont plain of Etchu and northeast of it the wetter lagoon-filled lowlands of Takata and Echigo. Southwest of Noto Peninsula is the Kaga Lowland. The Tokai or Pacific side has three conspicuous bays of fault origin, Ise, Suruga, and Sagami-Tokyo. The heads of the first and third have important alluvial lowlands, the Nobi and Kwanto plains respectively. At the head of Suruga Bay the great volcanic piles of Fuji and Ashitaka come down almost to the sea margins, and a bay-head lowland is lacking. The Sun-en coastal strip (excluding Izu Peninsula), between Kwanto on the north and Nobi to the south, is characterized by numerous small delta-plains and conspicuous diluvial terraces separated from one another by spurs of hill land.

Lowland Chubu is definitely within that part of Japan (south of 37°) where typical humid, subtropical climates (Caf) prevail. Abundant rainfall, long, hot summers, a frost-free season of 180–260 days, mild winters with January minimum temperatures hovering around the freezing point —such are the general characteristics. Lowland Chubu marks the approximate poleward limit of the subtropical broadleaf evergreen woodlands, although at higher elevations deciduous and mixed forests, typical of northern Honshu, prevail. Precipitation is heaviest along the Japan Sea side of Chubu, 80–100 inches being common. Here the seasonal accent is upon the winter months, when dark, overcast skies and heavy snows, like those of western Ou, prevail. Precipitation is somewhat less (60–80 inches) on the Pacific side, and there the warm season is accented, mid-summer being somewhat drier than early summer and fall. Southwestern Chubu has in the winter only a third to a fourth as much precipitation as the northwest side, and while snow falls on 13–20 days, there is no lasting snow cover. The Sun-en coastal strip, narrow and protected on the north and west by broad and high mountain masses, has somewhat milder winters than the extensive and more exposed plains of Kwanto and Nobi at its northeastern and southwestern extremities. Within the mountain core the graben basins of Fossa Magna have a variety of local climates, but on the whole temperatures are lower, frost-free seasons shorter, and rainfall less than on either of the coasts. In fact the 40–50 inches of pre-

Units of Japan" (in Japanese) in the *Geographical Review of Japan*, 3:1–22 (July, 1927).

cipitation, with a summer maximum, which is typical of these interior basins gives them the distinction, along with parts of Hokkaido and the Inland Sea depression, of being the least rainy sections of Japan.

In respect to occupance characteristics Chubu as a region is less distinctive than either Hokkaido or Ou, for it is merely the northern and eastern part of long-settled southwestern Japan, which has those landscape features commonly considered to be typical of Nippon. It has some distinction in that it includes the country's largest plain, Kwanto, and, coincident with it and the Nobi Lowland, two of the three largest compact population clusters in Nippon and three of its six great urban centers. Chubu's Pacific margins form the northern end of Japan's manufactural belt, including such industrial metropolitan centers as Nagoya, Tokyo, and Yokohama, the latter being also one of the country's two greatest ports.

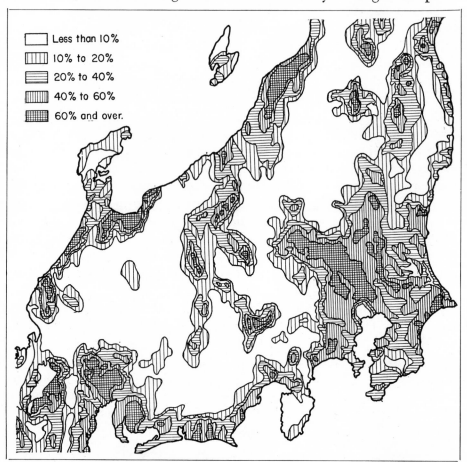

Less than 10%
10% to 20%
20% to 40%
40% to 60%
60% and over.

FIG. 197. Percentage of the total area of Chubu in cultivated crops. After Matui.

The Sun-en coastal strip, connecting the Tokyo-Yokohama industrial center with the Nagoya and Osaka-Kobe-Kyoto centers farther to the southwest, has the finest rail service in Japan, and its traffic, both freight and passenger, exceeds that of any other section. Tea growing reaches its maximum development on the Pacific side of Chubu, as does mulberry cultivation, for the country's silk industry is markedly concentrated in the graben basins of the Fossa Magna and on the Kwanto and Nobi plains. Over half of Japan's mulberry acreage is included within Chubu.

In contrast to the Tokai or Pacific side of Chubu, the Hokuroku littoral facing Asia is a less modernized, more provincial region, where life moves at a slower pace and at a somewhat lower level. It is often called the "back door" of Japan. No great urban centers and no large ports have developed, manufacturing has had small growth, commercial crops other than rice are few, foreign trade is insignificant, and in winter heavy snows, poor visibility, and stormy seas constitute serious handicaps to both land and sea transport. Snowsheds are very conspicuous features along all the rail lines.[2]

The Central Mountain Knot of Chubu

Three principal subdivisions of the broad mountain mass of central Honshu (Region A, Fig. 198) are here recognized: (1) the great transverse tectonic depression of Fossa Magna with its volcanic piles and graben valleys; and the mountain masses (2) to the east and (3) west of the depression.

The Transverse Tectonic Depression of Fossa Magna (Subregion 1, Fig. 198).—Geologically and morphologically the Fossa Magna stands out as the zone of division between northeast and southwest Japan. The western margin of the trough is marked by a tremendous fault-scarp, at or near whose base is a series of four graben basins. The eastern margin is less abrupt and distinct, though it too is marked by fault-scarps with two graben basins adjacent to the foot. Through the Fossa Magna runs the Fuji Volcanic Chain, whose numerous cones stand as boundary posts and further accentuate the division between northeastern and southwestern Japan. This volcanic chain is continued southeastward into the Pacific Basin as the Izu, Ogasawara, and Bonin Islands of the Tsushima Arc.

Hill and Mountain Masses of the Fossa Magna (Area *a*): *Izu Peninsula* (*a*[1]).—Forming the eastern margin of Suruga Bay, which is the south-

---

[2] Settlement forms and house types of Chubu are briefly described in *Nippon Chiri Taikei* (*An Encyclopedia of Japanese Geography*, Tokyo, 1930), 6:264–289.

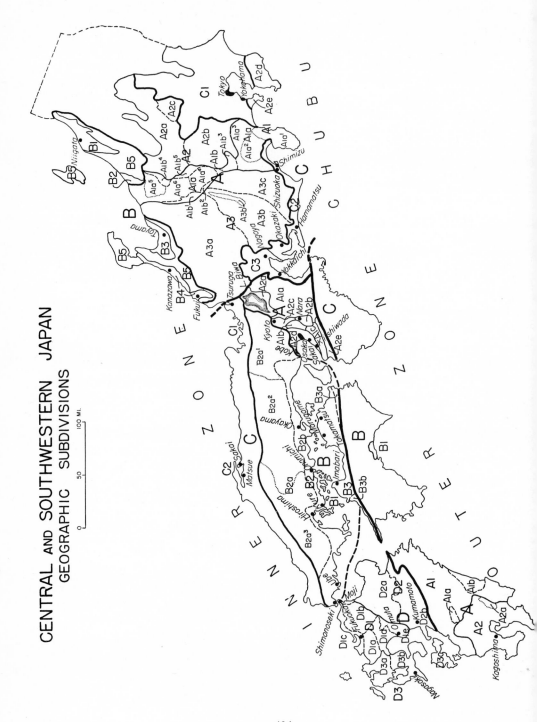

CENTRAL AND SOUTHWESTERN JAPAN
GEOGRAPHIC SUBDIVISIONS

434

FIG. 198. GEOGRAPHIC SUBDIVISIONS OF CENTRAL AND SOUTHWESTERN JAPAN

CHUBU OR CENTRAL JAPAN

. CENTRAL MOUNTAIN KNOT

A 1. Transverse Tectonic Depression or the Fossa Magna

A 1 a. Hill and Mountain Masses of the Fossa Magna

a¹. Izu Peninsula

a². Mt. Fuji

a³. Tertiary Mountains

a⁴. Yatsu Volcanic Group

a⁵. Myako Volcanic Group

a⁶. Northern Tertiary Hills

A 1 b. Fault Basins of the Fossa Magna

b¹. Matsumoto Basin

b². Suwa Basin

b³. Kofu Basin

b⁴. Nagano Basin

b⁵. Ueda Basin

A 2. Highlands East of the Fossa Magna

A 2 a. Nasu Volcanic Chain

A 2 b. Chichibu Mountains

A 2 c. Ashio Mountains

A 2 d. Boso Peninsula

A 2 e. Miura Peninsula

A 3. Highlands West of the Fossa Magna

A 3 a. Hida Highlands

A 3 b. Kiso Mountains

b¹. Ina Trench

A 3 c. Akaishi Sphenoid

B. HOKUROKU LOWLANDS AND HILL LANDS

B 1. Echigo or Niigata Plain

B 2. Takata Plain

B 3. Etchu or Toyama Alluvial Piedmont

B 4. Kaga Plain

B 5. Tertiary Hill Land (including Noto Peninsula and Sado Island)

C. LOWLANDS OF THE TOKAI COAST

C 1. Kwanto or Tokyo Plain

C 2. Sun-en Coast

C 3. Nobi or Nagoya Plain and Associated Lowlands Bordering Ise Bay

INNER ZONE OF SOUTHWEST JAPAN

, KINKI OR EASTERN SETOUCHI

A 1. Hilly Uplands

A 1 a. Omi-Iga

A 1 b. Ikoma

A 1 c. Izumi

A 2. Fault Basins

A 2 a. Biwa (Omi) Basin

A 2 b. Yamato or Nara Basin

A 2 c. Kyoto (Yamashiro) Basin

A 2 d. Osaka or Settsu Plain

A 2 e. Kino Graben

CENTRAL SETOUCHI (INLAND SEA)

B 1. The Islands

B 2. Sanyo District

B 2 a. Interior Hill Lands of Southern Chugoku

a¹. Tamba Upland

a². Kibi Upland

a³. Western Chugoku

B 2 b. Coastal Margins of Southern Chugoku

B 3. Inland Sea Margins of Shikoku

B 3 a. Yoshino Rift Valley

B 3 b. Matsuyama Plain

C. SANIN LITTORAL OF NORTHERN CHUGOKU

C 1. Wakasa Bay Area

C 2. Shinji Horst and Hiinokawa Plain

D. NORTHERN KYUSHU

D 1. Tsukushi Hill Lands and Associated Plains

D 1 a. Seburu Horst

D 1 b. Chikuho Block

D 1 c. Coastal Margins

D 1 d. Tsukushi Plain

D 1 e. Miike District

D 2. Northern Volcanic Region

D 2 a. The Lava Plateaus

D 2 b. Mt. Aso Region

D 3. Insular and Peninsular Northwestern Kyushu

D 3 a. North Hizen

D 3 b. The Peninsulas

D 3 c. Amakusa Islands

PACIFIC FOLDED MOUNTAINS OR OUTER ZONE OF SOUTHWEST JAPAN

SOUTHERN KYUSHU

A 1. Kyushu Folded Mountains

A 1 a. Hitoyoshi Fault Basin

A 1 b. Sadowara (Miyazaki) Coastal Plain

A 2. Southern Ash Upland and Associated Highlands

A 2 a. Miyakonojo Basin

B. SOUTHERN SHIKOKU

B 1. Kochi Plain

C. KII PENINSULA

ern extension of the depressed zone of Fossa Magna, Izu Peninsula is a rugged hilly and mountainous country composed largely of andesite rock with conspicuous volcanic cones and lava flows. Slight subsidence has resulted in numerous small coastal indentations at whose apexes are diminutive delta-plains, well cultivated, which are the sites of small agri-cultural-fishing villages. Other than the coastal margins the principal focus of occupance is the meridional lowland, which closely follows the axis of the peninsula, where weak Tertiary rocks are prevalent. Dispersed agricultural settlement appears to predominate. At the northern extremity of Izu the hill slopes overlooking both Sagami and Suruga bays are devoted to the culture of Satsuma oranges, this being about the northern limit of important citrus cultivation in Nippon.

Associated with the recent volcanic activity of the region are the numerous hot mineral springs. These spas and the general scenic beauty surrounding them, to which imposing Mt. Fuji contributes much, have led to the establishment of numerous resorts, well known to foreigners as well as Japanese. Miyanoshita Spa in the Hakone district at the extreme northeastern margin of Izu is only the most famous.[3] The entire Hakone district, located as it is near the populous regions of Japan and served by excellent rail facilities, is one of the most frequented resort areas in all Nippon. Renowned Mount Hakone is a dissected volcano lying between Sagami Bay and Fujiyama. Its enormous crater, 12.8 kilometers from north to south and 7 kilometers from east to west, contains six central cones and an atrio lake, Ashino-ko, on the west. Inside the crater are a number of villages, whose combined populations number 9,000 or more. The Fuji-Hakone-Amagi Volcanic Range, extending southward to form Izu Peninsula, interposes the most serious natural barrier to land transport along the whole Tokaido route from Tokyo to Kyoto. During Tokugawa days Hakone Pass over this mountain, which was followed by the famous Tokaido post-road, was of strategic importance and was guarded by a great barrier gate, where all travelers along the Tokaido were carefully inspected. This gate is located within the volcano's crater, at its south end where the road occupied a narrows between Lake Ashino and the steep southern wall of the crater. Its importance is suggested by the fact that from it are derived the geographical terms *Kwanto* (Tokyo-Yokohama region), meaning "east of the gate," and *Kwansai* (Osaka-Kyoto region), "west of the gate." In 1935 the Tanna railway tunnel under the Hakone barrier was completed. It is one of the longest tunnels in the world, 7,807 meters.

[3] *Guide-Book Excursion B-2: Hakone* (Pan-Pacific Science Congress, Japan, 1926).

Mt. Fuji (a^2).—Occupying the heads of most of the large bays along the southeast coast are important aggradational plains. Suruga Bay, on the contrary, is terminated at its landward end by the symmetrical cone of Fujiyama and its lower eroded satellite, Ashitaka. Fuji, which rises by symmetrical concave slopes from sea level to an elevation of 3,778 meters, is the highest mountain in Japan and one of great beauty, being a nearly perfect cone. Both at home and abroad Fuji is almost a symbol of things Japanese. The comparatively smooth interstream uplands of the volcano's lower ash aprons are partially under cultivation, tea and mulberry as well as the usual summer and winter annuals being conspicuous. Along Fuji's eastern and western flanks numerous small hydroelectric plants occupy sites in the relatively steep-gradient valleys, providing power for important manufacturing plants.[4] To the north of Fujiyama, occupying portions of a semicircular trough between the flanks of the volcano and the Tertiary mountains, are the five lovely Fuji lakes.[5] Numerous small villages occupy the trough, most of which specialize in silk reeling. Maize is locally significant, and in October yellow ears of corn hanging under the wide eaves of the houses are a common sight. Crops occupy both the old lake plains and alluvial fans and the lower ash uplands.

The Tertiary Mountains (a^3).—Encircling Fuji on the west, north, and east is a semicircular belt of mountains which is unlike many regions of Tertiary rocks in that it is relatively high and rugged, having maximum elevations of 1,200–1,900 meters. Occupance is meager.

The Yatsu and Myako Volcanic Groups (a^4 and a^5).—Midway across Honshu in the Fossa Magna depressed zone is the Yatsu volcanic cluster, and farther north beyond Nagano city is the Myako group. The former consists of four large cones, the highest of which has an elevation of 2,899 meters. The northern aggregation is comprised of three large conical volcanoes and several smaller ones. Throughout both volcanic groups, wild and rugged country prevails and inhabitants are sparse except along the lower margins adjacent to the graben basins.

The Northern Tertiary Hills (a^6).—This unit, which occupies the northern part of the depressed zone, comprises a well dissected hill country including considerable areas of moderate slope and valley-bottom land. Hence cultivation is fairly widespread and intricate in pattern. Dispersed settlement is common. Mulberry is very important, for the region is a part of

---

[4] See Glenn T. Trewartha, "A Geographic Study in Shizuoka Prefecture, Japan," in the *Annals of the Association of American Geographers*, 18(1928):156–170.

[5] *Guide-Book Excursion B-4: The Lake District around Mt. Fuji* (Pan-Pacific Science Congress, Japan, 1926).

the sericulture region of central Honshu.

The Fault Basins of the Fossa Magna (Area *b*).[6]—These intermontane basins of 250–700 meters elevation, drier and cooler than the coastal lowlands, have many natural and man-induced features in common. One characteristic they all have is the large amount of alluvial and diluvial piedmont material, often coarse is texture and steep of slope, which comprises much of their areas. Varying amounts of this detritus are diluvium, carved by streams into terraces at various levels, but fan and cone configuration are conspicuous in both recent and old river deposits (Fig. 199). Soil materials tend to be coarse or even stony, a feature which, in conjunction with the sloping piedmont surfaces, the cooler, shorter summers, and the smaller amount of rainfall, somewhat handicaps rice cultivation, although it by no means excludes it (Figs. 200, 201). On some of the steeper fans the paddy fields are artificially terraced, their outer retaining walls being composed of smooth, waterworn boulders excavated from the fan materials. Normally the rice fields produce only one harvest during the annual cycle, although

FIG. 199. The basins of the Fossa Magna are characterized by steep fans and cones. The numerals indicate individual fans. From *Nippon Chiri-Fuzoku Taikei.*

---

[6] For a more detailed study of a representative basin see Glenn T. Trewartha, "The Suwa Basin: A Specialized Sericulture District in the Japanese Alps," in the *Geographical Review,* 20(1930):224–244.

many of the dry upland fields are planted to wheat and barley in autumn after summer vegetables and other warm-season crops have been harvested. But of greatest importance is the mulberry crop, for these mountain basins of the Fossa Magna are the very heart of Japan's silk-producing region. In not a few of the villages (referring here to a political subdivision and not a settlement) mulberry occupies 40–60 per cent of the cultivated land. Mountainous Nagano Prefecture, in which all but one of these grabens are located, is easily the ranking prefecture in sericulture in Nippon. In 1939 it included 14 per cent of the country's mulberry acreage, produced 18–19 per cent of its cocoons, and reeled 23–24 per cent of its raw silk (Fig. 202).[7]

Over Japan as a whole the rearing of silkworms is auxiliary to gen-

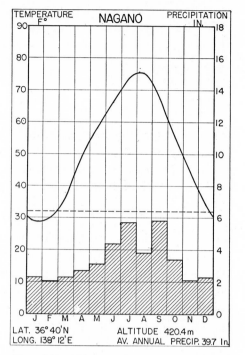

Fig. 200. Nagano has a continental climate (Daf) with average winter-month temperatures below 32°F. Rainfall is low for Japan and there is a conspicuous summer maximum.

eral farming, but in these basins of central Honshu it is more often the chief occupation. This specialization in sericulture and silk production reflects in part the relative inaccessibility of the region and the predominance of slope land. Raw silk, being a relatively compact and highly valuable commodity, can absorb higher transportation costs than most products. Moreover, since mulberry is tolerant of most soils and does not require irrigation, it is well adapted to the thin, rocky hillside soils and the coarse stony soils of the alluvial cones and fans. The two most common mulberry locations are (1) a zone several hundred feet wide along the foothills of the bordering mountains and (2) the higher and stonier parts of the fans, where irrigation is difficult. (Figs. 203, 204). Because of the shorter growing season in these high altitude basins[8] an

[7] *Norinsho Tokeihyo,* 1939, pp. 71, 74, 88. The discrepancy between mulberry and cocoon percentages on the one hand and raw silk on the other reflects an import into the reeling centers of Nagano of cocoons from other parts of the country.

[8] The growing season is just slightly over 5 months at Matsumoto, as compared with 7 months and 8 days at Tokyo near sea level.

early-budding, quick-maturing dwarf variety of bush is grown, which yields less per unit-area and from which only one picking is possible. Since late spring frosts are a real hazard to mulberry at these altitudes, the emphasis is upon summer and autumn worms rather than upon the spring crop, which is more important for the country as a whole. Partly because of the unusually high degree of specialization in silk and the fact that fewer substitute crops can be grown here, there has been less decline in mulberry acreage in these mountain basins than in the country as a whole. In 1939, when the mulberry acreage of the country as a whole dropped to 65 per cent of what it had been in 1930, Nagano Prefecture, in which most of these basins are located, retained 81 per cent of its acreage.

The interior basins of Chubu, like those of Tohoku, are very conspicuous on a population map, their dense settlement standing out in contrast to the meagerly inhabited surrounding highlands (back endpapers). Because of its depressed nature, the Fossa Magna and its basins are important not only as a region of population concentration, but as a route connecting the opposite coasts. No single rail line follows the depressed zone throughout its entire length, although both the eastern and western grabens are served by lines focusing upon Tokyo, the eastern one reaching Takata and Niigata on the Japan Sea coast. Rail connection is also made with Nagoya by way of the Kiso Valley, and beyond that with the whole Kinki region, but because ties are strongest with the Kwanto cities, these basins become an important part of Yokohama's hinterland for silk export.

The village type of settlement predominates on the whole, although

FIG. 201. Coarse, stony soils characterize the upper parts of the alluvial-diluvial fans in the basins of the Fossa Magna. Such sites and soils are better suited to a crop like mulberry than to irrigated rice. Suwa Basin.

isolated farmsteads are not uncommon, especially on the steeper
fans and on the diluvial terraces.
Culture forms associated with
the silk industry are conspicuous in many of the settlements.
The tall galvanized-iron smokestacks of the filatures are discernible, even from a distance.
Closer scrutiny brings into view
the low, unimpressive, shed-like
reeling plants and the huge bar-
rack-like cocoon warehouses three
to six stories high, with batteries
of windows, protected by wide
eaves, marking each story. Because of their cheap and flimsy

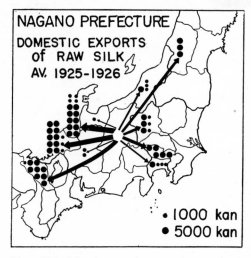

FIG. 202. Nagano Prefecture is the center
of Japan's raw silk industry. One kan = 8.27
pounds. From *Nippon Chiri-Fuzoku Taikei*.

construction and their lack of heating equipment, the filatures are usually
closed during the two or three winter months.

Matsumoto Basin (*b¹*) is the northernmost of the genuine basins lying
at the foot of the western fault-scarp which bounds the Fossa Magna,
although the very narrow Himekawa rift valley extends on to the north
coast. The features of the Matsumoto Graben are in general similar to
the representative conditions previously described. Alluvial and diluvial
fans and terraces are conspicuous. The metropolis, Matsumoto city (72,795),
from which the basin takes its name, is a castle town which is famous
today as an important center of the raw silk industry in its various phases.

Suwa Basin (*b²*) is next in line south of Matsumoto. Its lowest and central portion is occupied by a lake of the same name, upon whose southern
and northwestern margins delta-fans are encroaching. The one at the
north has so steep a slope as to warrant being called a cone. The Tenryu
River, one of the largest in Japan, has its source in Suwa Lake and drains
to the Pacific. Suwa Basin is nationally famous, for it is the greatest silk-
reeling center in Nippon and probably in the world. The filatures are
highly concentrated at Okaya (40,033), located on the Tenryu River at
the point where it leaves Lake Suwa (Fig. 205). This concentration of
raw silk production in Suwa has its roots in the past.[9] Lying between the

[9] See Trewartha, "The Suwa Basin," *op. cit.*, 238–239; also Katsue Mizawa, "The
History of the Suwa Silk Industry from the Geographical Viewpoint" (in Japanese),
in the *Geographical Review of Japan*, 2(1926):813–834, 925–951.

cotton-producing plains along the Pacific coast and the non-cotton-producing region to the west and northwest, at a natural sag in the dividing range and near the heads of a number of radial valleys which ascend from the Pacific coast, the Suwa region after the middle of the eighteenth century became a center for the relaying, distributing, and cleaning of this fiber. After Japan was opened to world trade, cotton was imported instead of grown locally and Suwa lost its position as a cotton-distributing and processing center. Gradually it turned to another fiber, raw silk. Within Okaya the filatures tend to be concentrated along the Tenryu River, where before the development of hydroelectricity the stream supplied direct waterpower. Kamisuwa, a castle town on the lake, is famous as a resort and boasts several excellent inns. Hot sulphur springs, skiing and skating facilities in winter, and the general scenic effect of lake and mountains all combine to make the place attractive.

One unfavorable feature of the basin is the fact that it is visited every few years by floods which do extensive damage to the rice fields on the basin floor, especially those on the lower delta-fan at the southern end of the lake. This flooding has given rise to an unusual practice known as *tuka-dukuri* or mound cultivation (Figs. 206, 207). Many small circular mounds of earth, about a foot high and four to seven feet in diameter, dot the paddy fields. On each is planted a single fruit tree, usually quince, though also apple, pear, and grape. Vegetables, too, may be grown on the mounds. These crops furnish the farmers some food and income even when the floods have seriously damaged the rice crop.[10]

Kofu Basin (*b*³),[11] next to the south, is separated from Suwa by the Yatsu Volcanic Group, so that the connection between the two grabens is reduced to a relatively constricted valley. But there is sufficient settlement on the ash slopes and river terraces bordering the connecting valley to constitute a corridor which is evident on a population map. Kofu, the most southern and least elevated of the grabens, is warmer and less frosty and snowy than the others. Kofu city has only 11.7 days of snow on the average as compared with Matsumoto's 46.5 and Nagano's 82, and its growing season is 194 days as compared with 157 and 167 at the other two Fossa Magna stations. Besides its specialization in sericulture

[10] Taizi Yagawa, "On the Tuka-dukuri (A Type of Land Utilization) on the Suwa Basin, Nagano Prefecture" (in Japanese with English summary), in the *Geographical Review of Japan*, 14(1938):490–506.

[11] S. Kowada, "Some Geographical Considerations Concerning Kofu Basin" (in Japanese), in the *Geographical Review of Japan*, 7(1931):19–31; K. Tanaka, "The Kofu Basin" (in Japanese), in the *Geographical Review of Japan*, 1(1925):946–975; 2(1926):17–46.

FIG. 203 (*top*). The lower slopes of Suwa's mountain foothills are devoted almost exclusively to mulberry; the higher slopes have a woodland cover. Photograph by Yagawa.

FIG. 204 (*center*). A closer view of the mulberry belt along the lower slopes of Suwa's foothills. On the plain in the foreground are rice fields. Rural villages concentrate at the base of the slopes.

FIG. 205 (*bottom*). The city of Okaya, on Lake Suwa in the Suwa Basin in the heart of the Nagano silk district, is Japan's greatest silk-reeling center. Filatures and cocoon storehouses are very conspicuous features of the city.

the basin has a reputation as a grape-growing district. Kofu city (102, 419), a castle town, is an important cocoon market as well as a filature center.

The Nagano and Ueda Basins (b^4 and b^5).—Along the eastern margins of the transverse depression, at the foot of less conspicuous fault-scarps, is a north-south corridor constricted to valley dimensions in some places but containing two wider basin-like sections designated the *Nagano Basin* to the north and the *Ueda Basin* farther south. Both regions are thoroughly specialized in the various phases of raw silk production. The city of Nagano (76,861) contains one of the most famous Buddhist temples of Japan and is to some extent a mecca for pilgrims.

The Highlands East of the Fossa Magna (Subregion 2).—In this region of confused and formidable mountain country where the three distinct and parallel highland chains of northern Honshu fuse, it is less easy to distinguish individual mountain areas.

Fɪɢ. 206. *Tuka-dukuri* in the midst of rice fields, Suwa Basin. The trees are Chinese quince.

Fɪɢ. 207. Distribution of *tuka-dukuri* in the Suwa Basin. After Yagawa.

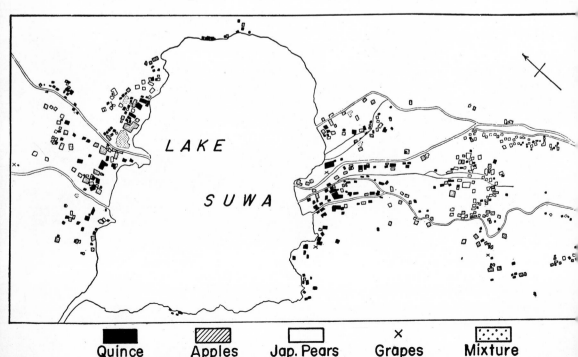

LAKE

SUWA

| Quince | Apples | Jap. Pears | Grapes | Mixture |

The Nasu Volcanic Chain (Area *a*).—This range, crescentic in shape, with its convex side toward the southeast, is composed of numerous volcanoes of various types and stages of evolution. It is for the most part meagerly occupied, although some land is tilled not only in the restricted valleys but also on the lower slopes of a number of the smoother ash aprons. Mulberry is the most important crop. At the southwestern extremity of the range, under the shadow of active Mt. Asama, is the city of Karuizawa, famous throughout Japan as a summer hill station (3,180 feet) for both foreigners and Japanese. Nikko, a town containing the most magnificent aggregation of colorful and ornate Buddhist temples, mausolea, and pagodas to be found anywhere in Japan, is located on the western flanks of the Nasu Range in the midst of noble cryptomeria groves.[12] The Japanese have an expression, "Who has not seen Nikko must not speak of splendor." Excellent accommodations cater to the throngs of tourists who come to see the sights not only at Nikko but throughout the surrounding region of mighty volcanic cones, beautiful lakes, torrential rivers with waterfalls, splendid forests, and hot springs.

The Chichibu and the Ashio Mountains (Areas *b* and *c*), although separated by the Tone Lowland, which forms the western arm of the Kwanto Plain, are similar geologically and greatly resemble the Outer Zone of southwest Japan, being composed of ancient, folded sedimentary rocks so faulted and tilted that block form is the result. In general the Chichibu Mountains present a rugged landscape, some peaks exceeding 2,500 meters elevation. Occupance is meager except in certain small areas of weak Tertiary rocks, such as the Chichibu Basin, where relief is much less and valleys more open. In these locations a relatively dense dispersed type of rural settlement is characteristic.

The Ashio Block with its back slope toward the Kwanto Plain is lower (highest elevation 1,526 meters), and its valleys are much wider. The region is therefore better populated than the Chichibu area. Along igneous intrusions at the northern boundary is one of Japan's largest copper deposits. In 1939 one mine in this locality, the Ashio, produced 12,762 tons of blister copper, or 16.4 per cent of the entire copper output of the country.[13] It also had a considerable output of gold, silver, and zinc. Close to 4,000 laborers are employed at the Ashio mining camp, which is one of the largest in Japan. Dressing mills are located in the

[12] Leopold G. Scheidl, "Das Gebiet von Nikko in Mittel-Japan," in *Petermanns Geographische Mitteilungen*, 85(1938):141–152.
[13] "Kohle und Metalle im Yenblock-Gebiet," in *Vierteljahrshefte zur Statistik des Deutschen Reichs*, 1941, p. 89.

neighborhood of the town of Ashio, and the smelter is at Honzan a few miles distant.[14]

The Boso and the Miura Peninsulas (Areas *d* and *e*).—These remnants of an old east-west horst, the fracture and partial subsidence of which resulted in Tokyo Bay and Uraga Channel, have fairly typical Tertiary landscapes. Elevations are usually less than 400 meters. Dissection is mature, and isolated farmsteads and cultivated lands occupy both the labyrinthine valleys and the lower hill slopes. Minor sinking has produced an irregular coastline with numerous small cultivable deltas at the head of indentations, upon whose seaward margins are located the ubiquitous agricultural-fishing villages. Misaki, at the southernmost extremity of Miura, has considerable fame as a fishing port. Wave-cut platforms and sea cliffs are conspicuous features of the Tertiary headlands. To the left of the narrow entrance to Tokyo Bay and guarding this greatest population unit of Japan on the Kwanto Plain is the naval and air base of Yokosuka, a city of 193,358 people which has become one of the principal centers of the new war industries. Both the Boso and the Miura Peninsula are renowned for their seaside resorts, which attract patrons from nearby Tokyo, Yokohama, and other Kwanto cities. A rail line skirts the entire periphery of Boso Peninsula, making the coastal settlements easily accessible. Sea bathing is the principal attraction. More than three million people make use of the Boso resorts every summer.[15]

The Highlands West of Fossa Magna (Subregion 3): *The Hida Highlands* (Area *a*).—The easternmost part of Hida, where it terminates abruptly in a fault-scarp overlooking the Fossa Magna, is the highest range in Japan and is often called the Japanese Alps. Some of its peaks exceed 3,000 meters. At the present time no glaciers exist, although cirque-like features can be observed. Numerous volcanoes, some very youthful in appearance, cap the range. Occupance is extremely meager. Where the mountains reach the Japan Sea they terminate abruptly in formidable sea cliffs.

Westward from the fault-scarp overlooking the Fossa Magna the altitudes decline, and a broad area of rugged hill country prevails, whose elevations in general are less than 1,000 meters. But valleys are still narrow, and there are few waste-filled basins. The agricultural population is therefore meager; indeed this is one of the emptiest regions in Old Japan. Mining of copper, lead, zinc, and silver is characteristic of a number of localities,

[14] *Guide-Book Excursion C-1: The Ashio Copper Mine* (Pan-Pacific Science Congress, Japan, 1926).

[15] T. Osaki, "The Seaside Resorts of the Boso Peninsula" (in Japanese with English summary), in the *Geographical Review of Japan,* 14(1938):668–692, 745–760.

but it is usually on a small scale; only one mine has an annual output approaching 2 million yen. Here and there in the isolated and inaccessible valleys of Hida is still to be observed a feature that is now comparatively rare, the large patriarchal-family house. These relict forms are probably most numerous in the Nakakiri district of Gifu Prefecture, almost due south of the Toyama Plain. A representative large house in this locality covers 78 by 48 feet and has a height of 46 feet, which allows for four or five stories. Such a house must have accommodated from forty to fifty or more persons, although at present few have more than twenty occupants.[16]

The Kiso Mountains (Area *b*).—Essentially a horst, this is a granitic mass of rugged mountains with elevations approaching 3,000 meters. It is only sparsely occupied, the principal agricultural sites being the river terraces in some of the larger valleys. The single railroad reaching the basins of the Fossa Magna from the Kinki district follows the canyon-like Kiso Valley, the route of the once-famous Nakasendo Highway. Close to the eastern margins of the Kiso Mountains is the detritus-filled *Ina Trench* (*b*[1]), which presents a landscape that in its major lineaments closely resembles the grabens of the Fossa Magna.

The Akaishi Sphenoid (Area *c*).—In its high relief, steep slopes, and meager settlement, Akaishi almost duplicates Kiso. It is also a horst, but is a highly folded mass of sedimentary and metamorphic rocks rather than granite. Geologically it belongs to the folded mountains of the Outer Zone of southwest Japan and is the easternmost part of this zone. Along the eastern border of Akaishi, where it overlooks the western margin of the Fossa Magna, are nine of Japan's sixteen peaks of more than 3,000 meters elevation. These high peaks rise like monadnocks from flattish old-erosion surfaces of about 2,600 or 2,800 meters elevation.[17]

The Hokuroku Lowlands and Hill Lands of Chubu

Between Wakasa Bay to the south and the area where the Echigo Mountains reach the seacoast, a little north of latitude 38°, is a series of coastal alluvial plains whose immediate hinterlands are thoroughly dissected Tertiary hill country of no great elevation. Noto Peninsula and Sado Island are also in this subdivision (Region B). Back of these plains and the hill lands rise the mighty mountains of central Honshu and farther north the Echigo Range. From north to south the plains are the Echigo or

[16] *Nippon Chiri Taikei* (1930), vol. 6, pp. 286–288; vol. 6b, pp. 167–170.
[17] Sinjo Uyeda, "Geomorphology of the Akaishi Mountains" (in Japanese with English summary), in the *Geographical Review of Japan*, 12(1936):504–526.

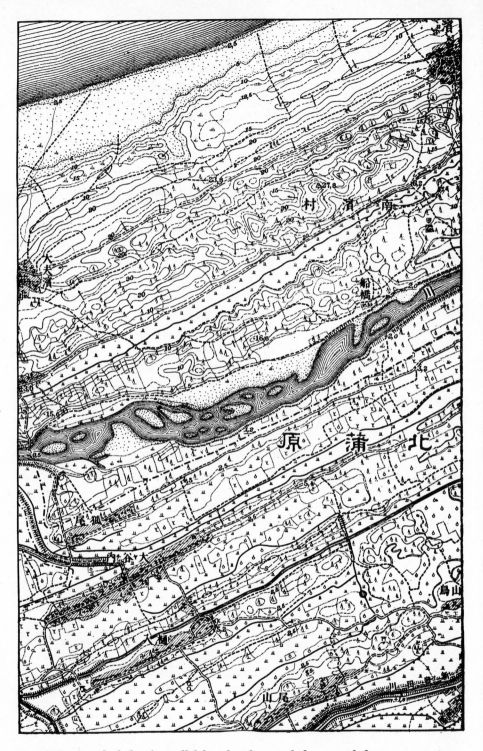

Fig. 208. A wide belt of parallel beach ridges and dunes with long, narrow intervening lowlands characterizes the seaward margins of most Hokuroku plains. A section of the Echigo or Niigata Plain. Japanese topographic map, scale about 1:50,000.

Fig. 209. Belt of dunes in the background, with lagoon and wet plain in foreground. The lagoon plains, when not too wet, are planted in rice. Echigo Plain.

Niigata Plain, one of the largest in Japan, the Takata Plain, the Etchu or Toyama Plain—all to the north and east of Noto Peninsula—and the Kaga Plain, west of Noto. All the lowlands to the northeast of Noto occupy fault depressions which have been partially filled with sediments brought down by rivers from the central highlands. The Kaga Plain includes not only the narrow lowlands to the north and south of Kanagawa city but also the alluvial lowlands of the Kuzuryu River, on which the city of Fukui is located, and the narrow Oochigata Graben, which cuts across Noto Peninsula and divides it into a northern and a southern section. All the principal lowlands except Etchu are bordered on their sea sides by extensive belts of beach ridges and sand dunes thrown up by the strong winter monsoons (Fig. 208). In part, therefore, the plains behind these coastal barriers are filled lagoons, which are subject to frequent flooding and in general have poor drainage (Fig. 209).

The climate of Hokuroku in many ways resembles that of western Ou. Being somewhat farther south, winter temperatures are a little milder, and

Table 136.—Maximum Depth of Snow Cover on the Ground at Selected Stations in Hokuroku
(in centimeters)

Station	November	December	January	February	March	April
Fukui	—	37	74	84	38	—
Okoti	4	80	178	233	155	68
Takata	0	66	136	177	134	37
Onagadani	14	114	238	235	94	23

Source: T. Okada, *The Climate of Japan*, 124–125.

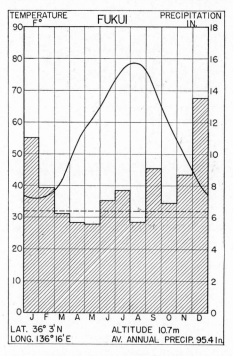

LAT. 36° 3' N   ALTITUDE 10.7m
LONG. 136° 16' E   AV. ANNUAL PRECIP. 95.4 In.

FIG. 210. Hokuroku has a subtropical climate (Caf), average temperatures of winter months being above 32°F. Precipitation is excessively heavy and the maximum occurs in winter.

midwinter month temperatures average a few degrees above freezing rather than below, as in Ou. The January mean at Niigata is 34.7; at Takata 33.3; at Aikawa (Sado Island) 36.0; at Kanagawa 36.9; and at Fukui 36.3. In the United States similar January means are to be found in Kentucky, Virginia, and Maryland. August temperatures average 77° or 78°, so the summers are distinctly hot. Hokuroku has some of the heaviest precipitation in Japan, the mean for the year generally being between 80 and 100 inches. The winter half year has more than the summer half, December and September ordinarily being the wettest months of the year (Fig. 210). Lying as it does very nearly at right angles to the strong winter monsoons and backed by some of the loftiest mountains in all of Japan, Hokuroku is the snowiest of all the lowland regions of Japan (Fig. 211). Rail traffic is impeded by the heavy snows to such an extent that the tracks are laid on an elevated roadbed, and snow fences and snowsheds are common. As pointed out in an earlier chapter, this part of Japan is climatically unique among the subtropical regions of the earth by reason of its excessively deep snow cover. A large majority of the winter days are overcast and depressing, and blue sky is almost phenomenal. A considerable part of the winter

FIG. 211. The Hokuroku and western Ou regions facing the Japan Sea have deep snow.

precipitation falls as rain, so that the number of days with snowfall, an average of 15–20 in the midwinter months, is less than farther north in Ou, where the amount of snow is actually less. The northern portion of Hokuroku, which lies in the lee of Sado Island, has somewhat less snow-fall than the more exposed regions farther south (Fig. 212). Snowfall also increases inland as the mountains are approached. For example, in January the maximum depth of snow cover at Niigata on the coast is only 35 centimeters, whereas at Nagaoka farther inland it is 109 centimeters and at Odiya still farther up the Shinano Valley 151 centimeters. Thawing of the heavy snow cover in spring creates violent floods that inundate the plains.

Culturally Hokuroku bears many resemblances to Tohoku or Ou, in that it too lags behind the rest of Japan. It is decidedly the back door of Nippon. Separated as it is by a high wall of mountains from the urbanized industrial and commercial sections along the Pacific side, where Westerni-

FIG. 212. Maximum depth of the snow cover on the Echigo Plain and surrounding highlands. Note the rapid increase in snow depth inland toward the mountains.

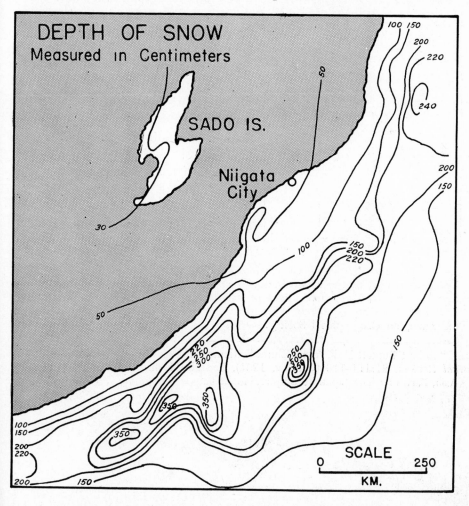

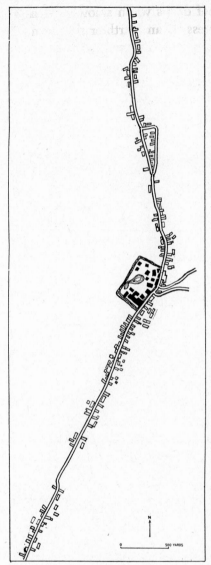

zation is farthest advanced and large domestic markets have developed, it is in an isolated position. In addition, the excessive precipitation, resulting in frequent floods, and the generally poor drainage on the lowlands imposes serious limitations upon agriculture and leads to frequent crop losses. The long, gloomy, snowy winters with their strong winds and the attendant boisterous seas, impeding ocean shipping, add further to the disadvantages of life in Hokuroku. Supplementing these physical handicaps is one of human origin. During the feudal period in Japan wealthy landlords in this region in western Ou came to possess much of the agricultural land. Partly this is attributable to laxity in the enforcement of the laws passed to discourage the accumulation of large estates. Partly it was a result of the fact that the large expenditures necessary to drain extensive areas of the Japan Sea lowlands tended to discourage small individual holdings. Today this section of Japan has some of the country's largest and wealthiest landowners and it is here that the conditions of the landless peasant farmers are the worst (Fig. 213).[18] It is a region of numerous disputes between tenants and landlords.

FIG. 213. A shoestring type village (buraku) along a highway on the Echigo Plain. The long walled estate, whose buildings are shown in solid black, belongs to the local landlord. The other buildings of the buraku, shown only in outline, are the homes of the tenants. Map by Hall, from the Geographical Review, published by the American Geographical Society.

[18] Robert Burnett Hall, "Some Rural Settlement Forms in Japan," in the Geographical Review, 21:111–116 (January, 1931). See also Hall, "Agricultural Regions of Asia, Part VII: The Japanese Empire," in Economic Geography, 10(1934): 334–335.

Fig. 214. Serpentine-shaped settlement occupying the levees of an abandoned river meander, a dry site on the poorly drained Echigo Plain. From Japanese topographic sheet. *Geographical Review*, published by the American Geographical Society.

The settlements and houses on the Hokuroku plains have certain distinctive characteristics. Because of the superabundance of water on the lowlands, settlements tend to be concentrated on elevated dry sites. Most common of these dry sites are the serpentine levees along present or abandoned stream channels, the beach ridges and dune ridges bordering the sea margins of the plains, and the older beach ridges back from the coast, marking ancient strand lines (Fig. 214). Since most of the elevated dry sites have a linear character, the settlements on them likewise have a shoestring or *strassendorf* form. Such settlements frequently consist of a single row of rather closely spaced houses lining either side of the road, which follows the crest of the ridge. Many of them extend unbroken for more than a mile, and a few for more than five miles with only an occasional break. Over 90 per cent of the settlements on the Echigo Plain are of this shoestring or *strassendorf* form.[19] Dry fields planted to vegetables and other unirrigated crops usually flank these linear villages on either side. As a protection against the strong winter winds and heavy snows, the rural settlements, whether elongated or compact, agglomerated or dispersed, are surrounded by high, dense hedges of trees. From a distance the rural settlements look like islands of woodland rising out of the inundated paddy land.

The representative house of stormy Hokuroku is somewhat more substantially constructed than in most of subtropical Japan. Heavy board siding is conspicuous. Thatched roofs are less numerous, being replaced by roofs of heavy wooden shingles weighted down by cobblestones. Usually the roof is asymmetrical with the shorter slope facing the

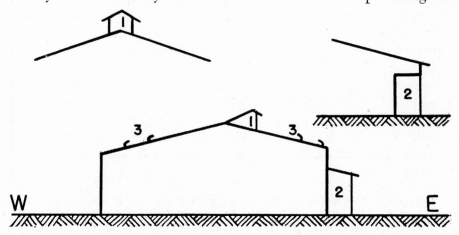

FIG. 215. Unique features of house construction are characteristic of snowy Hokuroku. After Yasuda.

thoroughfare. This arrangement lessens the danger of large masses of snow sliding into the street. It is also a common practice to place on the roof some kind of barrier or obstruction to anchor the snow. These *nadedome*, as they are called, may take the form of a row of hooked tile on tile roofs or of long wooden cleats on thatch roofs (Fig. 215).[20] On the

---

[19] Hall, "Some Rural Settlement Forms in Japan," *op. cit.*, 112.

[20] Hatuo Yasuda, "The Landscape of the City of Takada, Niigata Prefecture" (in Japanese with English summary), in the *Geographical Review of Japan*, 15:509–523 (January, 1939).

shingle roofs cobblestones serve the same purpose. Another fairly common feature of the roofs in this region of heavy snow and much dark winter weather is the *takamado*, a kind of skylight which rises well above the roofline and serves to bring additional light into the house (Fig. 215).[21] Because of the strong westerly winds, frequently accompanied by driving snow, the *takamado* usually face east. In many of the older towns in those areas where the snow accumulates to a depth of more than 50 centimeters, the houses in streets with shops are equipped with *gangi*, the wide board awnings or overhangs which allow the easy passage of pedestrians (Fig. 215). This feature seems to be gradually disappearing, however.

Agriculture in Hokuroku also has certain distinguishing features. Because the lowlands are poorly drained, they are more specialized in rice than are the plains in most parts of the country (Fig. 94). Thus whereas in Japan as a whole paddy fields occupied not quite 53 per cent of the total cultivated area in 1939, in Niigata Prefecture 75 per cent was so utilized. In Hokuroku rice is not only the principal food crop but the important cash crop; large amounts leave the region annually for the markets in the great urban industrial areas on the Pacific side of Honshu. On such naturally inundated plains the problem of irrigation is simple, but deep flooding frequently does great damage to the rice. A conspicuous feature of these wet plains that specialize in rice are the rows of small dwarf trees, commonly water oaks, that are planted along the footpaths and the irrigation and drainage canals (Fig. 216). The lower branches have been removed so that usually all that remains is a small crown of foliage at the top. On these *hasagi*, the rice is hung to dry after it is harvested,[22] for the heavy fall rains make portions of the plains so wet that ordinary methods of drying are unsuitable. In the most deeply inundated areas only the tallest varieties of rice can be grown, and frequently the harvesting must be done by boat. Small elevated platforms are built in each paddy on which the rice is stacked as it is cut.[23] Undrained marshy areas are commonly cropped to lotus.

What dry fields there are on the Hokuroku plains are chiefly confined to such dry points as the belts of beach ridges and dunes along the seaward margins, to relict forms of the same origin farther inland, and to the serpentine levees of present-day streams or those marking the

[21] *Ibid.*, 514, 523.
[22] Hatuo Yasuta, "Distribution of Hasagi in Hokuroku District" (in Japanese with English summary), in the *Geographical Review of Japan*, 16:657–672 (October, 1940).
[23] Hall, "Agricultural Regions of Asia, Part VII: The Japanese Empire," *op. cit.*, 336.

courses of abandoned meanders. Apparently vegetables constitute the principal crops in the dry fields. Soybeans are relatively important and small amounts of cereals and tea are grown. The Niigata region is about the northern limit of tea cultivation, however, and since winter cropping is not common in most parts because of the heavy snow and the poor drainage of the plains, unirrigated cereals are not widely planted. Mulberry growing, and the silk industry in general, is less important in Hokuroku than in central and eastern Japan.

The Echigo or Niigata Plain (Subregion 1) is the largest area of compact new alluvium in all Japan. It is the product of the Shinano River, the longest in Nippon, and a number of smaller streams fed by the heavy precipitation in the high mountains to the south and east. The plain is coincident with the greatest population nucleus north of latitude 37°. Occupying in part a fault basin, and having a belt of parallel beach ridges and dunes one to three miles wide along its sea margins, the lowland is poorly drained and contains a considerable area of swamp and shallow lake. Across its flat surface wander numerous large and small streams, the story of whose shifting courses can be read in the scars of old channels and the oxbow lakes. At the city of Niigata on the coast, partly because it lies to the leeward of hilly Sado Island, and partly because the plain is relatively wide, the snow cover is less deep than at any weather bureau station along the northwest coast. Interior some distance, and therefore closer to the hill lands and mountains where the polar air masses of the winter monsoon are thrust abruptly upward, the snowfall is much heavier and the snow cover much deeper.

Like a series of giant corrugations, the dozen or more parallel beach ridges 20–25 meters high, with their intervening wet, trough-like lowlands, form the widest belt of wave- and wind-deposited materials along the plains of Hokuroku and western Ou (Fig. 208). The outer ridges are often dune-capped, and fence-like windbreaks are necessary in some places to prevent the drifting of sand. Large areas are planted with a cover of trees, which performs the dual service of anchoring the loose sand and protecting the settlements from strong sea winds. A distinctly linear arrangement of the culture features prevails. Rice and some Japanese-pear orchards occupy the wet parallel lowlands; the intervening sandy ridges, where these are not in woods, are the sites of villages and dry crops, vegetables being prominent, especially such sand-tolerant ones as melons, legumes, and tubers (Fig. 217). On the ocean side of the last ridge the wide expanse of sloping beach is also in vegetables (Fig. 218). In contrast to some of the other plains, the drier and less snowy north-

FIG. 216. A poorly drained Hokuroku plain with *hasagi*.

FIG. 217. Rice occupies the low poorly drained lagoon plain in the foreground. The beach ridge beyond is specialized in unirrigated crops. Echigo Plain.

FIG. 218. The outermost portion of the Echigo Plain, seaward from the westernmost dunes. The Japan Sea is visible in the background. Vegetable crops are grown on the very sandy soils.

western Echigo has an appreciable acreage of fall-sown wheat and barley, which occupy its unirrigated fields during the cool season.

The settlements of this coastal subdivision of the Echigo Plain bear the earmarks of poverty. Often they are only loose agglomerations of huts without well defined streets, completely hedged in by walls of bamboo trees. Compact villages are by no means lacking, however. Where there are no windbreaks and there is less protection from strong winds, stone-weighted roofs are common. Among the vegetable patches in many of the coastal villages wells with great wooden sweeps are conspicuous, reflecting the necessity for artificial watering of these porous sandy soils.

On the poorly drained lowland back of the belt of beach ridges is one of the greatest rice-growing areas of Japan. Because of the wetness of the plain, yields are high, although the grain is not of the highest quality, being somewhat soft. Along the field margins, rows of bare poles or small trees with only tufts of foliage at their tops serve as supports upon which to hang bundles of rice or rice straw to dry. An early-maturing, glutenous type of rice called *mochi*, which is used for pastry, is extensively planted, and by early August the ripening fields of this variety are conspicuous by reason of their yellowish color. Low isolated remnants of beach ridges rise slightly above the alluvium in some places, and these dry sites become islands of upland crops in the midst of the paddies. Irregularities representing abandoned stream courses, as well as riparian belts of variable width along the present diked streams, are also the sites of unirrigated crops. In the vicinity of villages, small artificially elevated plots of vegetables, fruit, and mulberry are conspicuous.

Compact villages, many of them small and tree-enclosed, are the prevailing settlement form on the new alluvium. *Strassendorf* types are especially common, paralleling highways on the wet plains and occupying dry sites along the dikes of streams, relict levees, and the low remnants of beach ridges. The numerous villages, often protected by hedges and trees, and the rows of trees along rivers, canals, and even some field boundaries preclude extensive vistas.

The city of Niigata (150,903) occupying both sides of the Shinanogawa near its mouth, is located in the midst of the beach ridges. Canals and bridges are numerous. Its hinterland includes not only the immediate Echigo Plain, the largest in northern Japan, but the adjacent productive Tertiary hill country and the northern grabens of the Fossa Magna. Most conspicuous among the city's industrial plants is an oil refinery and its storage tanks, for Niigata is the outlet for the nearby Echigo oil fields. Associated with the industry are the repair shops for the oil field machinery and equipment. There is also an engine works and a metal-industry plant. Situated as it is on a silting river mouth, exposed to serious floods and to strong winter winds, Niigata is seriously handicapped in ocean shipping, although it is the ranking port of the Japan Sea coast of Honshu. Large boats lie at anchor in the open roadstead and discharge by lighters; small ones enter the river. In winter the larger vessels avoid Niigata and use instead the supplementary port of Ryotu (Ebisu) on Sado Island. The port is primarily engaged in coastal trade, the principal domestic exports being rice and petroleum. Its foreign trade, chiefly with

TABLE 137.—FOREIGN TRADE OF NIIGATA, 1938

Exports in Yen		Imports in Yen	
Machinery and parts	1,067,290	Oils, fats and waxes	4,529,951
Lumber and wood	554,135	Coal	2,285,689
Sulphur	420,423	Bean cake	2,066,035
Minerals	323,602	Logs and lumber	1,761,615
Mandarin oranges	213,468	Soy beans	1,567,922
		Sulphate of ammonia	1,080,450
Total, including others	4,241,869	Phosphorite	622,996
		Fodder	523,995
		Wheat bran	520,518
		Total, including others	16,123,313

Source: *Annual Return of the Foreign Trade of Japan*, pt. 3 (Department of Finance, Tokyo, 1938)

Asiatic countries, amounted in 1938 to only 20.4 million yen. Almost 80 per cent of this represented imports, chiefly petroleum, coal, and bean-cake. Machinery and lumber constitute the chief foreign exports. Two other cities of over 25,000 population, Nagaoka (66,987) and Sanjo (36,541), have interior locations on the Echigo Plain.

The Takata Plain (Subregion 2).—Although much less extensive, the Takata Plain in most respects closely resembles the Echigo, its larger northern neighbor. Snows are very heavy, especially toward the interior, as the lowland narrows toward the mountains. This seems to be the approximate southern limit of the *gangi* or covered sidewalks. Naoetsu is a minor port of call for coastwise steamers. It exports considerable oil produced in the adjacent Tertiary hills, and imports not only for the immediate plain but for the northern basins of the Fossa Magna. The metropolis of the plain, Takata (30,152), is an inland city. Kashiwazaki, on the coast between the Niigata and the Takata Plain, is of some importance for its electrochemical industries.

The Etchu Alluvial Piedmont (Subregion 3).—Of all the coastal low-lands of Hokuroku and western Ou, the Etchu or Toyama Plain just to the east of Noto Peninsula is the one that is untypical: 1. Unlike the others, which are all low, wet, filled lagoons, it is composed of a series of fairly steep alluvial and diluvial fans which form an extensive alluvial piedmont belt. 2. The usual wide belt of parallel beach ridges and dunes along the seaward margins is lacking. 3. There is a remarkable development of dispersed rural settlement.

Toyama is a bay-head plain partially occupying a depressed block between Noto Peninsula and Honshu proper. The lack of a marked belt of beach ridges and dunes along the outer margins of the plain is due to (1) the deep waters of Toyama Bay and (2) a weakening of the strong winter winds and waves as a result of the protection offered by Noto Peninsula.[24] It is probable that the high Hida Range immediately to the rear of Toyama, with its heavy precipitation, numerous short vigorous streams, and abundance of fluvial materials, largely accounts for the well developed alluvial-diluvial piedmont belt.[25] Coarse diluvial sediments in the form of fans and benches at various levels, resting unconformably upon Tertiary prongs, characterize the inner margins of the plain. In some places relatively broad and smooth depositional surfaces still persist; in others stream erosion has produced roughened surfaces. Conspicuous cliffs, providing excellent cross-sections of assorted fluvial materials, are not infrequent, but gradual transitions from one level to another are more common. Red loams resulting from a weathering of the diluvial sands and gravels cover these older deposits.

The new fans, also composed of coarse stony materials, and resting upon eroded diluvium or upon Tertiary surfaces, merge along their upper slopes with the older formations without a very perceptible disconformity. Broad boulder-strewn stream courses containing vigorous rivers occupy both fan-crest and inter-fan areas. Scars of old stream channels testify to river vagaries. Toward the sea margins the conspicuous crescentic or scalloped arrangement of features which is characteristic of compound fans gives way to a flattish plain.

On the steeper alluvial fans of Toyama the completely dispersed settlement type, with the individual isolated farmstead as the unit of occupance, is the rule (Fig. 220).[26] This feature is most perfectly developed in the

[24] Conversations with Mr. Harada, geographer at the normal school in Toyama.

[25] A. Watanabe, "Consideration of the Elevated Delta-Fans of Japan" (in Japanese), in the *Geographical Review of Japan*, 5:1–13 (January, 1929).

[26] Isamu Matui, "Statistical Study of the Distribution of Scattered Villages in Two Regions of the Tonami Plain, Toyama Prefecture" (in Japanese), in the *Japanese Journal of Geology and Geography*, 9:251–266 (March, 1932). See the valuable bibliography on page 251.

upper part of the western fans in the vicinity of Fukuno, where the individual farmstead is the only form of settlement outside a few fairly large market towns. There appears to be no system or pattern in the arrangement of the residences. Each house is hidden in a tall hedge of conifers which completely surrounds and protects it against the sea winds and the downcast foehns which arrive from the interior. From an elevated vantage point the fan appears to be dotted with tiny groves, so hidden are the farmsteads in foliage (Fig. 220). In such regions of disseminated population it is common for peddlers to carry provisions from the market town to the rural farmstead. Gradually, as the fans flatten out upon approaching the sea, small agglomerations become more prominent at the expense of isolated farmsteads, until finally on the flattish ocean margins of the lowland little rural villages are the rule. In most cases the hamlets and villages, like the individual farmsteads, are hedge-enclosed.

As noted earlier, dispersed settlement in Japan often indicates relatively recent occupance. Retarded settlement on the steeper, coarser parts of fans is probably attributable to the stony infertile soils and the flood hazards associated with vagrant rivers. But here again Toyama seems to be the exception. From a study of old maps Dr. Ogawa concludes that the scattered rural residences are not indications of recent occupance, but relict features associated with the ancient *jori* system of land division in which one cho (2.45 acres) was the common unit of landholding. It has become a tradition in the Toyama area for a farmer to cultivate a single block of land, which he owns or perhaps partly owns, in the immediate vicinity of his dwelling. Dr. Ogawa further suggests that the

FIG. 219. The braided channel of one of the Toyama rivers. An irrigation canal at its point of origin in the left foreground.

FIG. 220. Isolated farmsteads, each enclosed by a wall of trees, dot the upper portion of the Toyama Piedmont. View looking seaward from a higher diluvial level.

strong foehn winds descending from the Hida Range and the attendant fire hazards may help to explain the persistence of isolated farm residences.[27]

The *gangi* or enclosed sidewalk is not known in this region, although the roofs of thatched houses are steeply pitched to prevent deep accumulations of snow. Tile and shingle roofs are less steep, their greater conductivity permitting the snow to melt off. Two cities, Toyama (127,859), a feudal castle town and the present political capital of the prefecture, and Takaoka (59,671) are the commercial centers. Toyama contains an aluminum smelter and a metal-manufacturing plant. The smooth coastline of the plain offers little in the way of natural harbors; the local port of the lowland, Fushiki, occupies a river mouth site adjacent to the southeastern margin of Noto Peninsula.

More exclusively than the terrain features would lead one to expect, rice is the dominant crop in the Toyama region; so much so that large amounts are exported to other parts of Japan. Not only on the lower, flatter areas are paddies conspicuous, but even on the higher parts of the fans and the crests of the diluvial terraces, where, however, mulberry, vegetables, and even woodland, offer competition. Only small amounts of wheat and barley are grown as winter crops. Since stones are prominent on the fans, many of the farmsteads are surrounded by low walls of smooth, water-worn boulders, and the retaining walls of the terraced paddies are similarly constructed. What with the numerous tree-enclosed, isolated farmsteads and small villages, and the lines of trees along roads and waterways, the plain has a disordered appearance and affords no wide vistas.

The Kaga Plain West of Noto Peninsula (Subregion 4).—Physically and culturally the relatively narrow strips of alluvium west of Noto Peninsula have more in common with the Echigo and Takata plains and with those of western Ou than with Toyama. Essentially they are filled lagoons, still poorly drained in some places, whose seaward margins, unprotected by Noto Peninsula, have wide belts of parallel beach ridges and dunes with smooth harborless coastlines. Where fan configuration is conspicuous, lagoon features are lacking and the belt of beach ridges is narrower. The vigorous winter winds and associated waves and currents of the Japan Sea littoral not only produce conspicuous shoreline features, but result in such characteristic culture forms as dense windbreaks around the settlements, boulder-covered house roofs, and piles of kindling and firewood anchored securely to the ground. Small compact settlement

[27] *Nippon Chiri Taikei,* 1930, vol. 6B, p. 267.

units, tree-enclosed, are most common. On the elevated sandy belt back of the protective rows of conifers which cap the outermost of the beach ridges, considerable areas are planted to unirrigated crops, especially vegetables and mulberry. Similar cropping practices are common on the fragments of diluvial terrace which border the Tertiary hills to the rear of the plain. On the poorly drained lagoon plain, rice almost monopolizes the cultivated land.

Kanazawa (186,297), the metropolis of this plain and of the entire west coast of Honshu, was for three centuries the feudal capital of one of the greatest and richest daimyos. Today it is the capital of Ishikawa Prefecture, headquarters of the Ninth Army Division, located in the castle grounds, and center of an important silk-weaving industry. Fukui (97,967), another castle town farther down the coast, is still more famous as a silk-weaving center (Fig. 221). Nor is the industry confined to these two cities. In the smaller towns as well, small weaving plants abound, making these lowlands west of Noto Peninsula in Ishikawa and Fukui prefectures the country's foremost center of silk-cloth production (Fig. 130). This specialization in the fabricated product is not based upon large-scale cocoon production in the immediate hinterland, but is rather an inheritance

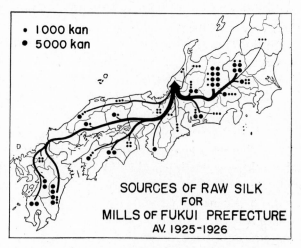

FIG. 221. The Fukui silk-weaving industry draws its raw material from much of southwestern Japan. One kan = 8.27 pounds. From *Nippon Chiri-Fuzoku Taikei*.

from the feudal past. Fukui Prefecture is also an important producer of rayon, and within the last two decades many of the small establishments in the Kaga region which formerly made silk cloth have become producers of rayon cloth and of silk-and-rayon mixtures.

At the point where the Saikawa River breaks through the dune barrier is situated the little river-mouth port of Kanaiwa. Its harbor is of little value, being too shallow even for some coastwise ships. In winter it is quite useless. Of much more importance is the port of Fushiki on Noto Peninsula, with which the Kanazawa hinterland is connected by rail.

The Tertiary Hill Land of Hokuroku (including Noto Peninsula and Sado Island (Subregion 5).—Surrounding the plains of Hokuroku and forming an intermediate step between them and the high mountains to the rear is a mass of hilly land, composed of a series of blocks with intervening fault valleys, whose general trend is northeast-southwest. A local relief of 200–400 meters is common. For the most part dissection has been fairly complete, and hence settlement is relatively dense for a hill region, both compact and dispersed forms being numerous. In some places the upland slopes are relatively mild, and here there is considerable cultivated land, terraced paddies being intermingled with dry fields. Artificial ponds for irrigation are numerous. A very complicated dendritic pattern of paddy land coincides with the valley floors. The wider graben valleys contain much fan material and conspicuous river terraces, thus resembling the fault basins of the Fossa Magna. Similarly, also, mulberry is a very important crop.

In the Tertiary hills bordering the Echigo Plain is Japan's second most important oil field, although it is insignificant in world production. For several years after 1931 the output of the Niigata wells declined sharply, but since 1935 the prospects in the Niitsu and the Higashiyama centers have looked brighter and in 1939 new drilling derricks were set up there.[28] In 1935 there were seven active producing centers in the Niigata field. There are two refinery and cracking-plant units, one at Niigata and the other at Kashiwazaki, 70 or 80 kilometers down the coast from Niigata.

Noto Peninsula, which forms the principal irregularity of the northwest coast of Honshu, is a low, warped dome having faulted margins in some places. A narrow graben valley, alluvium-floored and covered with rice fields, divides the peninsula into a northern and a southern half. The highest elevations, close to the north coast and along the faulted margin of the southern upland overlooking the graben valley, barely exceed 500 meters. Average elevations are 200–300 meters. The valleys, developed in intricate dendritic patterns, are given over almost exclusively to paddy rice. On upland sites where slopes are not too steep, terraced, pond-irrigated paddies are intermingled with dry fields.[29] Dispersed settlements are common. The indented coasts of Noto contain numerous fishing villages, as well as two important local ports, Fushiki and Nanao, which

[28] "Das japanische Mineralölwirtschaft," in *Wirtschaft und Statistik*, 21:138 (April, 1941).

[29] K. Tanabe, "A Morphological Study of Cultivated Land on Noto Peninsula" (in Japanese), in the *Geographical Review of Japan*, 16:396–411 (June, 1940).

serve the adjacent plains, whose smooth coasts provide no satisfactory natural harbors. Fushiki, at the northwestern extremity of the Toyama Plain, where it makes contact with Noto, can accommodate boats of 3,000 tons at its quays. Its chief domestic export is rice, reflecting the principal specialization of the adjacent Toyama Plain, which is its main hinterland. Its domestic coastwise traffic is valued at several times its foreign trade. The latter in 1938 amounted to 17.2 million yen, imports being from four to five times the value of exports. Ores and metals constitute the single greatest import of foreign origin; and coal, bean-

TABLE 138.—FOREIGN TRADE OF FUSHIKI, 1938

Exports	Amount in Yen	Imports	Amount in Yen
Calcium carbide.	889,787	Ores and metals	5,105,720
Lumber and wood.	409,362	Coal	2,520,330
Metals.	360,900	Beancake	1,277,631
Printing paper	136,973	Flax	1,129,307
Shirting	124,596	Logs	1,106,904
Machinery	112,036	Sulphate of ammonia	766,750
		Phosphorite	627,644
Total, including others. . .	3,033,295	Salt	406,847
		Soybeans	246,641
		Total, including others . . .	14,220,569

Source: *Annual Return of the Foreign Trade of Japan*, pt. 3 (Department of Finance. Tokyo,1938).

cake, flax, and logs follow in the order named. Nanao, strategically located at the eastern end of Noto Graben and, like Fushiki, protected by the peninsula, is connected by rail with Kanazawa and its productive Kaga Plain hinterland, which region it serves as a port. Ships of about 3,000 tons can draw alongside the pier, where the water is six meters deep. In 1938 its total foreign trade amounted to little more than a quarter million yen, imported phosphorite comprising 75 per cent of the total. Nanao's coastwise trade is much greater.

Sado Island (Subregion 5),[30] lying thirty-two miles offshore from Niigata and the Echigo Plain, owes its peculiar anvil shape to the fact that it is composed of two parallel ranges of hill land and mountain separated by a depression floored with deposits of old and new alluvium. The maximum elevation exceeds 1,100 meters. Where Tertiary rocks prevail there are extensive upland surfaces of low relief, but in the regions of andesite and liparite, sharp, angular forms predominate. Con-

[30] Robert Burnett Hall, "Sado Island," in the *Papers of the Michigan Academy of Science, Arts, and Letters*, 16(1931):275–297.

spicuous marine erosion terraces border that part of the coast where hills come down to tidewater. A large proportion of the more than 100,000 inhabitants are concentrated on the alluvial floor of the central graben plain and along the shores of the island. Rice is the great crop of the central lowland, and more than a fourth of the annual output is exported. Rice is also grown on the marine terraces bordering the mountain coasts and in the valleys of the short streams descending from the highlands. Next to agriculture fishing is the mainstay of the population, and coastal settlements engaged in both agriculture and fishing are numerous. The Aikawa gold and silver mine in Sado has been producing for nearly 350 years and as late as 1936 the output was still important, although it was exceeded by nearly a score of other mines in Japan. The little port of Ryotu (Ebisu) at the eastern end of the central plain is a supplementary winter "outport" for Niigata. Its total foreign trade in 1938 was only 259,000 yen, all of it being imported petroleum.

CHAPTER XIII

Tokai: the Pacific Side of Chubu

THIS subdivision of central Japan (Region C, Fig. 198) includes the Kwanto or Tokyo Plain at its northeastern extremity and the Nobi or Nagoya Plain (sometimes called the Mino-Owari Plain) at its southwestern limits. Between these two relatively extensive lowlands lies a narrower coastal lowland region composed of smaller discontinuous alluvial and diluvial plains separated by spurs of hill land. The region embraces some of the heartland of Japan, notably the nation's capital, three of its six metropolitan centers, and two of its four great industrial nodes. Throughout its length ran feudal Japan's greatest highway, the Tokaido. Today this old route is approximately paralleled by the double-tracked Tokaido railway and the modern Tokaido motor highway.

THE KWANTO OR TOKYO PLAIN

This largest lowland of Nippon (Subregion 1), embracing about 13,000 square kilometers or slightly over 5,000 square miles, is also coincident with the country's greatest compact population cluster. As of about 1940 over 15 million persons, or about 21 per cent of the population of Japan Proper, lived on the Kwanto Plain. The plain, which occupies a tectonic depression, is composed of unconsolidated fluvial, estuarine, and marine deposits in alternating clay, sand, and gravel strata, totaling several hundred meters in thickness. Overlying the water-laid sediments are several meters of subaerially or shallow-water deposited volcanic ash. Until recent geological times the southern margin of the Kwanto depression was a continuous east-west highland composed of Tertiary rocks, for the Uraga channel entrance to Kwanto and Tokyo Bay is the result of recent subsidence.

Physical Characteristics

Emergence and elevation of the sediments has not been symmetrical; the plain gradually increases in elevation from the center, where it is scarcely 20 meters high, to elevations of 30 to 50 meters along the seaward margins, and to still greater heights toward the west, where fan configuration is conspicuous. Cross-valley profiles show steep terraces, indicating haltings during emergence. Rivers have cut broad valleys into the uplifted diluvial sediments, and later depression of the land has transformed these into estuaries, which have ultimately been filled. Long estuarine remnants of swamp and lake still persist along the lower stream courses. The most recent crustal movement has been a slight uplift that has produced along the sea margins narrow belts of new coastal plain with smooth coastlines. These coastal strips are bordered on their land sides by wave-cut diluvial cliffs or headlands which, turning inland along the rivers, form the margins of the floodplains. Generally speaking, Kwanto is a relatively uniform plane surface ending in more or less continuous steep bluffs along the river valleys and the narrow coastal strips. Only along these steep bluffs is the ash cover so thin as to expose the diluvial beds of sand and gravel. The peculiar double-crescent configuration of the eastern coast is the result of a rock sill forming the projecting point known as Cape Inubo.

In spite of active stream erosion, ash-covered diluvial terrace 20–50 meters above sea level still covers the larger part of Kwanto. This most extensive plain is distinctive among Japanese lowlands in that it is so

FIG. 222. Three distinct levels on Kwanto are here shown: (1) the low new alluvium of the floodplains; (2) the lower diluvial terrace, designated as *Musashino;* and (3) the higher and more dissected *Tama* terrace.

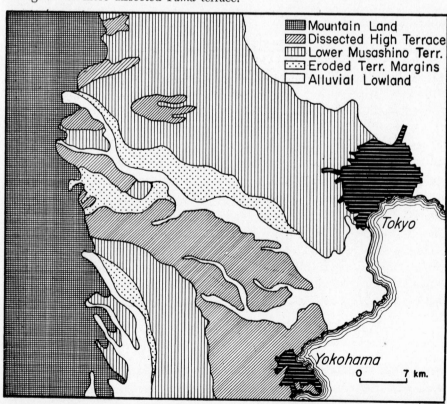

predominantly of old rather than of new alluvium. Japanese geographers recognize two general terrace levels separated from each other by a line of dislocation, (1) the higher Tama, and (2) the lower Musashino, terrace (Fig. 222). The latter, which covers much the larger part of the plain, consists of a series of wide, smooth, tabular surfaces, lying between broad, shallow, alluvium-filled valleys. Toward the mountain borders on the north and west the surface gradients steepen perceptibly and alluvial fan configuration is conspicuous. West of Tokyo Bay and south of the Tama River, which lies about midway between Tokyo and Yokohama, are remnants of the higher Tama terrace, whose altitudes approach 200 meters at the foot of the Kwanto Mountains, but descend eastward to approximately 30 meters elevation along the ocean margins. Smaller erosion buttes known as the Sayama and the Asayama Hills, resembling the Tama terrace, rise above the general low terrace level north of the Tama River. In general these higher terraces are maturely dissected and lack extensive smooth summit areas, which is the principal feature distinguishing them from the Musashino levels.[1] This higher Tama upland reaches the sea in the vicinity of Yokohama, where it terminates in precipitous cliffs (Fig. 222).

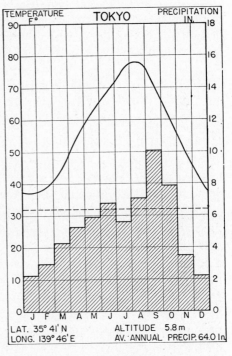

Fig. 223

Five contrasting landform types of Kwanto have been recognized: (1) the broad, shallow, alluvium-filled stream valleys, often with steep margins; (2) the low Musashino terrace; (3) the higher and more dissected Tama terrace; (4) diluvial fans at the base of the mountains; and (5) narrow belts of new coastal plain along the seaward margins of the plain.

Except the immature new alluvium, the soils of Kwanto are derived chiefly from weathered volcanic ash which mantles the diluvial sediments.

[1] "Fossil-Localities in the Environs of Kioroshi," in *Guide-Book Excursion C-6* (Pan-Pacific Science Congress, Tokyo, 1926); "Kamakura and Enoshima," in *Guide-*

They are emphatically ruddy in color, except perhaps for a humus-impregnated veneer; they vary in texture from loams to clays, and are relatively infertile, having been leached of the soluble plant foods. Virgin ash soils yield only low returns. Because of the presence of active colloidal substances they are able to imbibe and retain large amounts of water. which in years of excessive rainfall makes them wet and soggy even to the point of injuring crops.[2]

Cultural Features

Considering the long period of Japanese history, the occupance of Kwanto has been both recent and relatively slow. When Japanese culture attained its fruition ten centuries ago in Nara and Kyoto, old national capitals in the Kinki region, Kwanto was still in large part a wilderness known as Musashino. It was not until the latter part of the sixteenth century, when Yedo, now Tokyo, was made the residence of the ruling Tokugawa princes, that development of the adjacent lowland was markedly accelerated. The predominance of infertile, ash-covered diluvial upland, whose soil and relief characteristics are not well suited to irrigated rice, is the chief cause for the retarded settlement of the largest plain of Nippon. In addition, the diluvial terraces of Kwanto are notoriously deficient in water, which has further discouraged their use for agriculture.[3] Even today, although Kwanto, because it is the largest of the lowlands, has the greatest population cluster in Japan, the general density of settlement is probably no more than half as great as that of other important plains along the Pacific coast, which are predominantly of low, fertile, easily irrigated new alluvium. Large areas of Kwanto's flattish diluvial uplands still have a cover of planted woodland or wild grasses.

The Rural Land Utilization of Kwanto.—Low-level occupance of the floodplains and high-level occupance of the more elevated diluvial terraces, marked by contrasting land-use features, is distinctive of Kwanto (Fig. 224). It is on the low floodplains and deltas with their superior soils

Book *Excursion C-5* (Pan-Pacific Science Congress, Tokyo, 1926); H. Yabe, "Geological Growth of the Tokyo Bay," in *Bulletin of the Earthquake Research Institute* (Tokyo Imperial University), vol. 9 (1931), pt. 3, pp. 333–339; H. Yabe and R. Aoki, "The Great Kwanto Earthquake of September 1, 1923, Geologically Considered," in the *Annual Report of Saito Gratitude Foundation* (Sendai, Japan), No. 1, May, 1926, pp. 70–83.

[2] T. Seki, "Distribution of Volcanic Ash Loams in Japan Proper and Their Characteristics and Agricultural Value," in the *Proceedings of the Third Pan-Pacific Science Congress*, Tokyo, 1926, 2:1936–1941.

[3] G. Imamura, N. Yazima, and Y. Tuzimoto, "Underground Waters and Rural Habitations," in *Comptes Rendus du Congrès International de Géographie*, Amsterdam, 1938, vol. 2, sec. A, pp. 98–100.

and easy access to abundant irrigation water that the highest population densities are found. In such locations on Kwanto the ratio of people to area is similar to that on the other crowded lowlands (350–1,000 per square kilometer). The western half of Kwanto, therefore, which contains the larger share of the new alluvium, is the most crowded region, with the greatest concentration of population on a belt extending in a north-westerly direction from Tokyo along the complicated floodplain nets of the Tonegawa, Nakagawa, and a number of other closely spaced rivers.[4] Settlements on the new alluvium tend to be compact village units. Because of the swampy nature of the floodplains the rural villages are concentrated on dry sites (1) at the base of the diluvial uplands where they make contact with the floodplains or (2) along river levees and elevated highways. The location at the contact zone between alluvium and diluvium is advantageous not only because of the better drainage, but also because it gives the farmers in the village easy access to both the wet fields below and the dry fields above. Except for the riverine belts, where the elevation is slightly greater, surface irregularities more pronounced, and soils sandier, the low-level floodplains are largely devoted to irrigated rice. In the peri-urban belt adjacent to Tokyo and Yokohama there are numerous artificially elevated dry fields planted to vegetables. This is a part of the capital city's market-gardening zone. Much of the paddy land of Kwanto remains fallow after the rice harvest or has only a crop of *genge*, a green manure crop. In part this reflects the poorly drained nature of much of the Kwanto alluvium. It is also the result of intensive vegetable farming, which leaves the farmers little time for fall draining and cropping of their rice fields. In some of the recently reclaimed lands along the seaward margins of the larger deltas there are typical polder areas where master dikes enclose extensive areas of wet land devoted almost exclusively to rice. In such areas the rectangular fields laid out in grid patterns suggest the recency of reclamation. Where drainage is deficient, as it is in many places, the rural villages, characteristically situated on the dikes, are of shoestring form. Where better drainage permits, there are scattered isolated farmsteads; this feature, together with the rectangular arrangement of fields and roads, reminds one of paddy landscapes in Hokkaido.

The high-level or second-story type of occupance characteristic of the smooth, although not necessarily level, surfaces of the younger Musashino terraces is in contrast to that of the floodplains. Settlements are of both the dispersed and the agglomerated type. The isolated farmstead is the older

[4] Hidezo Tanakadate, "Topographical Analysis of Density of Population in Kwanto" (in Japanese), in the *Journal of Geography* (Tokyo), 50:541-555 (December, 1938).

form and was a natural development, whereas the compact farm villages
are of later origin and were planned and fostered by the government of
the shoguns.[5] Since scarcity of drinking water offered the chief problem
to the settlers on the terraces, the early occupants located their farmsteads along the margins of the terraces, where shallow wells could provide the necessary water. In the interiors of the uplands, where water was
farther below the surface, government officials charged with village planning were forced to select sites where there were abundant sources of
underground water.[6]

A striking feature of the compact settlements on the terrace uplands is
the large number of long, narrow, shoestring villages, composed of a row
of closely spaced dwellings on either side of and paralleling a highway
(Fig. 225). One comes to associate this form of settlement with elongated
dry sites such as river levees, beach ridges, and elevated highways on wet
paddy lands. On the Kwanto terraces, however, it appears to have its
origin in the difficulties of obtaining a sufficient water supply. Numerous
shoestring villages have no easily available source of subsurface water;
canals have therefore been built which carry underground water from
areas on the uplands, where wells are relatively abundant, to the sections
that are deficient in water. The canals tend to parallel the highways, with
the result that settlements become linear in form. The farms and fields
of the families occupying such villages are also linear, with their long
dimension at right angles to the highway and the village.[7] It is common
for such farms to show a definite belted arrangement of land use, mulberry occupying the fields next to the village, dry fields of vegetables and
grains lying beyond the mulberry, and woods or wasteland located at
still greater distances. The growing of the mulberry closest to the farm
home makes the picking and carrying of bulky fresh mulberry leaves a
less time-consuming job.[8] A conspicuous feature of settlements on many
parts of Kwanto is the dense hedges of planted trees surrounding many
of them. The isolated farmstead thus appears as a tiny grove of trees, and
the village takes on the appearance of a larger grove. In some sections
of Kwanto near Tokyo which have been studied, as many as 70 per cent
of the farmhouses had tree mantles, usually surrounding them on all sides.[9]

[5] G. Imamura, et al., op. cit., 300.   [6] Ibid., 99–100.

[7] Nikiti Yazima, "A Study of the Newer Settlements of the Musashino Upland" (in
Japanese with English summary), in the Geographical Review of Japan, 15 (1939):
807–821; T. Yamazaki, "Patterns of Settlement on Musashino Upland" (in Japanese),
in the Geographical Review of Japan, 9 (1933):766–774.

[8] T. Yamazaki, op. cit., 766–774.

[9] Taiji Yazawa, "On the Distribution of Wind Mantles in the Vicinity of Tokyo"
(in Japanese with English summary) in the Geographical Review of Japan, 12 (1936):

FIG. 224. Two-story occupance on the Kwanto Plain. Small irregular rice fields characterize the low alluvium. The higher diluvial upland is occupied by larger and more rectangular plots of dry crops and planted woodlands. A sinuous belt of woodland marks the escarpment between the two levels. From a folio of airplane photographs published by the Tetto-Shoin Publishing Company, Tokyo.

473

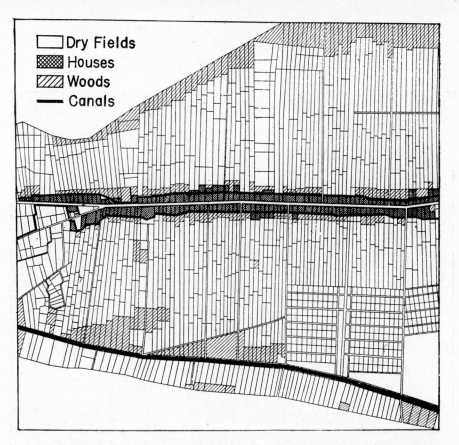

Fig. 225. A shoestring settlement on the lower terrace of Kwanto. A single row of houses fronts upon either side of the highway. At the rear of the houses pass the canals supplying the village with water. A hedge of trees flanks the village on the north and south. Beyond are the long fields with their long dimension at right angles to the highway. After Yazima.

The densest planting is on the north and west, which is the direction of the strong, cold winter winds.

Over the flattish upland surfaces of the lower terrace, paddy fields are very few. The dearth of water precludes a crop requiring inundation. Even now a large amount of the land on the terraces is uncultivated and given over to woods or left in tracts of moor-like waste. Much of the woodland appears to be planted, for the trees are small and arranged in geometric pattern (Fig. 224). But in spite of these non-cropped areas Kwanto is still the single largest compact region of unirrigated crops anywhere in Old Japan. The usual variety of unirrigated annuals common to subtropical Japan is characteristic here. Summer crops of vegetables,

47–66, 248–268. See also Ryukiti Ito, "Types and Functions of *Yasiki-mori* (Forest in Farmyard) on the Musashino Upland, Western Suburb of Tokyo" (in Japanese with English summary), in the *Geographical Review of Japan,* 15 (1939):624–642, 672–685.

beans, peas, sweet potatoes, millet, and buckwheat are followed by autumn-sown wheat and barley. In the suburban belts of Tokyo and Yokohama a very intensive rotation of corps by inter-tillage methods is practiced. To protect against frost and the cold northwest winds which

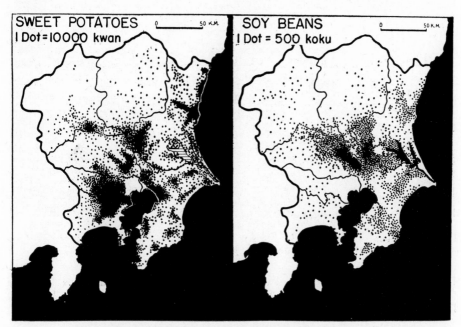

FIG. 226. Distribution of sweet potatoes and soybeans on Kwanto. From *Nippon Chiri-Fuzoku Taikei.*

often injure vegetable crops on Kwanto, ingenious coverings have been devised to shield the plants against cold and wind without shading them entirely from sunlight. Vegetables are also planted on the southern side of rows of barley, which offer protection against the northwest winds.[10] The steep margins of the terraces, where danger of wash is serious, usually have a woodland cover. Thus airplane views of Kwanto characteristically show a narrow sinuous belt of darker colored woodland marking the steep winding terrace margins, which serve as the boundary between the flood-plains with their small, irregularly shaped paddy fields and the diluvial uplands, characterized by a coarser and more rectangular dry-field layout (Fig. 224). Certain sections of the Kwanto terraces not only grow the usual food crops, but specialize in one or more commercial crops, some of them perennials (Fig. 226). Thus the uplands of western Kwanto are one of the country's most specialized regions of mulberry growing and silk produc-

[10] S. Sugai, "Forms of Cultivation in the Vicinity of Tokyo" (in Japanese with English summary), in the *Geographical Review of Japan*, 12 (1936):527–540.

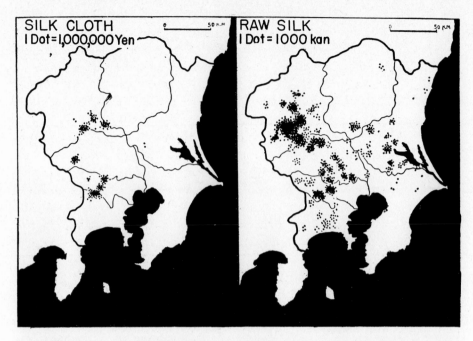

FIG. 227. Western Kwanto is highly specialized in the production of raw silk. One kan = 8.27 pounds. From *Nippon Chiri-Fuzoku Taikei.*

FIG. 228. Distribution of tea and tobacco on Kwanto. What mulberry and silk are to western Kwanto, tea and tobacco are to its eastern parts. One kan = 8.27 pounds. From *Nippon Chiri-Fuzoku Taikei.*

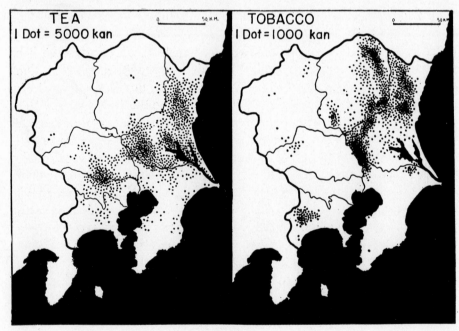

tion (Fig. 227). In certain sections mulberry appears to be the most important crop, occupying as much as 30–50 per cent of all the cultivated land. The central and eastern part of Kwanto is Japan's most important tobacco-raising district, Ibaraki and Tochigi prefectures having between a quarter and a third of the nation's tobacco acreage. Eastern Kwanto is also somewhat specialized in tea production (Fig. 228).

On the older, higher, and more dissected terraces of the Tama group, chiefly concentrated in southwestern Kwanto west of Tokyo Bay, the pattern of population distribution is in contrast to that on the younger terraces. Within the Tama terrace, where the character of the terrain is that of low hill country, settlements are markedly concentrated in the relatively narrow valleys. Both dispersed and compact forms of rural settlement are present. Paddy rice largely monopolizes the valley bottoms, and a composite sketch of the rice land exhibits an intricate dendritic pattern.

Unirrigated crops are cultivated to some extent on the slopes, but the larger part of the hill land is in woods or covered with wild grasses and shrubs.

On the more recently emerged strips of coastal lowland bordering the plain proper, settlements seek out the dry sites on the parallel lines of low beach ridges. Because of the considerable amount of low wet land, rice is an important crop and characteristically occupies the troughs between the sandy beach ridges. The latter in turn support crops of vegetables and mulberry, or are crowned with rows of trees which act as windbreaks and prevent the blowing of the sandy soil. This parallel arrangement of terrain and culture features is not everywhere prevalent on the new coastal plain.

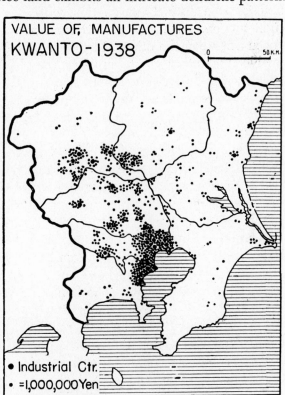

FIG. 229. From *Nippon Chiri-Fuzoku Taikei.*

Urban Units of Kwanto

Not only is Kwanto by far the largest node of population in Nippon, but it also far surpasses any other region in total urban population. Twenty-eight cities of over 25,000 population are located on Kwanto or its borders. Ten of these are under 50,000, fourteen between 50,000 and 100,000, one between 100,000 and 200,000, and one between 300,000 and 400,000. Two others, both on tidewater, rank among the nation's six metropolises (over 950,000 population): Tokyo, Nippon's capital and largest city, and Yokohama, one of the three greatest ports. Both are manufacturing centers of consequence and together comprise one of Japan's two greatest industrial nodes (Fig. 229). It needs to be emphasized that although Tokyo and Yokohama are separate political entities, in a very real sense they, together with Kawasaki, which is situated between them, comprise and function as a distinct conurbation, with a total population of more than eight million. Each unit of this combination is complementary to and dependent upon the others. In this respect Tokyo-Yokohama closely resembles that other great binuclear conurbation in Kinki, composed of Osaka and Kobe. In each combination the larger city functions principally as the main business and industrial center, the other as its deepwater port. In addition, Tokyo, to a greater extent than Osaka, is a political and administrative center.[11]

Although the Kwanto Plain, which is the immediate hinterland of Tokyo-Yokohama, is Japan's single greatest settlement unit, with over one-fifth of the country's inhabitants, the service area of these cities is by no means confined to that plain, but in a very genuine sense includes all of northern Japan. The almost complete absence of significant ports in northern Honshu testifies to the overshadowing influence of the Kwanto ports in that region. In radial pattern from this great *Keihin* urban center on Tokyo Bay, rail lines spread out across Kwanto, tapping the more distant hinterlands beyond. The famous Tokaido Line follows the coast to the southwest; two lines progress westward toward the Fossa Magna and beyond to the Hokuroku coast, so that Nagano silk is drawn off toward Yokohama. Other routes to the north tap the important meridional basins of Tohoku, also specialized in sericulture.

TOKYO

For reasons previously stated, Tokyo, formerly Yedo or Edo, remained an insignificant fishing village for centuries after Kyoto and Osaka, the

[11] L. Mecking, "Japans Seehafen und ihre neueste Entwicklung," in *Meerskunde,* vol. 26, no. 8.

great cities of the southwest, had reached maturity. It became a daimyo's headquarters in the mid-fifteenth century and a strongly fortified castle was erected on the site of the present Imperial Palace. But it was not until late in the sixteenth century, when Yedo became the capital of the usurping Tokugawa shoguns, who ruled the country for two and a half centuries, that rapid development of the city began. During this period Yedo was a vast military encampment with the nearly impregnable shogun's castle on a diluvial bluff overlooking the bay, and the fortress-like dwellings of the daimyos or feudal lords spread out on the floodplain below it. In its most prosperous days under the shoguns the population of the capital city exceeded a million. After the fall of the shoguns, Yedo's threatened decadence was averted when the restored Mikado made it his "East Capital" and renamed it Tokyo.

The capital city of Tokyo is located on shallow water at the head of Tokyo Bay. Up until 1932 the political city occupied only about 85 square kilometers and had a population of two million, but the inclusion acts of 1932 and 1936 have enormously increased Tokyo's area and population until at present it includes 577.9 square kilometers and in 1940 boasted a population of 6.8 million. It thus ranks fifth among the cities of the world in area and second only to New York in population. The city occupies two contrasting kinds of sites. Much of the eastern or commercial, business, and manufacturing portion of the city is located on low floodplain and delta sediments of the Sumida River; the western half, chiefly residential, is built on the summit and dissected margins of a diluvial upland whose crests are 20–40 meters above sea level. Relatively steep grades mark the transitions from one level to another. Considerable areas of recently reclaimed land border the bay. The moat- and wall-enclosed Imperial Palace, strategically located on the extreme eastern margin of the diluvial plateau, has been the core around which accretion has taken place and even yet it is near the geographical center of the modern city. The Imperial Palace is also the focal center of a cobweb pattern of urban transport lines. Even beyond the city limits these radial highways localize urban development in the form of modified *strassendorf* settlements, so that octopus form is conspicuous. Throughout the commercial and industrial sections, which occupy floodplain and delta sites, the city plan is somewhat more rectangular than in other parts. Canals and canalized rivers thoroughly intersect the lowland district, making hundreds of bridges necessary. Many of the buildings of downtown Tokyo are supported on piles.

As a result of the three-day fire following the earthquake of September

1, 1923, nearly half the city, largely the commercial and industrial section, was destroyed. The known dead numbered 58,104; 370,000 houses were destroyed; 38,824 persons were reported as missing or injured; the total property loss amounted to 3.7 billion yen, and the city's population declined by over 950,000. Such wholesale destruction had at least one good result; it permitted a thorough execution of a new city plan so that Tokyo between 1923 and 1930 became a city in metamorphosis, an Oriental city being remodeled on Occidental lines.

The fundamental idea underlying the reconstruction of Tokyo was to increase the ratio of street area to total city area. Prior to 1923 the aggregate area of streets was only 11.6 per cent of the city's area, but by 1930 it had been increased to 25 per cent, nearly as large a proportion as in Berlin and Paris. The remodeled street system, especially characteristic of the destroyed eastern half of the city, consists of two principal thoroughfares, one running north-south with a breadth of 33–44 meters and the other east-west with a breadth of 33–36 meters. These two arteries are crossed by 52 secondary main thoroughfares, each with a minimum breadth of 22 meters, and 112 auxiliary roads 11–22 meters wide. The blocks thus formed are crossed by a number of minor streets each 6–11 meters wide. Over 500 quakeproof and fireproof bridges were built. In the western residential section of Tokyo, located on the upland and out-

FIG. 230. Tokyo city planning map. By Tokyo Municipal Office, 1936.

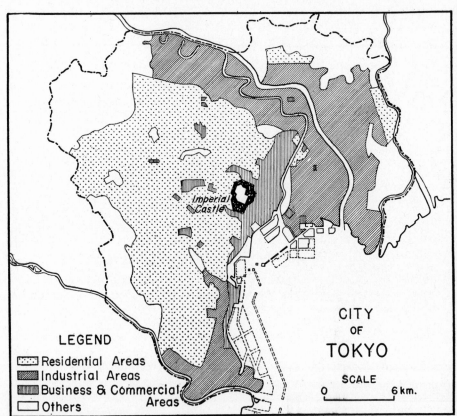

CITY
OF
TOKYO

SCALE

0   6 km.

LEGEND

Residential Areas
Industrial Areas
Business & Commercial
Others   Areas

Imperial
Castle

side the burned area and in the suburban districts, the cobweb pattern consisting of radial streets and girdling boulevards has been maintained as the basic pattern for whatever remodeling has been done. Within the burned sections, in addition to the remodeling of the street system, extensive replatting was undertaken, during the course of which over 203,000 buildings were moved, 14,400 meters of canals and river improved, and extensive areas of park established.[12]

The business or commercial core of the city occupies a north-south elongated strip of low-lying alluvial land bounded by the Sumida River and Tokyo Bay on the south and east, and by the diluvial uplands on the west (Fig. 230). It is in this section of Nippon's capital that Occidental influence has been felt most. New, modern, fireproof buildings four to eight stories in height with large display windows are numerous (Fig. 78). Taxis, busses, and tram cars crowd the streets. Smaller, isolated, but compact, business areas exist within the general manufacturing and residential areas, and throughout all parts of the city combination shops and residences seem to flank almost all of the principal streets and many of the secondary ones as well. Thus to a much greater extent than in American cities, the commercial pattern outside the core is coincident with the street pattern. Structures along such business streets are predominantly small open-front shops, with families living in the second stories or in the back rooms.[13]

Industrial Tokyo occupies two distinctly separate areas: (1) the larger and more important one east of the commercial district and between the Sumida and the Arakawa waterways, and (2) a less important area south of the commercial core along the west coast of Tokyo Bay. This is the northern end of a coastal manufacturing belt connecting Tokyo, Kawasaki, and Yokohama (Fig. 230).[14] By no means are these areas devoted exclusively to manufacturing, for they contain the homes of thousands of industrial workers, as well as local business centers and business streets. The manufacturing districts occupy low floodplain and coastal plain sites; factories are commonly located either along the Bay or on the canals and rivers draining into it (Fig. 231). Considerable portions of these industrial

[12] *Japan-Manchukuo Year Book,* 1940, p. 485; *Tokyo, Capital of Japan: Reconstruction Work, 1930* (Tokyo Municipal Office).

[13] H. Sasaki, "Reconnaissance of the City Center of Tokyo" (in Japanese), in the *Geographical Review of Japan,* 9:755–765 (September, 1933). See also Sinzo Kiuti, "A Study of the Landscape of Tokyo" (in Japanese with English summary), in the *Geographical Review of Japan,* 12 (1936):96–125.

[14] See map opposite page 52 in *Tokyo, Capital of Japan: Reconstruction Work, 1930* (Tokyo Municipal Office). See also Y. Takemi, "Distribution of Factories in Greater Tokyo" (in Japanese), in the *Geographical Review of Japan,* 6:369–386 (July, 1930).

Fig. 231. View across the Sumida River, over the industrial district of northeastern Tokyo. Numerous waterways, carrying much bulky freight, intersect the industrial areas. The large building along the river front is a brewery. Photograph by D. H. Davis.

districts are on reclaimed land along the margins of the Bay. To some degree, also, manufacturing plants are concentrated along the outer belt-line of railroad which encircles Tokyo on the west. Most decidedly the localization of factories has been influenced by availability of cheap transport facilities, particularly by water, even though only shallow draft barges can be accommodated on most of the rivers and canals of the industrial district. To an unusual degree the Tokyo industrial plants are served by water transportation, so that barges and lighters can unload fuel and raw materials at their very doors.

The total value of manufactural output in Tokyo Prefecture in 1938 was about 3.2 billion yen[15] and probably as much as 2.5 billion of this amount was from Tokyo City.[16] The capital city had become the greatest manufactural city of Nippon, even exceeding its rival, Osaka. Following the general national pattern, Tokyo experienced a remarkable expansion in manufacturing during the decade of the thirties and an equally remarkable change in industrial composition. Between 1931 and 1938 the value of Tokyo's manufactural output was more than tripled. Along with the swelling of the total volume and value of industrial production went a shift in emphasis from small-factory light industries to heavier industries housed in larger plants. As a result the industrial districts of Tokyo are more like an Occidental manufacturing district in appearance than they were in 1930. At the beginning of the 1930 decade Tokyo was largely a city of small industrial establishments; more so than Osaka was. The large

[15] *Kojo Tokeihyo*, 1938, p. 24.   [16] *Tokyo* (Tokyo Municipal Office, 1940), 41.

factory was the exception. Textiles were more important than metal and machine industries, and the metal industries that were important in Tokyo were chiefly those specializing in highly fabricated products that could be carried on successfully in smaller workshops.[17] But after 1932, when the country was launched on a policy of forcible expansion on the continent of Asia and heavy and strategic industries necessary for the prosecution of war were fostered by the government, even at the expense of consumer-goods industries, Tokyo obtained her share, if not more than her share, of these new war industries. Thus by 1938 the three ranking industrial groups in Tokyo were machines and tools, metals, and chemicals, with food manufactures fourth and textiles fifth. With this shift in manufactural emphasis large-scale factories became more and more conspicuous on the skyline of the factory districts, where previously small one-story buildings had been the rule.[18] The composition of Tokyo's industry and the importance of the leading industrial groups is shown in Table 139. The number of small industrial establishments is still a conspicuous feature in spite of the increase in larger plants.

TABLE 139.—THE INDUSTRIES OF TOKYO AT THE CLOSE OF 1937
(Excluding those with fewer than five operatives)

Kind of Industry	Number of Factories	Number of Workers	Value of Production (in thousands of yen)
Textile	1,232	38,468	191,856
Metal	2,854	62,941	537,112
Machines and tools.	4,597	169,709	712,586
Ceramic.	418	9,308	24,691
Chemical	1,385	42,994	468,591
Sawing and woodworking	672	9,301	33,794
Printing and bookbinding	1,114	24,993	126,098
Foodstuffs.	778	12,884	172,258
Total, including others	14,329*	403,093	2,404,519

Source: *The Japan Year Book*, 1940–41, p. 835.
* In addition there were 29,633 small establishments with fewer than five employees, whose total number of workers was 47,251.

The coastal industrial district of southern Tokyo in Shinagawa, Ebara, Omori, and Kamata wards is continued southward along the coast toward Yokohama in the Kawasaki industrial center. Kawasaki, a city of 300,777 in 1940, has grown with extraordinary rapidity during the past decade

[17] John Orchard, *Japan's Economic Position* (New York, 1930), 157–158.
[18] For a summary of some of the more important manufacturing plants with a strategic significance see T. E. Lloyd, "Kyushu and Honshu Islands, Focal Points of Japan's Industry," in *Iron Age*, April 30, 1942, pp. 83–94. See also "Design for Bombing Japan," in *Steel*, August 28, 1944, p. 115.

(114,294 in 1930), as a consequence of the concentration there of industrial enterprises of a strategic nature. Primarily it is a center of heavy industry with blast furnaces and steel mills, oil refineries, cement plants, great ship-building yards, chemical plants and the like.

Residential Tokyo, in contrast to the commercial and industrial sections, occupies chiefly upland locations in the western part of the city, but throughout its whole extent business streets are very numerous. Residential types are predominantly Japanese in architecture; only in certain newer sections do houses give evidence of foreign influence.

The Port.—Since Tokyo is at or near the mouths of several rivers at the head of a shallow silting bay, its harbor is so shallow that until recently it could accommodate only the smallest ships. This handicap led to the development of a deepwater port at Yokohama almost 20 miles down the bay; from Yokohama barges and lighters brought the discharged cargo to Tokyo. Within the past decade, however, important improvements of Tokyo's harbor have been made, and on May 20, 1941, the ports of Tokyo and Yokohama were combined into one port under the name of Keihin.[19] Yokohama is no longer listed as an open port and is replaced by the port of Keihin. Yokohama opposed the improvement of Tokyo's harbor and the amalgamation of the two ports into one, for it probably means that she will be robbed of some of her previous trade. Henceforth, however, Yokohama will chiefly accommodate overseas trade from more distant sources which arrives in large ships, while Tokyo will handle primarily commerce with Manchuria, China, and the Japanese Empire. A dredged channel 22,600 meters long, 600–700 meters wide, and 6.7–7.6 meters deep has been developed in the shallow waters of the bay

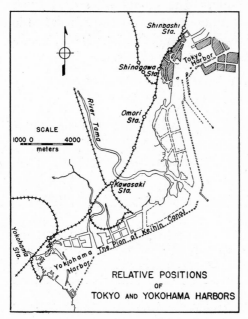

FIG. 232. From the *Far Eastern Review,* September, 1941.

[19] "The Port of Tokyo," in the *Far Eastern Review,* 38:42–44 (September, 1941). See also the *Geographical Journal,* 98 (1941):165.

between Yokohama and Tokyo (Fig. 232).[20] Vessels enter the new channel from off Yokohama. Ships of about 10,000 tons can navigate the dredged channel, although Tokyo harbor has been dredged only to accommodate ships of up to 6,000 tons. Two miles of quays have been constructed and ships of that size or under can come alongside and discharge their cargoes.[21] The forty-six mooring buoys in the harbor and the quays can accommodate 80 vessels of the 6,000-ton class at one time.[22] During 1938 the total tonnage of ships entering Tokyo harbor was 7.9 million. In 1922 the comparable figure was only 300,000 tons.[23] Being primarily a great consuming market and an important distributing center, it is to be expected that Tokyo port will import much more than it exports. Incoming cargo handled in 1938 amounted to 6.3 million tons, whereas exports were only 904,532 tons or one-seventh as much. Most of the incoming cargo is raw materials for industry, food, and semi-processed goods, items characteristic of a great industrial and population center. The total cargo tonnage handled through the port was about equal to the railway freight hauled into and out of Tokyo.[24]

YOKOHAMA

Yokohama is one of those few Japanese cities which had little or no contact with the feudal period, since it was called into existence by the exigencies of the modern era. Although only a fishing village of 350 population in 1859, when it was declared an open port, by 1940 it was a metropolis of 968,091, and one of the nation's three really great ports. Preeminently it is a port city and its growth has been closely associated with its expanding services as a foreign-trade port, not only for Tokyo and the Kwanto region, but for all of northern Honshu as well. Lying in a small indentation along the west side of Tokyo Bay, it has adequate depth of water and docking facilities to permit the largest Pacific boats to anchor alongside the piers (Fig. 232). Most freighters, however, anchor at buoys and load and unload with the aid of lighters.

The Port.—Before the earthquake and fire of 1923, which razed a fourth of the urban area, Yokohama was, by a slight margin, the ranking port of Japan. At least partly as a result of the catastrophe, many coasting vessels which had formerly docked at Yokohama proceeded directly to Tokyo, and Kobe succeeded in diverting to itself a portion of the Kwansai silk

[20] "The Port of Tokyo," *op. cit.*, 43.
[21] *Tokyo* (Tokyo Municipal Office, 1940), 58.   [22] "The Port of Tokyo," *op. cit.*, 43.
[23] *Far East Year Book*, 1941, p. 492.
[24] *Japan-Manchukuo Year Book*, 1940, p. 487.

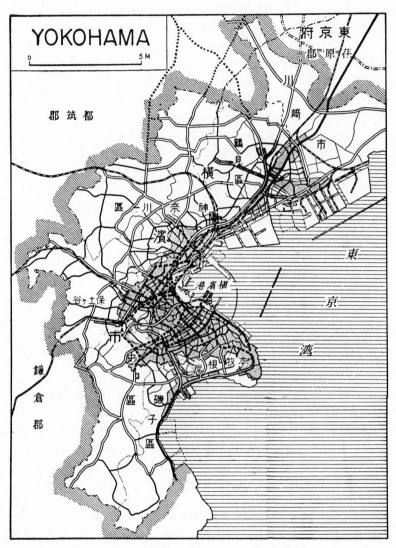

FIG. 233. The city of Yokohama is built around a small indentation in the coastline of western Tokyo Bay approximately twenty miles down the bay from Tokyo. Note the land that has recently been reclaimed for industrial expansion along the coast at the northern end of the city. From *Nippon Chiri-Fuzoku Taikei.*

export which had belonged to Yokohama.[25] As a result the Kwanto port dropped to second place, handling only 31 per cent of the country's foreign trade in 1929 as compared with 36 per cent for Kobe. In 1938, for the first time since 1923, Yokohama again forged into first position, which it had previously held for a decade and a half. Yokohama Port profited greatly from the important industrial expansion in the Kwanto region after 1932. Since as much as 70 per cent of the nation's silk exports

TABLE 140.—FOREIGN TRADE OF YOKOHAMA 1939

Exports	Value in Thousands of Yen	Imports	Value in Thousands of Yen
Raw silk	386,480	Machinery	152,005
Flour	30,075	Raw Cotton	37,740
Refined sugar	12,077	Beans	37,365
Canned food	52,706	Soybean cake	30,226
Copper	6,998	Gutta percha	22,972
Cotton yarn	7,396	Coal	17,164
Cotton cloth	6,961	Wool	13,436
Silk textiles	18,266	Leather	10,118
Rayon textiles	22,187	Lumber	9,932
Insulated wires	7,335	Phosphate rock	9,602
Rolling stock	33,310	Pulp	6,609
Machinery	63,224	Oil-extracting materials	6,015
Total, including all others	950,977	Total, including all others	929,127

Source: *Japan Advertiser Annual Review*, 1939–40, pp. 38, 63.

normally passed through Yokohama, that port had a trade in which exports consistently exceeded imports, at least before the marked decline in the raw silk trade starting in 1930. Beginning in 1934, when the industrial boom in the Kwanto region began to get under way, the scales tipped in favor of imports and in the six years following 1933 only two years showed an excess of exports and then by only trifling amounts. The expanded industrial structure of the Kwanto region has caused Yokohama to become increasingly important as a gateway of industrial raw and finished materials destined for its immediate manufactural hinterland and for central and northern Japan as well. Even the Nagoya industrial node is, to a considerable degree, served through Yokohama.

The composition of Yokohama's foreign trade for 1939, the last year for which statistics are available, is shown in Table 140. Clearly the Kwanto port is still Japan's, and even the world's, greatest silk port. In 1939 raw silk destined largely for the United States comprised 40 per cent of the

[25] It has been estimated that 60 per cent of the filatures of Japan are nearer to Yokohama than to Kobe.

value of outgoing cargo. This preponderance of raw silk in the export trade reflects the specialization of southern Tohoku and central Honshu, its natural trade territory, in sericulture. The third item in importance, canned food, was also for non-Asiatic markets, chiefly the United States and Europe. Machinery, rolling stock, flour, and refined sugar went chiefly to Yen-Bloc countries. Yokohama's imports were dominated by machinery, a cargo item largely originating in the United States.

TABLE 141.—YOKOHAMA'S TRADE BY PRINCIPAL COUNTRIES
(Value in thousands of yen)

Country	1938 Value	1939	
		Value	Percentage of Total for 1939
EXPORTS			
United States	277,956	412,466	43.4
Kwantung.	116,551	160,899	16.9
Manchuria	44,758	103,794	10.9
China.	47,892	79,009	8.3
England	45,426	49,832	5.2
India	22,659	26,046	2.7
Australia	17,131	18,365	1.9
France	21,792	16,230	1.7
IMPORTS			
United States	382,622	395,830	42.6
Manchuria	72,267	99,257	10.7
Germany	99,044	79,814	8.6
Canada	25,285	48,109	5.2
China	20,789	32,470	3.5
Dutch East Indies	28,974	22,502	2.4
India	21,237	19,999	2.2
Sweden	14,514	18,807	2.0
Straits Settlements	22,154	17,059	1.8
Kwantung.	9,638	12,399	1.3

Source: *The Japan Advertiser Annual Review*, 1939–40, p. 64.

To a much larger degree than is true of any of the other principal ports, Yokohama's trade is across the Pacific and with the United States. Over 43 per cent of her exports in 1939 were sent to the United States and nearly 43 per cent of her imports had their origin there. Yen-Bloc countries—Kwantung Leased Territory, Manchuria, and China—ranked next to the United States in receipts of Yokohama's exports, but this same group supplied much less of her imports.

Not only in foreign trade, but also in coastwise traffic does Yokohama rank high as a port. In 1938 the value of coastwise shipping at Yokohama was 76 per cent of its foreign trade, exports leading imports in the ratio of about 5 to 4. Domestic exports are made up of a large variety of goods with petroleum products, drugs and dyes, minerals, and metals leading in the order named. Domestic imports represent fewer types of products, metals and minerals and their manufactures comprising 56 per cent of the total by value, and beverages, food, and tobacco adding another 15 per cent.[26] In normal periods exports to other parts of Japan greatly exceed imports, which reflects the importance of Yokohama as a distributor to other sections of Nippon, chiefly by water, of the foreign goods received at its wharves. A considerable part of the domestic export trade is with Tokyo, three-fourths of the freight shipments to that city being carried by several thousand lighters which are a part of the equipment of Yokohama Port.

City Plan.—In 1939 the city of Yokohama more than doubled its area through the annexation of outlying districts. Its present area is greater than that of any of the five other great Japanese cities, with the exception of Tokyo. A large proportion of the 264,000 increase in the city's population between 1935 and 1940 is the result of this increase in area. The city occupies three kinds of sites: (1) in complete and compact fashion three small wedge-shaped delta-plains opening out upon Yokohama Bay; (2) spurs of diluvial upland 40–60 meters high which separate the three delta-plains, these being much less completely urbanized; and (3) a coastal strip, a considerable part of which has been recently reclaimed from the sea, extending northward along the coast (Fig. 233). This, too, is only urbanized in part. The small streams which have formed the three delta-plains occupied by the city do not carry enough load to seriously silt the harbor. On the other hand, they provide a splendid network of waterways throughout the lowland portions of the city, offering exceptional transport advantages to business and industry. The heart of Yokohama, containing its commercial core, is on the southernmost of the three alluvial plains, immediately back of the principal piers. Before the earthquake this business section had many Occidental-style buildings but it was here that damage, particularly from fire, was most severe. Like Tokyo, Yokohama, in the decade and more after 1933, became an Oriental city in metamorphosis; however, progress in reconstruction work was somewhat less rapid than in the capital. Numerous large fireproof and quakeproof buildings were erected, though the proportion of small Japanese structures is still greater than it is in Tokyo. In spite of the fact that many foreign firms moved their offices and plants to Kobe fol-

[26] *The Annual Statistical Report of the Yokohama Chamber of Commerce and Industry,* 1939.

lowing the earthquake, the large number of foreign business houses that still have offices in Yokohama testifies to its cosmopolitan nature.

Although the low delta-plains and the diluvial spurs are both sites for residential areas, it is the flanks and crests of the uplands that are most exclusively residential and have the most attractive living quarters. From the crests of the 40–60-meter-high plateau splendid views may be had of the lowland city and its harbor.

Industry.—Throughout most of its history Yokohama has been chiefly a port city and manufacturing has been overshadowed by trade. One reason for the slower development of industry has been the restricted

TABLE 142.—INDUSTRIES OF YOKOHAMA, 1937

Industry	Factories	Workers	Production (in thousands of yen)
Spinning	189	6,658	17,892
Metals	107	8,918	111,496
Machine and tool	213	32,850	246,245
Ceramics	20	1,746	15,976
Chemical	89	6,135	178,024
Woodworking	90	1,328	6,409
Commodities	108	3,558	60,231
Total, including all others	1,067	64,920	689,142

Source: *The Japan Year Book*, 1940–41, p. 853.

area of level land suitable for factory sites. The local plains are of small size and surrounded by steep uplands; hence, the expansion inland of factory building has been restricted. As a result the principal direction of industrial expansion has been northward along the coast. Large numbers of small plants of workshop dimensions occupy canal sites throughout the lowland city but the most exclusive industrial section, where large factories are relatively numerous, is an attenuated and incompletely urbanized coastal belt extending northward and joining with that of Kawasaki and Tokyo. A northward extension of Yokohama's boundaries in 1927 brought this industrial area, including the principal Tsurumi center, within the city limits. Large areas of newly reclaimed land along the coast of Tokyo Bay provide desirable sites for a considerable number of large and modern factories. Excellent deepwater canals and spur railroad tracks serve these reclaimed lands, the splendid transport facilities having been one of the principal items attracting factories to these new sites. The large size of the factories in this area give it a typically industrial appearance.

Great shipbuilding yards, cement plants, breweries, petroleum refineries, blast furnaces and steel mills, engineering works and chemical plants, are representative of the types of industry to be found in this newer manufacturing district on the northern margins of the city. At the end of 1936, the machine and tool industry far outranked in importance any other group; chemicals were second and metals third. Japan's petroleum industry is chiefly concentrated in Yokohama, the refineries of the locality probably representing between 50 and 75 per cent of the nation's crude and cracking capacity and more than three-quarters of its iso-octane capacity. The city's oil tankage capacity is the greatest in the country. Its shipbuilding yards are among the largest.

THE SUN-EN COASTAL STRIP

Along the Tokai littoral from Izu Peninsula to Ise Bay[27] (Subregion 2) the high mountains of central Honshu come close to the sea so that extensive plains do not exist and the small fragments of coastal alluvium that are present are isolated from each other by spurs of highland and high terrace (Figs. 234, 235). But in spite of its configuration the Sun-en district has had an importance in Japanese life far out of proportion to its restricted area of level land. Its importance and fame have grown largely out of its being the corridor through which in Tokugawa days passed Japan's most famous road, the Tokaido, connecting Tokyo (then Yedo) and the old capital at Kyoto (Fig. 236). Because of the numerous highland barriers separating the plains, the route was not an easy one. It still retains its importance as a transit route, situated as it is between the great Kwanto cities to the northeast and Nagoya and the Kinki cities to the southwest. The Sun-en strip is traversed by two of Japan's most modern and efficient thoroughfares, the double-tracked Tokaido railway and the Tokaido motor highway (Fig. 237).

A number of relatively important rivers descending from the central mountain core have built a series of small delta-fans which are the focal points for population concentration. Unusually high population densities of 400–550 per square kilometer are characteristic. Each of these plains is also a center of rice culture. The Oi Plain is distinctive because of its striking fan configuration with relatively steep slopes and even more so because its farm population resides mostly in isolated farmsteads rather

[27] Most of this region has been treated in detail in Glenn T. Trewartha, "A Geographic Study in Shizuoka Prefecture, Japan," in the *Annals of the Association of American Geographers,* 18:127–259 (September, 1928). See also Robert B. Hall, "Tokaido: Road and Region," in the *Geographical Review,* 27:353–377 (July, 1937).

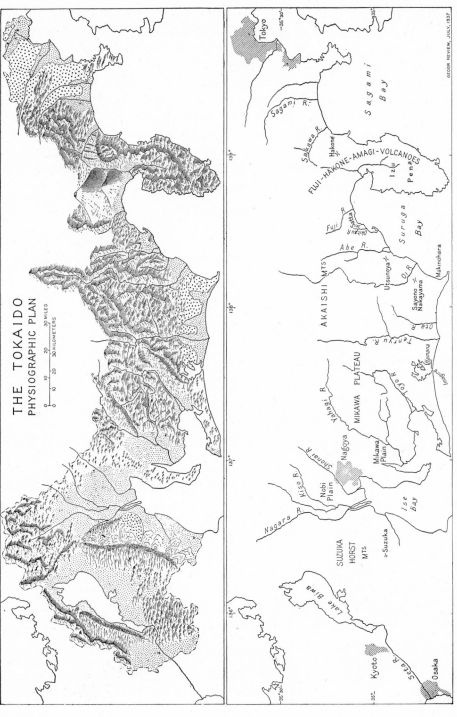

THE TOKAIDO
PHYSIOGRAPHIC PLAN

0 10 20 30 MILES
0 10 20 30 KILOMETERS

Tokyo

Sagami R.

Sakawa R.

Hakone

FUJI-HAKONE-AMAGI-VOLCANOES

Izu
Peninsula

Sagami Bay

Fuji R.

Satta

Okitsu R.

Suruga Bay

Abe R.

AKAISHI MTS

Utsunoya

O.R.

Sayono
Nakayama

Makinohara

Tenryu R.

Oi R.

Imagire

Hamana

Toyo R.

MIKAWA PLATEAU

Yahagi R.

Shonai R.

Nagoya

Mikawa
Plain

Nobi
Plain

Kiso R.

Nagara R.

Ise Bay

SUZUKA
HORST
MTS

Suzuka

Lake Biwa

Kyoto

Seta R.

Osaka

35°30′

139°

138°

137°

136°

35°30′

35°

GEOGR. REVIEW, JULY, 1937

Fig. 234 (*above*). Physiographic diagram of the Tokaido District. Map by R. B. Hall, from the *Geographical Review*, published by the American Geographical Society.

Fig. 235 (*below*). Location map to accompany Figure 234. From the *Geographical Review*, published by the American Geographical Society.

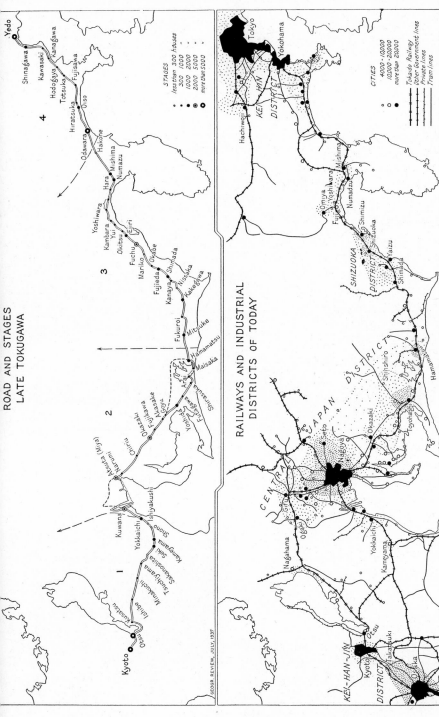

ROAD AND STAGES
LATE TOKUGAWA

Yedo
Shinagawa
Kawasaki
Kanagawa
Hodogaya
Totsuka
Fujisawa
Oiso
Hiratsuka
Odawara
Hakone
Mishima
Numazu
Hara
Yoshiwara
Kambara
Yui
Okitsu
Ejiri
Fuchu
Mariko
Okabe
Fujieda
Shimada
Kanaya
Kakegawa
Nissaka
Fukuroi
Mitsuke
Hamamatsu
Maisaka
Arai
Shirasuka
Futagawa
Yoshida
Goyu
Akasake
Fujikawa
Okazaki
Chiriu
Narumi
Atsuta (Miya)
Kuwana
Yokkaichi
Shono
Kameyama
Seki
Sakanoshita
Tsuchiyama
Minakuchi
Ishibe
Kusatsu
Otsu
Kyoto

1 2 3 4

STAGES
less than 300 houses
300 1000
1000 2000
2000 5000
more than 5000

(GEOGR. REVIEW, JULY, 1937)

RAILWAYS AND INDUSTRIAL
DISTRICTS OF TODAY

KEI-HIN DISTRICT
Tokyo
Yokohama
Hachioji
Omya
Fujisawa
Mishima
Numadzu
Shimizu
Shizuoka
Yaizu
Shimada
Hamana
SHIZUOKA DISTRICT
Shinshiro
CENTRAL JAPAN DISTRICT
Toyohashi
Okazaki
Nagoya
Seto
Gifu
Ogaki
Nagahama
Yokkaichi
Kameyama
KEI-HAN-JIN DISTRICT
Otsu
Kyoto
Takatsuki
Osaka

CITIES
4000-10000
10,000-20000
more than 20000
Tokaido Railway
Other Government lines
Private lines
Tram lines

Fig. 236 (*above*). Road and stages of the Tokaido region in the late Tokugawa period. Main agricultural regions are indicated by numerals: (1) lands of very ancient cultivation, rice preponderant; (2) area of diversified agriculture but a preponderance of mulberry and silk; (3) tree culture (tea, oranges, Japanese pears); (4) dry-crop area specialized in truck gardening. Map by R. B. Hall, from the *Geographical Review*, published by the American Geographical Society.

Fig. 237 (*below*). Map by R. B. Hall, from the *Geographical Review*, published by the American Geographical Society.

Fig. 238. A section of the Oi Plain in Shizuoka Prefecture showing the dispersed farmsteads. Win~ grain in foreground.

Fig. 239 (*left below*). An elevated field of mulberry on the Tenryu Plain, Shizuoka Prefecture. R~ stubble in the foreground.

Fig. 240 (*right below*). A terraced hillside planted with orange groves in eastern Shizuoka Prefectu~ near Okitsu (Fig. 236).

than in rural villages (Fig. 238). On alluvial plains in Japan the clustered type of rural living is so universal that the Oi Plain with its dispersed farm dwellings has been the subject of considerable discussion among Japanese geographers.[28] All seem to be agreed that this settlement feature is in some way associated with the vigorous and errant Oi River and the frequent floods that it produced. The present scattered settlements date from the great inundations of 1604 and 1627 which laid waste the Oi Plain. It is possible that the advantages offered by isolated dry sites, or the scattered nature of fertile spots, also had some effect in dispersing the homes of the new settlers on a plain made desolate by water and gravel.

The delta of the Tenryu River in western Shizuoka Prefecture is unique because of the unusual number of elevated dry fields which rise like tiny rectangular buttes two to four feet above the lower inundated paddy fields (Fig. 239).[29] These thousands of elevated fields owe their origin to the fact that the Tenryu has refused to be contained within its dikes. The sand and gravel spread over the plain in time of flood was first scraped off and piled up into heaps, and at subsequent periods leveled off and converted into dry fields. Succeeding inundations, in which the rice crop in the paddy fields was ruined, but crops on the raised fields were uninjured, proved the positive value of elevated sites.[30] The delta of the Tenryu reminds one of a huge checkerboard, great numbers of whose irregular squares have been pushed up above the surface of the board. In some places the elevated plots occupy nearly as much area as the paddies. It is a two-storied type of land utilization, for the raised fields are devoted to an intensive rotation system involving summer vegetables and fall-sown crops of grain and rape.

Along the coasts of the alluvial plains fronting upon the open ocean west of Cape Omae, wide belts of sandy beach ridges and dunes are characteristic, coastal settlements are few, and fishing meagerly developed. Such formidable belts of dunes are absent along the protected coasts facing on Suruga Bay, and here the lower beach ridges are important sites for settlements and for specialized truck and market gardening developments. Fast rail service carries the perishable products to the great urban centers lying both to the northeast and to the southwest. Particularly famous as truck gardening centers for out-of-season vegetables is the narrow plain at the base of Kuno Mountain, southeast of Shizuoka City,

[28] K. Kodera and H. Iwamoto, "On the Scattered Settlements (Strendorf) on the Alluvial Fan of Ooi-gawa River" (in Japanese with English summary), in the *Geographical Review of Japan*, 15 (1939):686–710, 760–783. See also Trewartha, "A Geographic Study of Shizuoka Prefecture, Japan," *op. cit.*, 240–242.

[29] Trewartha, *ibid.*, 251–252.   [30] *Ibid.*, 252.

and Miho Spit a little farther to the east, which forms the protected harbor of Shimizu.[31]

Diluvial terraces composed of sand and gravel strata resting upon a base of Tertiary rocks, with a surface veneer of volcanic ash, are very conspicuous features of the Sun-en littoral. Some of them rise by almost precipitous slopes 150–250 meters above the surrounding plains. The names Makinohara and Bandenohara, which have been applied to certain of these diluvial uplands, suggest that they may have been originally covered with wild grasses instead of forest. East of Hamamatsu in eastern Sun-en these diluvial uplands, as well as the lower slopes of the hard-rock hills bordering the alluvial plains, are the sites of an important bush and tree type of agriculture specializing in tea and citrus (Figs. 114, 115). No other area in Japan is so specialized in tea, for 40 per cent of the nation's entire area of tea gardens is contained within Shizuoka Prefecture. Numerous inconspicuous tea-firing plants are widely scattered throughout the rural villages and the towns of Sun-en. Over 21 per cent of the nation's crop of mandarin oranges is from Shizuoka and the region is likewise a relatively important producer of bitter oranges and navel oranges. A large part of the tree-crop acreage is comparatively new, the fields being recently reclaimed forested slope lands or wild grasslands (Fig. 240). Much the larger part of Japan's tea export is from this eastern Sun-en district, the bulk of the export leaving through the little local port of Shimizu. There is also a fairly large shipment of mandarin oranges to foreign countries. Other tree crops of some importance in eastern Sun-en are peaches, biwa or loquats, and Japanese pears, although the latter are confined to the wet paddy fields and are not grown on the uplands and slopes. Some of the diluvial terraces of Sun-en have developed as specialized centers of commercial vegetable growing.

What tea and tree crops are to the uplands of eastern Sun-en, mulberry and silk are to its western parts. The region from Hamamatsu westward to Ise Bay is an eastward extension of the larger Ise Bay region of specialized silk production. Toyohashi (142,716) and vicinity are nationally famous as a filature center.

Included within the nation's industrial belt, though it is one of its more attenuated sections rather than a major node, Sun-en has a variety of industries. Three or four local concentrations can be noted. First, in eastern Sun-en, at the base of Fuji and Ashitaka volcanoes, are 20 to 30

[31] Shinkichi Yoshimura, Kenkichi Iwasaki, and Gohei Ito, "Microclimatic Observations on Strawberry Fields of Southern Foot of Mt. Kuno, Shizuoka Prefecture" (in Japanese), in the *Journal of Geography* (Tokyo), 47:158–168 (April, 1935).

small hydroelectric plants, several large paper mills and more small ones, and a number of filatures and other textile plants. The principal advantages of the location are the abundance of cheap hydroelectric power and clean water, as well as the close proximity to rail and ocean transportation. The ancestors of the present paper factories from which these modern ones have evolved chose the location because, in addition to available waterpower, the adjacent volcanic slopes supported a wild shrub or bush used as raw material. A second concentration of industry is in and around the castle town of Shizuoka city (212,198), where a number of plants for refiring, blending, and packing tea are located. This is the tea capital of Nippon. Fish and fruit canning, woodworking, lacquer wares, soybean-oil plants, and textile manufacturing also characterize this locality. Third, Hamamatsu, the western metropolis (166,346), also a castle town, is the local center of a relatively important textile region, specialized particularly in the weaving of inexpensive cotton cloth. Within the city and its vicinity are hundreds and perhaps thousands of small weaving establishments, a great majority employing fewer than ten workers, all using electric power. Many of the weaving establishments are no more conspicuous than an implement shed on an American farm. The present power-loom weaving industry of the Hamamatsu region is the offspring of an earlier household-industry forbear, although availability of cheap electric power within the past few decades and greatly expanded markets have immensely stimulated its growth. Hamamatsu likewise has some fame as a center of the dyeing industry, has some heavy industries, and is well known for its musical instruments.

The local port of Shimizu (68,617) has a superbly protected natural harbor lying behind the compound recurved Miho Spit. Large ocean-

FIG. 241. Loading tea at the port of Shimizu in Shizuoka Prefecture.

going transpacific vessels make Shimizu a port of call during the period from May to September to take on tea, and again in November and early December to collect crates of mandarin oranges (Fig. 241). Loading is done exclusively by lighters. In 1938 Shimizu's foreign trade amounted to nearly 28.5 million yen of exports and 25.5 million of imports. Exports are almost exclusively locally derived, with green tea, paper, canned citrus, canned tuna, and black tea ranking in that order. More than four-fifths of the imports are soybeans, which are the raw material for a large vegetable oil mill within the city.

TABLE 143.—FOREIGN TRADE OF SHIMIZU, 1938

Exports	Value in Yen	Imports	Value in Yen
Mandarin oranges.	335,348	Soybeans	20,966,579
Green tea	8,621,878	Small beans	323,687
Black tea.	1,904,648	Coal	543,034
Canned tuna fish	2,857,388	Logs	582,851
Canned citrus.	3,674,145	Fodder	321,401
Sake.	412,928	Beancake	1,641,644
Canned mackerel	193,016		
Paper	6,907,674		
Wood and lumber.	1,032,537		
Total, including others. . .	28,480,032	Total, including others . .	25,500,595

Source: *Annual Return of the Foreign Trade of Japan*, pt. 3 (Department of Finance, Tokyo, 1938)

THE ISE BAY BORDERLANDS

This area (Subregion 3) includes the Nobi or Nagoya Plain,[32] next to Kwanto the largest lowland in southwestern Japan, and the lowlands bordering the tectonic bay of Ise, including its bay-head delta-plain. It is one of the nation's major compact settlement units, containing its third largest city, Nagoya (1.3 million) and one of the four important nodal centers in its industrial belt. Industrially, what Tokyo is to Kwanto, and Osaka to Settsu, Nagoya is to Nobi, but unfortunately, here there is no comparable deepwater port such as Yokohama or Kobe serving as a gateway for ocean trade. In the neighborhood of five million people comprise this Ise Bay population cluster, most of them on the Nobi Plain proper.

The eastern and western borderlands of Ise Bay are composed of narrow fringes of new alluvium bordered on their landward sides by wider belts of diluvial terrace and Tertiary hills. In the Kinki area to the

[32] Sometimes called the Owari or the Mino-Owari Plain.

west, as well as in the vicinity of Ise Bay, much of the area shown on many earlier geological maps as Tertiary is really dissected higher and older diluvial terrace, composed of unconsolidated sediments. Large areas of this high dissected terrace have been reduced by erosion to almost a badland type of surface and occupance is meager. In the valleys there is some mulberry and rice, the rice often being irrigated from artificial ponds. Most of the surface appears to be in trees or left waste. On the smoother lower terraces, rice as well as dry crops, including tea, oranges, and much mulberry, are conspicuous. Settlement is both dispersed and agglomerated. The low new alluvium bordering the eastern and western margin of the bay is largely in paddy fields.

On the west side of the bay, 23 miles south of Nagoya, is the roadstead port of Yokkaichi (102,771), serving not only a restricted local hinterland, but likewise, in a small way, functioning as the outer port of industrial Nagoya. Recently, with the improvement of Nagoya harbor, the latter function is waning, so that in 1938 the value of Yokkaichi's foreign trade was only 23 per cent that of Nagoya's. Some large transpacific steamers which call at Yokkaichi do not proceed farther up Nagoya Bay. In normal years it holds the rank of sixth or seventh among the Japanese ports. Imports, largely raw materials for manufacture, are usually five to ten times the value of exports. Yokkaichi and other towns of the Ise Bay coasts are within the general Nagoya industrial region, and like it are engaged in textile manufacture, both silk and cotton. The greatest foreign imports are textile raw materials, wool from Australia and raw cotton from British India leading, with oil seeds, soybeans, beancake, peanuts, and Indian corn also ranking high. Reflecting the hinterland's specialization in cheap porcelain manufacture, Yokkaichi's second most important export

TABLE 144.—FOREIGN TRADE OF YOKKAICHI, 1938

Exports	Value in Yen	Imports	Value in Yen
Canned salmon	4,340,614	Millet	309,922
Vegetable oils	477,683	Indian corn	1,383,432
Woolen or worsted yarns	114,769	Soybeans	898,296
Twines and cordage	270,007	Ground nuts	1,420,875
Fishing nets	1,903,602	Oil seeds	3,176,495
Underwear	405,983	Sulphate of ammonia	231,000
Cement	131,603	Raw cotton	6,778,968
Pottery	3,119,359	Wool	15,494,061
Enameled iron ware	448,062	Coal	337,849
Oil cake	243,520	Beancake	717,875
Total, including others	12,267,790	Total, including others	30,961,195

Source: *Annual Return of the Foreign Trade of Japan*, pt. 3 (Department of Finance, Tokyo, 1938).

(after canned salmon) is pottery. On the eastern side of Chita Peninsula, which flanks Ise Bay on the east, is the little port town of Taketoyo, which also serves as a gateway to the general Ise Bay region. Its total foreign trade of 22.6 million yen is almost exclusively imports, with maize, soybeans, and millet together comprising over 75 per cent.

The Nobi Plain

The relatively large plain of 1,800 square kilometers at the head of Ise Bay, also called Nagoya or Mino-Owari, is composed chiefly of new alluvium, although there is a fringe of diluvial terrace, chiefly along its eastern margins. Four important rivers, the Kiso, Hida, Nagara, and Ibi, with their many tributaries, gather the drainage from the high mountains of Central Honshu and pour their waters through the western part of Nobi. Conspicuous on the plain are the scars of abandoned stream channels with their bordering levees suggesting the capricious migrations of swollen rivers in time of flood. From ancient times western Nobi has been known as a region of disastrous floods, which not infrequently have inundated it three to five meters deep.[33] At such times the plain had the appearance of a lake. Losses of life and property were frequently great. The reasons for the numerous floods are the height of the surrounding mountains and the unusually heavy precipitation that occurs in them.

The region at present is a polder or *waju* region with immense dikes flanking the watercourses. Construction of dikes in western Nobi was begun about a thousand years ago, the original work having been done chiefly by the Buddhist temples which owned the greater part of this region. Dikes sometimes reach a height of ten meters and resemble large hills in their dimensions. Individual extensive polders are sectioned into subdivisions by cross dikes so that different forms of land use can be carried on within the same general polder. The central and eastern part of Nobi, unlike the western sections of the lowland, lacks a number of large rivers, so that deep inundation is not so common. Moreover, the eastern section of the plain is not so low or flat as the western part. Portions of it have distinct fan configuration and there is a certain amount of surface irregularity, giving rise to a small relief of several meters.

Land use on Nobi varies from one section to another. In the western part with its polder or *waju* land the poorly drained nature of the country and the frequent inundations have been important factors in influencing land use. In early days it was used largely as a region for hunting water-

[33] Atsuhiko Betsuki, "Waju or the Polder in Japan," in *Comptes Rendus du Congrès International de Géographie*, Amsterdam, 1938, vol. 2, sec. 5, pp. 47–49.

fowl; in the period around 1700 and later it was utilized as pasture land which supported a specialized horse-breeding industry, and more recently, as population has increased, it has been devoted increasingly to the growing of rice.[34] Within the polders much the larger part of the land is in paddy fields, which are poorly drained and remain as marsh land or even ponds after the rice harvest. Since the surrounding rivers are higher than the polder surfaces irrigation is easy. Drainage is very difficult, how-ever, and the lower parts of the polders are made cultivable only by use of power pumps. In places where the soil is unsuitable for rice, green manure crops of *genge* and clover are planted. The colorful blossoms of these crops in spring resemble gardens of flowers. In some polders portions of the wet land are used for pasturing cattle. Unirrigated crops of vege-tables and mulberry occupy the dikes.

Settlements in western Nobi are of two kinds, those occupying dry sites on the dikes and those located on the wet polders. The dike villages are inclined to have shoestring dimensions, whereas those on the wet lands are clump villages or *haufendorf* in type. This latter compact form is favorable for defense against inundation. Each house in the village is built upon an elevated earth platform, and special *miyazu*, or waterhouses, built upon high earthen foundations are commonly erected as storage places for articles of value or even of foodstuffs in time of flood. Sur-rounding the villages are dense screens of trees which protect against the winter winds and which may become temporary places of refuge in times of serious flood.[35]

The better drainage and somewhat more uneven terrain of central and eastern Nobi have induced more complicated land-use patterns in this region. Perhaps the most impressive feature is the large amount of land de-voted to unirrigated crops, particularly vegetables and mulberry. Patches of pine woodland are also conspicuous (Fig. 242). No doubt rice still remains the most important crop over the eastern part of the plain as a whole, but certainly it is not so exclusive as on most Japanese lowlands. In places the unirrigated crops occupy artificially elevated individual plots in the midst of the paddies, as they do on the Tenryu Plain, but there are also more extensive areas on contiguous dry fields. Mulberry is especially conspicuous, for the Ise Bay region is one of the most specialized silk areas of Nippon (Fig. 243). It is somewhat unusual for mulberry to occupy extensive areas on an alluvial lowland; being soil-tolerant and not requiring irrigation, it is usually forced, through crop competition, onto such sites as diluvial uplands or hill slopes. But here on the Nobi Plain

[34] *Ibid.*, 68–69.　　[35] *Ibid.*, 49.

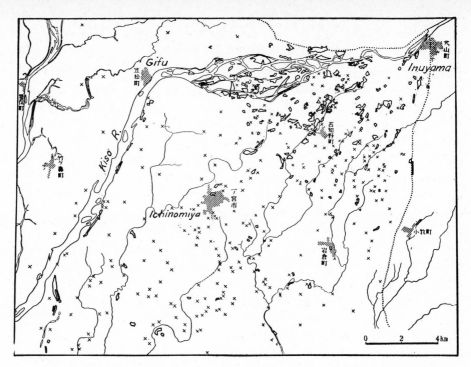

FIG. 242. Distribution of pine forest on the western part of Nobi Plain. Each *x* represents less than 240 acres of pine forest, each little enclosed area more than 240 acres. Map by Kagami.

FIG. 243. Distribution of mulberry in northeastern Nobi. Percentage ratio of area in mulberry to total area. Map by Kagami.

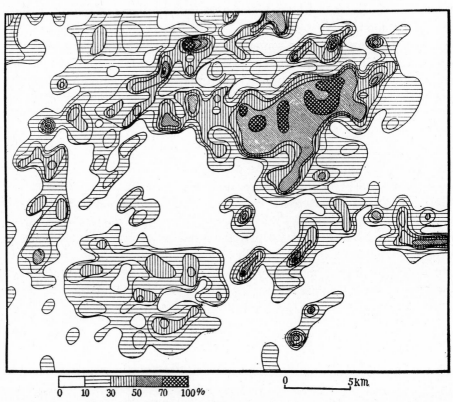

it appears to occupy large areas of potential rice land. It is significant, however, that the largest and most exclusive mulberry districts, and the largest and most numerous patches of pine forest, are found in the eastern part of the plain on the fan of the Kiso River, where both the slope of the land and the coarser soils make rice cultivation more difficult.[36]

The most specialized truck gardening area of Nobi does not appear to be in the immediate environs of Nagoya city but in central Nobi some 10 kilometers to the northwest of the city in the vicinity of Iwakura and Ichinomiya (Fig. 244). Several centuries ago the political centrum of Nobi was at Iwakura and a specialized vegetable culture developed adjacent to this market. At the beginning of the Tokugawa Era, more than three hundred years ago, the political center shifted southward to Nagoya. However, the vegetable center near Iwakura remained and continued to supply the new market to the south. The famous Biwazima market situated between the specialized vegetable area and Nagoya does an annual business of about four million yen.[37]

Cities.—On the Nobi Plain proper there are at least five cities of over 25,000 population (Nagoya, 1.3 million; Gifu, 172,340; Ichinomiya, 70,792; Ogaki, 56,117; Kuwana, 42,167); five others in this class (Seto, 45,775; Yokkaichi, 102,771; Okazaki, 70,792; Honda, 49,153; Tajimi, 26,820) are on its margins. Most of the cities as well as their satellite towns are centers for one or more phases of the textile industry, the Ise Bay area being Japan's greatest focus of textiles.[38] Cotton spinning and weaving, the manufacture of woolen yarn and the weaving of woolen cloth, the reeling of silk and the making of silk fabrics, rayon manufacture, and the processing of rayon cloth and rayon mixtures—all of these phases of the textile industry are importantly represented in the Nobi region. The weaving industry, including silk, wool, and cotton fabrics, is particularly concentrated in the central and northern part of the plain along the Nagara and Kiso rivers, with Gifu and Ichinomiya as principal centers.[39] The Ise Bay district has national and even world fame as a pottery or ceramics center, and is the most important point for these manufactures

[36] K. Kagami, "Geographical Significance of the Pine-Forest Distribution of the Nobi Plain, Aiti and Gihu Prefectures" (in Japanese), in the *Geographical Review of Japan*, 11:127–154 (February, 1935).

[37] Masahide Sugiyama and Kwanzi Kagami, "Vegetable Fields in the Owari Plain" (in Japanese with English summary), in the *Geographical Review of Japan*, 12:193–217 (March, 1936).

[38] Nobuhiko Obara, "Contributions to the Study of the Textile Industry in the Owari-Mino Plain, Japan," in *Comptes Rendus du Congrès International de Géographie*, Amsterdam, 1938, vol. 2, sec. IIIa, pp. 271–276.

[39] *Ibid.*, 272.

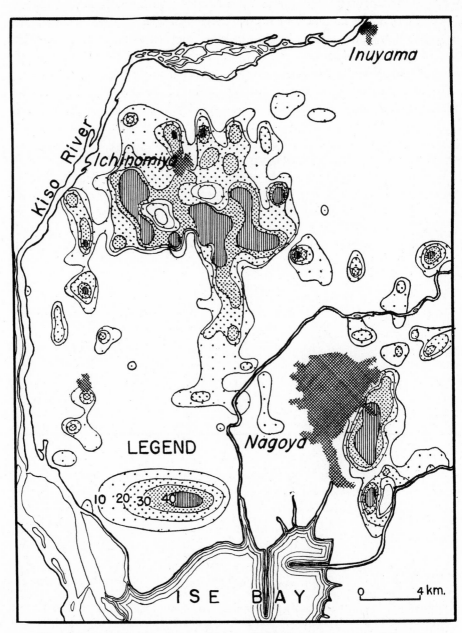

FIG. 244. Distribution of vegetables on Nobi. Percentage ratio of the area in vegetables to the total area. Map after Kagami.

in Japan. About 59 per cent of all the country's pottery products by value are from the Nobi region; it provides a still larger proportion of porcelain materials for export. The center of the industry is at Seto, a city located about ten miles east of Nagoya in the hills bordering Nobi, where there is a large deposit of kaolin. Nagoya, Gifu, and Yokkaichi are also important in pottery manufactures. The individual plants are small and relatively inconspicuous. Gifu city, in addition to being a textile center, specializes in the production of two typically Japanese products, umbrellas and lanterns.

NAGOYA

Site.—The metropolis and primate city of the Ise Bay area is located on the southeastern margin of the Nobi Plain, with its core area about four miles from tidewater. The political boundaries of Nagoya enclose 160 square kilometers or nearly 62 square miles and extend southward to the Bay. However, the geographical city is considerably smaller in area and only in recent years, with the annexation of Atuta, a port town, and the attempt to develop a deepwater harbor there, has urban development reached to the coast. Even yet the city's shape is that of a funnel, with the broader central portion several miles inland. Only a long, thin appendage of partially urbanized city extends south to the harbor (Fig. 245).[40] The site of Nagoya is a very low diluvial terrace whose relatively smooth surface is only five to fifteen meters above sea level. There is adequate level land for expansion. The city's funnel shape, tapering rapidly toward the south, is the result of intentional coincidence with the drier terrace upland, which protects it from the serious floods that have scourged the adjacent alluvial lands. At the same time the diluvium is not high enough to entirely preclude the development of canals in the city, although they are fewer than in either Tokyo or Osaka. At the north end of the city, occupying a diluvial eminence 20 meters high which gives it great prominence, is a magnificent feudal daimyo castle, a relic of the Tokugawa Era when Nagoya was already a large and prosperous city on the Tokaido Highway linking the Kwanto and Kinki capitals. The castle is the principal tourist attraction in Nagoya. The commercial core of the city, conspicuous on a map because of its remarkably rectangular street grid, lies just south of the castle grounds.

Although Nagoya is preeminently an industrial city, and situated in a region which is expanding in manufacturing more rapidly than almost

[40] K. Kagami, "Structure of City Development," in the *Geographical Review of Japan,* 13:375–390 (May, 1937).

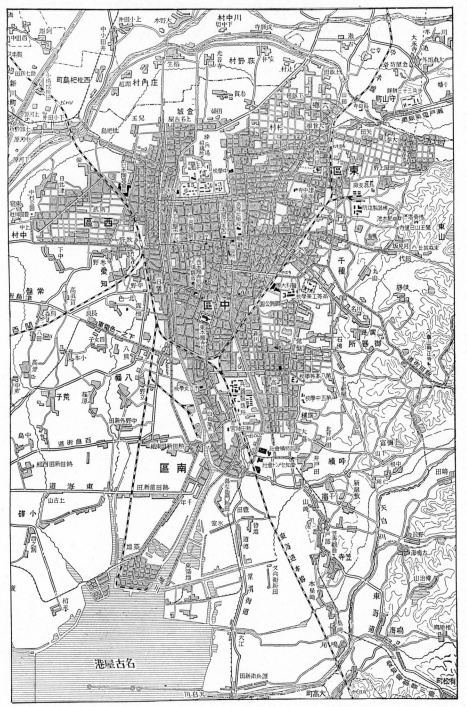

FIG. 245. Nagoya city and its harbor. From *Nippon Chiri Taikei*.

any other part of Japan, this present accelerated development is largely a case of making up for an earlier retardation which resulted from inferior water transport facilities and a late improvement of them. Like Tokyo and Osaka, Nagoya is located on a bay-head plain where silting rivers have shallowed the coastal waters so that ocean boats could not approach the coast; but unlike Tokyo and Osaka, Nagoya had no adjacent deep-water port such as Kobe or Yokohama. Manufacturing industries first became important in those parts of Japan provided with adequate water transport. Not only was the original city nucleus of Nagoya located four miles inland from shallow tidewater, but within the city itself the network of canals was not comparable to that of either Osaka or Tokyo. The movement of bulky goods was thereby made more difficult. The city was thus largely dependent upon rail transport and it was not until after the development of efficient rail service that Nagoya's modern expansion began. Today it is an important rail center on the main Tokaido Line. Its trade territory is primarily the borderlands of Ise Bay with their five million inhabitants. These comprise a major settlement area and consuming center. Largely because of the proximity of Osaka and Kobe, the outer hinterland of Nagoya is somewhat limited. Through a rail line following the Kiso Valley, however, it has extended its influence toward the Matsumoto and Suwa grabens of the Fossa Magna, and by way of the Biwa depression to the Japan Sea coast.

Harbor improvement within recent years has resulted in Nagoya's becoming the nation's fourth or fifth port, but it is far behind Yokohama, Kobe, or Osaka in importance and normally handles less than 5 per cent of the nation's foreign trade, as compared with 25–30 per cent for each of the "big three." The narrow dredged channel up the bay, 8.5 meters deep, and the restricted turning space in the harbor still discourage the large transpacific boats from calling at Nagoya. Consequently their cargoes destined for that city usually pass through Kobe, Yokohama, Osaka, or Yokkaichi and eventually reach Nagoya by rail or lighter. A large part of the raw cotton and wool consumed in the textile industries of the Nobi Plain enters the country by the Kwanto or Kinki ports, while the immense amount of raw silk produced in the Ise Bay section has its chief outlet through Yokohama. It seems very doubtful that Nagoya's harbor will ever permit it to compete with Yokohama, Kobe, or Osaka as a port city. However, boats up to 10,000 tons can now be accommodated, some using the new dock, more of them anchoring at buoys and being serviced by lighters. Connecting the harbor with the city proper is a railroad line and several canals. The older canals are at present too shallow to be of much value, but the new Nakagawa Canal completed in 1930, 6,391 meters long, 63–91 meters wide, and about 2 meters deep at low tide, may be destined to play a genuinely important role. A strip 51 meters wide on either side of the canal has been converted into landing stages, with warehouse sites and roads, and beyond these strips the land has been filled in and prepared for factory sites.[41]

Trade.—Partly as a result of harbor and port improvements, but related as well to the accelerated growth of the Ise Bay region as an industrial area, the total water-borne commerce of Nagoya, foreign and domestic, increased from 28 million yen in 1908 to 297 million yen in 1926 and 592 million in 1937, when it reached its all-time high. In the latter year the value of the city's water-borne trade was about equally divided between foreign and domestic trade. Following 1937 there was a decline in the city's foreign trade; in 1938 it was only 64 per cent, and in 1939, 71 per cent of its 1937 peak. Almost the whole decline was in imports, much of it in such textile raw materials as wool and wood pulp for artificial silk. The textile industries were being converted to war production. For example, the value of imported wool, which reached 73 million yen in 1937, was down to 22 million in 1938 and 15 million in 1939. Since 1937 exports have greatly exceeded imports, although in earlier and more normal years this was not the case.

An analysis of Table 145 showing Nagoya's foreign trade indicates that exports were chiefly manufactured goods, with textiles, especially cotton goods, pottery, and glass far in the lead. Both of these are specialized industries in the immediate hinterland. Among imports industrial raw materials and food are dominant. Wool amounted to nearly one-half the total in 1937 and pulp for artificial silk came next in rank. It is significant that the raw cotton import of Nagoya amounted to only 3.7 million yen in 1937 and this in spite of the large specialization of the Ise Bay region in cotton textiles. The explanation is that much of the raw cotton for this region entered by more easily accessible ports than Nagoya, some coming through Yokkaichi, but also through the Kinki and Kwanto ports.

Nagoya's trade is predominantly with Asia; 42 per cent of its 1937 commerce was with that continent, followed in order by Oceania, North America, and Africa, the remaining trade being about equally divided among the three. The prominence of Asia, Oceania, and Africa as markets for Nagoya's exports reflects the preeminence of cheap cotton textiles in the outgoing cargo. Exports were predominantly to Yen-Bloc countries, Manchuria and Kwantung Leased Territory leading the list, followed by

[41] *Guide to Nagoya* (Nagoya Municipal Office, 1931), 34.

India, China, the United States, and the Dutch East Indies. Five of the first six were, therefore, Asiatic countries. Manchuria also led the list of countries which were source regions for Nagoya's imports, followed in order by the United States, Dutch East Indies, India, Kwantung Leased Territory, the Philippines, and China. Six of the first seven import sources were in eastern and southeastern Asia.

TABLE 145.—FOREIGN TRADE OF NAGOYA, 1937

Exports	Value in Yen	Imports	Value in Yen
Pottery	42,101,608	Wool	72,555,807
Cotton tissues	40,218,785	Pulp for artificial silk	12,640,470
Woolen tissues	6,090,418	Wood	7,991,538
Spinning and weaving	5,767,071	Maize	7,327,318
machines.		Coal.	5,529,807
Veneer boards	4,469,074	Oil cake	3,789,859
Artificial silk	3,802,813	Cotton.	3,717,129
Shooks for wood boxes. . . .	3,705,571	Peas and beans	3,356,588
		Iron.	3,273,018
		Oil seeds	3,068,939
		Machinery	3,067,800
Total, including others. . .	147,909,395	Total, including others. . .	148,328,796

Source: *The Annual Statistical Return of Nagoya for the Year 1937* (Nagoya Chamber of Commerce and Industry, 1938), 183, 186.

TABLE 146.—DESTINATIONS OF EXPORTS FROM NAGOYA IN 1939

Country	Value in Yen
Manchuria	24,000,000
Kwantung	23,155,635
India	19,910,425
China	15,419,880
United States.	12,690,939
Dutch East Indies.	9,852,805

Source: *The Japan Advertiser Annual Review*, 1939–40, p. 64.

Industry.—Nagoya is the manufacturing metropolis of the Ise Bay region, the nation's industrial node of third rank. Although the Nagoya region is about on a par with the North Kyushu Node in value of manufactural output, or exceeds it slightly, it is only one-third as important as either the Kwanto or the Kinki center. Compared with the latter Nagoya's chief handicap in industrial development is probably the lack of a deepwater harbor. By contrast with Tokyo, Yokohama, Kobe, or Osaka, Nagoya's industrial sections have a distinctly small-town appearance. This is because the city specializes in types of industries that do not require large and conspicuous plants. In particular, the heavy metal and machine industries are lacking, although within the last decade, under government stimulation, there has been considerable conversion to industries having strategic military significance. In 1937, although textiles still ranked first, the machine and tool industry was next in importance and chemicals was third. Until the latter part of the thirties decade, however, Nagoya was preeminently a textile center and Japan's number one textile city, specializing in both the cotton and the woolen industries. In 1935 her output of cotton fabrics was valued at 221 million yen and woolen fabrics at 182 million yen. In addition there were cotton yarns amounting to 115 million yen in value, woolen yarns valued at 32 million yen, and an important output of rayon yarn as well. Much of Nagoya's woolen industry is relatively new, having developed since World War I. Australian wool is chiefly used. That much of Nagoya's textile industry, especially the weaving, is of the workshop type is indicated by a comparison of

TABLE 147.—THE INDUSTRIES OF NAGOYA

| Class of Industry | Factories with Five or More Workers, 1937 | | Value of Output, 1938, including Plants with |
	Factories	Workers	Value of Output (in thousands of yen)	Fewer than Five Workers (in thousands of yen)
Textile	758	32,053	194,529	821,340
Metal.	528	9,031	33,478	43,660
Machine and tool . . .	1,070	49,901	161,640	284,700
Pottery	223	12,895	28,317	61,370
Sawmills and woodwork.	769	8,195	36,274	—
Chemicals.	182	6,254	48,486	92,940
Total, including others	4,173	133,416	614,745	1,496,980

Source: *The Japan Year Book*, 1939–40, p. 894; *Nagoya Industry* (Nagoya Chamber of Commerce and Industry), April, 1940, p. 18.

columns three and four in Table 147. The total value of textile output, including that of the workshops, is four times the output of factories employing more than five workers. Reflecting the city's specialization in textiles, there had developed in Nagoya an important textile machinery industry. Pottery declined relatively in importance during the latter half of the last decade, but in 1935 it ranked next to textiles in importance. Bicycles, motorcycles, and motor tricycles, clocks, toys, and wood products all figured significantly in Nagoya's industrial structure. It is clear that most of the city's manufactures were of such a type that hydroelectric power instead of coal could be utilized as a source of power. An important development of the thirties decade has been the rise of Nagoya as one of the country's foremost aircraft manufacturing centers. Even in 1935 the manufacture of airplanes ranked next to pottery among the classes of industry.

Regional concentration of factories is less conspicuous than in Tokyo or Yokohama (Fig. 246). In general, however, they have had a tendency to collect in a Y-shaped industrial area which includes the narrow southern end of the city and its southeastern and southwestern margins, where canal and rail facilities are best developed.[42] Sawmills and dyeing and bleaching establishments are particularly attracted to waterway sites. The newest factory area appears to be on the reclaimed land around the harbor and along the improved Naka-gawa Canal, completed in 1930, which leads northward to the city proper from the harbor.

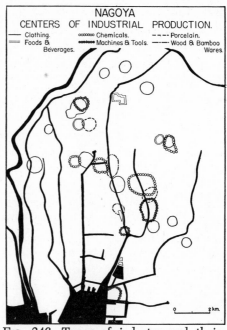

FIG. 246. Types of industry and their regions of concentration in Nagoya. After Kagami.

[42] K. Kagami, "The City of Nagoya as Viewed from Production and Sales of Merchandise: A Study of Municipal Functions" (in Japanese with English summary), in the *Geographical Review of Japan,* 15:35–63 (January, 1939).

CHAPTER XIV

The Inner Zone of Southwest Japan

PART 1

THIS triparted region of Nippon, containing as it does portions of Honshu, Shikoku, and Kyushu, is for the most part the borderlands of *Setouchi* or the Inland Sea, from which location it derives a considerable portion of its unity. Only northwestern Kyushu and the northern portion of Chugoku (Sanin) have sea frontage other than upon the Inland Sea. The region is hilly rather than mountainous, much the larger part being less than 1,000 meters in elevation. Because of the abundance of granite, rounded rather than sharp terrain features are conspicuous. The most dense and complicated fault net to be found anywhere in the country appears in this region. The whole Inland Sea, with its ragged, picturesque shoreline and numerous islands, is the result of block crustal movements along some of these fault lines. There are few lowlands of conspicuous size, the Settsu or Osaka Plain (at the head of Osaka Bay) at the extreme eastern end of the Inland Sea, and the Tsukushi Plain in northwestern Kyushu being the largest. Minor alluvial fragments occupying small coastal indentations are more characteristic. Along the entire southern boundary of the region in all three islands, separating it from the Pacific Folded Mountains, is a very conspicuous morphological fault.

All lowland parts of the region belong climatically to the humid sub-tropics (Köppen's Caf). Temperature contrasts between various parts are not conspicuous, the whole littoral of Japan south of about latitude 35°–36° having summer-month temperatures varying between 75° and 78°F. and winter months in the neighborhood of 40°F. A frost-free season of 200–240 days is characteristic. The most important regional contrasts in climate are associated with cloudiness and precipitation, the Sanin or Japan Sea littoral of northern Chugoku differing from the Inland Sea borderlands in having more winter precipitation and cloud, so that snow lies on the ground in winter several centimeters deep. Brighter, clearer winters with no snow cover, and a total annual precipitation of only 40–50 inches concentrated in summer typify Inland Sea conditions. This

FIG. 247. Percentage of total land under cultivation in central and southwestern Japan. After Matui.

is one of the driest and sunniest parts of Nippon. A subtropical broadleaf evergreen forest, similar to that of lowland Chubu, originally mantled most of this region. In northern Kyushu is the one locality of important mineral wealth, the largest part of the nation's coal originating in that region.

More than any other section of Japan, that part of the Inner Zone within the basin of *Setouchi,* or the Inland Sea, is considered the heart of Old Japan, and the features resulting from the work of men's hands are here present in great abundance. The two ancient capitals, Nara and Kyoto, which from 710 to 1192 were the centers of national government, still bear in their temples, shrines, and palaces evidences of Imperial occupance. Considering the small area of low-lying tillable land, population is denser than in most parts of Japan, although there are few conspicuously large clusters of concentration on the demographic map, because extensive plains are almost entirely lacking in this region. It is on the lowlands of Kinki at the eastern end of Setouchi, where Osaka, Kyoto, and Kobe are located, that population concentration is most marked. As a corollary of the dense rural population, land holdings are small, averaging less than two acres in many of the prefectures. Artificial terracing of the hillsides to permit their agricultural ultilization is widely practiced and is a feature of the rural landscape which amazes Americans. Paddy fields are commonly winter-cropped. As along the warm, sunny Sun-en coast, such crops as tea, citrus, and mulberry are here prevalent on the hill slopes and diluvial terraces.

Within the Inner Zone is the southwestern half of Japan's industrial belt, containing two of the four important nodes of concentration, the Osaka-Kobe-Kyoto center at the eastern end of the Inland Sea, and the North Kyushu center at the western end of that waterway. Transpacific and round-the-world boats all touch at Kobe, one of the nation's first ports, using the Inland Sea as the most direct route to and from the Asiatic mainland. In most respects it is the northern Chugoku or Sanin coast which is not in harmony with the preceding description, for, isolated as it is, great industrial and urban centers have not developed there, and the general refinements of civilization are less advanced.

KINKI, OR EASTERN SETOUCHI

Semi-isolated alluvium-filled structural basins and associated hill lands of horst structure are characteristic of Kinki (Region A).[1]

The Hilly Uplands (Subregion 1): *Omi-Iga* (Area *a*), *Ikoma* (Area *b*),

[1] Sumner W. Cushing, "Coastal Plains and Block Mountains in Japan," in the

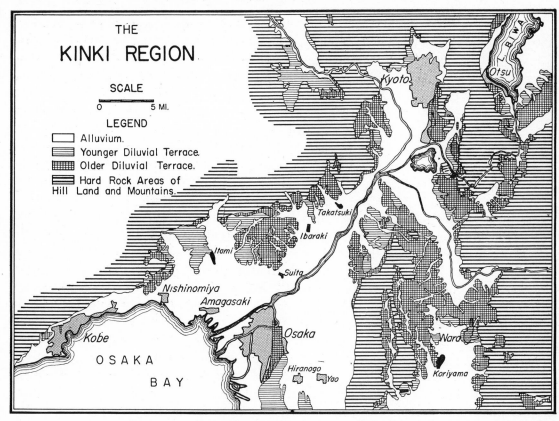

Fig. 248. Chief features of surface configuration in the Kinki region.

and *Izumi* (Area *c*).—Lying between the Nobi Plain on the east and the Kyoto and Nara (Yamato) Basins on the west, and bounded by fault-scarps on both margins, the Omi-Iga upland is composed of tilted blocks and true horsts which have been reduced to complicated hill country by stream erosion. Along the eastern margins there are some summit elevations which exceed 1,000 meters but much the larger part of it is little more than half that height. Granite is the predominant rock; rounded cupola forms and bare whitish hills with a veneer of loose rock waste, imperfectly covered with vegetation, are characteristic. Where there are Tertiary rocks, elevations are lower and the drainage net much finer. Population is relatively dense for a hilly country, and compact farm villages as well as dispersed farmsteads crowd the valleys and the small fault basins. Pond irrigation is widely practiced.

The Ikoma Hills separating the Nara Basin from the Osaka Plain, and the Izumi Horst between the latter lowland and the Kino Graben are similar in most respects to the Omi-Iga Hills.

Annals of the Association of American Geographers, 3 (1913):43–61. See also Kyoto, Nara, Osaka, Kobe, *Guide-Book Excursion D* (Pan-Pacific Science Congress, Japan, 1926).

The Fault Basins (Subregion 2). The *Biwa (Omi) Basin* (Area *a*).—This largest of the Kinki depressed areas, containing the most extensive fresh-water lake in Nippon, provides the narrowest and most complete break in the mountain barrier of Honshu, which separates the Pacific from the Japan Sea coasts (Fig. 4). A narrow belt of hills, some nine to ten miles wide, cut by numerous north-south fault valleys, is all that separates the Omi Basin from the deep tectonic indentations of Wakasa Bay on the Japan Sea coast. In ancient days this hilly belt was the site of a barrier gate comparable to the one on the Tokaido. A still narrower and lower mass of hills, two to three miles wide, forms the southern divide which separates the Omi from the Yamashiro (Kyoto) Basin. From ancient times down to the present this corridor between north and south coasts has been an important transit route for both military and commercial pur-poses. It is followed today by the Hokuroku, and in part by the Tokaido, railroads, which negotiate the northern and southern barriers by means of tunnels. It is by this natural lowland route through the Biwa Basin that the Japan Sea Hokuroku coast is made tributary to the industrial port cities of Osaka, Kobe, and Nagoya.

The asymmetrical basin occupied by Lake Biwa has higher and more precipitous walls on the west than on the east, with the result that the alluvial and diluvial fringe surrounding the lake is much narrower, and the individual fans steeper on the western margin, where the waters are also deeper. The shoreline is definitely scalloped by the numerous advancing fronts of the delta-fans which the radial drainage lines are producing. On the eastern margins a few hardrock outliers rise above the alluvium or

FIG. 249. In the foreground a section of the lower terrace of Kinki on which rice fields and dry fields are intermingled. In the background is the higher terrace (1), chiefly in woods or wasteland. Still further in the background, and rather indistinct, are the higher granitic mountains (2). Scene near the southern end of Lake Biwa.

FIG. 250 (*left*). A section of the relatively barren higher terrace of Kinki. Note the stunted character of the tree cover. Near the southern end of Lake Biwa.

FIG. 251 (*below*). A cultivated valley in rice in the dissected higher terrace along the western side of Lake Biwa.

out of the shallow water of the lake. Within the Biwa area (and for Kinki as a whole) three distinct depositional forms are recognized, (1) the delta-fans of new alluvium, those along the eastern margins of the lake being broader and flatter, (2) the lower and younger, and (3) the higher and older diluvial terraces (Fig. 249).[2] The last are composed chiefly of coarse fluvial deposits with some intervening clay beds, the total thickness often being over 100 meters. Where gravels predominate, the surfaces are likely to be rugged, exhibiting badland characteristics, although level

[2] *Guide-Book Excursion D*. See especially the geological map of Kinki.

to undulating crests are also represented (Figs. 250, 251). Unlike the Shizuoka terraces these of Omi unfortunately have no mantle of volcanic ash. The lower terraces, which represent a second stage of uplift, have smoother surfaces and finer, better mixed soils with less sand and gravel. Elevated streams, whose beds are 20 feet or more above the alluvial lowlands and flanked by high dikes are characteristic of the delta-fans. In some instances railroads and highways are carried under the elevated river beds by tunnels rather than over them by bridges. Thick groves of bamboo characteristically parallel the river courses, their roots serving to hold the levees in time of flood. Ruthless cutting of the timber from the surrounding granite hills to supply wood for the rebuilding of the Buddhist temples of Mt. Hieh and for the great urban centers of Kinki led to disastrous floods in times past which deposited sand and gravel on the fertile plains below. It was here in the Biwa Basin that some of the first work of torrent correction was begun under the direction of a Dutch engineer in 1871, but even yet bare, whitish granite slopes are conspicuous.

Climatically the basin subdivides into two parts, a northern half, down to about the Aichi River, which is similar to the Hokuroku coast, and a southern half which is similar to the Pacific side of southwestern Japan. In winter especially the contrast is marked, for at that time the strong monsoon blows over the low range of intervening hills into the northern end of the Omi Depression, giving gray, overcast, snowy weather, typical of Nippon's windward Japan Sea coast in that season. During the three winter months precipitation near the southern end of the lake is not much more than half what it is along the northern margins only 35 or 40 miles distant, where snow lies deep on the ground.

This climatic contrast leads to major contrasts in land use as well, for while in the south half of the Omi Basin most of the rice fields are winter-cropped and resown to wheat, barley, and rape in fall, those in the snowier north remain fallow after the rice harvest. In northern Biwa, as on the Japan Sea coast, are to be seen along the paddy-field margins the rows of *hasagi,* bare upright poles or slim, almost branchless trees, upon which the rice is hung to dry after harvest. The low terraces are somewhat less completely utilized than the new alluvium but nevertheless bear important crops of rice, mulberry, summer vegetables, and winter grain, as well as some tea. In such locations pond irrigation is common. The ruddy-colored high terraces, as well as the steeper, stonier upper parts of the alluvial fans, have much wasteland and woodland. Where the high terraces have been much dissected, a complicated pattern of cropped land frequently coincides with the intricate valley system, terraced paddies watered from artificial ponds being very numerous. Bamboo is relatively abundant, and in favorable locations some dry crops are cultivated, even on the level crests of these higher uplands.

The lake itself, together with its rugged *umland*, and the legend, history, and art which are associated with its classic shores, make the Biwa region attractive to resorters, tourists, and sightseeing groups from the adjacent metropolitan centers. Two funicular railways carry tourists to the top of Mt. Hieh, where there is the attraction of ancient Buddhist temples set in groves of magnificent cryptomeria. From Hieh's elevation of 2,800 feet one can behold a panorama of almost the entire Biwa Basin and of Kyoto as well. Small tourist boats, carrying some freight, ply between various towns along the lake shore. Biwa is well stocked with fish; although most of the catch is consumed by the local population, some is sent to the adjacent cities. Crude, arrow-shaped bamboo-and-reed fish traps are numerous in the coastal waters. Biwa's waters find their only natural outlet by way of the Seta River at the extreme south, although two parallel canals, one providing the city with its water supply, the other a carrier of trade, connect the lake with Kyoto by means of tunnels through the intervening hill barriers.

Although Omi Basin is not a principal focus of manufacturing, industries are not absent. The old, long-established industry of the Basin is the weaving of various kinds of cloth for the Japanese market. Small inconspicuous plants of workshop dimensions are characteristic of these textile trades. In contrast are the several large-scale modern rayon factories concentrated at the south end of the Biwa Basin in the vicinity of Otsu and Zeze. This location is favorable for rayon factories, because of the large amount of clean soft water which is readily available, and because of proximity to the ports of Kobe and Osaka, through which the pulp is imported. Otsu city, strategically located within the lowland corridor connecting rural rice-specialized Hokuroku and urbanized industrial Kinki, has fame as a rice distributing center, more than 500 rice dealers having their headquarters there.

The Yamato or Nara Basin (Area *b*).[3]—In gross morphology Nara Basin is similar to other Kinki basins. Its floor is composed of flat-lying new alluvium with marginal fragments of both young and old diluvial terrace, the latter being much more abundant. In materials and forms the diluvium of Yamato resembles that of Biwa. A belt of dissected high terrace, known

[3] This subdivision has been studied in detail by Robert Burnett Hall. See his published study, "The Yamato Basin, Japan," in the *Annals of the Association of American Geographers*, 22 (1932):243–291.

as the Nara Hills, forms the boundary between the Yamato and Kyoto plains. Population is extremely dense here even for Japan, 70 per cent of the people living in small, rectangular rural villages, enclosed by hedges and sometimes moats. Following the *handen* system of land partition introduced from China prior to the seventh century, the land was divided and subdivided into rectangular plots, all boundary lines being oriented north-south and east-west. Villages were planted at rather regular intervals, drainage lines were brought into conformance with the rectangular land subdivisions, and literally thousands of small irrigation ponds were dug, which have given the entire landscape a distinctly checkerboard aspect. This *handen* system, with its evenly-spaced compact villages, is found throughout lowland Kinki and other parts of southwestern Japan, but in Yamato it seems to exist in its most exclusive and least altered form.

On the higher parts of the alluvial basin floor, where drainage is more perfect, 72 per cent of the land is replanted to winter crops while 10 per cent yields three crops.[4] Because the lowest parts have inadequate drainage, most of the paddy fields are left fallow in winter. The larger part of the old diluvium has been left in trees and waste, while more of the lower, smoother, new diluvial terraces are cultivated. Both irrigated rice and dry crops, such as watermelons, mulberry, vegetables, tea, persimmons, and oranges, are common. The wonder is that in such a long-occupied and densely peopled region more complete land utilization, at least of the low terraces, has not been accomplished.

Nara city (61,465), the metropolis of the basin, and the first permanent capital of Japan (710–784 A.D.) is a hallowed spot, famed not only for its ancient temples and other antiquities, but for its natural beauties as well. Several million pilgrims and tourists visit the city each year. An excellent foreign-style hotel caters to Occidental visitors.

The Kyoto (Yamashiro) Basin (Area *c*).—Separated from the Nara and Osaka plains only by narrow belts of old diluvial terrace, Kyoto Basin is like Nara in many of its natural and occupance features. In the central-eastern part shallow, swampy Ogura Lake, remnant of a larger body of fresh water which at one time occupied the entire lowland, is rapidly being reclaimed for rice fields. Conspicuous along the river courses as well as on the bordering terraces are the groves of bamboo. Along the eastern margins of the plain are extensive orchards of Japanese pears, their branches and fruit supported on horizontal trellises. On the diluvium in the vicinity of Uji, between Kyoto and Nara, tea gardens are abundant, for this region is famous throughout Japan for teas of extraordinarily high

[4] *Ibid.,* 267–268.

quality. The *handen* system of land partition has left an indelible imprint upon the rural landscape, especially in the rectangular arrangement of its culture features.

Kyoto (1,089,726), one of Japan's six great cities, and the seat of Imperial residence for nearly eleven centuries (to 1869), still retains its Imperial grandeur and beauty. The fact that it is the only one of Japan's six great cities that does not have direct access to tidewater suggests that its growth is based upon somewhat different conditions than those affecting the other five metropolises, whose industrial growth is linked with their seacoast location.

Kyoto is primarily a political, religious, and cultural center, pervaded by a charm of quiet and refinement. Until very recently, it was scarcely a part of modern industrial Japan at all, the changes of the last decades having largely passed it by. During the feudal period it developed as a handicraft center for such products as lacquer, porcelain, bamboo, cloisonné, bronze, and silk textiles. Today it is still a city of craft industries, catering to a wealthy Japanese and foreign tourist trade.

TABLE 148.—INDUSTRIES OF KYOTO, 1937
(excluding workshops with fewer than five workers)

Kind of Industry	Number of Factories	Number of Operatives	Production (in thousands of yen)
Textile	1,446	30,722	90,943
Metal	157	2,314	23,636
Machinery	279	10,792	38,064
Ceramics	73	1,679	6,322
Chemical	117	2,489	23,032
Sawmill and woodwork	167	1,491	8,008
Printing and bookbinding	100	1,603	3,844
Foodstuffs	514	3,871	33,958
Total, including all others	2,809	56,912	239,660

Source: *Japan Year Book*, 1940–41, p. 847. In 1936 the output of all factories, including those with fewer than five workers, was about a hundred million yen greater than that of the larger factories.

The representative industrial plant of Kyoto is the workshop, employing fewer than a score of workers. Except for a few large cotton-spinning mills on the outskirts of the city, large factories scarcely exist—in fact, they are excluded by law. The workshop industries are scattered throughout the city rather than being strongly localized. Foremost among them is textile manufacturing, including the twisting of silk thread, the dyeing, bleaching, and weaving of silk cloth, and the production of high-grade linen and woolen fabrics. A large part of the cloth dyed and bleached in Kyoto is woven outside the city. Other peacetime industries are embroidery, lacquer ware, and fine potteries.

In the period since 1930 there has been some modification of the above picture, for as the nation prepared for war not only did Kyoto's industries expand their output but there were also numerous conversions from peacetime to wartime production. The workers in art metal have learned to make guns and precision machinery, and the lacquer workers have turned to the manufacture of gunpowder and other munitions. Within the city and its environs there are now scores of small metal and machine-and-tool shops, metal smelters, wire mills, powder magazines, and a gun-powder plant.[5] Table 148 portrays the character of Kyoto's industrial structure in 1937. Since that time there has been a further trend toward the strategic wartime industries.

Like Nara, Kyoto is a pilgrimage and tourist center, for its environs are classic ground upon which fifteen hundred years of Japanese history have left their mark. The old Imperial Palace, ancient and famous Buddhist temples and monasteries, the mausoleum of the Emperor Meiji—these are only a few of the revered spots which attract foreigners and Japanese alike. The city stands at the far northern end of the Yamashiro Basin under the shadows of the surrounding hills, on a somewhat higher portion of the alluvial floor, where streams debouch onto the plain. Its rectangular outline, as well as the grid arrangement of its north-south and east-west streets, indicates *handen* influence. Kyoto is more distinctly Japanese in its features than either of the other five great cities, although in the commercial core Occidental-style structures are not uncommon.

The Settsu Plain

The Osaka or Settsu Plain (Area *d*) is larger than the Nara or Kyoto Basin, but like them has an alluvial floor with borderlands of both old and new diluvium. Osaka Plain has the outstanding advantage of fronting on tidewater. Commonly the Settsu or Kinai Plain is thought of as also including the lowland on which Kyoto is located, since only a narrow belt of dissected old diluvium separates the two. Essentially the Settsu Plain is the advancing bay-head delta of the broad and diked Yodo River and its numerous distributaries, with amphibious ocean margins and shallow water offshore. Although *handen* influence is discernible in settlement forms and land subdivisions, it is not dominant. Population is exceedingly dense. Myriads of irrigation ponds dot the diluvial borderlands and there are some on the alluvial floor of the plain as well. A relatively

[5] T. E. Lloyd, "Kyushu and Honshu Islands Focal Points of Japan Industry," in *The Iron Age,* April 30, 1942, folded map opposite p. 84.

wide and continuous belt of diluvial terrace borders Osaka Bay on the
south and east, and in places the terrace reaches the water's edge and terminates in low, wave-cut cliffs. Toward the north, approaching Osaka, as
the diluvial bench gradually withdraws from the coast, there is a progressively wider strip of sandy coastal plain, principally devoted to market
gardens, between the sea and the terrace. Much of the smooth rolling surface of the low diluvium is in rice, vegetables, and other dry crops, while
the belt of higher and more dissected diluvium farther back from the coast
is a specialized orange-growing region with rice occupying the maze of
intricately dendritic valleys. To be sure, woodland and wasteland comprise

the most extensive type
of cover, but cultivation
seems to be more general
than on most of the older
terraces of Kinki.

Here on the Settsu
Plain at the eastern end
of Setouchi is an indus-
trial concentration which
ranks as the equal of
that of Kwanto. While
principally focused at
Osaka city, manufactur-
ing plants form a cres-
centic industrial belt, attenuated in spots, along
the margins of Osaka
Bay from Kobe on the
northwest to beyond
Kishiwada on the south-

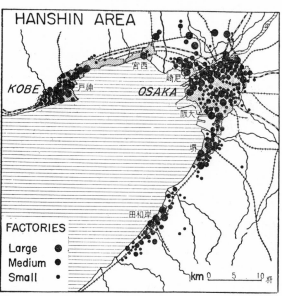

Fig. 252. The great Hanshin industrial node at the
eastern end of the Inland Sea along Osaka Bay.
From *Nippon Chiri-Fuzoku Taikei.*

east. Kobe, Nishinomiya, Amagasaki, Sakai, and Kishiwada are the principal secondary nodes. The region has no local power or raw-material resources; its location in a densely populated region where labor is relatively abundant, and on tidewater, served by lighters and rail from Kobe
and Osaka as foreign-trade ports, must be classed as its major advantages.

Probably in no other part of the country are transportation facilities so
excellent and well developed. In 1938, 30 per cent of the nation's total
value of manufactured goods was produced within this general Osaka-
Kobe-Kyoto industrial area. A great variety of industries is characteristic,
with metals, machines and tools, chemicals, and textiles all ranking high.

OSAKA

Site.—Osaka (3,252,340) is located on the Yodogawa Delta at the head of shallow Osaka Bay, where a score or more streams debouch along a coastal strip of 20 kilometers. The delta's projecting front creates the principal irregularity of the otherwise crescentic littoral. Much the larger part of the city is built on flat delta sediments, only slightly above sea level, so that large modern buildings must be supported on piers. Throughout this lowland section Osaka is intersected by a remarkable network of rivers and canals crossed by over 1,300 bridges; a veritable Venice, but a smoky, dirty one. Only along the city's extreme eastern margin are the site conditions different. Here residential forms occupy a north-south spur of diluvial terrace, 1–2.5 kilometers broad and 10–20 meters high (Fig. 253). At its northern tip, now the northeast corner of the city, there is an abrupt descent to the lowland. From this strategic site one commands a view of the entire city and its environs. Here has survived one of Japan's greatest feudal castles. Its wall- and moat-enclosed grounds are now occupied by permanent army barracks. From the old heart of the city, at present some 5 kilometers from the delta front, a narrow belt of urbanized land extends southwestward between the Ajikawa and Shirinashi channels, following the principal lines of communication connecting the city proper with its harbor. In this feature Osaka resembles Nagoya.

Only in Kyoto is the grid pattern of intersecting north-south and east-west streets more extensively developed than in Osaka. It is in the newer western part of the city that departure from this pattern is most marked. Most of the streets are still typically Japanese in their narrow widths, although several of the great thoroughfares have been widened to 20–25 meters. In 1936 streets comprised only 7.4 per cent of the total area of Osaka as compared with approximately 25 per cent in reconstructed Tokyo.

Crowded, flimsy structures comprise most of the city. There has been no recent earthquake and resulting widespread fire, as in Tokyo, to permit a thorough remodeling of the city structure. Throughout the business core, however, close to the geographical center of the city, Occidental-type structures predominate to a greater degree than in most Japanese cities. This is in spite of the fact that Osaka has almost no foreign residents. The large and relatively tall buildings and the traffic-crowded streets cause an American traveler to feel much at home. Nevertheless the numerous narrow streets and bridges are a severe handicap to fast-moving traffic. Shallow canals in rectangular pattern intersect the business section, providing a convenient means of receiving the necessary commodities. The best and most exclusive residential areas are on the diluvium at the eastern margins of the city and along the coast toward Kobe. Manufactural Osaka encircles the older part of the city on the north and west and is served by numerous deepwater canals and distributary channels. Mecking estimates that one-third of the urban area is primarily manufactural.

Background.—Osaka's commercial and industrial preeminence is of long standing. During much of the fourth century A.D. it was the capital city of Japan and consequently the political, as well as the economic center. During the long Nara-Kyoto period of political preeminence Osaka, then called Naniwa, was their principal port and commercial and financial center. Very early it became the port of entry for official envoys from Korea and China. In the sixteenth century Hideyoshi, predecessor of the Tokugawa shoguns and a great tycoon of the feudal period, chose the city for his residence, built Osaka castle, and induced the merchants of Sakai and Fushimi to locate there. Throughout the whole feudal period, even after Yedo (Tokyo) became the Tokugawa capital, Osaka continued to grow as a commercial center, the daimyos erecting huge warehouses there for the storage of the products from their respective fiefs. Osaka merchants acted as middlemen and bankers in the distribution of these products so that their city became the commercial hub and they the merchant princes of the country.

Kyoto, seat of Imperial residence, and a city of a million or more throughout much of the feudal period, required tremendous quantities of supplies, all of which passed through the port of Osaka, only 27 miles distant. Thus at the time Japan was opened to foreign trade three-quarters of a century ago, Osaka was the greatest trading mart in the country, but it was all domestic trade carried on in shallow, clumsy junks and required little in the way of port facilities. In 1868 the city was opened to foreign trade, but the large foreign boats could not enter its shallow and generally unimproved harbor and consequently Osaka's business suffered. It was at this time that Kobe, 16 miles down the bay on deep water, rapidly grew into prominence as the transshipping port for foreign cargoes.

Modern Osaka harbor is entirely of artificial construction. Two converging moles extending seaward some 3 kilometers, with a narrow entrance between their terminals, enclose a harbor of limited dimensions, 500 meters east-west by 400 meters north-south (Fig. 253). It has been dredged to a maximum depth of 9 meters at low water. More than thirty anchor buoys provide facilities for the berthing of vessels up to 20,000

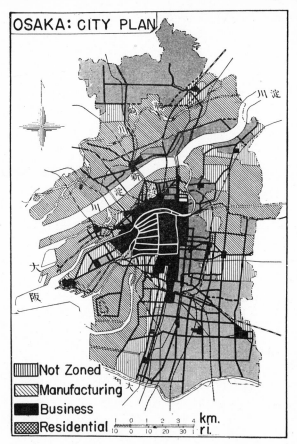

FIG. 253. The city planning map of Osaka.
From *Nippon Chiri-Fuzoku Taikei*.

tons, and piers and quays can accommodate smaller boats.[6] Private and municipal warehouses line the waterfront. The Shirinashi and the Ajikawa River debouch within the harbor, and these waterways provide entrance for lighters and also for cargo boats of 3,000–4,000 tons into the industrial heart of the city, where they can unload at the quays of the manufacturing plants. Plans have been made for considerably expanding the harbor area and improving the port facilities; how much of the plan has been actually accomplished is not known.[7]

Trade.—Considering all water-borne commerce, domestic and foreign, Osaka is normally the greatest port of Japan, for the coastwise traffic of the city is unusually large. In 1929, for example, when Osaka's share of the country's foreign trade was only about 21 per cent as compared with over 30.4 per cent for Yokohama and 37 per cent for Kobe, the value of the city's foreign shipping was only 57 per cent of that of her coastwise traffic. Since 1929 Osaka has increased more rapidly as a foreign-trade port than the other two great gateway cities. In 1939 it handled about a quarter of Japan's expanded overseas commerce, which placed it on a par with Kobe and only slightly behind Yokohama. Osaka therefore is no longer the poor

[6] *The Port of Osaka.* Compiled and Issued by the Municipal Harbor Department, Osaka, Japan, 1930.
[7] *Nippon Chiri-Fuzoku Taikei* (Geography and the Customs and Manners of Japan). Volume on Kinki region, p. 673, Tokyo, 1939.

third in the triumvirate of great ports but is instead an equal. In 1939 its exports exceeded those of any other port, although its imports were slightly less than those entering Kobe, and considerably less than those of Yokohama. Even though Osaka is the principal focus for one of the greatest manufactural concentrations in Japan, a considerable part of the raw wool, cotton, iron and steel, and machinery destined for Osaka is unloaded at the harbor of its deepwater rival, Kobe, and lightered or trucked to Osaka, thus arriving at the latter city as domestic rather than foreign imports.

Tramp rather than line traffic predominates and passenger boats are few, for Osaka is almost exclusively a freight port. Normally exports exceed imports, though this is contradictory to what one has come to expect of a port serving a great manufactural hinterland. The explanation is that while the bulky industrial raw materials from the United States, Canada, British India, and Australia are commonly brought by larger steamers that unload at Kobe, the exported finished products, destined principally for Asiatic markets, are carried mostly in smaller boats that leave directly from Osaka.

The single most important item in the import list is raw cotton, chiefly from the United States, British India, and Brazil, which amounted in 1938 to 20 per cent of the total value of imports. Raw wool, principally from Australia, machinery, vehicles, chemicals, petroleum, lumber, and oil-yielding seeds from Manchuria and China are other important items of import. Among exports cotton cloth far surpasses any other single item, amounting to 30 per cent of the value of the outgoing cargo. Its destination is chiefly eastern and southern Asia. Machinery, largely for Manchuria and China, metals, iron manufactures, artificial silk cloth, cotton yarn and thread, chemicals, and paper are other high-ranking exports.

Osaka's trade is predominantly with eastern and southern Asia, 88 per cent of its exports going to, and nearly 35 per cent of its imports coming from that continent. Next in rank is North America, which supplies 41 per cent of Osaka's imports, though taking only 0.5 per cent of her exports. It becomes clear from an analysis of Table 150 that the Yen-Bloc countries are Osaka's principal trade area and particularly so in the matter of exports. Outside of the Yen-Bloc countries, the United States is by far the most important of Osaka's trade areas, outranking every other country except Kwantung as a source of imports, though claiming a very unimportant position in the port's export trade.

Industry.—As stated earlier, Osaka, Japan's most highly industrialized great city, is only the principal unit of the general Kinki manufactural

TABLE 149.—IMPORTANT ITEMS IN OSAKA'S FOREIGN TRADE, 1938

Exports	Value in Thousands of Yen	Imports	Value in Thousands of Yen
Cotton tissues	243,000	Raw cotton	103,629
Machinery	60,000	Machinery and instruments	41,137
Iron manufactures	30,000	Chemicals and drugs	25,394
Metals	54,635	Vehicle and parts	23,627
Artificial silk tissues	37,308	Petroleum	22,671
Paper	27,006	Wool	16,363
Cotton yarn and thread	29,972	Oil-yielding seeds	11,291
Chemicals and drugs	28,999	Coal	7,679
Woolen tissues, including mixtures	16,646		
Pottery and glass	14,057		
Staple fiber tissues	21,232		
Dyes and pigments	10,809		
Total, including all others	800,328	Total, including all others	518,076

Source: *Annual Return of the Foreign Trade of Japan*, pt. 3 (Department of Finance, Tokyo, 1938).

TABLE 150.—REGIONAL DISTRIBUTION OF OSAKA'S FOREIGN TRADE, 1939

Imports	Value in Thousands of Yen	Exports	Value in Thousands of Yen
United States	225,796	Kwantung	280,743
China	92,769	Manchuria	221,680
Manchuria	51,919	British India	96,810
Canada	45,625	Netherlands Indies	75,773
British India	37,769	United States	12,160
Egypt	16,501		
Australia	10,260		
Germany	10,098		

Source: *Glimpses of the East*, 1940–41 (Tokyo, 1941), 97.

TABLE 151.—COMPOSITION OF OSAKA'S MANUFACTURAL INDUSTRIES, 1937
(including plants with fewer than five workers)

Industry	Number of Factories	Number of Employees	Output (in thousands of yen)
Textile	5,525	44,047	221,244
Metals	6,105	65,365	779,640
Machinery	9,470	90,899	502,123
Ceramics	727	15,445	55,523
Chemicals	2,273	27,267	327,975
Milling and woodwork	938	12,942	46,950
Printing and bookbinding	758	12,414	62,444
Foodstuffs	969	14,133	96,600
Total, including all others	52,363	320,922	2,225,702

Source: *The Japan Yearbook*, 1940–41, p. 893.

528

node at the eastern end of the Inland Sea. This node includes not only the deepwater port of Kobe and the industrial metropolis of Osaka, but also a number of lesser cities and towns which are satellites of Osaka. To the south of Osaka along the coast are Sakai (182,147) and Kishiwada (46,468), while westward toward Kobe are the coastal cities of Amagasaki (181,011) and Nishinomiya (111,796). Bordering Osaka on its land side are the industrial centers of Fuse (134,724), Suita (65,812), Toyonaka (45,031), and Itami (33,579). Until less than a decade ago the satellite cities and towns, not including Kobe, were specialized in the lighter industries, especially textiles, and in goods for sale in the home market. The spinning and weaving of cotton was dominant. It is likely, however, that the unusual expansion of the nation's heavy industries during the decade of the 1930's has modified this specialization as it has in the primate city itself. In 1930 nearly a quarter of Osaka's factory workers in plants with over five laborers were employed in cotton-spinning mills, while 18.1 per cent were in the machine industries, and 16.1 per cent in metallurgical industries. By 1936, however, textiles had dropped to 15 per cent, while the machine and metallurgical industries were far in the lead with 25 and 22 per cent respectively of the industrially-employed in factories with more than five workers.

By the second half of the thirties decade, therefore, Osaka had become a focus for heavy industry to an even greater degree, though remaining one of the nation's great textile centers. Ranked in terms of industrial output, and including factories of all sizes, the metal industry in 1937 stood at the top, with 37 per cent; the machine industry was next, with nearly 23 per cent; chemicals were close to 15 per cent, and textiles 10 per cent. From an analysis of Table 151 it becomes clear that Osaka is a city specialized in a great variety of manufactures. Within the textile group it is cotton spinning which far outranks all other phases of the industry. In cotton spinning large factories are the rule. Cotton weaving, on the other hand, is of little importance in Osaka city, although the satellite cities and towns are highly specialized in the production of cotton tissues, much of the cloth being produced in small factories and workshops. The compact nature of both the raw material and the finished product, as well as the need for only a small unit of labor, make location of weaving plants outside the metropolis more economical. In a very real sense the spinning industry of Osaka and the weaving industry of its hinterland are interdependent and complementary in nature. In addition to cotton spinning, the dyeing and bleaching of cotton cloth and the manufacture of knit goods, woolen cloth, and woolen mixtures are all well represented. Silk reeling and silk spinning and weaving appear to be the only phases of textile manufacture not present.

Osaka and adjacent Amagasaki have at least three blast furnace plants and four steel mills so that a considerable part of the steel required in the machine and the engineering industries of the Kinki metropolis are locally produced. However, neither the iron ore nor the coal required in the iron and steel industry of Osaka is obtained from locally adjacent sources. Very emphatically it is the large local market for such items as industrial machinery, electrical apparatus, and hardware that has stimulated this specialization in metals. Bridges and structural steel, marine engines, and railway equipment are additional metal products of more than local importance. Although overshadowed by Kobe as a shipbuilding center, largely because the deeper water at that port permits the launching of large vessels, Osaka fabricates a considerable number of smaller boats. At least four shipyards are located along the city's waterfront.

A host of other industries, including chemicals, cement factories, printing and bookbinding, wooden and bamboo articles, bicycles, food and drink products, bring the total number of manufacturing establishments in the city to over 52,000, almost a fourth of which employ more than five

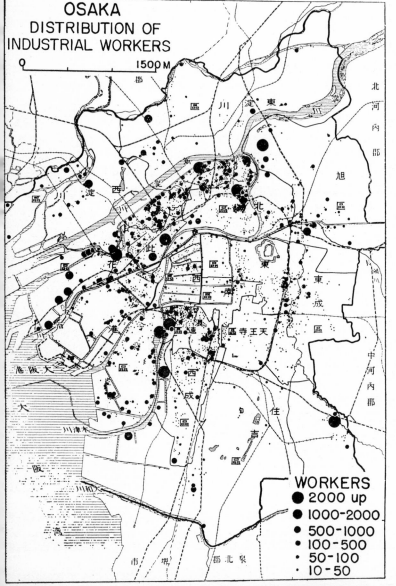

FIG. 254. The principal industrial sections of Osaka lie to the north, west, and south of the business core. They occupy flat alluvial land where there are numerous rivers and canals that can be used for transport purposes. From *Nippon Chiri-Fuzoku Taikei.*

FIG. 255. Osaka harbor.

operatives. In spite of the predominance of small plants, large and conspicuous factories are more numerous here than in any of the other principal manufacturing centers except North Kyushu. In contrast to the Tokyo-Yokohama area, factory buildings in Osaka are older and in poorer physical condition, because of the earlier development of factory industry here. They are generally also of flimsier construction. These features, together with the smoky, murky atmosphere and the filthy waters of canals and streams fouled by the waste of factories, give to Osaka a thoroughly industrial aspect.

Unlike Tokyo and Yokohama, where one result of the Great Earthquake and fire has been a planned modernization of the industrial sections, Osaka's factories are less concentrated in differentiated industrial districts. Instead, manufacturing plants are rather widely scattered throughout the city (Fig. 254). The newer and larger factories, however, have a degree of concentration along (1) the deepened Yodogawa and its distributaries in the northwestern part of the city, and (2) in relatively close proximity to the harbor (Figs. 253, 255).[8]

On first thought the reasons for Osaka's industrial preeminence may not be so obvious. Without coal or notable raw materials within its immediate *umland,* two of the most conspicuous advantages for manufacturing are absent. To a much greater degree than in the Kwanto and Nobi industrial areas, which are nearer the principal center of hydroelectric development, Osaka and vicinity depend directly or indirectly upon coal.

[8] A. Bekki, "Geographical Distribution of Industries in Osaka" (in Japanese), Geographical Bulletin (*Chiri Ronso*), Kyoto Imperial University, No. 4, 1934, pp. 175–218.

Rather, (1) the wide expanse of level land on which the city is located provides adequate room for city growth and industrial expansion, (2) the adequate facilities for both internal and external water transport make it accessible to bulky fuel and raw materials, and (3) the large supply of available labor and capital (the latter first accumulated by merchant families during the feudal period) have favored the centering of industry at Osaka. To this list of advantages should also be added Osaka's excellent rail facilities, for it is the hub of a widespread rail net which taps an extensive and densely populated hinterland.

KOBE

Kobe (967,234), on deepwater 16 miles down the bay from Osaka, is a new Japanese city brought into existence by the demands of the modern commercial and industrial era. In that respect it is like its rival deepwater port, Yokohama. When, after the middle of the last century, Japan was opened to foreign trade the present site of Kobe harbor was occupied by only insignificant fishing villages. Hyogo harbor, south of the Minato Delta, and now a part of expanded Kobe City, was, to be sure, an important settlement and port city, profiting by its proximity to the flourishing metropolis of Osaka, for several hundred years prior to the restoration. Since Osaka's shallow harbor was unable to admit large foreign vessels, an adjacent deepwater port to serve the general Kinki region became necessary, and it was on the slight coastal indentation known as Kobe Bay, 16 miles distant from Osaka, that such a development took place. The port and modern city were to a considerable degree developed by British and American merchants. Even in recent years foreign concerns were relatively more important there than in any other city, the non-Japanese population in 1936 being 8,030. In 1940 Kobe was practically tied with Yokohama for fifth rank among Japanese cities, with slightly less than a million population. For fifteen years, up until 1938, Kobe was the first port of Japan.

The site of the city, a narrow coastal and alluvial piedmont strip backed by a high and precipitous granite horst, has determined its linear shape—12 kilometers long by 1.5–2 kilometers broad (Fig. 256). Its immediate hinterland is relatively barren of settlement, which again serves to emphasize the fact that Kobe's *raison d'etre* is the populous Kinki region and, more especially, industrial Osaka. The industrial and commercial sections of the city occupy the flatter land along the waterfront, while residential Kobe occupies the piedmont slopes to the rear (Fig. 256). The retail commercial core, much of it emphatically Occidental in appearance, occupies a mid-position along the coast just back of the principal piers, dividing the industrial strip into eastern and western parts. Portions of the city along the waterfront are built upon reclaimed land, with the larger buildings resting upon piles. Since all parts of the business and industrial section are so near salt water, the lack of an extensive system of canals such as serves most of the great Japanese cities, is not a serious handicap.

Industry.—Primarily commercial, and somewhat overshadowed industrially by the metropolis of Osaka, Kobe is nevertheless one of the nation's principal manufacturing cities. It lies at the western extremity of the great Hanshin industrial belt and represents the second most important point of manufactural concentration within that belt. The value of Kobe's industrial output in 1938 was 770 billion yen, about a third that of Osaka's.

TABLE 152.—KOBE'S INDUSTRIAL PRODUCTION, 1936

Commodity	Value of output (in thousands of yen)
Textiles.	28,007
Metals	125,272
Machines and tools.	146,786
Ceramics	1,273
Chemicals.	81,664
Wood and wood manufacturing	5,231
Printing and bookbinding.	3,412
Foodstuffs.	65,651
Total, including others	486,505

Source: *Glimpses of the East*, 1939–40 (Tokyo, 1940), 115.

Over 70 per cent of the factory production was in the heavy industries, for Kobe's plants had by that time been geared to production for war.[9] Heavy industries accounted for only 56 per cent of the city's manufactures in 1936, but by the next year the proportion had risen to 62 per cent.[10] Foremost among its industries even in 1936 was machines and tools, followed by metals and chemicals, and the importance of these three increased relatively in the succeeding years.

As compared with Osaka, Kobe has been much less specialized in textiles, which group of industries furnished less than 6 per cent of the city's industrial output in 1936 as against 30 per cent for the machine industries, 26 per cent for the metal industries, and 17 per cent for chemicals. Since 1936 the relative position of textiles has further declined. Among the heavy industries of the engineering type shipbuilding is outstanding, the

[9] *The Japan Advertiser Annual Review*, 1939–40, p. 40.   [10] *Ibid.*, 40.

huge Kawasaki and Mitsubishi shipyards being among the largest in Japan. Thus the Osaka Bay district, with both Kobe and Osaka as centers, is Japan's shipbuilding concentration of first rank. Associated with the great shipyards are large marine-engine and motor plants, airplane factories, and locomotive plants. Kobe is also an important producer of primary iron and steel, having at least one large blast furnace unit and two steel mills. More than 150 machine shops and machine tool plants and over 70 metal plants are located in the city.[11] Other than metal and machine factories there are also plants of conspicuous size manufacturing matches, bean oil and cake, rubber goods, especially automobile and airplane tires, flour, sugar, and industrial chemicals. All of these industries profit by Kobe's importance as a port city, in that imported raw materials are easily accessible. The lack of further available level land within the city for factory sites is the most serious handicap to Kobe's continued expansion in industry. High hills prevent expansion inland and to the west. In recent years there has been a rapid filling in of the region between Kobe and Osaka, such lesser cities as Amagasaki and Nishinomiya having expanded there. Numerous large modern factories and extensive dormitories for their workers characterize this newer section of the Hanshin industrial belt.[12]

The Port.—Kobe's position as one of the three ranking ports of Japan is associated with two items of location: (1) its Kinki hinterland, one of the two most populous, urbanized, and industrial regions of the country, and (2) its location on the famous Inland Sea steamship route, which is followed by boats operating between Asia and North America. It has, as a consequence, become the terminus for much of the Japanese line traffic and a port of call for all foreign-line boats operating in East Asian waters.

Kobe's harbor in a number of respects resembles more that of Yokohama than that of Osaka, Nagoya, or Tokyo (Fig. 256). Like Yokohama it is removed from the head of the bay, where relatively large streams debouch and shallow the water. Natural depths of 10 meters are found at a distance of one-half mile to one mile seaward from Kobe. The port is located in a slight natural indentation that offers a degree of protection. In addition, a series of breakwaters with a total length of 4.5 miles encloses a commodious harbor 3.6 square miles in extent which provides adequate anchorage and turning space within an area of quiet waters. The four principal foreign-trade piers, enclosing basins 350 meters long with water depths of 9–12 meters, lie opposite the commercial core in the central

[11] T. E. Lloyd, "Kyushu and Honshu Islands Focal Points of Japan Industry," in *The Iron Age*, April 30, 1942. See folded map.
[12] *The Japan Advertiser Annual Review*, 1939–40, p. 40.

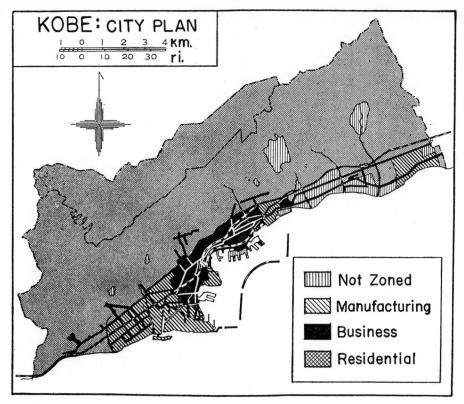

FIG. 256. The city planning map of Kobe. From *Nippon Chiri-Fuzoku Taikei.*

part of the city. It is principally the large mail and passenger ships which dock at the piers; the smaller freighters usually adopt the less expensive procedure of anchoring at one of the 23 buoys, where they unload and load from lighters. Other wharves and piers are provided for ships engaged in coastwise traffic. Much of the city's industry is located close to the waterfront. In 1937, an average of 74 ocean-going vessels slipped in and out of Kobe harbor daily. The docking and warehouse facilities are the largest and among the most modern in Japan.

That Kobe is an industrial port serving the Hanshin and Ise Bay industrial nodes is suggested by the amount and character of its trade. Among foreign imports industrial raw materials overshadow everything else; on the other hand, Kobe's exports are largely factory products. Although Kobe itself is not a textile center, in 1937 nearly 46 per cent and in 1938, 41 per cent, of its incoming cargo was raw cotton, chiefly from British India, the United States, and Egypt. This raw material was destined not only for the mills of Osaka and the general Kinki region, but also for those of the Nagoya center and others in smaller cities in southwestern Japan. Ores, oil, chemicals, and machinery also ranked high among imports.

Among foreign exports there is no single item that has such a commanding position as raw cotton in the imports, though cloth of various kinds comprises about 30 per cent of the total value of exports. Cotton fabrics, in which Kobe itself is not specialized, lead in the export list, with nearly 16 per cent of the total value, followed by raw silk with 11 per cent, clothing with nearly 11 per cent, and machinery with close to 9 per cent. Until Yokohama was demolished by the earthquake and fire of 1923 that port had almost a monopoly on the raw silk trade. Profiting by its rival's misfortune, Kobe at that time took, and has continued to retain, a considerable proportion of the silk trade from those regions in southwestern Japan which are naturally more tributary to it than they are to Yokohama. Kobe's total foreign trade in 1937 amounted to about 2.25 billion yen and its coastwise trade was nearly equal to its foreign. The following year showed a sharp decline. A considerable part of Kobe's

TABLE 153.—LEADING ITEMS IN KOBE'S FOREIGN TRADE, 1938
(in thousands of yen)

Exports	Amount	Imports	Amount
Cotton tissues	121,483	Raw cotton.	292,414
Woolen tissues, including mixtures .	21,640	Oils	53,341
Silk tissues, including mixtures . . .	25,700	Ores and metals.	81,140
Artificial-silk tissues,		Machinery, instruments and vehicles .	52,023
including mixtures.	57,251	Pulp for artificial silk	26,184
Staple-fiber tissues,		Paper and paper manufactures . . .	28,873
including mixtures.	4,544	Rubber	22,811
Raw silk	84,991	Soybeans	14,046
Artificial silk	6,254	Hides and skins.	14,834
Paper and pulp	21,105		
Clothing	81,990		
Machinery and instruments	67,574		
Chemicals and drugs.	24,972		
Oils	16,356		
Sake.	16,637		
Wheat flour	10,377		
Pottery and glass	10,404		
Metal manufactures	18,978		
Metals and ores.	9,067		
Total, including all others	774,038	Total, including all others	706,257

Source: *Annual Return of the Foreign Trade of Japan*, pt. 3 (Department of Finance, Tokyo, 1938).

water-borne domestic trade is lighter traffic with Osaka, and trade, carried by small steamers or sailing ships, with the local ports along the margins of the Inland Sea, for which Kobe acts in the capacity of an entrepôt. In value, exports and imports are very similar; on the other hand, in volume or tonnage the bulky raw-material imports greatly exceed the exports.

Kobe's principal trade is with southern and eastern Asia, with the

United States a close second. In contrast to Osaka's trade, however, Kobe's is much more largely with countries outside the Yen-Bloc. In 1939, for example, only 30 per cent of its exports went to Yen-Bloc countries and only 20 per cent of its imports were derived from those regions. This suggests a fundamental contrast between the ports and harbors of Kobe and Osaka. The more commodious and deeper harbor of Kobe, and its superior port facilities, attract the larger and faster ships that are accustomed to operate on the long runs.

Since Kobe's position as a commercial city is so thoroughly dependent upon the Kinki industrial hinterland, programs of harbor improvement begun by Osaka and Nagoya, and their growing importance as ports, are sources of some concern to Kobe. Ocean freight rates to Osaka and Kobe are identical, even when transshipment from Kobe to Osaka is necessary. Consequently, if Osaka harbor is ultimately improved to such a degree as to admit large ocean steamers, Kobe will necessarily suffer, since its own local industrial hinterland is limited.

Kino Graben (Area *e*) is a narrow spear-shaped, waste-filled valley lying between the Izumi Horst on the north and the Kii Folded Mountains on the south, and coinciding with the great fracture zone and morphological fault which separates the Inner and the Outer Zone of Southwest Japan. Diluvial deposits carved by river erosion into a succession of terraces representing different stages of uplift, fill the northern part of the valley. As a consequence, the river and its narrow alluvial floodplain are crowded against the hardrock hills that bound the valley on the south. Rice predominates on the alluvial floor. Both lower smooth, and higher dissected, terraces are present, and on these elevated sites the usual dry crops of annuals, together with mandarin orange groves, mulberry fields, and woodland occupy the greater share of land, although pond-irrigated rice also competes for space. The north-facing hill slopes bordering the south side of the graben have even a greater concentration of orange groves than do the terraces on the north side, this Kino Valley being a part of that specialized Kinki orange district lying along the south side of Osaka Bay and bordering Kii Channel. Wakayama city (195,203), at the mouth of the valley, and an outlier of the Osaka industrial belt, is specialized in spinning, weaving, dyeing, and bleaching of cotton and silk fabrics. Wakanoura, on a small indentation about 5 kilometers south of Wakayama, is that city's port. Depths of 2.5 meters are maintained so that small boats engaged in domestic trade can enter with cargoes of coal and raw cotton and carry away lumber, fish, oranges, and straw materials.[13]

[13] Ludwig Mecking, *Japans Häfen* (Hamburg, 1931), 423–425.

CHAPTER XV

The Inner Zone of Southwest Japan

PART 2

CENTRAL SETOUCHI (INLAND SEA)[1]

IN THE various schemes for subdividing Japan geographically, *Setouchi* (Region B) is almost invariably recognized as a unit. It is Japan's Mediterranean. Literally translated the word *Setouchi* means "within the channels," referring to the straits, all of them fortified zones, which connect the Inland Sea with the ocean. Morphologically it is the lowest part of a subsiding land area which prior to subsidence had been a maturely dissected peneplaned surface cut by a complicated net of faults. Its archipelagic character, exceedingly irregular coastline, centripetal drainage, and relatively bright, dry, sunny climate, together with its borderlands of partially bare granitic hills, give to Setouchi Basin a considerable degree of physical uniformity.[2] Its waters are so shallow that an uplift of fifty meters would expose a land surface whose essential features would be like the lands now bordering its shores. Before submergence the region was a series of five large basins separated by dissected horsts, a pattern quite similar to that of Kinki. These basins are now the more open portions of Setouchi, called *nadas*. The archipelagic portions, composed of hundreds of islands arranged in roughly parallel rows, are the exposed crests of the intervening dissected horsts, and the narrow channels between the islands mark the fault lines. At present the deepest water is found not in the open *nadas*, but in the constricted inter-island channels, where depths are maintained by tidal scouring, tidal races being so vigor-

[1] H. Schmitthenner, *Die Japanische Inlandsee* (Hettner-Festschrift, Breslau, 1921); I. Watanuki, *Geography of Setouchi with One Hundred Illustrations* (in Japanese, Tokyo, 1932); Keiji Tanaka, "Some Geographical Notes on the Excursion to the Inland Sea (Setouchi) Region, including Miyajima" (unpublished manuscript); N. Yamasaki, "Morphologische Betrachtung des japanischen Binnenmeers Setouchi," in *Petermanns Geographische Mitteilungen*, 48 (1902):245–253.

[2] "The Besshi Copper Mine and Yashima," in *Guide-Book Excursion E-2* (Pan-Pacific Science Congress, Tokyo, 1926), 2–3.

ous in some places as to make navigation difficult if not actually dangerous.

Fortunate are those Japanese who reside along the shores of Setouchi, for the charm of its subdued landscape makes it one of the loveliest parts of Nippon. The beauty of the Inland Sea region has not been lost on the Japanese, judging by the large numbers of people who for centuries have crowded onto its diminutive plains and adjacent hill slopes. Clear blue skies and calm, island-studded waters, picturesque fishing craft, shining sandy beaches of disintegrated granite—these are ingredients of the Setouchi landscape, as are also the small carefully cultivated plains and closely spaced settlements, with several hundred feet of artificially terraced and cultivated slopes rising back of them. Probably in no other large area of Japan is terraced cultivation of steep slopes so extensively practiced (Fig. 257).

The quiet waters and numerous natural harbors, together with the dense population which occupies its margins, have been influential factors in Setouchi's development as an important commercial sea. Not only is it followed throughout its entire length by the transpacific steamers, but it is crossed from north to south by multitudes of small intercoastal

Fig. 257. The borderlands of the Inland Sea. Note the height to which terraced fields have been carried up the mountain slopes. Scene near Okayama.

and inter-island boats engaged in an important domestic trade. Since this is a segment of the nation's well populated industrial belt, cities are relatively numerous, although none of them is of first rank. Almost all the larger cities have coastal locations and are maritime in aspect, each being an important trade center for a local hinterland and having frequent boat service with neighboring ports.

At the extreme eastern and western ends of Setouchi, respectively, are the important twin ports of Kobe-Osaka and Moji-Shimonoseki. Between these, and much more engaged in domestic trade, are nearly a score of lesser ports. Most of these are located in the central portion of Setouchi, where they do not compete with the great "end ports," and in that portion where well populated islands are most numerous. Some of the more important ones are located opposite constrictions in the sea or on important channels. All of them have significant connections with Kobe and Osaka, through which they do most of their foreign trading, raw cotton for local textile industries being an important cargo item. Coal is the principal cargo received from the North Kyushu ports. Boats plying only between the local ports tend in general to follow north-south routes connecting opposite cities on the Chugoku and Shikoku coasts and touching at some islands between. The waterfronts of these minor ports are so crowded with small craft of various sorts that from a distance one has the impression of a forest of masts (Fig. 258). Sailing boats are often as numerous as engined craft (Fig. 259).

Industry appears to be neither very specialized nor very concentrated,

Fig. 258. Numerous small freight-passenger boats, both sailers and steamers, crowd the harbors of the local ports along the Inland Sea. Onomichi harbor.

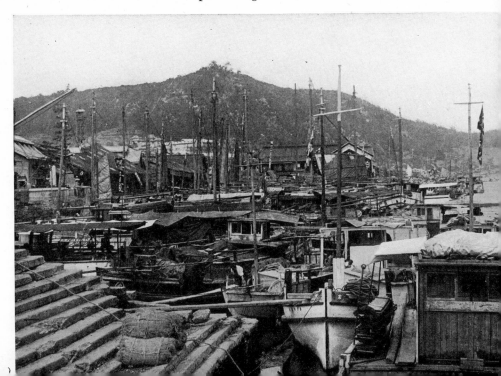

Fig. 259. Fishing boats in the harbor of a little village near Hiroshima on the shores of the Inland Sea.

although as one travels along the Setouchi coasts, he is conscious of frequent isolated or small clusters of manufacturing plants in the cities and villages. Cotton spinning and weaving probably rank highest among Setouchi's industries, but *sake,* beer, rubber, chemicals, tile, rayon, metal products, oil refineries, salt evaporators, and numerous other industries are represented. Two of the most distinctive local industries are the manufacture of salt from sea water and the weaving of reed mats for *tatami,*[3] made from a cultivated aquatic plant, *I,* grown almost exclusively in this region.

Within the basin of Setouchi is 90 per cent of the country's salt-field area—a total of some 4,000 hectares or approximately 10,000 acres (Fig. 260). Along some parts of the coast these diked salt-fields with their geometric pattern of evaporating basins and drainage ditches, their salt piles and the small boiling plants adjacent make a distinctive landscape (Fig. 261). The country's salt-fields are concentrated in Setouchi because of its prevailingly hot, bright, clear summer weather with less rain and lower relative humidity than in other parts of Japan (Fig. 262). Other favorable features are (1) the moderate tidal range, averaging about three meters, which permits periodic filling and draining of the canals of the salt fields;

[3] *Tatami* are the almost universal floor covering in Japanese homes.

(2) numerous small alluvial areas with clean sandy beaches and quiet shallow waters offshore; (3) the proximity of cheap Ube coal, which is used as fuel in the boiling stations.

The Islands

The hundreds of islands (Subregion 1) which dot the surface of Setouchi are a characteristic feature of this Japanese Mediterranean. To observe the characteristic insular landscape features, I made a crossing from Hiroshima in Chugoku to Imabari in Shikoku on a small intercoastal steamer which called at numerous island settlements. In no instance did the thousand-ton boat come alongside a dock at any of the island ports, but was always met by a sculled lighter. Most of the islands are several hundred feet high, with steep, forested slopes. Those composed of granite have somewhat softer contours with much bare whitish rock showing through the sparse woodland cover. Slopes frequently end abruptly at the water's edge, and hence low wave-cut cliffs or platforms are common features. Hidden away in little coves are alluvial accumulations on which small agricultural-fishing villages have grown up, although many of the tiny deltas are so small that expansion onto the adjacent lower hill slopes

Fig. 260 (*left*). Distribution of salt fields in the borderlands of the Inland Sea. From *Nippon Chiri-Fuzoku Taikei.*
Fig. 261 (*right*). View of the salt fields near Onomichi. Boiling plants are located along the margins of the salt field.

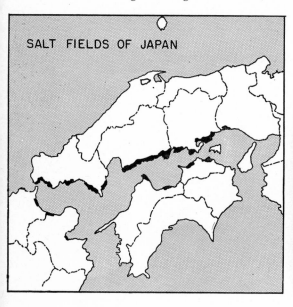

SALT FIELDS OF JAPAN

and to reclaimed land along the sea margin has been necessary. The little fishing boats belonging to the island villagers are protected by low stone breakwaters, which enclose a trifling bit of sea. Many small islands adjacent to a larger mother island have no settlements. Those that are used exclusively for rice cultivation are less likely to have permanent habitations than those on which dry farms prevail, for the latter require more constant attention. Since grass is much in demand for forage and fertilizer, it is the exclusive crop on many islands. Because island farms are more often reached by boat than by road, the cultivated spots are distributed in a most irregular manner, and are found wherever access to the sea is least difficult (Fig. 263).

Shrines, often dedicated to *Benten*, sea goddess and favorite deity

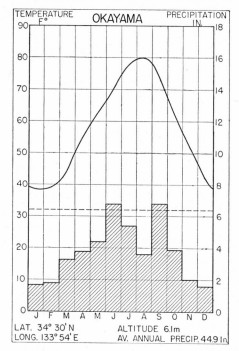

Fig. 262. Hot summers, mild winters, less than average rainfall, and a high percentage of sunshine are characteristic of the Inland Sea climate.

of the island peoples, occupy conspicuous promontory sites and in prelighthouse days served as landmarks for the navigators.[4] Conspicuous to a foreigner is the cultivation of steep slopes, made possible through artificial terracing. By this arduous means cultivation is often carried from four to six hundred feet up the steep hillsides. In such a slope environment unirrigated crops naturally predominate, although rice is grown wherever possible. Mandarin oranges are one of the most widespread crops of the terraced slopes.[5] On two islands of the Inland Sea, one on the route between Okayama and Takamatsu and the other about eleven miles northwest of Niihama in Shikoku, are located important copper smelters. In such island locations a minimum amount of damage is done to valuable

[4] Hikoichiro Sasaki, "The Cultural Landscape of Islands of the Inland Sea" (in Japanese with English summary), in the *Geographical Review of Japan*, 8 (1932):38–47.

[5] I. Watanuki, "Villages in Setouchi" (in Japanese), in the *Geographical Review of Japan*, 7:1053–1074 (December 1, 1931).

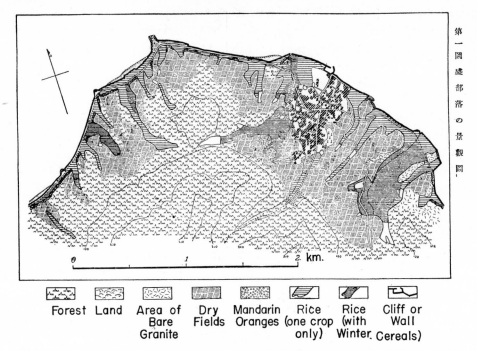

Fig. 263. Vegetation cover and features of agricultural land use on a small island in the Inland Sea. Map by Watanuki.

farm land by the smelter fumes. The smelter near Niihama handles chiefly ores from the famous Besshi copper mine in northern Shikoku.

Sanyo District

Chugoku Peninsula, or extreme southwestern Honshu, of which this Sanyo section (Subregion 2) facing Setouchi comprises the southern two-thirds, was formerly a complicated mountainous region composed of igneous and sedimentary rocks. It has been peneplaned and subsequently fractured into a series of blocks, some rising, others depressed. The principal fault system trends northeast by southwest, but it is intersected roughly at right angles by another series of parallel faults. The uplifted oblong blocks or horsts are recognized in Japan under such names as Tamba and Kibi plateaus. Although in some places remnants of the ancient peneplains still persist in the form of uneven upland surfaces, much the larger part of the area has been reduced to relatively rugged hill country whose elevations rarely exceed 3,000 feet. Major drainage lines, determined principally by the fault net, have a striking lattice pattern, their entrenched, steep-sided, and narrow valleys indicating rejuvenation. Where two fault-line valleys intersect, wider alluvium-floored stretches result, this feature of the drainage lines being characteristic. Unlike Kinki, Chugoku is not a region of numerous alluvium-floored grabens. Passes and saddles across stream divides, resulting from frequent instances of stream capture, are numerous.[6]

In this study, roughly the crest of the divide in Chugoku is accepted as the line separating the northern or Sanin slopes from those of Sanyo to the south. This boundary, geological and cultural as well as morphological, makes for an asymmetrical partition, since the highest land is much closer to the north than to the south coast. In general the sedimentary rock areas of Chugoku are somewhat lower in elevation, and in them dissection has been more complete, resulting in a finer-textured terrain than in the bolder, granitic areas. For purposes of discussion the interior hill lands of southern Chugoku are treated separately from the coastal margins.

INTERIOR HILL LANDS OF SOUTHERN CHUGOKU

The complicated terrain features and land-use patterns of this region (Area *a*) make broad generalizations on the basis of reconnaissance observation not only difficult but somewhat hazardous. Five rail lines cross Chugoku from north to south, connecting the trunk lines which parallel the Sanin and Sanyo coasts. Except in the higher parts, where coarser-textured slopes prevail, the hill lands of southern Chugoku are well occupied, both dispersed and semidispersed settlements being found in the rural areas. The settlement pattern is unusually complicated, coinciding as it does with the intricate system of drainage lines. Slope cultivation, with terraced hillsides planted in mulberry, tea, tobacco, orange groves, summer vegetables, and winter grains, is characteristic. Rice occupies all irrigable sites. The region is not thoroughly specialized in any one crop, variety being a distinctive feature.

Some fame is attached to the region because it has the highest density of cattle population of any large part of the country, although even in the most specialized regions of cattle raising the average is only one animal per farmer and the largest herds usually contain not over ten head. The animals are of native stock, usually black, and are raised for beef and for draft purposes. Cattle markets are held regularly in many towns. During the three summer months, especially after rice planting, the animals forage for their food on the wild pastures and wooded slopes; during the remainder of the year they are kept at the farmstead.

[6] K. Tanaka. Unpublished manuscript on Setouchi, cited in note 1.

The *Tamba Upland* (*a*[1]) in eastern Chugoku differs from the other sections in that it is composed largely of sedimentary rocks. Its high eastern margin with elevations of over 1,000 meters is the fault-scarp overlooking the Biwa, Kyoto, and Osaka depressions. The fault net is here less dense and the texture of slopes less fine than elsewhere in Chugoku, and settlement is therefore more concentrated, being confined largely to stream valleys and to small waste-filled fault basins such as Kameoka, Tamba, Sasayama, and Fukuchiyama. The wide interfluves are largely devoid of settlement, and are left principally in woods or in wasteland.

The *Kibi Upland* (*a*[2]), in central Chugoku, is bounded on the north by a long and continuous much-eroded fault-scarp which separates it from the higher and more formidable hills or low mountains which are the principal divide of the peninsula. Kibi is a hilly land with elevations usually under 500 meters. The original peneplain surface is in an early stage of dissection, steep-sided valleys separating rather extensive areas of somewhat uneven upland surface, above which monadnocks rise. Fault features are not conspicuous. Most of the upland is in trees or cut-over wasteland, although its more flattish parts have been brought under cultivation. In low spots where water can be accumulated, rice is grown (Fig. 264). In such regions settlement is usually in the form of isolated farmsteads or loose clusters of farmsteads; genuinely compact villages are not numerous. Even in many of the larger alluvium-floored valleys, settlements lack compactness, the houses being located in irregular fashion along the margins of the valley or even on the bordering lower hill slopes. Although Kibi is the heart of Chugoku's cattle country, I did not see a single animal grazing on the hill slopes during my trip across the region in midsummer. This suggests that even in this specialized cattle-raising region, cattle are not numerous according to non-Japanese standards. Forest industries seem to be important, to judge from the bundles of wood and charcoal which one sees piled on the platforms of railway stations.

Near the eastern and western extremities of the Kibi district are two rel-

Fig. 264. Near the crest of the Kibi Upland in inland Chugoku. Note the semi-dispersed character of the farmhouses. Rice is the crop in the foreground.

atively large areas of lower elevation, in general less than 300 meters, where weak Tertiary rocks are prevalent. Typical Tertiary landscape, with wide, open, alluvium-floored valleys separated by hills of moderate to low elevation, is characteristic. A relatively dense dispersed rural population cultivates not only the valley floors but the hill slopes as well. Miyoshi and Tsuyama are the metropolises of the western and eastern basins, respectively, and lie strategically near the focus of radially converging valleys.

Western Chugoku (a³), with its dense fault net and highly developed morphological fault structure, consists of a series of narrow northeast-southwest horsts, highest in the north-central part (over 1,300 meters), but descending step by step to the Japan Sea and Setouchi coasts. Although fault valleys are numerous, there are no graben basins. The rural population, commonly living on isolated farmsteads or in loosely knit rural villages, is relatively dense. Toward the extreme western end of Chugoku, where sedimentary rocks rather than granites prevail, elevations are generally lower. In some limestone areas typical karst features have developed.

THE COASTAL MARGINS OF SOUTHERN CHUGOKU

The irregular southern coast of Setouchi (Area *b*) has resulted from the sinking of a hilly land whose original features were caused by faulting and stream erosion. Along certain stretches islands are abundant, but where *nadas* prevail these are largely lacking. Many former irregular arms of the sea, or archipelagic channels, have been filled with detritus, forming a complicated and seemingly almost patternless system of alluvial valleys and basins, or small plains studded with hardrock hills. None of the delta-plains is sufficiently large to warrant its consideration as a separate unit. Alluvial deposits accumulate here with surprising rapidity because of the rapid weathering of the rounded and often bare granitic hills. A relatively dense population has kept the vegetation cover of these slopes impoverished for centuries, and reforestation is therefore extremely difficult. The hills come down to the water's edge so frequently that many

Fig. 265. Slope cultivation along the Sanyo margins of the Inland Sea. Orange groves are conspicuous. Note the semi-dispersed nature of the farmhouses.

stretches of the Sanyo trunk-line railway, paralleling this coast and connecting Kobe and Shimonoseki, are inland at variable distances from the shore and separated from it by hills. Diluvium is not extensive along the coast of Chugoku except toward its extreme eastern end between Himeji and Kobe. There in the basin of the Tamba River is a relatively large area of old diluvium and Tertiary deposits which have been so thoroughly dissected that almost all smooth upland surfaces have been obliterated. A labyrinthine pattern of alluvium-floored valleys has thus been developed. On these sites is found a relatively dense dispersed population. Numerous artificial ponds in the adjacent hills provide water for irrigation of the paddy fields.

The arable land is completely occupied, although there are no large compact units of population, since there are no extensive plains. Various forms of rural settlement are represented, dispersed and compact as well as intermediate amorphous types. The unusual thing is that in such a long-settled region there should be so many isolated farm dwellings. These prevail on the hilly lands, but are also common on the more open plains. In no other part of rural Japan have I seen so many prosperous and attractive residences of more than average size. Whitewashed, with red tile roofs, many of them look more Mediterranean than Japanese. These do not predominate, to be sure, but they are sufficiently numerous to add brightness, color, and charm to the countryside. On the extreme outer margins of some of the larger deltas, where new land has recently been reclaimed for agricultural uses, the isolated rural dwellings and the rectangular pattern of land subdivision and lines of communication remind one of Hokkaido.

Some of the features of the agricultural landscape are distinctive. A striking characteristic is the prevalence of artificially terraced fields on the lower slopes of the hills, for this is one of Japan's principal areas of slope cultivation (Fig. 265). By this method unirrigated fields are carried up the slopes for several hundred feet. Conspicuous as a slope crop in western Sanyo, as on the islands of Setouchi, is the mandarin orange. Still more widespread are the fields of summer vegetables, many of which are replanted to cereals in the fall. Extremely high-grade rice is produced on the relatively coarse alluvial soils, which have been weathered from the adjacent granite hills. Winter cropping of both the paddies and the upland fields is very common. As a result this region has become one of the country's largest producers of naked barley and wheat, both fall-sown crops which are used for human as well as animal food. The cattle population is relatively dense for Japan, many farmers raising beef and draft animals for sale, thereby increasing their meager cash incomes. This specialization in cattle in southern Chugoku seems to date from the Sino-Japanese War of 1894–95 and the Russo-Japanese War of 1904 when army headquarters were located at Hiroshima and the region supplied large amounts of meat to the Japanese troops. A number of the coastal towns such as Onomichi, Chiya, Niimi, and Takahashi, are important cattle markets. The animals are kept chiefly at the farmsteads and fed on grass cut from the hill slopes and on crops grown on the tiny farms.

Competing with rice for low, easily inundated sites along portions of the Inland Sea margins is the reed crop, called *I*, from which *tatami* mats are made. Practically the country's entire production is confined to two prefectures, Okayama, in southern Chugoku, and Kagawa in northern Shikoku. No doubt the clear, hot summer weather, ideal for out-of-doors drying, is a major factor in this regional specialization, but local inhabitants attribute it partly to the supplies of white clay, used as a bleaching agent, which are available in the vicinity. The plant is dark green in color, three to four feet tall, and has a small cylindrical stem probably an eighth of an inch in diameter. Between Onomichi and Okayama the reed crop is particularly conspicuous; the dark green patches of the plant sometimes occur singly or in small groups intermingled with rice fields, but not uncommonly there are several acres of continuous reed fields (Fig. 266). In July, the harvest season, the reed fields are alive with workers engaged in cutting the plant, tying it into bundles, dipping it in white-

FIG. 266. Fields of the *I* reed, from which *tatami* are made. Note the cut reed drying along the edge of the roadside. Recently planted paddy field in foreground. Scene near Onomichi.

clay mud, and laying it out on the hillsides to dry. At this time many of the adjacent hill slopes are covered with the drying reed.

Sanyo for the most part is conspicuously lacking in mineral resources, the only one of significance being the coal in the relatively unimportant Ube (Onada) and Omine fields in the extreme western part of Chugoku, in Yamaguchi Prefecture, near Ube city. On a map published by the Japan Bureau of Mines entitled, "The Important Mines, 1935," only three mines were shown for the Ube Field. However, others of less importance were not included on the map. Two of the Ube mines together produced 1.8 million metric tons of coal in 1935, chiefly poor bituminous and lignite.[7] This no doubt was a large percentage of the entire Ube output. Since the production of this field in 1928 was only about 700,000 tons, the above figure indicates a considerable increase in output. Submarine seams at present are the largest producers. Most of the coal mined in the Ube Field is consumed in the manufacturing centers around the margins of the Inland Sea. On the map of important mines referred to above, three mines are shown for the Omine anthracite field located 20 to 25 kilometers inland and to the northwest of Ube city. For only one of these was a production figure given and that amounted to 221,000 tons (1935).[8] The anthracite mined at Omine is mostly fine, and usually rich in sulphur and ash. Some of it is manufactured into briquettes. In Yamaguchi Prefecture, in which the Omine and Ube fields are located, the total production of coal by mines with over 10,000 metric tons output amounted to only 2.5 million tons in 1935.[9]

CITIES OF SANYO

There are at least nineteen cities of over 25,000 population in that part of Sanyo lying west of Kobe. Only one, Hiroshima, has over 300,000 population; one has approximately 275,000 and four others exceed 100,000. Most of the nineteen are local ports and manufacturing centers of some significance.

Shimonoseki (196,022), at the western end of Chugoku, is strategically situated on the narrow Straits of Shimonoseki separating Honshu from Kyushu, which is the main route for transpacific vessels to and from Asia by way of Japan. Only a mile and a half from Moji on the Kyushu side of the straits, Shimonoseki is the southern terminus of the Honshu rail lines and an important ferry port with boats leaving at fifteen-minute intervals. A railroad tunnel under the straits, which was to have been completed in 1942, has probably modified this phase of the city's activity. Very recently

[7] *The Mining Industry of Japan, 1935,* Japan Bureau of Mines. [8] *Ibid.* [9] *Ibid.*

the open ports of Moji and Shimonoseki have been combined into a single port called Kammon. In this combination Shimonoseki handles principally the unusually large domestic trade, and acts as the country's terminus of shipping lines connecting with Fusan and Rashin in Korea. It has national fame as a fishing port, probably ranking as the greatest in western Japan.

TABLE 154.—VALUE OF IMPORTANT ITEMS IN SHIMONOSEKI'S FOREIGN TRADE, 1938

Exports	Value in Yen	Imports	Value in Yen
Woolen tissues, including mixtures	2,639,000	Ores and metals	531,000
Woolen knitting yarns	2,066,000	Machinery	208,000
Wheat flour	1,764,000	Steam boilers and parts.	99,000
Underwear	996,000		
Machinery	977,000		
Clothing and accessories	802,000		
Artificial silk	699,000		
Cotton tissues	558,000		
Socks and stockings	547,000		
Cotton thread	535,000		
Total, including others	22,897,000	Total, including others	1,279,000

Source: *Annual Return of the Foreign Trade of Japan*, pt. 3, (Department of Finance, Tokyo, 1938).

Shimonoseki's trade consists chiefly in exports to the Yen-Bloc countries. Industrially Shimonoseki is a part of that node of heavy manufacturing lying along the straits separating Kyushu and Honshu, but concentrated chiefly in northern Kyushu. Railroad shops, shipbuilding yards, breweries, and cement and fertilizer factories are some of its more important plants.

Ube (100,660), located near the coal field which bears the same name, is a minor coal port. The total foreign trade in 1938 was valued at only about a million yen with imports, largely salt (629,738 yen) and steam boilers and parts (238,794 yen), amounting to eight times the exports. A relatively large synthetic petroleum plant using the local coal is located at Ube. Between Ube and Hiroshima in the vicinity of the towns of Tokuyama and Kudamatsu are large petroleum refineries with associated cracking and iso-octane plants.

Hiroshima (343,968) is the metropolis of central Setouchi. It was an important castle town during the feudal era and its modern growth was stimulated when it became military headquarters of the Emperor and his general staff, and principal home base of operations during the wars with China and Russia.[10] It is still a military and political center, the fifth army

[10] H. Nozawa, "The Development of the City of Hiroshima" (in Japanese) in the *Geographical Bulletin* (*Chiri Ronso*), No. 5, pp. 47–93 (Kyoto Imperial University, 1934).

brigade occupying the daimyo castle grounds within the city. Although it is one of the principal local ports of Setouchi and is served by the trunk-line Sanyo Railway, Hiroshima is not primarily a commercial and industrial city. Its fame and charm are attributable to a colorful historic background, as well as to its present political and military functions. The city's hinterland is a much-faulted granite hill country with relatively dense settlement. A local rail line runs north from Hiroshima as far as Miyoshi, tapping that important interior region. The site of the city is a small multi-pronged delta, at whose sea ends are several land-tied islands (Fig. 74). Canals are abundant. Along the advancing delta fronts the waters are so shallow that it has been necessary to develop an outer port at Ujina on one of the land-tied islands, some 3 or 4 kilometers seaward from the heart of the city. Its manufacturing emphasizes textiles, rayon, cotton, and silk being represented. Small-size machinery and tools, rubber products, and canned foods are likewise of some consequence. It is very likely also that a synthetic petroleum plant belonging to the Imperial Army is operating at Hiroshima.

Kure (276,085), at the southern extremity of Hiroshima Bay, is strictly a fortified military city, being the site of a naval station, steel works, arsenal, and dockyards. It contains the greatest dry dock of the country. Near by is the Imperial Naval College.

Onomichi (48,726), with its outer port of *Itosaki,* is a center of oil storage and receives large imports of foreign petroleum. The principal exports, canned citrus and *tatami* mats, reflect local specialization of the region

TABLE 155.—VALUE OF FOREIGN TRADE OF ONOMICHI-ITOSAKI, 1938

Exports	Value in Yen	Imports	Value in Yen
Canned citrus	239,000	Vehicles and vessels	5,655,000
Tatami mats.	750,000	Petroleum.	5,498,000
		Soybeans	407,000
Totals, including others. . . .	1,566,000	Total, including others	12,840,000

Source: *Annual Return of the Foreign Trade of Japan*, pt. 3 (Department of Finance, Tokyo, 1938).

in mandarin oranges and in the *I* reed of which *tatami* are made. Imports amount to eight times exports in value, vehicles and vessels, and petroleum comprising a large part of the total.

Okayama (163,552), an old castle town, is today a local manufacturing center and, like Hiroshima, an important port in coastwise trade. Located on a delta with shallow water offshore, it has an outer port like many of the other local cities of Setouchi, located 15 or 20 kilometers to the south on a rocky coast. The foreign trade of this outer port, *Uno*, amounts to only 5 or 6 million yen, with paper, minerals, rubber-soled shoes, and firebrick ranking high among the exports, and clay, fodder, maize, and millet among the imports. Okayama is a railway junction point, the Sanyo trunk line here joining one of the trans-Chugoku lines which connects with Matsue on the Sanin coast. *Himeji* (104,259) at the eastern end of Sun-en is particularly well known as one of the newer centers of pig iron and steel production. It is estimated that over 10 per cent of the pig iron of Japan Proper and more than 7 per cent of its steel are processed in the Himeji plants. All raw materials must be imported.

Inland Sea Margins of Shikoku

Shikoku has two very dissimilar geographic subdivisions separated from each other by the great median dislocation line of Japan, which is bordered on either side by developed rift valleys. To the north of this morphologic boundary is a fractured granite area of hill land proportions, in most respects like southern Chugoku; to the south is a region of rugged folded mountains, a segment of the Outer Zone of Southwest Japan. The morphologic and geologic boundaries do not exactly coincide, for a small and lower portion of the Outer Zone of Pacific Folded Mountains lies north of the Yoshino Graben and Matsuyama Plain, which do coincide with the line of dislocation. The landform set-up of northern Shikoku (Subregion 3), with its two blunt granite peninsulas, *Tanakawa* and *Sanuki,* and broad *Hiuchi Bay* or *Nada* between them, is the result of differential fault-block movement, the two peninsulas being horsts and the bay a depressed block. It is noticeable that the granite peninsulas are in line with numerous islands in Setouchi, the archipelagoes marking tops of fractured sunken horsts. On the whole the coastline is less irregular than that of Sanyo.

Many of the natural and cultural forms, their patterns and associations, already described for southern Chugoku, are repeated in northern Shikoku with some modifications. It is chiefly the contrasting features of landscape, therefore, which here need to be stressed. The lowlands of North Shikoku, like those of Sanyo, are too small for individual analysis in this reconnaissance report. Significant contrast exists, however, between the two great peninsulas. The western one is compact and less fractured, contains very little valley alluvium, and presents a relatively smooth coastline, so that settlement is very meager except along the sea margins. On the other hand, Sanuki, the eastern peninsula, is like Sanyo in being much fractured and fragmented, with considerable areas of alluvium occupying broad valleys and what were formerly inter-island channels. As a consequence, settlement is much denser in the eastern peninsula than in the western. A distinctive feature of Sanuki's landforms are the conspicuous flat-topped and conical hills of andesite, which stand out in marked contrast to the more rounded and somewhat lower granitic hills. The conical hills, which are not numerous, may be remnants of volcanic plugs. The tabular hills, some of them rising 300 meters and more above the new alluvium which ties together the hardrock "islands," have precipitous upper slopes, where the andesite cap prevails. They become conspicuously less steep on the weaker granites which comprise the lower two-thirds or more of their total elevation.

Low diluvial terraces with smooth or rolling surfaces are more numerous, rivers are shorter and more variable in flow, and fan configuration of the detrital deposits is more conspicuous on the Shikoku coast than along Sanyo. In July, when I saw the region, most of the broad boulder-strewn river channels were either entirely dry or contained mere trickles of water. Supplementary irrigation from almost innumerable ponds appears to be very common on the alluvial delta-fans as well as on the terraces. The latter sites, although they are less completely utilized than the more fertile new alluvium, are extensively planted to both rice and dry crops, reflecting long occupance of the region by a relatively dense population.

Occupance patterns associated with the *handen* system of land subdivision are very numerous on the plains of North Shikoku. Evidences of this system are not lacking in Sanyo, but certainly the imprint there is not only fainter but less widespread than in North Shikoku. Even here it is not equally evident in all parts, and there are variations in forms. From the flat top of an andesite hill just north of Takamatsu one can look southward over one of the more extensive lowlands of the island and behold a rural scene where *handen* features, expressed in terms of rectangular land subdivision, road pattern, and irrigation ponds, are very conspicuous. The compact village so well represented in Kinki is not prevalent here; instead, there are numerous isolated farmsteads, many of them located along the grid pattern of highways as in Hokkaido. A similar rectangular pattern of land subdivision and roads is conspicuous on the Matsuyama Plain, but there compact villages are much more numerous and ponds are fewer. On the lowland adjacent to Imabari the mesh of the rectangular grid of roads and farms is considerably finer than in other sections.

Two small lowlands, the *Yoshino Rift Valley* (Area *a*) on the east and the *Matsuyama Plain* (Area *b*) on the west, border the great median dislocation line in Shikoku, separating the Inner Zone from the Outer Zone of Southwest Japan. In origin and landscapes they resemble the Kino Graben of Kii Peninsula. Yoshino, which is 80 kilometers long, is shaped like a very long, thin spear. A conspicuous belt of well cultivated river terraces and fans, with a relatively dense dispersed type of settlement, borders the north side of the lowland. The valley floor contains much coarse sand and gravel, and evidences of river floods and lateral stream migrations are common. Mulberry, tobacco, indigo, and other dry crops compete with rice in such an environment. Both of these fault valleys have local railroad lines, but they are not connected with any larger system. In fact, the whole railroad pattern of Shikoku is a series of fragments not organized into a system, the longest single stretch being the one that parallels the north coast.

CITIES

No cities of large size have developed in northern Shikoku, although six with populations of between 25,000 and 100,000 are important local business and industrial centers, and in most cases ports as well. Industries are varied, though cotton weaving and silk reeling are most prominent. *Tokushima* (119,581), at the seaward end of the Yoshino Graben and serving that specific hinterland, is an ancient castle town. Its location some 3 kilometers inland, on a shallow river, has necessitated the development of a deeper outer port, *Komatsushima,* 7 kilometers to the south along the rocky coast. This port, with which Tokushima has both lighter and rail connections, is engaged only in domestic trade. *Matsuyama* (117,534) in a similar way serves the local hinterland of the western fault valley, which has the same name as its principal city. It too has an outer port, *Takahama,* located not at the river mouth, but on an adjacent land-tied island. Two important local business centers, *Takamatsu* (111,207) and *Marugame* (26,928) serve the Sanuki hinterland, which coincides with the single greatest compact settlement unit in Shikoku. Next to Hiroshima, Takamatsu has the largest domestic water-borne trade of any of the local Setouchi ports. Here boats up to 3,000 tons can come alongside docks, so that an outer port is unnecessary. Marugame is not itself a shipping center, but is served by the adjacent port of *Tadotsu,* which is one of Shikoku's leading ports, though it is not large enough to be classed as a city.

Imabari (55,557), serving the narrow littoral plains flanking the western granite horst of Tanakawa, is, like Takamatsu and Tadotsu, strategically located for commerce at a narrows in Setouchi where islands are numer-

ous. It has particular fame as a cotton-textile-weaving center. Imabari is
one of the few open ports in Shikoku. Its foreign trade, amounting to
nearly 5.5 million yen, is equally divided between imports and exports.
Logs and lumber from the rugged hinterland comprise half the exports;
phosphate rock and ores and metals make up 90 per cent of the imports.

TABLE 156.—VALUE OF IMPORTANT ITEMS IN THE FOREIGN TRADE OF IMABARI, 1938

Exports	Value in Yen	Imports	Value in Yen
Logs, lumber, and wood products .	1,039,000	Phosphate.	1,112,000
Paper.	364,000	Ores and metals	817,000
Canned foods	262,000	Fodder	153,000
Mandarin oranges	143,000		
Total, including others	2,238,000	Total, including others	2,214,000

Source: *Annual Return of the Foreign Trade of Japan*, pt. 3 (Department of Finance, Tokyo, 1938).

Along the open coast of Hiuchi or Bingo Nada, where the precipitous
fault-scarp marking the northern boundary of the Pacific Folded Mountains comes close to the sea, there is only one city of significant size,
Niihama (42,392). The life of Niihama is associated with the important
Besshi copper mine located 12 miles to the south. Here are situated the
general offices of the mining company as well as ore-dressing and refining
plants.

THE SANIN LITTORAL OF NORTHERN CHUGOKU

Literally translated, the Japanese word *Sanin* (Region C) means "shady
side," and as applied to the northern littoral of Chugoku refers to the
darker, gloomier, stormier weather there as compared with that of
Setouchi. The contrasts between these two regions do not end with
climate, for Sanin differs from Sanyo also in its less indented coastline, more
limited hinterland, lower population density, fewer cities, more meager
development of manufacturing and commerce, and lack of salt manufacture and citrus culture.

Since Chugoku is asymmetrical, in that the drainage divide is closer to
the north than to the south coast, the total area of land tributary to Sanin
is neither large nor productive. Marginal downwarping, together with
deep water offshore, has tended to produce an abrupt coast where wave-
cut sea cliffs are conspicuous and large indentations rare (Fig. 267). No
insinking basins with relatively extensive alluvial accumulations, such as
exist along the Japan Sea coast of Tohoku and Chubu, are to be found in
Sanin. Where streams enter the sea, tiny accumulations of alluvium de-

velop behind outer belts of beach ridges and dunes, but strong waves and currents prevent their seaward extension beyond the protection of the headlands. Alluvial plains are even smaller and less numerous than they are along the Inland Sea. Two exceptions to this rather featureless shoreline should be noted: (1) In mid-Sanin, the Shinji Range, a horst 60 to 70 kilometers long, parallels the coast, attached to the mainland by a narrow isthmus of Tertiary rock and by river and wave sediments deposited in the intervening graben valley. (2) The extreme eastern part of the Sanin coast has suffered marked insinking, resulting in irregular Wakasa Bay. Fault-scarps mark both the eastern and western margins of the bay, and the deeply indented coastline of ria type indicates submergence of a hilly land with numerous fault-line valleys trending at almost right angles to the shore.

Four separate volcanic groups occupy caldron-shaped depressions along the Sanin coast. The mightiest of these is Daisen (1,773 meters), just to the east of Matsue, a youthful cone with some tilled land on its smooth ash-and-lava aprons. Hundreds of cattle and horses are pastured on its slopes. Hyonosen volcanic group (1,510 meters) south of Tottori is so thoroughly dissected that little if any of the original smooth slope remains, and a wild mountainous country is the result. Two smaller and less conspicuous groups of lava domes are found west of Matsue. Closely associated with volcanic activity are the fissure-type mineral deposits of Sanin, principally silver, copper, and tin. Most of the mines are small, but two of them, Ikuno and Akenobe in Hyogo Prefecture in eastern Sanin, employ several hundred workmen each. Ikuno produces silver, gold, and copper; 80 per cent of the country's tin comes from the Akenobe mine.

Lacking extensive plains, Sanin has no large compact settlement clusters. Small agricultural-fishing villages are strategically located on little alluvial patches at the mouths of rivers whose valleys provide access to the rugged local hinterlands. Considering the nature of the terrain, rural population is relatively dense. Settlements, both compact and dispersed, occupy shallow upland basins as well as valley floors. There is not the same abundance of open valleys with large concentrations of population extending back into the interior as there is in Sanyo. Artificial terracing for slope fields is common. General subsistence agriculture prevails, though some cash income is derived from the sale of cocoons, wood products, and tea. Since this region is a part of the Chugoku cattle area, the sale of cattle also provides some farm income. Slopes have not been so denuded of their forest cover as in the Setouchi borderlands, and

Fɪɢ. 267. The abrupt Sanin coast west of Matsue. Note the little shoestring village bordering the highway which occupies the meager belt of level land between sea and hills.

charcoal manufacture is therefore an important auxiliary to farming.

Since both manufacturing and commerce are relatively unmodernized in Sanin, no large urban centers have developed. Only three cities of over 25,000 population are to be found in the region, the metropolis Matsue having a population of only 55,506. Such industry as does exist, including cotton weaving, silk reeling, and porcelain and lacquer manufacturing, is housed in relatively small and inconspicuous plants and uses largely local raw materials. Railroad lines, constructed with difficulty because of the abrupt and hilly coast, parallel most of the Sanin littoral but are not continuous throughout its entire length. Ocean shipping is relatively un- developed and ports are rare. During the winter, weather conditions and boisterous seas make navigation difficult, and the general lack of deep indentations has caused a dearth of natural harbors. Five foreign-trade ports are located on the Sanin coast, but only one of these, *Tsuruga*

TABLE 157.—VALUE OF IMPORTANT ITEMS IN TSURUGA'S FOREIGN TRADE, 1938

Exports	Value in Yen	Imports	Value in Yen
Artificial silk tissues, including mixtures	2,389,000	Beancake	1,098,000
Cotton tissues	1,047,000	Coal	586,000
Machinery and parts	866,000		
Mandarin oranges	632,000		
Waste paper.	608,000		
Beer	337,000		
Thread and yarns	322,000		
Total, including others	8,507,000	Total, including others	2,047,000

Source: *Annual Return of the Foreign Trade of Japan*, pt. 3 (Department of Finance, Tokyo, 1938).

(31,346), has a significant amount of commerce. The two unimportant ports of *Hamada* (32,230) and *Hagi* (32,270) in western Sanin have foreign trade totals of only 80,000 yen and 428,000 yen respectively.

THE WAKASA BAY DISTRICT

This part of eastern Sanin (Subregion 1), located where Sanin makes contact with Hokuroku, is the exception to the general pattern of smooth, abrupt coast characteristic of northern Chugoku. The bay itself is the result of down-faulting and a subsequent invasion by the sea. Fault-scarps bound the bay on its eastern and western margins. Between Wakasa Bay on the north and Osaka and Ise bays on the south, the land barrier between the Japan Sea side and the Pacific side of Japan becomes narrowest and lowest. No lowlands of sufficient extent to permit concentrated settlement border Wakasa Bay. Two advantages partially counteract this handicap, however: (1) the long, deep, fiord-like indentations of the coast offer excellent protected harbor sites, and (2) a low and narrow range of hills some 15 kilometers wide, cut by tectonic depressions, is all that separates Wakasa Bay from the Biwa depression, which is the natural lowland route to the great industrial and commercial settlements of Kinki and of Ise Bay. Three or four small port cities occupy little alluvial patches at the heads of the deep bays, all of them of very minor importance except Shin-Maizuru, a fortified naval port, and Tsuruga, a commercial port. The latter has direct rail connection with Biwa and draws likewise from the small plain around Fukui just north of Wakasa Bay. Boats up to 6,000 tons are able to come alongside the dock. Tsuruga is one of the relatively few open ports on the west side of Japan, its chief trade being with Vladivostok, Korea, and the east coast of Manchuria. In 1938 exports, chiefly manufactured goods from the Kinki industrial region at the southern end of the Biwa corridor, were valued at more than four times the imports. Beancake and coal comprise more than 80 per cent of the total imports.

SHINJI HORST AND HIINOKAWA PLAIN

The other principal irregularity of the Sanin coast (Subregion 2) is located about midway along Sanin in the vicinity of the metropolis, Matsue. In this region the isolated Shinji block forming Shimane Peninsula is separated from the mainland by a wide rift valley occupied by Naka Lagoon, Shinji Lake, and the delta-plain of Kizuki or Hiino River (Fig. 268). A wide combination sand spit and bar separates the salty Naka Lake from Miho Bay, while Naka and Shinji lakes are separated by an isthmus composed of Tertiary rocks and alluvial materials. A channel

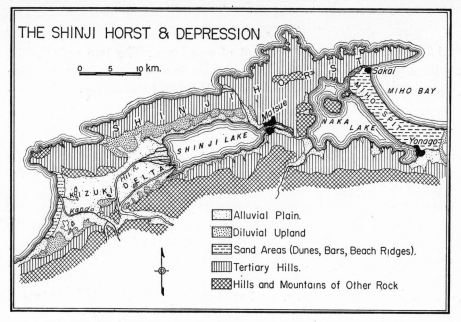

FIG. 268. The Shinji lowlands are coincident with the most important
population cluster along the whole Sanin coast.

connects the two lakes and there is also a connection between Naka Lake
and the sea. The western end of the Shinji graben valley is closed by a
bay-mouth bar with beach ridges and sand dunes. Back of the dunes is
the steeply inclined Kizuki or Hiinokawa delta-plain, which is rapidly
extending itself eastward into Lake Shinji. The alluvial sediments of the
Shinji Depression are the most extensive to be found along the whole
Sanin coast; it is not strange, therefore, that the single largest compact
population cluster anywhere in northern Chugoku coincides with these
lowlands. The elevated and diked Hii River, the master stream of the
delta-plain, is subject to violent floods and in these flood periods it has
frequently changed its course, sometimes flowing westward into the
Japan Sea and at other times eastward into Lake Shinji. For about three
hundred years, however, the river has had its present outlet.[11]

The Hiinokawa Plain is the fertile nucleus of Shimane Prefecture, containing one-seventh of its population, though it represents only one-
thirtieth of the prefecture's area. Density of population is over 1,600 per
square mile.[12] On the elevated sandy seaward margins of the plain, where
beach ridges and dunes are prevalent, protective groves of conifers and
unirrigated crops of cereals, mulberry, and orchards occupy much of the
land. The delta-plain proper is largely in rice, but there is also much mulberry along the present and the relict levees, and around the settlements.
The older western and central portion of the plain is a region of ancient
settlement. Eastward the settlements become progressively more recent,

[11] Robert Burnett Hall, "The Hiinokawa Plain," in the *Proceedings of the Fifth Pacific
Science Congress,* Toronto, 1933, 2:1360–1361.
[12] *Ibid.,* 1362.

since they have occurred as successive belts of newly formed land have
appeared on the margins of an advancing delta. Some settlements on the
easternmost part of the delta are less than twenty years old. A distinctive
feature of the Hiinokawa Plain is the dispersed settlement, each farmstead, as a protection against floods, occupying an artificially elevated
plot rising several feet above the general level of the paddy fields (Fig.
269). The prevalence of isolated farmsteads, instead of the compact rural
village, has resulted from the practice of selecting available dry sites on a
steeply inclined delta-fan where the flood danger is a frequent menace.
A similar dispersion of farmsteads on the steeply inclined and flood-
dangerous Oi Plain in Shizuoka and on the Toyama Plain in Hokuroku
has been noted previously.

A further distinctive feature of settlement on the Hiinokawa Plain are
the windbreaks in the form of pine-tree hedges 20 to 50 feet high which
surround each isolated farmstead on its northern and western sides. Seen
from a distance each farmstead appears as a small grove of trees (Fig.

269). The hedge is trimmed
squarely on top so that it has
an even crestline. At the bases
of the taller pine trees there is
a dense growth of lower trees
and bushes, making protection
against the winter monsoon

FIG. 269. *Right:* Isolated, hedge-
enclosed farmsteads on the Kizuki
Delta in the Shinji Depression. *Below:* A closeup view of one of the
above farmsteads, seen from the
south. Note the saddle roof and
the trimmed crest of the high hedge.

even more effective. Sometimes a hedge is lacking on the south and east, or the farmstead is protected only by a low hedge of broadleaf trees on these less exposed flanks. Great pride is taken by the farmer in the height and perfection of his hedge, for it is not only a utilitarian thing, but quite as much a feature of the local culture, and its quality and appearance is an indication of the prosperity of its owner. In the almost universal swaled roof crest of the rural houses of Hiinokawa there is strong resemblance to the architecture of southern Korea (Fig. 269). Only within the old province of Izumo, including the Shinji region, which has had the longest and most intimate contact with Korea, is this unique house type to be found. For purposes of transportation each of the isolated farmsteads has direct access to, and use of, one of the very numerous watercourses that interlace the plain. Each house possesses a boat, which in times of deep flood becomes the only means of communication.[13]

The eastern end of the graben back of Shinji is likewise blocked, in this case by a combination spit and bar with conspicuous parallel beach ridges. Here a linear pattern of settlements, communications, and agricultural features is very evident. Mulberry and vegetables are the prevailing crops. At the extreme northern tip of the spit and protected from the violent winter winds by the Shinji Hills is the local open port of *Sakai* (Fig. 267). Coal, wood, fertilizer, and petroleum are its significant imports. The foreign trade amounted in 1938 to slightly less than a million yen, nearly all of it imports of beancake and coal. From Sakai goods are taken by motorboat or by rail to Matsue, the prefectural capital and business center, and by lighter and rail to *Yonago* (47,051), a minor focus of industries, chiefly cotton textiles. Within the settlement cluster south of Shinji there is, therefore, a triumvirate of contrasting urban units: a port, a political center, and an industrial city. Matsue, located at the eastern end of Lake Shinji astride the channel leading to Naka Lake, is an ancient castle town, whose narrow streets and alleys were laid out with defense in mind. It has remained remarkably unaltered to the present day.

[13] *Ibid.*, 1370.

CHAPTER XVI

The Inner Zone of Southwest Japan

PART 3

NORTHERN KYUSHU

ALTHOUGH out of harmony with Chugoku and Shikoku in terms of the directional trend of the long axis of the island, the strike of Kyushu's principal morphological and geological features follows the general northeast-southwest direction exhibited in these other regions. Like Shikoku, Kyushu belongs to both the Inner and the Outer Zones of Southwest Japan; a morphological fault-scarp which forms the steep northern face of the Kyushu Folded Mountains provides a distinct boundary between them. South of this fault-scarp, landforms in general resemble the folded mountains of Kii Peninsula and southern Shikoku, although intersection with the Ryukyu Arc in southern Kyushu has resulted in modifications due to volcanic extrusions. North of the scarp, features resemble more closely the hill lands of Chugoku and northern Shikoku, granites being prevalent, although here, too, volcanics have added many modifications.

An extremely complicated and varied morphological and geological structure makes simple division of northern Kyushu (Region D) difficult. Three general divisions, each containing a considerable degree of variation, are here recognized: (1) The Tsukushi Hills and similar smaller but isolated areas in northwestern Kyushu are essentially a fragment of Chugoku. Granitic rocks are most prominent, although sedimentaries are not lacking, and fault-block structure is widespread. (2) South of Tsukushi and between it and the Kyushu Folded Mountains is a dissected lava-and-ash plateau with numerous large cones. This volcanic region occupies in Kyushu a position comparable to the Inland Sea basin between Chugoku and Shikoku. (3) Hizen Peninsula and the Amakusa Islands comprise the very irregular and loosely articulated region of western Kyushu. Geologically and morphologically this subdivision combines features of (1) and (2), for both recent volcanic and Tertiary rocks are prominent.

563

Climatically this northern Kyushu region is intermediate in character between Sanin and Sanyo, having more rainfall and less sunshine, particularly in winter, than Sanyo, but more sunshine than Sanin. It is less well protected than Sanyo from the northwest monsoon, and the damp, chilly winters with considerable cloud are disagreeable. Summer heat is also more humid and oppressive.

With the exception of the volcanic subdivision, the northern Kyushu region is a part of Japan's ancient and most important culture zone, which includes also Kinki and the borderlands of Setouchi. Population is dense, cities are numerous, and manufacturing relatively well developed, this being the fourth principal node in the country's industrial belt.

Tsukushi Hill Lands and Associated Plains

Composed largely of uplifted and dissected tilted blocks with depressed intervening lowlands, the Tsukushi district (Subregion 1) gives the impression of being a hill country, but without much order or system in the arrangement of its various units. Elevations rarely exceed 1,000 meters. In past geologic ages, particularly in the Tertiary epoch, some of the tectonic basins were estuaries which became partially filled with coal-bearing sediments. Since uplift these weak Tertiary strata have been thoroughly dissected, forming low hilly tracts with wide open valleys, in the midst of more formidable granitic hills. What were formerly very irregular coasts with numerous islands, both along the Japan Sea and Setouchi, have been considerably smoothed by alluvium deposited behind crescentic beach ridges and bars. Numerous islands have been thereby tied to the mainland. The coastline is still far from smooth, however, although good natural harbors are relatively rare.

SEBURU HORST

Two large and unlike hill masses, separated by the tectonic Mikasa Lowland, comprise most of Tsukushi proper. The western half, designated the *Seburu Horst* (Area *a*), is a compact and relatively rugged block possessing typically bold granitic features. Occupance is relatively meager, although some cultivation is carried on both in the narrow and intricate valleys and on portions of the upland surface, where slopes are not too steep.

THE CHIKUHO BLOCK

East of the dividing Mikasa fault valley, compactness of form is lacking, for Chikuho (Area *b*) consists of detached clusters of granite hills,

mostly fault-blocks, lower basin-like Tertiary areas of dissected hill country, and considerable alluvial lowland as well. Sedimentary rocks are more
common, and occupance is much more complete than in Seburu. Extending from north to south through the middle of this area is a basin 40–50
kilometers long and 10–12 kilometers wide, drained by the Onga River
and its tributaries. Low, rounded Tertiary hill masses, separated by
alluvium-floored valleys of variable widths, characterize the basin. The
supply of water from rivers and normal rainfall necessary to irrigate the
paddies, which tend to monopolize the alluvium, is supplemented by
numerous ponds located among the hills. On the hills, woods and wasteland prevail, although the lower slopes not infrequently have terraced
fields.

The particular fame of this Onga River basin, however, is that it contains the most important coal field, Chikuho, of northern Kyushu and of
all Japan as well; Chikuho produces annually one-third to one-half of
the nation's output (Fig. 270). Much the larger part of the field lies in
the basin of the Onga River and its tributaries, although three other
districts are located near the coast and are separated from the main part
of the field by rugged terrain.[1] These detached outlying fields are much
smaller and less important. The Chikuho coal is contained in Tertiary
shale, sandstone, and conglomerate strata deposited in basins within the
highlands composed of igneous and metamorphic rocks. Numerous
streams originating in the bordering highlands have produced a terrain
of low hills and open valleys. The coal-bearing sedimentaries have suffered two or three foldings, accompanied by numerous faults, resulting in
the formation of a number of local coal basins of small extent. The interrupted character of the coal seams and their steep angles of dip make
mining operations difficult and expensive. There are fifteen seams whose
thickness ranges from 0.6 to 1.5 meters. About fifty mines of respectable
size are in active operation; and scores of smaller ones are worked in a
somewhat desultory fashion. At least twenty mines produce annually
over 250,000 tons each. The larger mines are usually of the shaft type,
whereas the smaller ones engage in working surface outcrops. Most of the
coal mined is low-grade bituminous, and only small amounts are satisfactory for manufacturing even a low grade of coke. One mine, the
Futase, seems to produce the bulk of Chikuho's coking coal. Those characteristic features of mining areas—conspicuous top works with extensive
workmen's barracks, mine dumps, and long lines of coal cars in transit

[1] International Geological Congress, *The Coal Resources of the World* (Toronto,
1913). For a map of the field see Map 16 in the accompanying atlas.

or on sidings—are all to be seen, although the mines are so scattered and hidden among the hills that the scene remains distinctly more agricultural than saxicultural. There has been in recent years a gradual shifting of mining operations southward up the valley, as the older mines in the lower valley are worked out and abandoned.

Located only a few score kilometers inland from the Straits of Shimonoseki, the Chikuho Field has a distinct advantage in situation. Within the basin a complicated railroad system, dendritic in pattern, connects the coal field and its individual mines with the north coast, where the product is consumed locally in large quantities by the heavy industries of that region, or is exported to other parts of Japan through the ports of Wakamatsu, Moji, and Fukuoka. Coal from Chikuho dominates in the markets of Japan as far north as Nagoya; beyond that latitude coal from the Joban and Hokkaido fields begins to displace it, although even in the Tokyo-Yokohama district Kyushu coal is consumed in amounts almost equal to that from Hokkaido. There are no important manufacturing developments within the field itself; instead these are concentrated at tidewater along the Straits of Shimonoseki only a few score miles distant. Here necessary raw materials can be brought by boat without transshipment.

THE COASTAL MARGINS

Along the indented, island-studded littoral of Tsukushi (Area *c*), with its numerous small and very irregular fragments of alluvium, agricultural

FIG. 270. Important coal mines are indicated by small circles.

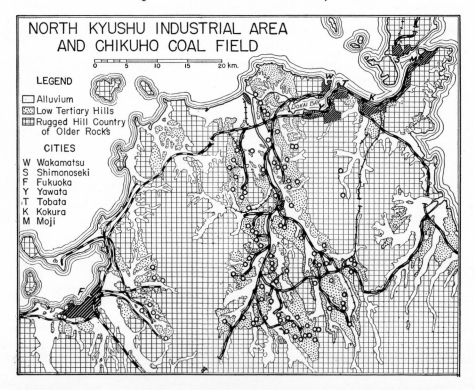

utilization is intensive but has few unique or distinctive features. Double cropping of the paddies is common, which causes the transplanting of rice to be delayed until as late as mid-July. Not only the alluvial plains, but the lower slopes of adjacent hills as well are cultivated, although not to the same degree as in Setouchi. Villages tend to concentrate along the drier inner margins of the lowlands adjacent to the hills or along the beach ridges. In the latter location they are commonly protected by a wall of conifers on their sea sides and surrounded by fields of unirrigated crops. The relatively small Fukuoka Plain is located at the north end of the Mikasa tectonic depression which separates Tsukushi into its two sections. The small Fukuoka Coal Field is situated in the plain's Tertiary rock borderlands, to the east of Fukuoka city. This is one unit of the larger Chikuho Field and has not more than a half dozen mines, each producing about 50,000 tons of coal annually.

Fukuoka city (323,217) comprises at present what were formerly two unlike urban units: (1) Fukuoka Proper, an old castle town of great fame and a modern political and university center, and (2) Hakata, a somewhat less elegant, but ancient port city, containing a number of manufacturing plants. The port still goes by the name of Hakata. This urban unit serves not only the Fukuoka-Plain hinterland, but also, by way of the Mikasa Valley, the Saga or Tsukushi Plain, the largest in all Kyushu, lying south of Seburu Horst. Fukuoka's spit harbor is relatively well protected, but its shallow waters, 2.5–5 meters deep, permit only shallow-draft boats to enter. Most of its sea trade is domestic, although a few foreign boats call; in 1938 the foreign trade alone amounted to nearly 9 million yen. Imports are only 40 per cent of exports in value and consist largely of petroleum products, since Fukuoka is the site of the Rising Sun Oil Company's distributing agency. The two largest export items are wheat flour and rubber-soled tennis shoes (Table 158, p. 572). Most of Hakata's overseas trade has been with the United States. The principal outgoing domestic cargo is coal derived from the adjacent coal field. Even the Hakata section of the city does not have a distinctly industrial aspect, for most of its manufacturing establishments are relatively small and do not require bulky raw materials. Hakata has long been renowned for its silk and cotton fabrics of special quality and form, such as brocades for the *obi*, or kimono sashes.

The Industrial Belt.—Though much of northern Kyushu coincides with the southern end of Nippon's manufacturing belt, industries are scattered and isolated over most of the area, as they are in the Inland Sea Basin. or along the Tokai coast between Tokyo and Nagoya. In one region, however, there is a very definite localization. This is along a narrow coastal strip bordering the Straits of Shimonoseki, which extends 25 or 30 kilometers from Moji on the east, to Orio or Yawata on the west, and includes Kokura, Tobata and Wakamatsu between these terminal cities (Fig. 270). Although not in Kyushu, Shimonoseki (across the Straits from Moji), is also a part of this industrial belt.

Special fame and distinction belong to this coastal strip, for it contains the nation's greatest concentration of heavy industries, with particular emphasis upon the refining of metals, especially iron. It is estimated that one-third of the pig iron and two-fifths to one-half of the steel produced in Japan Proper is from the North Kyushu center. The factors which have made this location particularly desirable for the development of heavy industry are: (1) the proximity and easy access to Chikuho coal, and (2) easily available water transport for imported bulky raw materials such as iron ore, pig iron, coking coal, wheat, petroleum, raw cotton, soybeans, and fertilizer and for similar heavy and bulky exports of coal and manufactured wares. Not only tidewater location but, more particularly, situation on the Straits of Shimonoseki, has encouraged the industrial development of this region. The Straits of Shimonoseki are the converging point for traffic between the Asiatic mainland, on the one hand, and Japanese ports, North America, and Europe, on the other. Rail traffic between Honshu and Kyushu also converges on the Straits, where ferry or tunnel service is provided, so that Shimonoseki is a crossroads of rail and water routes. Proximity to China, Manchuria, and Korea, the principal foreign regions trading with this industrial area, has likewise been advantageous.

Certain handicaps exist, however. Chief of these are: (1) the region's lack of protected and deepwater harbors, (2) the meagerness of level land for factory sites, and (3) peripheral location with respect to the principal domestic consuming markets. Most of the boats engaged in the Asiatic trade are of shallow draft, however, so that shoal roadstead harbors are not so much of a handicap as at first might appear to be the case. The markets for the finished products of this concentrated industrial region are largely within the country, where again the services of only small boats are required. It seems likely that North Kyushu's advantages in accessibility to fuel and to water transport will result in its continued growth as the principal center for heavy manufactures, probably at the expense of certain other less strategically located centers.

Throughout the narrow industrial belt, scarcely ever more than a mile wide and characterized by hills almost reaching the water's edge in places, urban forms are nearly continuous. Since industrial and commercial functions demand the level waterfront locations, residences are usually forced to occupy adjacent hill-slope sites. With one exception, Kokura, all these industrial cities are of relatively recent origin and owe their exceptional growth to modern manufacturing and, in a less degree, to ocean trade. Lacking any connection with pre-modern Japan, they have no Oriental charm; on the contrary they are dirty, grimy, smoke-stained, and wholly unbeautiful. In many Japanese industrial areas, where workshops rather than factories are the rule, the ugly features common to manufacturing districts can be partially hidden or camouflaged. This is impossible in North Kyushu, where the very size and nature of the industries—blast furnaces, steel mills, machine shops, cement factories, flour mills, sugar refineries, and others—preclude any softening of their starkness. The region with its huge, dirty buildings, unsightly chimneys belching black smoke, piles of coal and iron ore, huge waste dumps, and scores of railroad tracks, all covered by a murky sky, looks completely industrial.

The retail commercial sections of the cities occupy inner portions of the coastal strip, with manufacturing plants, docks, piers, and warehouses along the sea margins. The larger plants are often at the water's edge, where cargo boats or lighters can unload directly onto their docks. Some have specially arranged slips, so that freight cars ferried across from Shimonoseki can be brought alongside their warehouses. Those plants which are forced to locate a few hundred feet back from the waterfront because of lack of room are served by canals or canalized rivers. Convergence and crossing of rail and boat routes at Shimonoseki Straits cause this region to be conspicuously specialized in transport forms as well as in industrial features. Numerous craft of almost every description dot the Straits, many in transit, others anchored at buoys loading and discharging cargo by lighters. Scores of fishing boats and lighters, jammed closely together, occupy protected anchorage basins behind breakwaters. Moji, Wakamatsu, and Yawata are all freight ports of some consequence, the first mentioned ranking fourth in foreign trade for the nation in 1938.

Moji (138,997), on the south side of the Straits of Shimonoseki (less than 2,000 meters wide), and backed by relatively high fortified hills, is a veritable Gibraltar. It has had its principal development since 1887, when it was made the northern terminus of the Kyushu railroads and the Kyushu ferry terminus as well. The city's site has determined its dimensions, for though it parallels the coast for three or four kilometers, its width ranges from 500 to 1,000 meters. Moji Port serves not only its own industries but those of the whole manufacturing belt of which it is a part, for some of the industrial cities such as Tobata and Kokura are not open ports and consequently are served by lighters, principally through Moji. Along that part of the city's waterfront which extends farthest west, coal wharves dominate the scene; nearer the heart of the city are the general freight docks where boats of 3,000 to 13,000 tons can anchor.[2] Some Japanese transpacific liners stop at Moji and are serviced by lighters.

In normal years imports, chiefly raw materials for the industrial hinterland, are nearly double exports, which consist very largely of manufactured goods destined for Oriental markets, principally the Yen-Bloc countries (Table 159, p. 572). Imports are more varied in origin, with the Far East leading as the principal source, although the United States has in many years been the most important single country supplying imports. The large import of petroleum is suggestive of Moji's oil storage facilities; oil refining is not an important industry in northern Kyushu. Moji has become one of the greatest coal shipping ports of Japan. A considerable part of this cargo leaves the harbor in the form of bunker fuel, but in late years over a million tons annually have been carried by small boats and lighters to the industrial centers along the Inland Sea and as far north as Tokyo. Moji also has national fame as a fishing port of first rank.

Concentrated in the western one-fourth of the city, Moji's industrial section is in the vicinity of the great coal docks. A considerable variety of manufacturing plants occupy characteristic waterfront locations—among others, there are a steel plant, sugar refinery, brewery, bottle factory, flour mill, alcohol distillery, rice mill, machine shops, and a copper-wire establishment. On the island of Hikoshima in the Straits of Shimonoseki opposite Moji two shipyards are located.

Kokura (178,604), just west of Moji, is a castle town which has been largely metamorphosed. In earlier days it was the northern terminus of the great Kyushu highway, and at that time it was from Kokura rather than from Moji that crossing was made to Shimonoseki. The coastal strip is somewhat wider here, so that the city is less linear in dimensions than Moji and is bordered on its land side by low paddy fields instead of terraced hillsides. Its harbor facilities are undeveloped and it must therefore be served by lighters, principally from Moji. Its industrial belt is continuous with that of Moji's, the principal waterfront plants being blast furnaces, steel mills, and chemical factories. Located on the landward side of the city, but served by canals, are a rice mill and plants manufacturing porcelain and lime.

Beyond Kokura there is a slight break in the urban belt until *Dokai Bay* and its industrial littoral are reached (Fig. 271). This nearly land-locked,

[2] Ludwig Mecking, *Japans Häfen* (Hamburg, 1931), 314-317.

well protected body of water, 6 kilometers east-west by 2 kilometers north-south, with an eastern entrance only 300 meters wide at its narrowest point, is probably a sunken river valley, shallow, and handicapped by rapid silting. Constant dredging is necessary to keep it open for even the small ocean freighters which serve the industrial plants along its shores. The western one-third, where extensive mud flats are exposed at low tide, is not dredged and is consequently too shallow for navigation. In this part the shores are not urbanized and the few industrial plants located there are served by rail exclusively. From a vantage point on the hills back of Wakamatsu on the north side of Dokai Bay one is able to get a complete panoramic bird's-eye view of the region, although the smoky air tends to obscure details and photographing is forbidden, for this is a fortified zone. Features of this industrial landscape which stand out most distinctly are: the large factories with their conspicuous smokestacks, chief among them the great iron and steel works at Yawata; the extensive coal docks and the huge piles of coal along portions of the waterfront; the numerous small freighters, some anchored at buoys, others alongside the docks; the hundreds of lighters and small sailing vessels lying behind low breakwaters; and scores of railway tracks with long lines of moving or stationary coal cars.

Three important industrial cities occupy portions of the Dokai littoral. *Wakamatsu* (88,091) is on the north side of the narrow entrance and *Tobata* (84,260) just opposite; *Yawata* (261,309), continuous with Tobata, extends farther south and west along the south side of the bay. Occupying a large part of the Tobata waterfront is the government-operated iron and steel plant and the great coal docks, modernly equipped with electric cranes. In addition there are numerous coke ovens, a sugar refinery, and bottle, brick, cotton thread, and plate glass factories. Wakamatsu, across the channel from Tobata, occupies not only a narrow coastal strip and considerable reclaimed land, but the adjacent hill slopes as well. Most of the plants,—an oil refinery, steel mill, machine and tool shops, and a small shipbuilding and repair yard,—occupy reclaimed land near the channel entrance. Wakamatsu Port, which includes both sides of the channel, has special fame as Japan's greatest coal exporting center, all of the product coming from the adjacent Chikuho Field by rail. Loading is done from piers on both the Wakamatsu and the Tobata sides. Most of the exported product is carried to the numerous ports of southwest Japan in small coastwise steamers and sailers. Some larger boats anchor at buoys and are serviced by lighters, although many small steamers load at the docks, chiefly on the Tobata side.[3] Wakamatsu held fifth rank among

[3] *Ibid.*, 295.

TABLE 158.—IMPORTANT ITEMS IN HAKATA'S (FUKUOKA'S) FOREIGN TRADE, 1938

Exports	Value in Yen	Imports	Value in Yen
Wheat flour	2,224,000	Petroleum products.	2,731,000
Rubber-soled tennis shoes and other		Soybeans	322,000
rubber boots and shoes	2,014,000	Small beans	125,000
Lumber, logs and wood products.	831,100		
Tabi (Japanese socks)	625,000		
Paper.	343,000		
Machinery and parts	319,000		
Shell fish	192,000		
Confectioneries	156,000		
Total, including others	8,555,000	Total, including all others. . .	3,314,000

Source: *Annual Return of the Foreign Trade of Japan*, pt. 3 (Department of Finance, Tokyo, 1938).

TABLE 159.—IMPORTANT ITEMS IN THE FOREIGN TRADE OF MOJI, 1938

Exports	Value in Yen	Imports	Value in Yen
Wheat flour	7,843,000	Ores and metals.	60,068,000
Paper	5,880,000	Petroleum and petroleum	
Ores and metals.	4,628,000	products	58,022,000
Cement	4,826,000	Salt	12,930,000
Sugar	4,479,000	Machinery	8,091,000
Pottery and glass	4,113,000	Crude rubber.	6,937,000
Locomotives	3,916,000	Oil cake	5,064,000
Dyes and pigments	3,341,000	Sulphate of ammonia	4,717,000
Machine oil	3,036,000	Cotton.	3,856,000
Automobile tires	2,532,000	Vehicles and parts	3,822,000
Rubber-soled shoes	1,815,000	Soybeans.	2,287,000
Electric wire	1,701,000		
Electric motors and dynamos. .	1,263,000		
Total, including others. . . .	89,362,000	Total, including others. . . .	188,299,000

Source: *Annual Return of the Foreign Trade of Japan*, pt. 3 (Department of Finance, Tokyo, 1938).

TABLE 160.—IMPORTANT ITEMS IN THE FOREIGN TRADE OF WAKAMATSU, 1938

Exports	Value in Yen	Imports	Value in Yen
Metals.	18,646,000	Ores and metals.	45,497,000
Sugar	2,741,000	Coal.	17,501,000
Creosote	1,492,000	Soybeans.	8,349,000
Vegetable oil	1,394,000	Salt	6,145,000
Coal.	766,000	Vehicles and parts.	2,233,000
Machinery	577,000	Oil-yielding seeds	2,105,000
Logs and lumber	525,000	Dolomite and magnesite . . .	1,226,000
Railway cars and vehicles . . .	470,000		
Steam vessels.	324,000		
Cement	155,000		
Electric wire	148,000		
Total, including others. . . .	28,465,000	Total, including others. . . .	85,776,0 0

Source: *Annual Return of the Foreign Trade of Japan*, pt. 3 (Department of Finance, Tokyo, 1938).

foreign-trade ports in 1938. Primarily an import port for a large industrial hinterland, the value of the incoming foreign cargo is three times that of the exports. The latter are largely manufactured goods for the markets of eastern Asia, whereas imports are chiefly industrial raw materials and coal. Significantly, ores and metals comprise 53 per cent of the value of incoming cargo.

Yawata, which is the largest and most important industrial city along the Straits of Shimonoseki, is the site of the great government-owned Imperial Iron and Steel Works and is the principal focus of iron and steel manufacturing in Japan. No other blast-furnace and steel unit in Japan even closely approaches in capacity the one at Yawata. Although its *relative* importance in the nation's iron and steel output declined during the decade of the thirties as a result of greater expansion elsewhere, the greatly enlarged Yawata plant may still produce as much as one-quarter of the pig iron and 30 to 40 per cent of the steel of Japan. However, in 1926 the Yawata plant, plus its subsidiary at Tobata, produced 79 per cent of the total output of pig iron in Japan Proper and 58 per cent of the steel.[4]

The plant is located along the waterfront and has its own docks which receive, from foreign sources, its requirements of iron ore and some coking coal as well.[5] Unfortunately the steel mills rather than the blast furnaces occupy the shore side of the plant so that the ore must be carried by aerial cables over the steel mills and rolling mills to the blast furnaces. Several hundred by-products coke ovens are associated with the Yawata plant. Most of the coal, including that for coking purposes, comes from the adjacent Chikuho Field. About 10 per cent of the supply arrives from the Kaiping Field in North China, and this imported product is mixed with the domestic coal to make a satisfactory coke. The rolling mills at Yawata, which produce most forms of steel, are one of the principal sources of raw materials for machine, tool, and hardware manufacturing plants scattered throughout the country. The numerous iron-products fabricating plants within the North Kyushu industrial zone reflect the advantage of proximity to necessary bulky raw materials produced at Yawata. Westward from the Imperial Steel Works along the shores of Dokai Bay, manufacturing plants are not so numerous, since this is near the western limit of the local industrial zone.

THE TSUKUSHI PLAIN

This largest alluvial lowland in Kyushu (Area *d*), lying just south of the main Tsukushi Range and drained by the Chikugo River, spreads over

[4] U. S. Department of Commerce, *Trade Information Bulletin,* No. 612, pp. 8–12, 30–34.

[5] Statistics for imports and exports at Yawata are not available.

1,200 square kilometers and contains about two million inhabitants. Features of *handen* influence are conspicuous. Small compact villages are numerous, and extensive vistas rare. On the low newly-reclaimed land along the sea margins, however, where rice is the exclusive crop, villages are few. The fragment of dissected low diluvial terrace in the vicinity of Kurume has considerable areas planted in groves of *hazi* trees, from whose berries a wax used in the manufacture of glossy paper is obtained. The tree is distinctly subtropical in its habitat requirements, being confined to the milder parts of Japan; over one-half of the total crop acreage is in Saga and Fukuoka prefectures of northern Kyushu. Both Kurume (89,490) and Saga (50,406), the latter an old castle town, have industries of some consequence, chief of which is cotton textiles. In the smaller towns and cities of the plain as well factories are not lacking.

THE MIIKE DISTRICT

To the south of the Tsukushi Plain in the vicinity of Omuta is a small area (Area *e*) which in its lithic and landform characteristics appears to be

Fig. 271. The industrial area around Dokai Bay in North Kyushu. Note the location of the government iron and steel plant, the largest in Japan, at Yawata. From *Nippon Chiri-Fuzoku Taikei.*

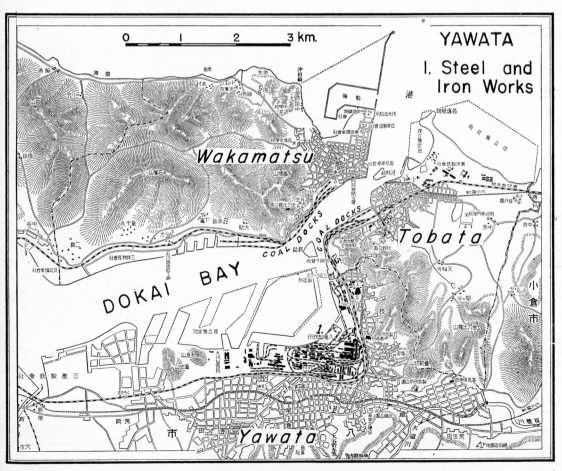

a detached fragment of the Tsukushi Range, although lower in elevation. The granitic rock upland rises to elevations of 400–500 meters. In the tilted Tertiary shales, sandstones, and conglomerates which flank the granites on their sea side, are found important coal measures, the mining area being designated as the Miike Coal Field.[6] It is only about 10 square miles in area, but usually ranks fourth or fifth in production (after Chikuho, Ishikari, Joban), with an annual output of between 2.5 million and 3 million tons. In 1935 the output of the larger mines, employing a total of 10,400 workers, was 2.5 million tons. The terrain of the coal field is that of hill country, with elevations varying from 30–150 meters. Half a dozen large mines with conspicuous top works and dump heaps are to be seen in the vicinity of Omuta, but in normal times not more than half that number are operating, the others having largely been worked out. One of the three large mines, the Yatsuyama, located right at the water's edge, is working submarine seams (Figs. 272, 273). The Miike coal is subbituminous in quality but is, nevertheless, some of the best produced in Japan. An outer belt line of railroad around Omuta collects the coal at the Manda and Miyanomura pits and takes it to the harbor and port of Miike a mile or so to the south of Omuta.

TABLE 161.—IMPORTANT ITEMS IN THE FOREIGN TRADE OF MIIKE, 1938

Exports	Value in Yen	Imports	Value in Yen
Coal.	6,693,000	Coal.	805,000
		Ores and metals.	652,000
		Salt	425,000
		Firebrick.	266,000
		Steam boilers and parts	146,000
		Sugar	140,000
Total, including others. . . .	6,891,000	Total, including others. . . .	2,566,000

Source: *Annual Return of the Foreign Trade of Japan,* pt. 3 (Department of Finance, Tokyo, 1938).

At Miike the Mitsui interests which own the mines have constructed an entirely artificial harbor especially equipped with modern machinery for coal export, at which 10,000-ton boats can be loaded by derricks in the outer harbor, and 5,000-ton vessels can load at the piers in the inner harbor. (Fig. 274). Miike is emphatically a coaling port, this one item comprising 97 per cent of the value of its foreign exports. Its imports, much smaller in value, are in part raw materials for Omuta industries.

[6] "The Miike Coal Field," in *Guide-Book, Excursion E-3* (Pan-Pacific Science Congress, Tokyo, 1926).

Directly associated with the available supply of coal for power is the concentration of industries within the city of Omuta (177,034), which lies within the Miike Coal Field. Its dirty, smoky appearance and its conspicuously large factories remind one of the north-coast industrial cities; unlike them, it is located inland and must therefore depend upon adjacent Miike harbor. All of the factories are owned and operated by the Mitsui interests who control the mining properties. A number of relatively large industrial plants, including coke ovens using some Chinese and some Chikuho coal, a dye factory making use of by-products from the coke ovens, machine shops, a zinc refinery, a nitrate fertilizer plant, a ferroalloy steel mill, a fireproof brick establishment, and a cotton-spinning factory, are all concentrated in the same vicinity on the northern margin of the city, where cheap land is available. They do not occupy tidewater or canal sites. One of the largest and most recent industrial developments in Omuta is a synthetic petroleum plant, believed to be by far the largest in Japan, making use of the local coal supply.

The Northern Volcanic Region

Between the Tsukushi Hills to the north and the Kyushu Folded Mountains to the south, and rising out of and completely burying the western end of Setouchi depression, is an extensive area of ash-and-lava deposits (Subregion 2). So diverse and complicated are the forms that any brief description must be inadequate.

THE LAVA PLATEAUS

In gross anatomy the northern portion (Area *a*) is composed of several relatively high strato, shield, and lava-dome volcanoes, with associated andesite plateaus believed to be the product of fissure eruptions. The *Lava Plateaus* have been altered by faulting and erosion with the result that they present a great confusion of features. Mesa and butte forms with steep bordering cliffs are common. Where dissection has opened up relatively wide valleys or basins there is a considerable rural population,

FIG. 272 (*left*). The Yatsuyama Mine, Miike Field.
FIG. 273 (*right*). Miners' dormitories at Yatsuyama Mine.

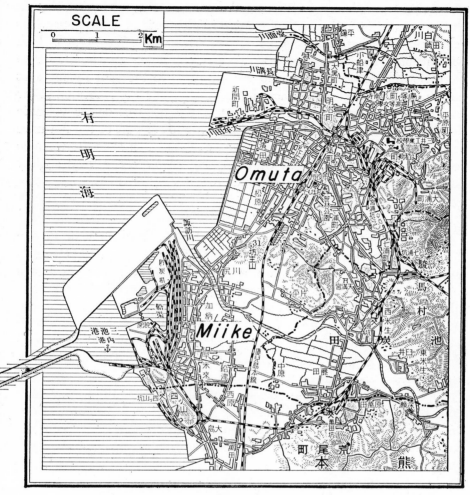

FIG. 274. The industrial city of Omuta and adjacent Miike harbor and port. From *Nippon Chiri-Fuzoku Taikei.*

isolated farmsteads and loose agglomerations of them being more prevalent than compact rural villages. In places artificial terracing for rice as well as for dry crops is remarkably developed. Circular Kunisaki Peninsula, projecting into the Inland Sea, is composed of a maturely dissected conical volcano with perfect radial drainage and an equally perfect radial culture pattern coincident with the drainage lines. Slight submergence along the northeastern side of Kunisaki has drowned the lower ends of the radial valleys, producing an irregular coastline. For the most part, however, the coast of the volcanic region is regular and is bordered by low diluvial terraces whose smooth but sloping surfaces are planted in deciduous orchards, mulberry, and the usual dry crops. *Beppu city* (64,724), on the east coast just to the south of Kunisaki Volcano, is a famous hot-springs resort center.[7] There are 1,300 hot-spring vents within the city, of which 800 are used for bathing purposes. Numerous hotels and inns cater to resorters and convalescents who are attracted to the spot by the spas and by the mild winter weather of the locality. The city is located at the base of a steep symmetrical fan composed chiefly of coarse volcanic detritus. Terraced paddies which occupy the lower part of the fan have retaining walls made of black andesite boulders taken from the volcanic sediments. Beppu, as well as *Oita* (76,985), an old castle town slightly farther down the coast, are ports of call for coasting steamers.

THE MT. ASO REGION

The southern and southwestern part of this Northern Volcanic Region is largely composed of the mighty cone of active *Mt. Aso*[8] (Area *b*) and its associated lava, mud, and ash uplands, extending across almost the entire width of Kyushu and covering an area of nearly 2,000 square kilometers (Fig. 275). Most of the lava is hidden under subaerially deposited ash but it is exposed along the sides of valleys. Aso's crater, which measures 16 kilometers east-west by 24 kilometers north-south is one of the world's greatest calderas. From the crater floor rise five new volcanic cones, some of them active and one reaching an altitude of nearly 1,600 meters. Two crescentic basins, a north and a south, occupy positions between the crater walls and the central cones; both atrios at one time held lakes in which volcanic and water-borne sediments were deposited (Fig. 275). These elevated lacustrine plains within Aso's crater are now well occupied by a dense rural population growing rice upon the lower, wetter portions and dry crops at the higher levels. Winds are strong at these elevations and as a consequence the villages are tree-enclosed. The intercoastal railroad line passes through the crater by way of the north atrio, and the ascent along the gorge-like valley which drains the crater to the west is both difficult and spectacular.

The outer slopes of the volcano are relatively mild in gradient, nowhere more than 10°, and to the east often only 2°–3°. Radial drainage is conspicuous. The original ash-mantled lava and mud surface was at first, no doubt, smoothly rolling, but rivers have incised relatively steep-

---

[7] "Beppu, The Hot-Spring City," in *Guide-Book, Excursion-1*, 5 (Pan-Pacific Science Congress, Tokyo, 1926).

[8] "Aso Volcano," in *Guide-Book, Excursion-4* (Pan-Pacific Science Congress, Tokyo, 1926).

walled valleys, between which are wide remnants of the slightly roughened upland. Local relief is usually not over 300 or 400 feet. The higher portions of the ash uplands close to the crater, where showers of ash are frequent; are covered with coarse wild grasses upon which horses and cattle are grazed. At lower elevations, more accessible and less subject to current showers of ash, cultivated land is more abundant, although there is evidence that occupance has been relatively recent. The valley floors are covered with an intricate dendritic pattern of rice lands, whereas the cultivated ash uplands are devoted to dry crops. Dispersed settlement is common.

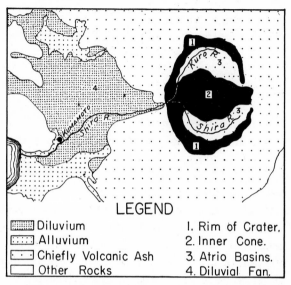

LEGEND

Diluvium	1. Rim of Crater.
Alluvium	2. Inner Cone.
Chiefly Volcanic Ash	3. Atrio Basins.
Other Rocks	4. Diluvial Fan.

Fig. 275. Mt. Aso and vicinity in the volcanic region of northern Kyushu. Note the new inner cone within the old crater and the two crater basins. The river draining Aso's crater has formed a large diluvial fan to the west of the crater.

The Shiro River, which flows westward from Aso, draining the two atrio basins, has deposited along the western foot of the volcano a large diluvial fan (Fig. 275). At its crest, where it makes contact with Aso lava 25 kilometers from the coast, the fan's elevation is about 200 meters. Much of its surface is relatively smooth, although in places streams have incised shallow gorge-like valleys and have developed a number of terrace levels, often separated by steep declivities. Dry-crop agriculture prevails on the upland surfaces, mulberry being especially prominent. Considerable areas are left in woodland. *Kumamoto* (210,038), capital of the prefecture of the same name, located near the sea margin of the fan, is not primarily an industrial city. In addition to being a capital and local business center, it is headquarters for an army division which has a large maneuver field on a flattish section of the diluvial fan. The little port of Misumi at the western end of the peninsula and southwest of Kumamoto serves as the gateway to the Kumamoto-Aso locality. Its foreign exports, valued at 1.7 million yen annually, consist chiefly of logs, lumber, and wheat flour. Imports valued at 2.8 million yen in 1938 were more varied in character, fertilizers such as beancake and phosphate rock taking first rank, followed by beans, maize, coke, fodder, and ores and metals.

Insular and Peninsular Northwestern Kyushu

Fragmentation has been so complete in this transition region of sedimentary and volcanic rocks (Subregion 3), and culture patterns are so complex and variable, that it is almost impossible to make a broad and simple synthesis of its geographic features. It is the westernmost extremity of Japan's densely populated industrial zone and in spite of its hilly nature occupance is therefore moderately abundant. Its extremely irregular outline, with deeply indented coasts and nearly enclosed arms of the sea, is the result of subsidence of a land surface made asymmetrically irregular by erosion, faulting, and volcanic activity. Natural harbors are very numerous and fishing is a major occupation of the coastal villagers.

NORTH HIZEN

The northern portion of Hizen Peninsula (Area *a*) is a region of weak Tertiary rocks considerable areas of which are capped with basaltic lava flows. Since it is a military zone, no published maps with contours are available. Having skirted the coast by small motorboat and traversed a portion of the area by car, I conclude that it is a hilly country of varying relief, in general under 200 meters. Where basalt is absent, typical Tertiary landscapes prevail. A relatively dense population living in dispersed settlements cultivates not only the intricate maze of valleys, but carries both irrigated and unirrigated fields up the adjacent terraced slopes as well. The prevalence of artificially terraced slopes reminds one of the Setouchi borderlands. Where flows of basalt cap the Tertiary rocks, somewhat irregular tableland surfaces, often precipitous from the crest down to the geological unconformity, are typical. The resulting features are mesa-like in form. On top of the tablelands, smooth in parts and uneven in others, both rice and dry crops are raised. The terraced rice fields often have retaining walls built from the surrounding basaltic boulders.

Within this Tertiary subdivision of Hizen are two coal fields, Sasebo on the west and Karatsu on the east. Each field annually produces about 2 million tons of sub-bituminous coal. The product from the Karatsu mines leaves Kyushu by way of the little north-coast port of *Karatsu* (31,342), with which the field has rail connections. Although an open port, Karatsu's foreign trade is negligible. Sasebo coal is mined not only on the mainland of Hizen Peninsula in the vicinity of Sasebo city, but also on several small islands along the coast. A portion of the output is used in the industrial plants of Sasebo and Nagasaki; some is shipped to China, and considerable quantities are consumed as bunker fuel. *Sasebo city* (205,989) is a fortified site and owes its size and importance to the fact that it is a naval station, equipped with dockyards and an arsenal.

The towns of Imari and Arita are Japan's principal centers of fine porcelain manufacture; the wares from this region are nationally and internationally famous. Abundant local supplies of kaolin are near at hand to supply the crude little potteries with their raw materials. Passing through these cities by train, one can often see numerous straw bundles containing porcelain standing on the station platforms awaiting shipment.

THE PENINSULAS

The southern portion of Hizen is composed of three sprawling peninsulas (Area *b*), Sonoki on the west, Nomo to the south, and Shimbara on the east, all joined to the northern Tertiary region by Tara Volcano (983 meters elevation), a dissected strato cone with associated lava domes. Radial drainage pattern approaches perfection on Tara, the lower portions of the diverging valleys being devoted to paddies, and the interstream ash-and-lava uplands sown to dry crops or left in woods. An almost continuous line of villages follows the volcano's shoreline; inland, there are scattered rural residences.

Shimbara, the eastern peninsula, is composed chiefly of Unzen Volcanoes.[9] The almost perfect elliptical curvature of the peninsula's north and east coasts is due to the conical elevation of the volcano. Physical and cultural patterns are rather similar to those previously described for Tara. Here the crescentic zone of cultivation on the lower, mildly sloping ash apron is as much as three miles wide in places. At an elevation of 2,200–2,300 feet in a gigantic explosion crater there has developed the nationally famous Unzen hot-spring resort. Cool summer climate, mountain scenery, and hot-springs, together with golf links and splendid hotel accommodations, make Unzen an attractive hill-station for foreigners and Japanese who desire to escape the tropical summer heat of the lowlands.

The sprawling Sonoki and Nomo peninsulas have earmarks of the Outer Folded Zone of southern Kyushu, for they are composed of old crystalline schists; on the other hand, they are joined to Hizen by volcanics and other rocks not characteristic of the Outer Folded Zone. In general the peninsulas are hilly regions and not well developed. Occupying the head of a deep and narrow indentation about three miles from the open sea is the old port city of *Nagasaki* (252,630) (Fig. 276). Its development has never

[9] "Unzen Volcanoes," in *Guide-Book, Excursion E-1, 3, 4* (Pan-Pacific Science Congress, Tokyo, 1926).

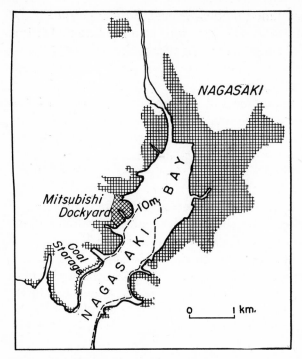

FIG. 276. Nagasaki occupies the meager coastal lowland and surrounding hill slopes at the head of narrow Nagasaki Bay. Note the location of the great Mitsubishi Dockyards and Engineering Works.

been closely associated with the immediate hinterland, which is prevailingly hilly, almost without alluvial plains, and meagerly settled. Furthermore, the city's isolation at the sea-end of a long and rugged peninsula has handicapped its modern development. During the long period of Japan's seclusion, Nagasaki was the only foreign-trade port of the Hermit Nation; through it filtered in elements of Occidental science and culture. Moreover, for years prior to the Russo-Japanese War Nagasaki was the wintering port for the Russian Asiatic Fleet; even at the present time the landscape of Nagasaki bears numerous evidences of the foreign influences to which it has been subjected.

The city is amphitheatre-like in form, occupying the steep slopes of the hills encircling the bay-head, as well as the narrow coastal strip itself. Mecking points out Nagasaki's strong resemblances in site and form to many Mediterranean coastal cities and villages. Its atypical slope site helps to make it one of the most picturesque of Japanese cities. Many of the narrow and irregular streets of the residential sections on the slopes are so steep that they require steps and terraces. Business, commercial, and industrial firms tend to concentrate on the flatter land bordering the bay. Here streets are wider and more regular in pattern.

A single great manufacturing combination, the Mitsubishi Ship Building and Dock Yards, with its associated steel works, machine shops, engine works, arms plant, and motor air brake and electrical appliance plant, has given Nagasaki its principal industrial fame. The Mitsubishi plant at Nagasaki is one of the largest of its kind in Japan. Nagasaki is one of the triumvirate of great shipbuilding centers in Japan, which includes also Kobe and Yokohama. Some of the largest ships of the country's fighting and commercial fleets have been fabricated there. The mighty wharves and docks of the plant occupy three kilometers of waterfront along the west side of the bay. Farther north, chiefly on reclaimed land at the mouth of the Urikamigawa, is a large textile mill, a number of sawmills with their associated piles of logs, and several ice-manufacturing establishments. Nagasaki is a very important fishing port and the ice manufactured here is used in the packing of fresh fish.

As a port city Nagasaki is in a period of retrogression. In 1900 it was the third-ranking port of the country in foreign trade; in 1938 it was tenth on the list. Significant causes for the decline are: (1) the development of competing manufactural, coal-exporting, and general port cities in the North Kyushu Industrial Belt; (2) the substitution of oil for coal as ship fuel, thus reducing the importance of Nagasaki's coaling services; and (3) the loss of foreign patronage when the Russian Fleet ceased to winter at Nagasaki. However, the city's excellent harbor, as well as its proximity to China and to the Sasebo coal field, are factors which may eventually turn the tide again in its favor. Its fame as a passenger port is closely associated with the very fast and frequent express-boat service with Shanghai, which is only 24 to 36 hours distant. Although fewer in number than in former decades, many boats still call at Nagasaki for bunker coal. Ships of 5,000–8,000 tons can lie alongside the wharves; larger ones anchor at buoys, where depths are 9–19 meters, and are serviced by lighters. The total foreign trade of Nagasaki in 1938 was only 32 million yen, with imports and exports divided in about the ratio of 6 to 4. Overshadowing all other foreign imports is petroleum, for Nagasaki is one of the largest oil storage points in Japan. Machinery and ores and metals rank next in importance, but far below petroleum. Among foreign exports, machinery, especially electric dynamos and motors, are most important, and canned

TABLE 162.—IMPORTANT ITEMS IN THE FOREIGN TRADE OF NAGASAKI, 1938

Exports	Value in Yen	Imports	Value in Yen
Machinery and parts	2,381,000	Petroleum	12,232,000
Canned sardines	841,000	Machinery and parts	1,755,000
Sake	309,000	Ores and metals.	1,445,000
Chemicals and drugs.	300,000	Cotton.	866,000
Beer.	271,000		
Total, including others. . . .	13,011,000	Total, including others. . . .	19,389,000

Source: *Annual Return of the Foreign Trade of Japan.* pt. 3 (Department of Finance, Tokyo, 1938).

sardines are second. Domestic water-borne trade is usually larger than the foreign trade.

AMAKUSA ISLANDS

On the Amakusa Islands (Area *c*) to the south of Hizen, hill country prevails, with numerous crests reaching elevations of 400–500 meters. There are only very meager alluvial patches, for the hills come down to the sea margins in most parts. Agricultural-fishing settlements, both dispersed and compact, dot the indented coasts.

CHAPTER XVII

The Pacific Folded Mountains or the Outer Zone of Southwest Japan

SOUTH and east of the great morphologic fault line which separates the Inner and Outer Zone of Southwest Japan is a region of relatively high and rugged folded mountains and hill country, composed principally of crystalline schists and other old sedimentaries.[1] Distinguishing characteristics of this region, setting it apart from the Inner Zone, are the well developed longitudinal valleys and ridges, following the axes of the folds and in general extending northeast-southwest, higher altitude, greater relief, steeper slopes, general scarcity of granitic and weak Tertiary rocks, and lack of a complicated fault net. Normal stream erosion acting upon the original folds has reduced the region to a stage of mature dissection with great relief, and has been chiefly responsible for the secondary landform features. Flattish upland surfaces are rare, river valleys are narrow, steep-sided, and characterized by entrenched meanders. Accumulations of alluvium, either along the coasts or in the interior valleys, are of small extent. Elevations are highest along the northern boundary, close to the Median Dislocation Line, and in general the several mountain groups forming the Pacific Folded Mountains in Kyushu, Shikoku, and Kii become successively less elevated from east to west. Along the margins of the channels leading to Setouchi, which separate the Outer Zone into three segments, the strike of the geological folds is at approximately right angles to the coastline, so that subsidence has resulted in a deeply indented shoreline of ria type. The Pacific borderlands, on the other hand, are usually smoother and more abrupt. Mineral deposits, chiefly copper, of bedded replacement type, characterize a narrow zone some 500 miles long by less than 20 miles wide.

At low elevations the Pacific Folded Mountains subdivision is the most nearly tropical region in Japan, humid midsummer months having average temperatures of about 80°F., while January averages between 40°F.

---

[1] Geologically and morphologically the Akaishi Mountains of Central Honshu are also a part of this Folded Mountain Zone.

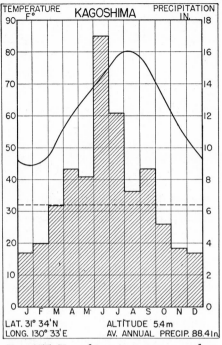

FIG. 277. Kagoshima in extreme southern Kyushu has one of the most subtropical climates in all Japan. Its heavy rainfall is markedly concentrated in summer.

and 50°F. (Fig. 277). Over much of the region, however, altitude considerably modifies these sea-level conditions. Rainfall is plentiful, 80–100 inches being common on the lowlands; at elevated stations precipitation is even higher. There is an emphatic precipitation maximum in the hot season, at the time of the onshore weak monsoon. Hurricanes are also most frequent in late summer and fall. Nearly eight months are frost-free; usually there are only 30 to 40 nights in winter on which frosts occur. Except at high elevations, subtropical evergreen forests with dense undergrowth originally covered the area. Palm, camphor, and *hazi* or wax trees, all indigenous to warm climates, are represented.

The semi-isolation and the elevated, rugged character of the region have resulted in a much wider spacing of settlements than in the adjacent Inland Sea district. Arable land is relatively meager. The few railroads are chiefly short isolated lines, and dependence upon coastwise water transport is therefore general. There are no really important ports, and manufacturing is relatively undeveloped.

SOUTHERN KYUSHU

Although it belongs to the Outer Zone of folded mountains, southern Kyushu (Region A) differs from Kii Peninsula and southern Shikoku (the other two subdivisions of the larger region), in that much of its southern part is a dissected ash and lava plateau with hard rock "islands" or steptoes protruding above its general level.

The Kyushu Folded Mountains

Highest toward its northern margin, where it terminates in a bold fault-scarp overlooking the Aso Ash and Lava Plateau, the Kyushu Mountains (Subregion 1) resemble a tilted block with upthrust on the north.

At the western end of the tilted block, the Kuma River flows northward against the general slope of the area, crossing it in a meandering antecedent gorge. This suggests that the river once flowed upon a peneplain surface, which was later tilted and folded to form the Kyushu Mountains. Slopes are usually steep, and the valleys narrow, although the crests of the ridges are often somewhat rounded.

At the heads of the deep coastal indentations bordering Bungo Channel, which separates Kyushu from Shikoku, there are small, isolated, triangular areas of dense settlement. These are coincident with the restricted alluvial accumulations wedged in between long spurs of meagerly occupied hill land. A similar settlement pattern is repeated on the east and west coasts of Shikoku and Kii Peninsula. The meager area of level land has led to the artificial terracing and cropping of the adjacent hill slopes, sometimes to elevations of several hundred feet. Orange groves are numerous on these slope sites.

Piles of logs and wood, and bundles of charcoal at the railroad stations testify to the importance of forest industries throughout this rugged region. The mining of semi-precious and precious ores is an industry of some importance in several localities. Large mines are not numerous, although there are several which employ more than 500 workers. The largest is the Saganoseki mine, employing 1,300 workers, in Oita Prefecture east of the city of Oita, which, in 1936, produced 14 per cent of the copper of Japan, 21.2 per cent of its gold, and 10.5 per cent of its silver. Some of the mineral deposits appear to be associated with a large granite intrusion.

The Hitoyoshi Fault Basin[2] (Area *a*), within the Kyushu Mountains, is not duplicated in any other part of the Outer Zone. Although it is a portion of the upper basin of the Kuma River, Hitoyoshi is relatively isolated, for it is surrounded by mountains on all sides. There is an outlet to the north by way of the gorge of the Kuma River as it cuts across the Kyushu Range. This basin, elongated east-west, and about 90 square kilometers in area, is composed largely of ash and diluvial uplands, which are in the form of piedmont terraces. The ash is relatively well dissected and much of it has been left in woods or waste, although portions have been reclaimed, principally for dry crops. The smoother diluvial surfaces are better cultivated, rice as well as dry fields being prominent. Considerable numbers of horses are pastured on the wild grasses of the ash and diluvial

---

[2] A section of Hitoyoshi Basin has been studied in detail by John Embree, an American anthropologist. His book, *Suye Mura,* is an intimate picture of village life in this somewhat isolated basin.

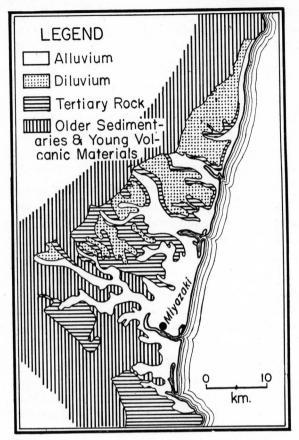

FIG. 278. The Miyazaki Lowland in
southeastern Kyushu.

uplands. Because of its isolation Hitoyoshi has many social features of an earlier era and in some ways is a decade or two behind rural districts farther north.

The Sadowara (Miyazaki) Coastal Plain (Area *b*).—Along a portion of the Pacific margins of the Kyushu Mountains is a wedge-shaped area of elevated coastal-plain sediments, terminated on its land side by a distinct morphologic fault (Fig. 278). The plain is composed of a basement of weak Tertiary rocks dipping in a northeasterly direction, upon which rest the diluvial sediments. Emergence has been halted at intervals, which has resulted in several terrace levels with more or less abrupt wave-cut fronts. In the broader southern section, earlier or more pronounced uplift has resulted in the removal of a larger portion of the original diluvial surface, and consequently large areas of seaward-sloping flattish upland are less prominent here than farther north on the coastal plain.

Low, rounded Tertiary hills and dissected ash plateaus, with associated wide-open and complicated valley systems, prevail toward the south, although smooth diluvial surfaces are not entirely absent. A lagoon-like strip of poorly drained alluvium, marked by beach ridges along its outer margins, lies seaward from the wave-cut terrace front. This strip of alluvium widens at the mouths of rivers and extends inland along the several steep-sided, but broad, parallel stream valleys which have been carved by a series of small rivers that descend from the mountains. The seaward strip of alluvium, containing many elevated remnants of beach ridges, likewise widens toward the south and, in the vicinity of *Miyazaki city* (66,497), has the dimensions of a plain.

Thirty years ago, before the rail line along the east coast of Kyushu was completed, this Miyazaki section was relatively isolated and not so well developed. Within the last quarter century or so, it has received important agricultural immigration, and these new settlers have reclaimed land both on the diluvial uplands and on the wet lagoon plain. The upland farms with isolated farmsteads in the midst of woodland and moors are planted almost exclusively to dry crops, chiefly soybeans, buckwheat, tea, sweet potatoes, and mulberry, as well as fall-sown wheat and barley. Horse breeding is a feature of the locality, as evidenced by the considerable numbers of horses pastured on the wild grasses of the uplands. The beach ridges are also sites for dry crops, whereas the wet lagoon lowlands, where reclaimed, are exclusively in rice. The larger area of alluvium back of Miyazaki city, because of its numerous elevated sandy spots (remnants of beach ridges), has a mixture of dry crops and irrigated rice. The Tertiary and ash hills to the rear are usually left in woods or wild grass; rice fields, often watered from artificial ponds, occupy the intricate valley systems.

Southern Ash Upland and Associated Highlands

This much-fragmented region (Subregion 2), complicated both geologically and morphologically, occupies a depressed area south and west of a crescentic fault-scarp which marks the southern boundary of the Kyushu Range. Essentially it consists of (1) several active or recently dormant volcanic cones, (2) areas of dissected andesite flow, irregular in outline, (3) an extensive lapillae plateau in a youthful stage of dissection, and (4) several steptoes, both sedimentary and granitic, which protrude well above the ash plateau level (Fig. 279). At the extreme south, Kagoshima Bay, enclosed between Satsuma and Osumi peninsulas, is a tectonic depression in the plateau surface.

Marking the highest elevations are the symmetrical volcanic cones, sometimes isolated, sometimes in groups. A number of them have slopes of such fresh lava or ash that they do not as yet support a forest cover and so appear stark and barren. On others forests are abundant, or, where cleared, the resulting moor-like areas provide pastures of low quality for horses. The andesite flows, confined to the northwestern part, have been so dissected as to produce a rugged hill and mountain country which contains little settlement. A conspicuous feature of the andesite hills is the

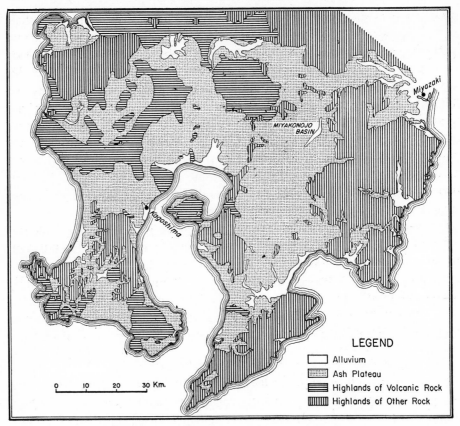

FIG. 279. The ash plateau of southern Kyushu.

numerous loose boulders, some of great size, which cover both flanks and crests. In the andesite country the hills often have tableland crests, which, though far from level, are conspicuously less steep than the slopes of the intervening valleys. South of the main lava mass are smaller flows, less formidable in aspect, which are intricately intermingled with the ash upland.

The steptoes, about a half dozen in number, are simply higher remnants of the fractured sedimentary and igneous surface, not yet submerged beneath the showers of ash or lava flows. They vary somewhat in appearance, but in general are rugged hill country, usually less than 1,000 meters in elevation, with few settlements.

Acting as a matrix binding together steptoes, volcanic cones, and andesite hills, the Southern Ash Plateau is not continuous over extensive areas. Considerable portions of the original depositional surface still persist as flattish or rolling uplands, 150–350 meters above sea level. Over a larger proportion of its area, however, stream erosion has reduced the region to slopes with a confused drainage pattern. It may be that part of

590

the surface irregularity is due to the original unevenness of the hardrock surface upon which the ash was deposited. However, subaerial erosion of the unconsolidated sediments, at a period when the whole region was probably at a somewhat lower elevation than at present, is certainly an auxiliary cause. A further conspicuous feature of the region is the wide, flat-bottomed, steep-walled valleys, whose sides show excellent cross-sections of the gray ash. Where the valley sides are not sheer they are often mantled in dense subtropical evergreen forest, which gives them an almost tropical aspect. Along the coasts where the ash plateau lies close to the sea are what appear to be old ash-covered fans or cones with incised stream valleys. The immediate sea margins are flanked with beach ridges, back of which lie partially filled lagoons.

Somewhat isolated from northern Kyushu and the rest of Japan by the formidable barrier of the Kyushu Range, this Satsuma region of southern Kyushu is rather provincial in outlook and at least a quarter century behind the rest of Japan. It remained a semi-independent state, relatively hostile to the new government in Tokyo, for some time after the Restoration. Even today the Satsuma dialect, which is not understood by other Japanese, is spoken in the homes of this region. Cultural connections have been with the Ryukyu Islands to the south, and evidences of this affiliation are to be observed in house features and social customs. Settlement types are varied; though compact villages are by no means absent, semi- and completely dispersed rural residences appear to predominate. Most settlements avoid the flat-topped ash uplands, where water is difficult to obtain and where the full force of the typhoons is felt in late summer and early fall. More commonly rural inhabitants seek the shelter of the valleys, building their dwellings close to the bases of valley walls, where there is the dual advantage of slight elevation, offering protection against floods, and the presence of spring water. When I saw the area in midsummer, large areas of rice were so deeply inundated as to be completely ruined.

Fig. 280. Farmstead of tropical aspect in the ash plateau region of southern Kyushu. After Hall in the *Geographical Review*, published by the American Geographical Society.

Fig. 281. The somewhat uneven crest of the ash plateau of southern Kyushu inland from Kagoshima. The crops are unirrigated.

Settlements located at the base of cliffs are in some danger from landslides at times of heavy rains or earthquakes.

Rural dwellings, often only crude huts of rough board and thatch with steep roofs and overhanging eaves, are tropical in aspect (Fig. 280). They are set in the midst of a subtropical vegetation of live-oaks, bamboo trees, and, occasionally, banana trees. Tile roofs are used only in the compact larger villages and cities. Rural settlements are commonly amorphous in structure; the farm residences may be areally grouped, but the individual units are often separated from one another by fields or woods, and connected only by trails (Fig. 67).[3]

Rice is relatively less important in this region of ash uplands than where alluvial areas are more extensive, for it occupies only 34–35 per cent of the cultivated area. It is confined largely to the valley bottoms and the coastal lowlands. On the flattish to rolling ash uplands dry fields of tobacco, sugar cane, beans, sweet potatoes, taro, vegetables, upland rice, fruit trees, and winter grains are usual (Fig. 281). This is the only part of Japan Proper in which sugar cane is a conspicuous crop. Both tobacco and sweet potatoes are specialized crops. Since the upland surfaces are not level, farmers have resorted to crude terracing in laying out the fields.

[3] Robert B. Hall, "Some Rural Settlement Forms in Japan," in the *Geographical Review*, 21:102–110 (January, 1931).

Horse breeding is of some importance in this area and portions of the ash uplands are used as pasture lands.

Cities are not numerous in southern Kyushu, for those important commercial and industrial services which cities perform are not well developed here. This is in marked contrast to northern Kyushu. *Kagoshima* (190,257) the metropolis of the Satsuma region, is located on a narrow coastal plain at the base of the ash plateau, fronting upon the quiet waters of Kagoshima Bay and situated almost under the shadow of imposing Sakurajima Volcano. Like scores of other cities and towns in southern Kyushu, it is an old castle town. Since Kagoshima is the only port of South Kyushu, it has a relatively extensive and populous hinterland. Its shallow inner harbor can accommodate ships of up to 2,000 tons; larger ones anchor outside the breakwater. Domestic trade far exceeds foreign. The

TABLE 163.—IMPORTANT ITEMS IN THE FOREIGN TRADE OF KAGOSHIMA, 1938

Exports	Value in Yen	Imports	Value in Yen
Logs, lumber, and wood products	3,118,000	Beancake	1,914,000
Dried fish	119,000	Soybeans.	1,405,000
		Animal bones	1 019,000
		Maize	412,000
		Bone dust	405,000
		Fodder	390,000
		Rice.	216,000
		Millet	175,000
		Salt	146,000
Total, including others. . . .	3,953,000	Total, including others. . . .	6.524,000

Source: *Annual Return of the Foreign Trade of Japan*, pt. 3 (Department of Finance, Tokyo, 1938)

principal shipping connections are with the Ryukyu Islands to the south and with the industrial ports of the Inland Sea. Kagoshima's foreign trade in 1938 amounted to about 10.5 million yen, with imports considerably exceeding exports. Outgoing cargo is nearly 80 per cent logs, lumber, and wood products. Imports are much more varied, but beancake, soybeans, and animal bones rank highest and in that order.

The Miyakonojo Basin (Area *a*).—Along the eastern margin of the ash plateau where it makes contact with a fragment of the Folded Mountains is the Miyakonojo Basin, containing the most important rural population cluster of the entire region. It is probably a tectonic depression partially filled with ash which has been carved into a series of low terraces by stream erosion. Rice fields occupy extensive areas on the smooth terrace surfaces as well as on the floodplains.

SOUTHERN SHIKOKU

Lacking a volcanic appendage like Kyushu's, southern Shikoku (Region B) is exclusively a region of folded mountains with a notable linearity of ridges and valleys.[4] It too has the profile of a dissected tilted and folded block, whose steeper slope faces the north. Deeply indented ria forms, indicative of subsidence, characterize both the east and west coasts; the tips of the two southern peninsulas have marked marine abrasion platforms, which terminate on their sea sides in wave-cut cliffs. Tosa Bay is a sunken block between the peninsulas.

In so rugged a region settlement is naturally meager. This is especially true in the higher northern parts, although even here there are occasional mining settlements and communities which derive their living from agricultural and forestry pursuits. In general the valley floors are so narrow that there is little level land for rice cultivation, although they occasionally open up into broader basin-like areas which become marked nodes of occupance. In a few areas rivers have so eroded parts of their basins as to form complex hill lands with appreciable proportions of valley floor and slopes of less declivity. In such areas the farm population is relatively greater. Along the deeply indented ria coasts, small isolated deltas at the heads of long, narrow bays provide the principal settlement areas. Farther south the marine abrasion platforms provide restricted areas of smooth surfaces for cultivation. Since so limited an amount of agricultural land is available, the mining, forest, and fishing industries are relatively important. The usual forest industries, such as the preparation of lumber, charcoal, and firewood, are rather well developed. Another and more distinctive enterprise is the manufacture of native paper from the fibers of two indigenous shrubs, *Edgeworthia papyrifera* and *Broussonetia kashinoki,* which occupy thousands of acres on the mountain slopes of southern Shikoku. Although this region specializes in paper manufacture to a greater extent than any other part of Japan, the industry is not very conspicuous, since it is housed in small plants.

The Kochi Plain

The single largest compact population cluster coincides with the small Kochi Plain (Subregion 1) at the head of Tosa Bay. In this vicinity a series of east-west fractures have produced a marked ridge-and-valley type of surface configuration, the long axes of the folds being parallel with

[4] Shingo Yehara, "Geologic and Tectonic Study of Shikoku," in the *Japanese Journal of Geology and Geography; Transactions,* VII, No. 1, pp. 1–42.

the coast. Subsequent sinking has resulted in a very irregular shoreline, but this has been considerably smoothed by river and wave aggradation, which has also filled the longitudinal valleys lying back of the coast. The dense rural population of the much-fragmented alluvial plain occupies both small agglomerations and isolated farmsteads. The dissected hill lands bordering Kochi have a considerable dispersed rural population This plain is distinctive in Japan, for it is practically the only part of the country in which two crops of rice are obtained during the course of a year. *Kochi city* (106,644), the metropolis of the plain of the same name, is a local port and distributing center. Although it is an open port, its foreign trade is negligible and consists almost entirely of logs and lumber. Isolation handicaps all of southern Shikoku, for there is no rail connection with the Inland Sea coast; small coasting boats and difficult bus service over the mountains are the only means of connection with neighboring areas. A few short and isolated fragments of railroad are all that exist at present.

In the narrow belt of crystalline schists along the northern higher margin of Shikoku's Folded Mountains lies the island's mineral wealth, principally copper of bedded replacement origin, and gold and silver. About a dozen mines in the region employ over 100 men each, and one of these, Besshi, is included among the country's greatest, employing between 3,000 and 4,000 workers. In 1936 Besshi produced 15.4 per cent of the nation's copper output, 3.5 per cent of its gold, and 5.5 per cent of its silver. Besshi is located in the rugged mountains 2,500 feet above sea level, twelve miles south of the little Inland Sea coast port of Niihama, with which it is connected by rail.[5] On the island of Shisaka, nine or ten miles due north of Niihama, is the smelter for this mining area, the isolated island location having been selected to obviate injury to crops from the smelter's fumes. The principal Besshi ore body, containing about 3 per cent metallic copper, outcrops near the summit of a rugged mountain ridge and is entered by an inclined shaft at an angle of 49°.

KII PENINSULA

In its isolation, rugged mountainous relief, lack of significant alluvial plains, meager population, and relative specialization in forestry and fishing, Kii (Region C) closely resembles southern Shikoku. Settlement is emphatically peripheral; inland from the coast Kii is one of the least occupied regions of subtropical Japan. In most parts the hills come down

[5] "The Besshi Copper Mine and Yashima," in *Guide-Book Excursion E-2* (Pan-Pacific Science Congress, Tokyo, 1926).

nearly to the water's edge and terminate in wave-cut cliffs. Narrow abrasion platforms are characteristic in some places, and not infrequently these are cultivated by farmer-fishermen living in isolated farmsteads. Where weak Tertiary rocks occur along the coast, slopes are less steep, dissection is greater, and occupance more complete. Portions of the shoreline are much indented, the small bay-head deltas providing sites for numerous little agricultural-fishing villages. Since there are only a few miles of railroad in the entire region, communication between settlements is largely by means of small coastal steamers or sailers from Osaka.

Index

Abashiri, climatic data for, 381; port of, 383
Abukuma Hill Land, 407–409
Abukuma Lowland, 414–415
"Adjusted" fields, 202
Agglomerated settlement, 153–159
Agricultural: income, 211; land, 193–198; acres per family, 194; scarcity of land, 209–210; population, density of, 139; practices, 202–209; rent, 210–211
Agriculture, 193–245; families engaged in, 193; in Hokkaido, 355–362; in Tohoku, 401–403; intensive character of, 208; shifting, 208–209
Aikawa gold mine, 456
Ainu, 122–123, 343–344, 351, 366
Air lines, 314–316
Air masses, 32–39; classification of, 34; equatorial, 39; Ogasawara, 37–39; Okhotsk, 36–37; polar continental, 35–37; polar maritime, 37; tropical continental, 38–39; tropical maritime, 37–39
Aizu Basin, 421–422
Akaishi Mountains, 11
Akaishi Sphenoid, 447
Akan coal field, 93, 385, 387
Akita, 400, 422; oil field of, 96, 422
Alluvial soils, 76, 78–79
Alluvium, area of, 7; relation to slopes, 7
Aluminum, 116
Alunite, 113
Amakusa coal field, 90
Amakusa Islands, 584
Animal industries, 242–245
Anthracite coal, 85–86
Aomori, 400; foreign trade of, 419; city of, 418–419
Aomori Plain, 418–419
Apples, 236; in Iwaki Basin, 425–427; in Tohoku, 427
Arc: Honshu, 10; Japan, 4; Karafuto, 10; Kurile, 4, 10; Ryukyu, 4, 10; Shikoku, 10; Tsushima, 10
Archean rocks, 4
Arcs and nodes, 3–4, 8
Area: of Japan Proper, 4, 6; of individual islands, 6
Arita, 581
Artificial fibers, 288–291
Asahigawa, climate of, 375–376
Asahigawa Basin, 377–379

Asayama Hills, 469
Áshino Lake, 436
Ashio copper mine, 445–446
Ashio Mountains, 445–446
Ash plateau of Southern Kyushu, 589–593
Aso Volcanic Region, 578–580
Aso Volcano, 578–580
Atsuma oil field, 380
Atuta port, 505
Automobiles, 307

Bai-u rains, 42, 49
Barley, 227–228; area of, 215
Bauxite, 116
Beach ridges, 20
Beppu city, 578
Bessemer steel, 295
Besshi copper mine, 556, 595
Birth rate, 130–131; artificial stimulation of, 132–133
Bituminous coal, 85
Biwa Basin, 14, 516–519; climates of, 518–519; manufacturing in, 519; terrain of, 516–518; as a traffic route, 516
Biwa Lake, 14, 519
Blast furnace industry, 292–295
Boreal forest zone, 66
Boso Peninsula, 446
Brandwirtschaft, 208–209
Bridges, 181
Briquettes, 86
Broadleaf forest, area of, 63
Building materials, 187
Buraku, 154–159; living standards in, 158–159; paddy type, 155–156; shopkeepers' type, 156, 158; social life in, 159; upland type, 156–157
Bushido, 124
Busses, 308

Caf climates, 57–60
Canals, 180–181
Castle: daimyo's, 171–172; towns, 170–172
Cattle, 242–245; raising of, in Chugoku, 545
Central and Eastern Hokkaido, 374–393
Central Fault Depression of Hokkaido, 375–379
Cereals in western Tohoku, 418
Charcoal, 83
Chemical industry, 301–302

Chichibu Mountains, 445–446

Chikuho Block, 564–566

Chikuho coal field, 89, 90, 565–566

China Sea, depth of, 8, 10

Chinaware industry, 303

Chrome, 113

Chubu (or Central Japan), 430–466; Central Mountain Knot of, 433–447; climates of, 431–432; cultivated area of, 432; location of, 430; Pacific side of, 467–511; surface features of, 430–431

Chugoku: cattle raising in, 545; coastal margins of, 547–553; interior hill lands of, 545–547; Sanin section of, 556–562; western section of, 547

Cities, 167–185; bridges in, 181; business cores of, 183; canals in, 180–181; distribution of, 174–176; fires in, 179; growth of, 181–182; in Hokkaido, 354–355; in Kwanto, 138; in Kinki, 138; in North Kyushu, 138; in Tohoku, 399–401; indigenous, 177–182; lack of zoning in, 179–180; locations of, 175–176; metropolitan, 182–185; morphology of, 176–177; of northern Shikoku, 555–556; of Sanyo, 550–553; of Settsu Plain, 524–537; by size groups, 176; on Kwanto Plain, 478–491; on Nobi Plain, 503–511; origins of, 167–174; street patterns of, 179; westernization of, 182–183

Climate, 32–60; altitudinal control of, 32; controls of, 32–43; influence of surrounding season, 39–41; latitudinal control of, 32

Climates: Caf, 57–60; Daf, 54–57; Dbf, 52–54; of the Fossa Magna basins, 57, 439; of central Honshu, 57; of Hokuroku, 449–451; of Tohoku, 54–57, 396–398; of western basins of Tohoku, 417–418; of western Tohoku, 423–424; of Asahigawa, 375–376; of Chubu, 431–432; of eastern Hokkaido, 387–388; of Hokkaido, 52–54, 342–343; of Hokuroku, 59–60; of Inland Sea, 59; of Obihiro, 391; of Sanin, 59

Climatic data, 44; elements, 43–51; regions, 52–60

Climatic types, 52–60; Fukui's, 52; Okada's, 52

Coal: anthracite, 85–86; bituminous, 85; coking, 85; consumption of, 82; distribution of, 88; exports of, 92–94; for Kwanto district, 274; for Osaka district, 274; importance among minerals, 83; imports of, 92–94; increase in consumption of, 83; production of, 87; mining, scale of operations, 87; quality of, 85–86; resources, 83–94; reserve of, 83–85

Coal fields: Akan, 385, 387; Amakusa, 90; Chikuho, 89, 565–566; distribution of, 86–93; eastern Hokkaido, 385–386; Fukuoka, 90, 567; Hokkaido, 90–93, 361; Honshu, 93; Ishikari, 89–93, 379–380; Joban, 93, 401, 408–409; Karatsu, 90, 580–581; Kushiro, 93; Kyushu, 90; Matsushima, 90; Miike, 90, 575; production of, 91, 92; reserves of, 86; Sakito, 90; Sanyo, 550; Sasebo, 90, 580–581; Shiranuka, 93, 385, 387; Takashima, 90; Tokachi, 385, 387; Ube, 93; Yubari, 379–380

Coal mines: distribution of, 89–90; output of large mines, 89–90; production of, in 1935, 87

Coastal fisheries, 247–252

Coastal fishing, distribution of catch, 253

Coastline, 28–30; length of, 28; minor features of, 29; of Inland Sea, 29; of Japan Sea, 28; of Kyushu, 29; of North Honshu, 28; of Pacific side, 29; relation of to natural harbors, 30

Coastwise trade, 318

Coking coal, 85

Colonization, 146–149

Commercial towns, 173

Communications, 305–317

Coniferous forest, area of, 63

Conservation of soils, 79

Controls of climate, ocean currents, 32–43

Copper, 112; from Ashio mine, 445–446; in Tohoku, 400, 416; mining of, in Tohoku, 416; in western Kyushu, 587; in Shikoku, 595

Copper mines, distribution of, 89

Cottage industries, 302–304

Cotton: spinning of, 284; spinning mill, 282; textiles, 282–286; thread, 285, 286; weaving, 282–286; weaving mill, 282

Crop boundaries in Tohoku, 403

Crops, areas of, 214–215; dry, 227–242; list of, 214; northern limits of, 217; unirrigated, 227–242

Cultivable land, 194

Cultivated area: changes in, 196; ratio of total area in Chubu, 432; ratio of, to total area in Tohoku, 402; ratio of, to total area in southwestern Japan, 513

Cultivated land, 193; area of, 193

Cultivation, frequency of, 205-206

Culture: origins of, 121–123; Western influence on, 121

Cyclones, tracks of, 41

Cyclonic storms, 41–43

Daf climates, 54–57

Daikon, 224
Daimyo, 124, 170–171; castle, 171–172
Dairying, 244; in Hokkaido, 357–358, 372
Dbf climates, 52–54
Death rates, 130
Debts of farmers, 211
Deep sea fisheries, 252–255
Deep sea fishing, distribution of catch, 253
Density of population, 138–146
Dewa Hills, 422
Diluvial soils, 76, 78–79
Diluvial terraces, 22–27; elevation of, 25; fertility of, 22–23; irrigation of, 26; materials of, 22, 26; older, 25–26; origin of, 23; skylines of, 25; soils of, 27; surface of, 25; use of, 26
Dispersed settlement, 151–153
Districts of Honshu and Shikoku, 204
Dokai Bay, 570–571, 574
Domestic markets, 262
Dry crops, 227–242; area of, 215
Dunes, 20; pine forest on, 21; on Niigata Plain, 20

Earth materials, 4–7
Echigo Mountains, 423
Echigo oil field, 464
Echigo Plain, 27, 456–459; dunes and beach ridges on, 456–457; rice specialization of, 458
Echigo-type settlement, 165–166, 169
Electric furnace steel, 295
Electric power, consumption of, 102; output of, 102; uses of, 106
Elements of climate, 43–51
Engineering industries, 297–300
Equatorial air masses, 39
Etchu Plain, 459–462; settlements on, 460–461
Exports, 324–328

Factories, size of, 261–262
Farm: families, number of, 193; implements, 200; population, 133–134, 143; tenancy, 209–211
Farmers, debts of, 211
Farms, 198–202; fields of, 200; open-field system of, 200; composition of, 198–200; sizes of, 197–198; in Tohoku, 401
Farmsteads, 190; in Hokkaido, 353
Fertilizer, 197, 206–208; cistern, 207
Feudal period, 124–126
Fields, sizes of, 200
Filatures, 279
Fish, kinds of, 247; canneries, distribution of, 251; products, processing of, 255

Fisheries, coastal, 247–252; deep sea, 252–255
Fishing, 245–256; in Hokkaido, 346; in Soviet waters, 255; regions, 246; villages, 248
Flour, uses of, 215
Fog, 53; in Hokkaido, 54
Foreign markets, 262
Foreign trade, 318–337; boom in, 323–324; of Aomori, 419; with Asia, 329–330; with China, 329; commodities of, 325, 327; discriminatory tariffs against, 322–323; with Europe, 329–330; of Fukuoka, 572; of Fushiki, 465; of Hakodate, 369; of Imabari, 556; importance of, with United States, 331–334; of Kagoshima, 593; of Kamaishi, 414; of Kobe, 536; of Kushiro, 390; of Miike, 575; of Moji, 572; of Muroran, 366; of Nagasaki, 583; nature of, 324–329; of Nagoya, 509; of Niigata city, 459; of Onomichi, 552; of Otaru, 369; of Osaka, 528; by ports, 335; with principal countries, 331, 332; principal items in, 326; regions of, 329–334; of Shimonoseki, 551; of Shiogama, 414; of Tsuruga, 558; with United States, 329–330; value of, 321–322; volume of, 321–322; of Wakamatsu, 572; with yen-bloc countries, 330–331; of Yokkaichi, 499; of Yokohama, 487–489
Forest: land, area of, 62; products, output of, 71
Forests, 62–74; area of broadleaf, 63; area of coniferous, 63; area felled, 70; composition of, 63; conservation of, 69; fuel from, 72; ownership of, 68–69; planted, 70; per capita acreage of, 66; protection, 69–70; used for pulpwood, 73; undergrowth in, 63; utilization of, 70–74
Forest zone: boreal, 66; subtropical, 63–65; temperate, 65–66
Forest zones, 63–66; altitudinal, 63–64; latitudinal, 63–66
Fossa Magna, 11, 431, 433–445; fault basins of, 438–444; highlands east of, 444–446; highlands west of, 446–447; tertiary mountains in, 437
Freezing isotherm, location of, 45
Frost, in subtropical Japan, 58
Frost-free season, see Growing season
Fruit, 234–236
Fuji volcano, 436, 437
Fuji Volcanic Chain, 11
Fukui, rayon industry, 291
Fukuoka: foreign trade of, 572; coal field, 90, 567
Fukuoka city, 567

Fukushima Basin, 414–415
Funakawa, 400, 428
Furano Basin, 379
Fushiki, 463; foreign trade of, 465
Fushun colliery, 93–94

Gangi, 418, 455, 462
Genge, 224, 225
Gen-ya, 62, 74
Geographic subdivisions: of Central and
    Southwestern Japan, 434–435; of Hok-
    kaido, 364; of Tohoku, 410–411.
Geology, 4–7
Gifu City, 505
Gifu Node, 11, 12
Gold, 111-112
Granites, area of, 4
Growing season, 46–47; at Asahigawa, 376;
    at Nemuro, 388; at Obihiro, 391; in
    Tohoku, 397; in Chubu, 431
Gun, 154

Hachiro lagoon, 427
Hakata, 567
Hakodate, 368
Hakone Mountain, 436
Hakone Pass, 436
Hamamatsu, 497
Hanawa Basin, 419–420
Handen features: in Kyoto basin, 521; in
    Nara Basin, 520; in northern Shikoku,
    554; on Settsu Plain, 522
Hanshin industrial area, 135–136, 274, 523
Hasagi, 455, 457
Haufendorf settlements, 164
Heavy industries, 291–302
Herring, 250
Hida Highlands, 446–447
Hidaka Mountains, 380–381
Hieh Mt., 519
Highway net, 312
Highways, 305–308
Hiinokawa Plain, 559–562; settlements on,
    561–562
Himeji, 553; iron and steel, 274; pig iron
    center, 293
Hiroshima, 551–552
Hitoyoshi Fault Basin, 587–588
Hizen Peninsula, 580–584
Hogs, 243, 245
Hokkaido, 341–394; area of, 342; surface
    features of, 341–342; climate of, 52–54,
    342–343; fog, 54; snow, 53; sunshine, 53;
    vegetation in, 343; coal mines in, 361; oil
    wells in, 361; coal fields in, 90–93; oil
    fields in, 98; population of, 136, 347–
    348; population density of, 143; popula-

tion distribution in, 349–350; Ainu in,
    343–344; emigration from, 347; immigra-
    tion to, 347; migration to, 147; coloniza-
    tion of, 343–353; military colonization of,
    345–346; cities in, 354–355; settlements
    in, 351–353; settlement types in, 351–353;
    distribution of settlement in 1885 in, 345;
    agriculture in, 355–362; farm houses in,
    353–354; farmsteads in, 353; soils of,
    343; potentially arable land in, 349; areas
    of crops in, 356, 360; cultivation in, 349;
    dairying in, 357–358; forage crops in, 357;
    rice in, 357, 359–361; agricultural regions
    in, 358–359; fishing in, 346, 362–363; lum-
    ber production in, 362; manufacturing in,
    362–363; railroads in, 361; railroad build-
    ing in, 347; geographical subdivisions of,
    363–393; in Meiji Period, 344–346; in
    Tokugawa Period, 344; coal, disposition
    of, 91; coal fields, production of, 92
Hokkaido Node, 10
Hokuroku, 433, 447–466; tertiary hill lands
    of, 464–466; climate of, 59–60, 449–451;
    snow cover in, 60, 449; sunshine in, 60;
    culture in, 451–452; population changes
    in, 135; houses in, 454–455; settlements
    in, 453–455; farm tendency in, 452; dry
    crops in, 455–456; rice specialization in,
    455
Honshu Arc, 10
Honshu coal fields, 92, 93
Horses, 243–245
Houses, 185–192; construction of, 186–187;
    interior of, 191; roofs of, 188; rural, 186–
    189, 190; sizes of, 186; urban, 188; in
    Hokuroku, 454–455
House types in Hokkaido, 353–354
Hydroelectric plants, capacity of, 104–105;
    distribution of, 103–105; size of, 103–105
Hydroelectric power, 101–106; distribution
    by rivers, 103

I reed, 541; in Sanyo, 549–550
Iburi oil field, 98, 380
Ikeda, 393
Ikoma Hill Lands, 514–515
Imabari, 555–556
Imari, 581
Imports, 328–329
Inawashiro Basin, 421–422
Income, agricultural, 211
Indebtedness, farm, 212
Indigenous cities, 177–182
Industrial belt, Nodes of, 271–275; power
    resources in, 271; of North Kyushu,
    567–573
Industrial crops, 236

Industrial development, 1931–37, 263–266

Industrial groups, relative production of, 276

Industrial production: distribution of, in 1938, 270; growth of, 262

Industries: wage earners in, 261; in Ise Bay district, 503, 505; of Kyoto, 521; of Nagoya, 509–511; in Omuta, 574–576; of Osaka, 527–532; in Tohoku, 399–401; of Tokyo, 481–483; of Yokohama, 490–491

Inland Sea, 12; climates of, 59; islands of, 542–544; nadas of, 538–539; as a trade route, 539–540; ports of, 540

Inland Sea district, 538–556; industry of, 540–542; salt fields of, 541–542

Inner zone, 11; of north Japan, 13; of southwest, 12

Inner zone of Southwest Japan, 512–584; terrain of, 512; climates of, 512, 514; culture of, 514; land under cultivation in, 513

Iron Ore, 106–111; distribution of, 89; imports of, 110; output of, 109–111, 292; reserves of, 106–109; Empire's supply of, in 1941, 111; origin of, 109–111; in Hokkaido, 111, 366; at Kamaishi, 110, 401, 405–406; at Kutchan, 111; at Ohinata, 111; at Sennin, 110, 401, 405

Iron pyrites, 112

Iron sands, 107–108, 109; at Kuji, 406–407; utilization of, 295

Iron and steel industry, 291–297; world rank in, 291; distribution of, 296; in Kinki, 274; at Kuji, 406–407; at Kamaishi, 406; in Kwanto, 272; at Muroran, 366; at Yawata, 573

Ise Bay, borderlands of, 498–500

Ise Bay District, 498–511; industries in, 503–505

Ishikari: coal field, 89, 90–93, 379–380; oil field, 98, 375, 380

Ishikari Plain, population of, 350

Ishikari River, 16

Ishikari-Yufutsu Lowland, 342, 371–374

Iwaki Basin, 424–427

Izu Peninsula, 433–436

Izumi Hill Lands, 515

Japan Arc, 4

Japan Current, 40

Japan Sea, depth of, 8, 10

Japan Submarine Trench, 9

Japanese: in Brazil, 146; immigration to foreign countries, 148; in foreign countries, 149; origins of, 121–123; physical characteristics of, 122–123; colonization, 146–149

Joban coal field, 93, 401, 408–409

Kaga Plain, 462–463

Kagoshima, 593

Kaiping collieries, 94

Kamaishi, 400; foreign trade of, 414; iron mine, 401, 405–406; iron ore, 107, 110; iron and steel works, 293, 406

Kamaishi port, 406

Kamikawa Basin, 377–379

Kanaiwa, 463

Kanazawa, 463

Karafuto, Japanese in, 147

Karafuto Arc, 10

Karatsu, 580; coal field, 90, 580–581

Karst, in western Chugoku, 547

Karuizawa, 445

Kawasaki, 138

Keihin industrial district, 135–136, 271

Keihin port, 484

Kibi Upland, 546

Kii Peninsula, 595–596

Kinki Region, 514–537; cities in, 138; terrain of, 514; industrial node, 273–274

Kino Graben, 537

Kiso Mountains, 447

Kitakami Hill Land, 404–407

Kitakami Lowland, 411–414

Kitami Mountain Land, 381–383

Kizuki Plain, 559–562

Kobe, 167, 177, 185, 532–537; foreign trade of, 334–337; functional areas in, 535; harbor of, 534; industries of, 533–534; port of, 534–537; site of, 532–533

Kochi Plain, 594–595

Kofu Basin, 442–444

Koitoi Oil Field, 375

Kojiki, 123

Kokura, 570

Komatsushima, 555

Koriyama Basin, 415

Kuji: iron sands, 109, 406–407; iron and steel plant, 406–407

Kumamoto, 579–580

Kure, 552

Kurile Arc, 4, 10, 13

Kuroshio, 40

Kushiro, 389–390, 393; coal field, 93, 390

Kutchan: iron mine, 366; iron ore, 111

Kutsharo Volcano, 383

Kwanto industrial node, 271–272

Kwanto Plain, 432, 467–491; coastal margins of, 477; terraces of, 468–470; terrain features of, 467–470; area of, 18, 27; cultural features of, 470–491; settlements on,

472–474; cities of, 138, 478–491; land utilization of, 470–477; market-gardening on, 471; silk production on, 476; soybeans on, 475; sweet potatoes on, 475; tea on, 476; tobacco on, 476–477; value of manufactures on, 477
Kyoto, 177, 183, 185, 521–522
Kyoto Basin, 520–522
Kyushu: cities of, 138; southern ash upland of, 589–593; subdivisions of, 563; climates of, 564; northern volcanic region of, 576–580; coal, disposition of, 91
Kyushu coal fields, 90; production of, 91
Kyushu Folded Mountains, 586–589; mining in, 587
Kyushu Node, 10

Lake Suwa, 441
Land, classification of, 196
Landforms, 19
Lead, 113
Lignite, 86
Limonite bog ore, 111
Lowlands, see Plains
Lumber, production of, by regions, 71–72

Machi, 154
Machine and tool industry, 272, 273, 274, 275, 299–300
Magnesite, 113
Manchuria, Japanese colonization in, 147
Manganese, 113
Man-land ratio, 194
Manufacturing, 258–304; causes for expansion of, 263–266; dependence of, upon foreign markets, 259; development of, in 1931–37, 263–266; development of, since 1937, 266–268; distribution of, 268–275; effects of World War I upon, 259–260; government influence in, 258–259; in Meiji Period, 258–259; Japan's advantages in, 263, 265; light industries in, 260; size of factories in, 261–262; state control over, 266; status of, in 1930, 260–262; technical efficiency in, 265–266; volume index of, 268; wage earners in, 261; wages in, 263, 265
Manufacturing belt, 268–271
Manufacturing industries, rank of, in 1936, 277
Marine products, processing of, 255
Market gardening, 232–233
Markets: domestic, 262; foreign, 262
Marugame, 555
Matsue, 562
Matsumoto Basin, 441
Matsushima Bay, 413

Matsushima coal field, 90
Matsuyama Plain, 555
Mature soils, 75–76
Mean annual precipitation, 48–49
Meiji Period, manufacturing in, 258–259
Merchant marine, 316–317
Mercury, 113
Metal industries, distribution of, 298
Metropolises, 182–185; growth of, 185
Miike coal field, 90, 575
Miike District, 574–576
Mikasa Valley, 564
Milk production, 243
Mineral resources, 81–117; of Sanyo, 550
Minerals: consumption of, 81; demand and supply of, 115; importation of, 81; power, 81–106; production of, 81, 82, 114. See also the specific minerals
Mining in Tohoku, 401
Mino-Owari Plain, 500–511. See also Nobi Plain
Misumi, 579–580
Miura Peninsula, 446
Miyakonojo Basin, 593
Miyanoshita, 436
Miyazaki Coastal Plain, 588–589
Mogami Plain, 428–429
Moji, 569–570; foreign trade of, 572
Molybdenum, 113
Monsoons, 32–39; summer, source of, 33; trajectories of, 33; velocity of, 33–34; winter, source of, 32
Moor soils, 77
Motor vehicles, 307
Mountain arcs, 3–4
Mountain lands, 14–18; area of, 14; cupola features in, 15; erosion surfaces in, 15; highest elevations in, 14; prevailing slopes in, 14; terrain features in, 15
Mountain rivers, 16–18; use of, for transport, 18
Mulberry, 240–242; decline of, 242; in basins of Fossa Magna, 439–440; northern limit of, 217
Multiple cropping, 204–205
Mura, 154
Muroran: foreign trade of, 366; iron and steel plant, 366; pig iron center, 293
Muroran port, 366–368
Musashino Terrace, 468; water supplies of, 472
Mutsu Plain, 409–411
Myako volcanic group, 437

Nadedome, 454
Nagano Basin, 444
Nagano Prefecture, exports of silk from, 441

Nagasaki, 581–584; industries of, 582–583; in feudal period, 125; port of, 583; site of, 582; trade of, 583–584

Nagoya, 177, 183, 185, 505–511; canals of, 507; harbor of, 506, 507–508; industrial node, 272–273; industries of, 509–511; site of, 505; trade of, 508–509

Nagoya Plain, 500–511. See also Nobi Plain

Naked barley, 227–228; area of, 215

Nara Basin, see Yamato Basin

Nara city, 520

Nasu Volcanic Chain, 445

Nayoro Basin, 377

Nemuro, 390; climate of, 388

Nemuro-Kushiro Terrace, 387–390

Nickel, 113

Night soil, 206–207

Nihongi, 123

Niigata city, 458–459; foreign trade of, 459

Niigata oil field, 96–98, 464

Niigata Plain, 456–459; dunes on, 20, 448

Niihama, 556

Nikko, 445

Nobi Plain, 432, 500–511; area of, 27; cities on, 503–511; early uses of, 500–501; mulberry growing on, 501–502; pine forests on, 502; polder lands of, 500–501; settlements of, 501; silk specialization of, 501; vegetable growing on, 501–502, 504

Node: Gifu, 11; Hokkaido, 10; Kyushu, 10

Nodes, 3–4

Nokkeushi Basin, 382–383

Nomo Peninsula, 581

North Kyushu industrial node, 275, 567–573

Noshiro-Omono Plain, 427–428

Noto Peninsula, 464–465

Oats, 227; in Hokkaido, 362

Obihiro, 393; climate of, 391

Ocean currents, 39–41; effects of, on Hokkaido climates, 387; effects of, on Tohoku climates, 396–397

Ocean deeps, 8–10

Odate Basin, 419–420

Oga Peninsula, 427–428

Ogasawara air masses, 37–39

Ohinata iron ore, 111

Oi Plain, 491, 494–495

Oil fields: Akita, 96, 422; Echigo, 464; Hokkaido, 98, 361, 375, 380; Iburi, 98; Ishikari, 98, 375; Koitoi, 375; Niigata, 96–98, 464; in Teshio hills, 375; in Tohoku, 422; distribution of, 95. See also Petroleum

Oita, 578

Okaya, 442–443

Okayama, 552–553

Okhotsk air masses, 37; in summer, 36

Okhotsk Current, 40

Older alluvium, see Diluvial terrace

Omi Basin, see Biwa basin

Omi-Iga Hill Lands, 514–515

Omine coal field, 550

Omuta, 574–576

Onada coal field, see Ube coal field

Onji soils, 75

Onomichi, 552

Orange, 234–236; northern limit of, 217

Orange growing in Sunen, 496, 498

Origin of Japan, 9–10

Osaka, 176, 183, 185; bridges in, 524; buildings of, 524–525; canals in, 524; castle of, 524; development of, 525; distribution of factories in, 531; distribution of industrial workers in, 530; foreign trade of, 334–337; functional areas of, 526; harbor of, 525–526, 531; industries of, 527–532; iron and steel industry of, 530; population of, 524; ship building in, 530; shipping facilities of, 527; site of, 524; streets of, 524; trade of, 526–528

Osaka Plain, see Settsu Plain

Oshima Hill Country, 363–365

Otaru, 368–369

Otsu, 519

Ou, see Tohoku

Outer Zone, 10; geological formations in, 11; of North Japan, 12–13; of Southwest Japan, 11–12, 585–596

Overseas shipping services, 317

Oyashio, 40; effects of current on temperature, 47, 387

Pacific Folded Mountains, 11–12, 585–596; climate of, 585–586; minerals in, 585

Pacific Mandated Islands, 147

Paddy lands, 213–226. See also Rice

Pearl culture, 255–256

Peppermint, 236, 382

Petroleum, 94–101; imports of, 97, 100–101; sources of, 101; production of, 96–98; reserves of, 94; storage of, 98; synthetic, 98–100; industry, 98; refining, 98–100

Petroleum fields, distribution of, 89, 95; production of, 97, 99

Physical endowments, see Resources

Physiographic subdivisions, 10–13

Pig iron: centers of, 293; import of, 294; output of, 292; output of, in Empire, 292; production of, 294; production of, by centers, 294

Plains, 18–28; coastal, location of, 18; interior, locations of, 28; materials of, 28; Kwanto, 18; materials of, 19; origin of,

18–20; rivers on, 21–22; seaward margins of, 20–22

Podsolized soils, 77–78

Polar continental air masses, 35–37

Polar maritime air masses, 37

Population, 121–150; age distribution of, 131; agricultural, 193; concentration of, on alluvial plains, 145; density of, 138–146; distribution of, 142–146; farm, 133–134; foreign migration of, 146–149; future growth of, 132; growth of, 127, 128, 129–130, 134; growth of, in 1920–40, 137; growth of since 1937, 132; in early Meiji period, 129; in Tokugawa period, 126–129; in Tohoku, 398–399; internal migrations of, 134–138; internal movements of, 134–138; maps of, 142–143; patterns of, 142–146; plan for increasing, 132–133; racial origins of, 121–123; regions of decline in, 135; regions of increase in, 135; reproduction rates of, 130–131; rural, 133–134; urban, 133–134; density, per unit of arable land, 139; numbers, 126–138

Population problems, 141; solutions for, 141–142

Porcelain, 303; industry in north Kysushu, 581

Ports, 334–337; distribution of, 335; foreign trade of, 335. See also the individual ports

Post-road towns, 173

Potatoes, 234

Poultry, 245

Power: minerals, 81–106; sources, 82

Precipitation, 47–51; distribution of, 48–49; mean annual, 48–49; seasonal distribution of, 49–51; variability of, 53

Prefectures, names and locations of, 140

Protection forests, 69–70

Pulpwood, 73

Rabbits, 245

Racial origins, 121–123

Rail net, 311–314

Rail travel, 311

Railroads, 308–314; rolling stock on, 319

Rainfall, see Precipitation

Raw silk, distribution of, 280; exports of, 325; regions of large production, 280. See also Silk

Rayon industry, 288–290; in Biwa Basin, 519

Rent, agricultural, 210–211

Resources, scarcity of, 3

Rice, 213–226; in Hokkaido, 359–361; in Hokuroku, 455; in western Tohoku, 424; boundaries of, 216–219; double cropping of, 595; fluctuations in yield of, 226;

harvesting of, 223; northern limit of, 217; ratio of, to cultivated area, 216; seed beds of, 218, 220; self-sufficiency in, 226; sources of irrigation water for, 219; transplanting of, 220–221; yields per unit area of, 208

Rice fields: fallowing of, 220–223; march of seasons in, 219–226; ridging of, 224–225; seasonal uses of, 222–226; weeding of, 222; winter cropping of, 222–226; winter crops in, 217, 219, 220–224

River terraces, 18

Riverine belts, 425, 426

Rivers: braided channels on, 21–22; levees of, 22; mountain, drainage basins of, 16; length of, 16; use of, for water power, 18

Roads, 305–308; feudal, 306

Rocks, 4–7; Archean, 4; area of different types, 6; older sedimentary, 5; Tertiary, 7; relation to slope of land, 6

Rural population, 133–134

Ryukyu Arc, 4, 10

Sado Island, 465–466

Sadowara Coastal Plain, 588–589

Saganoseki mine, 587

Sakai, 562

Sakata, 400, 428–429

Sakito coal field, 90

Salt fields of Inland Sea, 541–542

Sambongi plain, 409–411

Samurai, 124, 171

Sand dunes, see Dunes

Sanin, 556–562; terrain of, 556–557; volcanoes in, 557; settlements in, 557; cities in, 558; ports of, 558–559

Sanyo District, 544–553; terrain of, 544–545, 548; mineral resources in, 550; houses of, 548; cities of, 550–553; land use in, 548–550; cattle raising in, 548–549; orange culture in, 548; production of I reed in, 549–550; terracing in, 548; winter cropping in, 548; coastal features of, 547–548; coastal margins of, 547–553; interior hill lands of, 545–547

Sapporo, 373–374

Sardines, 250

Sasebo coal field, 90, 580–581

Satsuma-type settlement, 165, 168

Scrap iron: imports of, 292, 295; ratio to pig in steel mills, 296–297

Seaweed, 252

Seburu Horst, 564

Sendai, 413

Sendai Plain, 413

Sennin: iron mine, 401, 405; iron ore, 110

Sensible temperatures, 45–46

Seto city, 505
Setouchi, *see* Inland Sea
Settlement forms, 163–164
Settlements, 151–185; agglomerated, 151, 153–159; dispersed, 151–153; Haufendorf, 164; locations of, 161–163; semi-dispersed, 152–153; sites of, 161–163; strassendorf, 163–164, 165–166; on Hiinokawa Plain, 561–562; in Hokkaido, 351–353; in Hokuroku, 453–455; on new alluvium, 163; on the Nobi Plain, 501
Settlement type, definition of, 151
Settlement types, 164–167; Echigo, 165–166, 169; Satsuma, 165–168; Tokachi, 166–167, 170; Yamato, 164–166
Settsu Plain, 522–537; area of, 27; communications of, 523; cities of, 524–537; industries of, 523
Sheep, 243, 245
Shi, 154
Shifting agriculture, 208–209; in Tohoku, 403
Shikaribetsu Volcano, 385
Shikoku: Inland Sea margins of, 553–556; Pacific Folded Mountains in, 594; cities of, 555–556
Shikoku Arc, 10
Shimbara Peninsula, 581
Shimizu port, 496–497
Shimonoseki, 550–551
Shinano River, 16
Shinji Horst, 29, 559–560
Shinji Lake, 559–560
Shinjo Basin, 420
Shiogama, 400, 413–414; foreign trade of, 414
Shipbuilding, 300
Shipping services, 317
Ships, tonnage of, 320
Shiranuka coal field, 93, 385, 387
Shiranuka Hill Land, 385–387
Shizuoka: city, 497; prefecture, 496–497
Shoguns, 124
Shonai Plain, 428–429
Shrine towns, 172–173
Siberian air masses, 35–37
Silk: in basins of Fossa Magna, 439–440; on Nobi plain, 501; in southern Tohoku, 414–415; distribution of, 280; exports of, 242, 278–279; United States market for, 278–279; cloth, 281–283; industry, 240–242, 278–283; reeling, 279–280
Silk weaving, 281–283; in Fukui prefecture, 463
Silk worms, 241–242
Small grains, 227–232
Snow, 51, 55; days with, 51; in Hokkaido,

53; in Hokuroku, 60, 449–451; depth of, 51; in subtropical Japan, 59; in Tohoku, 55; in western Tohoku, 417–418, 423
Soil: conservation, 79; fertility, 78; maps, 74–75, 77; regions, 76–78; science in Japan, 74–75; types, 76–78
Soils, 74–80; alluvial, 76, 78–79; brown, 76–77; diluvial, 76, 78–79; mature, 75–76; moor, 77; Onji, 75; podsolized, 77–78; red, 76; of Hokkaido, 343
Sonoki Peninsula, 581
Southern Ash Upland of Kyushu, 589–593
Staple fiber, 288–290
Steamers, tramp, 320
Steamships, number and tonnage of, 320
Steel: output of, 292; output of, in Empire, 292; electric furnace type, 295; open-hearth type, 295; industry, 295–297; production of, in Korea, 297; production of, in Manchuria, 297
Steel making, by "hot metal" process, 295, 297; use of scrap iron in, 295–297
Storms, 41–43
Strassendorf settlements, 163–166
Submarine trenches, 8–10
Subtropical Japan, frost in, 58
Sulphur, 112
Sun-en District, 431, 433, 491–498; location, map of, 491, 492; physiographic plan of, 492; diluvial terraces of, 496; dunes of, 495; industrial districts of, 493; orange growing in, 496; tea growing in, 496; as a transit route, 491; truck gardening in, 495–496
Sunshine: in Hokkaido, 53; in Hokuroku, 60; in subtropical Japan, 59
Surface configuration, 3–31
Suwa Basin, 441–442
Suwa Lake, 441
Sweet potato, 234; northern limit of, 217

Tadotsu, 555
Takahama, 555
Takamado, 455
Takamatsu, 555
Takashima coal field, 90
Takata Plain, 459
Taketoyo, 500
Tama Terrace, 26, 468
Tamba Upland, 546
Tara Volcano, 581
Tax load, 212
Tea, 237–240; in Sun-en, 496, 498
Temperate Mixed Forest Zone, 65–66
Temperature gradients, 46–47
Temperatures, 43–47; summer, 46–47; winter, 45–46

Temple towns, 172–173
Tenancy in Hokuroku, 452
Tenants, 209–211
Tenryu Plain, 495
Terraces, wave cut, 25
Terracing, 202–204
Terrain features, 13–28
Tertiary-rock areas, 16
Tertiary rocks, 7; minerals in, 7; relation to slopes, 7
Teshio Delta, 375
Teshio Hills, 374–375
Textile production, volume index of, 276
Textiles, 260, 276–291; cotton, 282–286; decline in, since 1937, 266–267; in Nagoya area, 273; in North Kyushu, 275; silk, 281
Thermoelectric power, 102
Thunderstorms, 43
Timber: uses of, 73; imports of, 66–68
Tin, 113
Tobacco, 236; northern limit of, 217
Tobata, 571
Tohoku, 395-429; agriculture in, 401–403; central range of, 415–416; cities in, 399–401; clear and cloudy days in, 55; climate of, 54–57, 396–398; climate of western basins of, 417–418; crop boundaries in, 403; eastern highlands of, 404–409; eastern lowlands of, 409–415; extractive industries in, 401; forests of, 398; industries in, 399–401; lumber production in, 398; mining in, 401; population density of, 143, 398–399; shifting cultivation in, 403; sizes of farms in, 401; snow cover in, 55, 417–418, 423; subdivisions of, 404–429; terrain features of, 395–396; western intermontane basins of, 416–422; western plains of, 423–429; winter climate of, 54; western range of, 422–423; winter cropping in, 401–403; cultivated area of, 402
Tokachi coal field, 385, 387
Tokachi Lowlands, 390–393
Tokachi-type settlement, 166–167, 170
Tokachi Volcano, 385
Tokai, 467–511
Tokaido Highway, 467
Tokaido Railway, 467
Tokugawa Period, 124–126
Tokushima, 555
Tokyo, 176, 478–485; harbor of, 484–485; early development of, 479; residential area of, 484; port of, 484–485; trade of, 485; area of, 479; population of, 479; sites of, 479; earthquake, 479–480; streets of, 480; bridges of, 480; functional areas of, 480; business core of, 481; industrial areas of, 481–484; industrial output of 482–484
Tokyo Plain, see Kwanto Plain
Tokyo-Yokohama pig iron center, 293
Tombetsu Lowland, 376–377
Towns, 159–164; forms of, 163–164; appearance of, 160–161; shrine, 172–173; commercial, 173; functions of, 159–160; lack of zoning in, 160–161; temple, 172–173; castle, 170–172; post-road, 173
Toyama city, 462
Trade, 305–337
Trains, 310–311
Tramp ships, 320
Transportation, 305–317; rail, 308–314; water, 316–337
Trawling, 255
Tropical continental air masses, 38–39
Tropical cyclones, 42
Tropical maritime air masses, 37–39
Tsuchisaki, 428
Tsugaru Basin, 424–427
Tsugaru Horst, 422
Tsukushi Hill Lands, 564–576; coastal margins of, 566–573
Tsukushi Plain, 573–574
Tsuruga, 558–559
Tsushima Arc, 10
Tuka-dukuri, 442, 444
Tungsten, 113
Typhoons, 42

Ube city, 551
Ube coal field, 90, 93, 550
Ueda Basin, 444
Unirrigated crops, 227–242
Unzen Volcanoes, 581
Upland fields, 226–227; area of, 215
Uraga Channel, 446
Urban population, 133–134

Vanadium, 113
Vegetables, 232–234; production of, 215
Vegetation, 62–74; map, 65; in Hokkaido, 343
Villages: fishing, 248; forms of, 163–164. See also Buraku
Volcanic Chain of eastern Hokkaido, 383–385
Volcanic lands of southwestern Hokkaido, 365–370
Volcanic rocks, area of, 5
Volcanoes, 15–18; distribution of, 15–16; in Fossa Magna, 16; in Ryukyu Arc, 16; in Tsushima Arc, 16; number of, 9–10

Wages in industry, 262, 265

GF666
.T68

17552

DISTRIBUTION of POPULATION

by Francis Ruellan

(after the work of M. Tanaka,
K. Yamamoto and Glenn Trewartha)

SCALE

50   0   50   100   150   200 Km.

LEGEND

Each dot =
200 persons

Areas with more
than 200 persons
per sq. km.

Areas with more
than 500 persons
per sq. km.

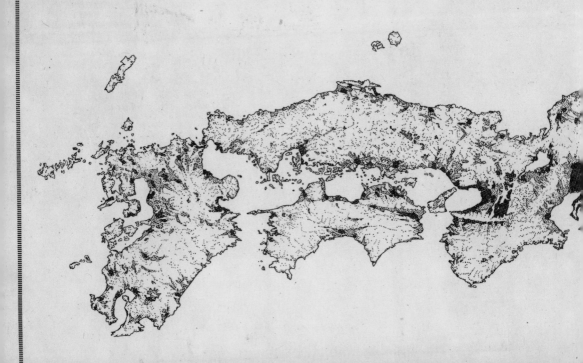